A.M.J. BUCHAN

Immunocytochemistry

Immunocytochemistry

Third Edition

Ludwig A. Sternberger, M.D.
The University of Rochester School of Medicine and Dentistry

A Wiley Medical Publication

JOHN WILEY & SONS

New York   Chichester   Brisbane   Toronto

Library of Congress Cataloging in Publication Data

Sternberger, Ludwig A.
  Immunocytochemistry.

  (A Wiley medical publication)
  Includes bibliographies and index.
  1. Immunocytochemistry. I. Title. II. Series.
  [DNLM: 1. Histocytochemistry. 2. Immunochemistry.

QW 504.5 S839i]
QR187.I45S77   1985   574.2'9   85-9496
ISBN 0-471-86721-7

Printed in the United States of America

10 9 8 7 6 5 4 3 2 1

To Nancy

Preface

The first edition of *Immunocytochemistry*, published in 1974, dealt mainly with methodology. When the second edition was released in 1979, immunocytochemistry had come of age and immunocytochemical findings became accepted, even when they were independent and not merely confirmatory of other knowledge. Yet, immunocytochemistry was still primarily an anatomical science, despite its capability of describing normal and pathologic structures with regard to chemical composition. Methods had become reliable, but specificity of antibodies was still a major problem.

The advent of monoclonal antibodies liberated immunocytochemistry from the need of detailed knowledge of the chemistry of each tissue constituent. Instead, immunocytochemistry itself could be used to explore yet unidentified chemical constituents. With monoclonal antibodies, different forms of single macromolecules can be discerned in situ. The scope of immunocytochemistry has been expanded. Immunocytochemistry is no longer only an anatomic science describing morphology in biochemical terms; it is also becoming a biochemical science that expands biochemistry by exploring in situ biochemical processes that traditionally required the use of isolated systems. Although we are still at the beginning of this expanding task for immunocytochemistry, the abundance of monoclonal antibodies used in immunocytochemistry has provided much of the data in this new third edition.

Meanwhile, even with the use of antisera, immunocytochemistry has become part of nearly any field of medical research. Immunocytochemistry has been especially useful in modern pathology and modern neuroscience.

The progress of immunocytochemistry during the last six years and the continually increasing number of publications that use immunocytochemistry required that the new edition not only possess more text and illustrations than the second edition, but that, in fact, it become a new book almost in its entirety.

Just as in previous editions, methodology has been described in detail. Because of the wealth of information, applications of immunocytochemistry had to be restricted to those aspects which I consider more stimulating to the pathologist or bioscientist, the student, or investigator. In the belief that basic and clinical knowledge should be inseparable, applications to pathology have been discussed in the same chapters as purely experimental material, rather than being delegated to separate chapters.

It is hoped that the book will be of equal value to the anatomist who likes to study structure functionally, to the molecular biologist who likes to relate his isolated system to a biologic pathway in situ, to the pathologist who likes to re-evaluate retrospective material, and to the surgical pathologist who hopes to enhance his diagnostic acumen and recommend optimal management of individual cases.

The second edition has been used as a textbook with some frequency. For this reason, the third edition again has been written with both the student and the investigator in mind. To aid the established investigator who may want to use the book "to look something up" rather than read it, extensive cross-references are found in the text. Consequently, knowledge of earlier chapters is not needed for someone who would like to start reading the book in the middle or use it as a reference for an item he or she has found in the index.

LUDWIG A. STERNBERGER

Rochester, New York

Contents

1. IMMUNOGLOBULIN STRUCTURE: INTRODUCTION TO IMMUNOCYTOCHEMISTRY   1

Common features of the four-chain immunoglobulin monomer   4
Immunoglobulin G   6
Immunoglobulin domains   10
Genes in fragments   11
Allotypy   14
Idiotypy   14
The primary function of antibodies: Affinity for antigen   16
The precipitin reaction   19
Electroblot immunocytochemistry   20
Radioimmunoassay   20
Immunoglobulin isotypes and the secondary, biologic functions
of antibodies   25
Affinity purification of antibodies   27

2. CONJUGATED ANTIBODY METHODS   32

Use of markers   33
Immunofluorescence   34
Conjugation of antibody with fluorescein isothiocyanate:
Principles   39
Preparation of fluorescein isothiocyanate-immunoglobulin
conjugate (FITC-Ig): Procedure   40
Conjugation of purified antibodies   42
Direct and indirect staining modes   42

Staining of living cells   44

Fluorescent cell sorting   46

Specificity   47

Immunofluorescence method specificity   48

Quantitative immunofluorescence   53

Immunofluorescence microscopy and photography   54

Enzyme-conjugated antibodies   56

Conjugation of peroxidase to immunoglobulin with
glutaraldehyde   63

The periodate conjugation technique   64

Use of antibody fragments in conjugation   64

Conjugation of peroxidase to Fab hinge regions with maleimide   65

Nonperoxidase enzymes for conjugation with antibodies   66

Signal intensification for light microscopy in conjugated
antibody methods   67

Conjugation of biotinylated peroxidase and antibody with avidin   67

Electron microscopy with peroxidase-conjugated antibodies   70

The immunoferritin method   72

Immunogold techniques   79

Method specificity of conjugates of antibodies with enzymes or
other proteins   83

3. THE UNLABELED ANTIBODY PEROXIDASE-ANTIPEROXIDASE
    (PAP) METHOD   90

Preparation of soluble PAP complex   96

Properties of PAP   100

Staining for light microscopy   103

Postembedding staining for electron microscopy   114

Pre-embedding staining for electron microscopy   126

Method specificity   142

Identification of background   145

Quantitative immunocytochemistry   146

Sensitivity   164

Resolution   175

Variations of the unlabeled antibody PAP method   180

Combination of PAP immunocytochemistry with tracer uptake
studies in the nervous system   186

Combination of PAP immunocytochemistry with
autoradiography   190

Staining of two antigens in the same section   193

Reversibility of the immunocytochemical reaction   200

4. TISSUE PREPARATION   210

Fixatives   212
Fixation strategies   217
Sectioning   218

5. SPECIFICITY OF ANTISERA   225

Causes of impaired specificity   226
Tests for specificity   230
Strategies for testing specificity of antisera   243

6. SPECIFICITY OF MONOCLONAL ANTIBODIES   245

Preparation of monoclonal antibodies: Principle   247
Methods of clone selection   250
Preparation of monoclonal antibodies for immunocytochemistry:
Procedure   252
Interpretation of specificity   256
Staining   258
Affinity purification of antigens   262
Strategies for use of monoclonal antibodies   262

7. THE IMMUNE RESPONSE—LYMPHOMAS   270

Common B- and T-cell functions   274
Specific B-cell functions   277
B-cell memory   280
B-cell tolerance   280
Specific A-cell functions   282
Specific T helper cell functions   283
Specific T suppressor cell functions   283
Memory T cells   284
Specific function of natural killer cells   284
B-cell differentiation   285
Distribution of lymphocytes in lymphoid tissue   285
Lymphomas   288
Clinical pathology of peripheral leukocytes   298

8. NEUROCYTOCHEMISTRY—NEUROPATHOLOGY   305

Antibodies to neurotransmitters and their biosynthetic enzymes   308
Serotonin   309
Taurine   313
Gamma-aminobutyric and glutamic acids   314
Catecholamines   316
Acetylcholine   317
Neurotransmitter colocalization   317
Identification of pathways   322
Neurotransmitter pathology   328
Familial dysautonomia   330
Olfactory protein   333
Neuron-specific enolase   333
Protein S-100   335
Glial fibrillary acidic protein   335
Brain tumors   339
Myelin   341

9. REGULATORY PEPTIDES—ENDOCRINE PATHOLOGY   357

The Scharrer concept of neurosecretion   358
Opioid and other stress-related peptides   359
Substance P   367
Somatostatin   367
Corticotropin-releasing factor   372
Oxytocin and vasopressin   379
Luteinizing hormone-releasing hormone   384
Thyrotropin-releasing hormone   388
Cholecystokinin   389
Vasoactive intestinal peptide   392
Polypeptide YY   393
FMRF-amide   394
Evolutionary aspects   394
Chemoarchitectonic patterns   395
Colocalization   397
Hormone receptors   401
Diabetes mellitus   414
Endocrine tumors   415

10. NEURONAL DIVERSITY   427

Identification of newly detected antigens   432
Heterogeneity of neurofilaments   438
Antigenicity of epitopes from heterogeneity regions of
neurofilaments   446
Monoclonal antibodies distinguish phosphorylated and
nonphosphorylated forms of neurofilaments in situ   448
Microheterogeneity of post-translational change   455
Epitopes of early and late appearance in development   458
Chemoarchitectonics and the scope of modern
immunocytochemistry   460
Alzheimer's disease   461

11. PROSPECTIVE PATHOLOGY   467

Antigenic expression of tumor differentiation   468
Carcinoembryonic antigen   470
Extragonadal germ cell cancer syndrome   471
Metastatic tumors   472

12. AUTOIMMUNE DISEASES   475

Deficiency of T suppressor cells   476
Idiotypic antibodies   477
Pathogenicity   478
Glomerulonephritis   478
Goodpasture's syndrome   479
Immune complex disease   480
Autoimmune thyroiditis   482
Lupus erythematosus   482
Myasthenia gravis   484
Multiple sclerosis   485
Experimental allergic encephalomyelitis   487
Demyelinating polyneuropathy   490

Author Index   495
Subject Index   511

Immunocytochemistry

Chapter One

Immunoglobulin Structure: Introduction to Immunocytochemistry

At the core of immunology is the *lymphocyte*. Subsets of this cell, along with other white blood cells, called collectively *mononuclear cells,* produce the substances that participate in immunologic reactions, recognize immunogenic stimuli, and mediate cellular interaction during antibody formation. The most prominent product of lymphocytes, secreted in largest amounts, is the *immunoglobulin* molecule. Immunoglobulin is capable of undergoing an immunologic reaction in the absence of its cell of origin. This is a bimolecular reaction that follows conventional chemical binding kinetics. The characteristics of this reaction is its selectivity or *specificity*.

Not all lymphocytes produce immunoglobulin. Immunoglobulin is the product of only one set of lymphocytes, called *B cells,* and even these do not secrete significant amounts of immunoglobulin unless they have been properly stimulated by encountering an outside substance that is *antigenic*. The encounter itself is an involved process that includes, in most cases, not only B cells, but also the participation of other mononuclear cells. Antigenic stimulation does not always proceed toward production and secretion of immunoglobulin. Whether or not immunoglobulin is secreted, the encounter, and the lymphocyte reactions that follow it, are called *immune response*. Often, especially when encountering substances produced by the same host as the lymphocyte, the immune response is specifically *suppressed*. This suppression is an active immunologic process. However, an immune response will generally occur, when substances foreign to the host are encountered, such as bacteria, viruses, proteins produced by other species, or tissues belonging to genetically nonmatched individuals of the same species. Yet even with these substances, an immune response does not always take place. Genetic factors determine whether the host produces lymphocytes that possess receptors to recognize a given substance. If such substance is recog-

1

nized, it is called an *antigen* and the specific sequence (such as seven amino acids) within an antigen so recognized is called *antigenic determinant* or *epitope*.

Even if an antigen leads to an immune response, the product of the response is immunoglobulin only if B cells are among those stimulated to become *effector* B cells. In addition to B cells, the immune system incorporates several other subsets of lymphocytes which are collectively called *T cells*. Certain subsets of T cells can become effector T cells. They do not secrete immunoglobulin, but undergo specific immunologic reactions via substances that are cell bound. Consequently, the cell must be in contact with the target with which it engenders an immunologic reaction (*cellular immunity*).

There is a great number of genetically determined specific receptors on lymphocytes. A given antigen stimulates only those cells that possess matching receptors. Therefore, only a small fraction of total lymphocytes will respond specifically to a given antigenic stimulant during a successful immune response, even though additional cells may participate in a nonspecific manner.

Specificity ensures that the products of the immune response, whether secreted immunoglobulin or cell-bound substances, react well only with substances possessing the antigenic determinant. They may react to a lesser extent with substances possessing epitopes similar to the original antigenic determinant, but binding will be weaker, the *affinity* will be lower, and the dissociation constant higher. This kind of reaction is called *cross-reaction,* which sometimes creates problems in immunocytochemistry. In general, products of the immune response react best with the antigen that has evoked them (*immunizing antigen*), and to a lesser but measurable extent with a highly restricted group of known or unknown cross-reactive substances, but fail to react measurably with most other substances encountered in nature. For instance, immunoglobulin reactive with epitopes on the surface of influenza type A virus will not react with those of type B virus, or for that matter with any other virus, such as polio virus. Similarly, immunoglobulins reactive with the dinitrophenyl group will not react with the phenylarsonate group, immunoglobulin reactive with D-lysine will not react with L-lysine, or immunoglobulin reactive with phosphorylated epitopes of neurofilaments will not react with nonphosphorylated forms of neurofilaments.

The reaction of immunoglobulin with antigen has certain consequences in vitro or in vivo. Sometimes, but not always, the reaction in vivo will initiate a number of events that lead to the elimination of the antigen. Immunoglobulins are one of the mechanisms (the others are cellular immunity and action of certain enzymes, such as lysozyme) that is important in defense of the host against invading microorganisms. For this reason, immunoglobulins are called *antibodies*.

Some proteins, like ovalbumin or hemoglobin, can be crystallized, suggesting that they are fairly homogeneous, at least when isolated from a given individual. Because of certain shared properties, many other substances, such as enkephalin precursor hormones (page 359), neurofilaments (page 438), or immunoglobulins were once considered homogeneous substances. Indeed, immunoglobulins possess a number of common characteristics that permit the classification of these proteins into a single *family* (1). These properties are relatively low solubility in ammonium sulfate, generally slow electrophoretic mobility compared to that of other serum proteins, and a subunit structure of four chains, two identical *light* (L) *chains* and two identical *heavy* (H) *chains*. However, antibody specificity would not be possible if all immunoglobulins had the same structure. It is probable that an individual mouse can produce in excess of 10 million different antibodies, hence over 10 million different immunoglobulins. This variability is due to differences in amino acid sequence within the specific combining sites of antibodies: immunoglobulins are a heterogeneous family of proteins. The differences are due to differences in mRNAs participating in the assembly of antibodies: specificity of antibodies is determined *pretranslationally*. Variations of the repertoire of antibody specificities among different individuals are largely determined by genetic factors, but may also involve somatic mutations (2,3).

The specificity of individual antibodies ensures, for example, that defense to microbial disease rejects only the invading microorganisms and not constituents of the normal bacterial flora of the host, and in general, not the host's own tissues. The specificity can also be used as an analytical tool to detect given epitopes in tissues: the use of antibodies as reagents to specifically detect epitopes within sections prepared for histology, to the exclusion of other epitopes, is the domain of *immunocytochemistry*.

While specificity of their combining sites is the characteristic feature of the variability of immunoglobulins, specific combining sites of antibody-like nature are not restricted to proteins of the immunoglobulin family, but are also encountered in other proteins that act as soluble and cell-bound factors during antibody formation (page 283) or as cell-bound factors during cellular immune reactions. However, immunoglobulins are the only epitope-specific substances secreted in large amounts, and, thus are readily available as central reagents for immunocytochemistry.

Extensive studies of the immune response and of the heterogeneity of immunoglobulin structure have been possible because immunoglobulins are soluble proteins and free-floating lymphocytes are readily available in the blood stream. Systems, other than the immune system, do not, in general, offer this convenience. The biochemical methods, so fruitful in the study of immunologic phenomena, cannot be directly applied to tissue-bound cells or their cell-bound products. To apply such methods, it is necessary to dissociate given cells from the remainder of the tissue, a process rarely leading to an entirely pure cell population, or to dissociate tissue-bound proteins into solution, a process that distorts the functional relation of proteins in their cellular interaction. It is not surprising, therefore, that information on heterogeneity of proteins outside the immune system has not come forth as rapidly as that of immunoglobulins. Interestingly, it is because of immunoglobulins themselves that exploration of tissue constituents in situ has now become possible through the use of modern immunocytochemistry. Parts of this book will deal with the contributions which immunocytochemistry has made in suggesting structural and possible functional heterogeneity of certain tissue constituents, hitherto considered homogeneous (pages 262 and 438). Thus, the immune system does not seem to be unique in expressing a high degree of functional heterogeneity. The brain, for instance, may have equal rights (page 427).

COMMON FEATURES OF THE FOUR-CHAIN IMMUNOGLOBULIN MONOMER

All immunoglobulins have a similar, basic alignment of peptide chains. Every immunoglobulin is either a monomer or oligomer of four peptides of which two are identical *L chains* and two are identical *H chains*.

While the variability of structure of specific combining sites in immunoglobulins determines selectivity for individual antigens, the variability of the remainder of the molecules is important for a number of other, secondary functions in the immune response of the host against foreign material which do not depend on specific antigen-antibody interaction. These secondary functions largely determine the disposition of antigen—that is, the manner in which the host will react to antigen once antibody has combined with it. It is of interest that in evolution these functions and specific antigen binding have been combined in a single molecule, the immunoglobulin molecule. The secondary functions of antibody mediate its binding to other effector substances of the host defense mechanism (via ligand or receptor interaction). The combination of specific antibody-binding and effector-binding reactivity in a single immunoglobulin molecule makes it possible for antibody to confer upon antigen those properties that make the host treat the antigen as a substance for elimination. While different genes are responsible for the antigen binding and the secondary functions of immunoglobulin, the genes for a single chain are linked, as shown by Honjo and Katoako (4), in a single chromosomal region, thus alluding to a common evolutionary ancestry. Indeed, immunoglobulins are rather recent in origin, being found only in vertebrates. Even within vertebrates, the presence of large amounts of circulating immunoglobulins are characteristic of warm-blooded animals. Earlier forms of vertebrates possess smaller amounts of circulating immunoglobulins, but their immune response, even though specific, is mostly dependent on cellular reactions.

Immunization, that is, the production of antibodies by injection of an antigen, is a selective process. A large number of differently structured antigen-combining sites pre-exist in the form of lymphocyte-bound receptors. No mature lymphocyte possesses more than one kind of specific receptor.

Immunoglobulins, secreted as a result of immunization, reflect, at least to a large extent, the structure of cell-bound antigen receptors. The variability of these receptors determines the large number of epitopes to which an animal is genetically predisposed to react. It dictates the minimum number of different antibody combining sites that can be expressed on immunoglobulin and, thus, a minimum degree of structural variability. Somatic mutations (3,4) increase the degree of variability. The variability for antigen resides in the *variable region* of the immunoglobulin molecule. No single immunoglobulin-producing cell secretes more than a single type (*idiotype*) of variable region.

When immunoglobulin binds with a specific antigenic determinant, probably only some of the amino acids in the variable region come into direct contact. These amino acids undergo highest frequency variation when one random immunoglobulin molecule is compared to another: their position in the immunoglobulin peptide structure defines the *hypervariable region* (5,6).

The variable region is the most characteristic part of the immunoglobulin molecule because of its essentiality for the specificity of the immune reaction.

The remainder of the immunoglobulin molecule is necessary for molding its individual peptides into a structural unit and for the secondary functions of antibodies before or after reaction with antigen in or on a cell or in circulation. These secondary functions include transport of immunoglobulin, immune elimination of antigen, and cytotoxicity. The secondary functions often provide mechanisms that explain observations obtained from staining pathologic tissue with immunocytochemical methods. The structural features in immunoglobulin that contribute to the secondary functions are also utilized extensively in the development of the various immunocytochemical methods we will discuss in the following pages. The secondary functions reside in relatively constant amino acid sequences of the immunoglobulin molecule. Antibodies of different specificities may share identical amino acid sequences in the *constant region*. The constant-region sequence does not contribute to antigen binding. The term constancy of amino acid sequence only implies invariance of composition of immunoglobulins irrespective of their specificities for binding antigenic determinants. However, there do exist a great number of different constant-region sequences that a vertebrate is capable of producing. While some of these variations determine unique secondary properties, others may be without specific biologic function. In general, the differences in amino acid composition of the constant region which determine differences in secondary functions are extensive. The constant region is characteristic of the *class* or *isotype* to which an immunoglobulin molecule belongs. Different isotypes of immunoglobulins are relatively easy to separate by chromatography. Nine isotypes of human immunoglobulins—called IgG1, 2, 3, and 4, IgM, IgA1 and 2, IgD, and IgE— can be distinguished on the basis of the H chains, $\gamma 1$, 2, 3, and 4, μ, $\alpha 1$ and 2, σ, and ε. In the mouse, the isotypes are called IgG_1, IgG_{2a}, IgG_{2b}, IgG_3, IgM, IgA_1, IgA_2, IgD, and IgE. The light chains may be either of κ or λ types or their subtypes. Two identical L chains are joined to two identical H chains in any immunoglobulin monomer. Thus, it is the H chain that determines the nature of the isotypes, while the L chain is either one of the two types in any one isotype (7,8). Despite the relative constancy in amino acid composition of each isotype-specific H chain and each type of L chain, there are several loci in L and H chains in which single amino acid substitution is determined by genetically inherited, allelic features: the difference in composition so determined is called *allotypy* (page 14).

When a single isotype of antibodies is purified from antiserum by chromatography, and when antibodies with a specific range of antigen reactivity is isolated from this fraction by reaction with specific antigen (page 27), the resulting material is still heterogeneous by electrophoresis. This heterogeneity is due to the fact that each epitope on antigen is capable of selecting a number of variable-region conformations from the available antigen receptor pool (page 275) during immunization, thus resulting in formation of a number of antibodies that react with varying portions of the epitope, exhibit varying degrees of affinities, and have different amino acid composition in the hypervariable region. Such heterogeneous antibodies are not suitable for the study of the amino acid sequence of the specific antigen binding sites of antibodies. The homogeneous antibodies that have contributed so much to the elucidation of immunoglobulin structure are the product of clones of antibody-producing cells derived from single antigen-recognizing cells. These antibodies are provided by monoclonal tumors of antibody-producing cells (plasmacytomas, multiple myelomas) or by cultures of single-cell clones selected from fusions of antibody-producing cells with non-immunoglobulin-producing myeloma cells (page 246).

Let us now discuss the amino acid composition of the chains of a typical monomeric immunoglobulin, such as IgG, and the manner in which they are attached to each other, before returning to our general discussion of antibody structure as related to antibody function.

IMMUNOGLOBULIN G

The bulk of antibodies obtained after hyperimmunization with most antigens resides in the immunoglobulin G (IgG) isotype. At pH 8.6, IgG possesses the slowest electrophoretic mobility among serum proteins. This property and its low solubility at low ionic strength facilitates its convenient isolation by passage through a diethylaminoethyl cellulose column at pH 6.5 to 8.0 in 0.005 to 0.02 M phosphate buffer. Under these conditions, the bulk of IgG is excluded from the column (eluting with the starting buffer along with haptoglobulin, an iron-conveying serum protein), while the remainder of serum proteins and other isotypes of immunoglobulins along with some of the IgG are retained. The molecular weight of IgG is 146,000. Its specific Y-shape (Fig. 1-1) is suggested by degradation studies and confirmed by electron microscopy (Fig. 1-2). There are four nitrogen-terminal amino acids (sometimes with masked amino groups), indicating that the molecule consists of four chains. Upon digestion with papain, one obtains a crystalline, homogeneous fragment called *Fc*, and two fragments *Fab* that are electrophoretically heterogeneous, if obtained from an IgG serum fraction, but homogeneous if obtained from myeloma IgG.

Because of the identity of both Fab fragments from any single IgG molecule, both specific combining sites are also identical. Each Fab fragment contains one specific combining site for antigen. Fab blocks the reaction of antigen with native antibody and competitively inhibits the secondary phenomena observed upon reaction of antigen with native antibody. Fab has been used as a specific blocking reagent in immunocytochemistry.

The cleavage into three fragments by papain is due to a preferential attack of the cysteine-activated enzyme on the *hinge region* of IgG. This region possesses unusual flexibility. It permits some degree of freedom about the angle that both Fab fragments form with each other. As a consequence, the distance between both antigen combining sites may change and an antibody may combine with two adjacent identical epitopes, even if this distance is not exactly identical to that of the most relaxed conformation of both Fab portions toward each other. Therefore, when identical epitopes are fixed within tissue or held on a cellular or subcellular membrane with high density, the chance is high that antibody, when used as an immunocytochemical reagent, will bind via *both* of its combining regions. As a consequence, it is possible to remove the bound antibody only if both sites are dissociated *simultaneously*. In effect, the affinity of the antibody is greatly increased, a factor that has contributed toward the sensitivity of immunocytochemical methodology (pages 164, 201, and 235).

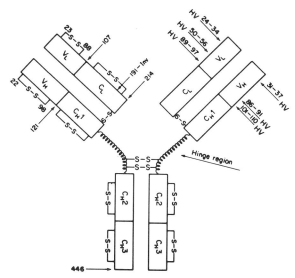

Figure 1-1. The complete amino acid sequence of a myeloma immunoglobulin G has first been reported by Edelman and his associates (7). The two identical heavy chains (H) are linked by a single sulfhydryl bond to the C-terminal end of a light (L) chain. The constant region of the H chains (C_H1, C_H2, C_H3) determines the isotype to which an immunoglobulin belongs (human IgG is shown in the figure). Light chains may be κ or λ types irrespective of the isotype of immunoglobulins in which they occur. Amino acid sequence analysis of a large number of κ chains has shown that except for the Inv allelic marker (in position 191) they are identical in the constant (C_L) regions. If we disregard the hypervariable regions (HV) in amino acid positions 24–34, 50–56, and 89–97, the variable portions of human κ chains (V_L) can be subdivided into three subgroups on the basis of amino acid composition. Different κ subgroups are always linked to κ and not to λ-type C regions. However, each subgroup may be linked to either of the allelic forms of the C_L region, providing one of the suggestions that at least two genes control the synthesis of a single polypeptide. Interestingly, differentiation into subgroups (3κ and 5λ subgroups) apparently occurred early in mammalian development, since the difference in amino acid composition of human κ-chain subgroups does not exceed the differences among human and mouse basic κ-chain sequences. Hypervariable regions of the light chain (H_v) are confined to amino acids 24–34, 50–56, and 89–97. The hypervariability determines the contribution of the L chain to the specificity of the immunoglobulin molecule in its reaction with antigen. Amino acids 23 and 88 are brought into juxtaposition by an intrachain sulfhydryl linkage. Thus, the hypervariable regions (24–34 and 89–97) are brought into approximation, apparently, assuring apposition to a relatively small epitope (5,6). In IgG the constant region of the heavy (γ) chain can be divided into three domains (C_H1, C_H2, and C_H3), each of which apparently can undergo a specific secondary function (independently of the specificity of the primary antigen-binding function of antibody). Thus, complement appears to be bound at the C_H2 domain. C_H2 is also the site of attachment of the carbohydrate that forms part of the constitution of IgG. H chains are divided into subgroups on the basis of variance of composition of variable-region amino acids other than those constituting the hypervariable region. Apparently any subgroup of H chain may be joined to any of the 9 known isotypes of heavy chains of immunoglobulin. An intrachain sulfhydryl bridge brings H-chain amino acids 22 and 98 into juxtaposition. As a consequence the three hypervariable regions from amino acids 31–37, 86–91, and 101–110 are brought together, thus apparently assuring their direct contact upon specific reaction with a relatively small epitope. Recombination studies of L and H chains have shown that both chains participate in the specific binding with antigen.

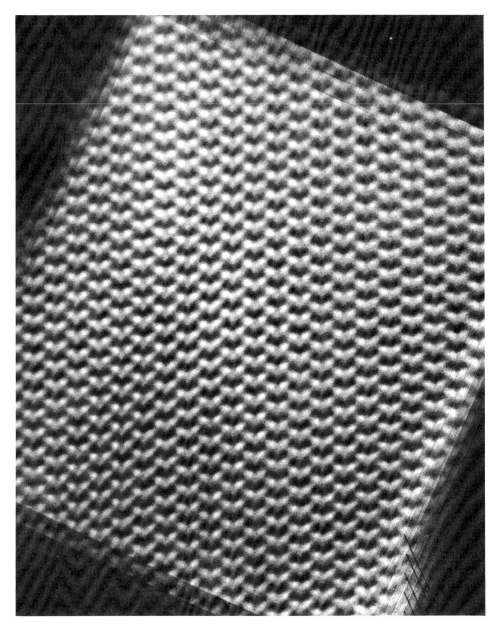

Figure 1-2. The structure of a myeloma IgG that crystallizes spontaneously on cooling has been studied by x-ray crystallography and negative-staining electron microscopy. In order to eliminate random noise of high-resolution electron microscopy, multiple exposures of the original micrograph were made on printing paper, moving the paper between each exposure in the direction of the crystal periodicity by a distance equal to the periodicity. This procedure was then repeated in different directions of periodicity [From Labaw and Davies (9)].

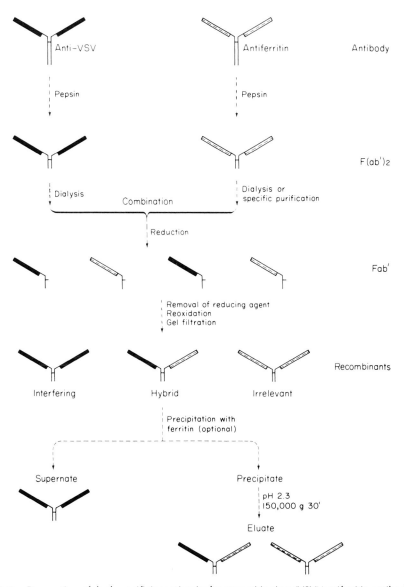

Figure 1-3. Preparation of dual specificity antivesicular stomatitis virus (VSV)/antiferritin antibody from anti-VSV and antiferritin IgG. Ferritin is one of the markers for antigen used in immunocytochemistry. When freed of interfering, single specificity anti-VSV, the dual specificity antibodies can be used to link ferritin to the VSV antigen.

On mild reduction in the presence of hydrogen bond-breaking agents, such as urea, IgG separates into two identical L chains (about 214 amino acids each) and two identical H chains (about 446 amino acids each). Both L and H chains have variable N-terminal and constant C-terminal regions. L chains are parts of the Fab fragment only and not of the Fc fragment. Each L chain is bound at its C terminal or pentultimate amino acid to an H chain with a single sulfhydryl bond. When separated L and H chains are acetylated, they still recombine on admixture. Therefore, urea or propionic acid must be present during the separation of L and H chains by gel filtration after reduction. The noncovalent bonding of the L and H chains is due to considerable homology of their amino acid sequences. This homology involves the constant as well as variable regions. Thus, when separated L and H chains from anti-A (antibody to A) and anti-B are allowed to recombine in a single mixture, the L chains from anti-A will home with a high probability to the H chains of anti-A and the L chains from anti-B to the H chains of anti-B.

The Fc fragment consists of the C-terminal portions of the H chains, which are constant—hence the crystalline nature of Fc even if obtained from nonhomogeneous IgG. Sulfhydryl bonds in the hinge region link both H chains. The number of these bonds depends on the isotype of the immunoglobulin. It is usually two, but may be one to four, except for IgE in which it may range from 5 to 15, thus suggesting yet undetermined subclasses among isotypes.

Limited digestion with pepsin fragments the Fc portion of IgG while leaving the Fab portions and the hinge region intact (9). The resulting $F(ab')_2$ fragment (Fig. 1-3) contains both specific antibody combining sites still bound covalently by sulfhydryl linkage. Fragments containing only one specific combining site (*Fab'*) can be obtained from F(ab')$_2$ by mild reduction even in the absence of hydrogen bond-breaking agents, since both H chains are held together by only a small sequence of amino acids. Upon reoxidation, F(ab')$_2$ is reconstituted. As the linkage is in a constant region of the H chains, Fab' fragments of different antibody specificities may recombine: The antibodies of dual specificities so obtained have been proposed for use in immunocytochemistry. Antibodies of dual specificity can also be obtained physiologically upon fusion of an antibody-producing spleen cell with an immunoglobulin-secreting myeloma cell (page 261).

IMMUNOGLOBULIN DOMAINS

Results of x-ray crystallography and of limited proteolysis have shown that immunoglobulin chains are folded into globular domains linked by more exposed areas (9,10). Light chains have two domains (one consisting of the variable, V_L, and the other of the constant, C_L, region, see Fig. 1-1), while the H chains have four domains (V_H, C_H1, C_H2, and C_H3), except for μ and ε chains, which have a fifth domain (C_H4). The globular structure is due to intrachain sulfhydryl bonds that bridge approximately 60 to 70 amino acid residues in each domain (5,6). Each domain itself consists of approximately 110 amino acids. Interestingly, in each immunoglobulin of the same heavy-chain isotype and light-chain type (such as IgG1κ), any two of the four constant domains C_L, C_H1, C_H2, and C_H3) possess about 30% amino acid homology, suggesting that the full chains have evolved through gene duplication from a common, smaller protein. In fact, a 115 amino acid polypeptide page 13, which possesses a high degree of homology with the C_H3 domain of IgG, has been isolated from human serum. The protein is also present on the surface of lymphocytes, is within major histocompatibility antigens (page 282), and while having no antibody function of its own, is related to recognition mechanisms in the immune response.

GENES IN FRAGMENTS

Separate chromosomes control the expression of λ, κ, and H chains. If different genes existed for each variable region in L or H chains, arranged linearly in the chromosome, a large number of nucleotide sequences that control the constant regions would have to be repeated. Alternatively, more than one gene would program a single polypeptide. Hozumi and Tonegawa (11) provided the original evidence for the latter mechanism by hybridization experiments with the labeled cDNA formed by reverse transcriptase from mRNA for the κ chain of the antiphosphoryl choline-producing mouse myeloma MOPC 321. Upon hybridization with embryonic DNA, cleaved by restriction enzymes and separated by gel electrophoresis according to molecular weight, two fractions of apparent molecular weights 3.9 and 6.0×10^6 were labeled. This suggests two gene fragments participating in the synthesis of the mRNA. On the other hand, upon hybridization with DNA from the MOPC 321 myeloma, only one restriction enzyme fragment of molecular weight 2.4×10^6 was labeled. The experiment shows that during expression of mRNA for production of MOPC 135 antiphosphoryl choline, at least two gene fragments are translated, but become ligated into a single sequence prior to formation of the mRNA.

Extension of this approach has shown, in fact, that a number of genes control each L and H chain. In the mouse, the λ chain, although more rarely expressed, is simpler than the κ or H chain. The λ chain genome possesses only two variable region genes. There are many variable region genes for the κ and H chain. Four genes participate in the expression of the total L chain mRNA: a leader segment, a variable segment (V), a junction segment (J), and a constant segment (C). In H chains, a terminal D segment is added. A large number of different germ line V segments are found in the genomic DNA. All segments are separated by nonexpressed *introns*. In the maturation of the lymphocyte (to become a cell capable of producing antibodies of single idiotypes), only one of the V genes is selected. A maturing cell is already committed to producing a certain idiotype, even before encountering antigenic stimulation.

No such commitment has occurred in the H chain constant region. Honjo and Katoako (4) have shown that the genes from mouse γ1, γ2a, and γ3 are represented as one copy per haploid genome in normal mouse tissue and in myelomas producing IgM or Ig3. However, IgG1 myeloma contains only half a copy of the genes for γ3, IgG2a and 2b myelomas contain only half a copy of the genes for γ3 and γ1, and IgA myeloma contains only half a copy for γ3, γ1, and γ2a. These findings are explained by assuming that only one of the alleles (page 14) is expressed. Thus, if an allele has been excised, the hybridization probe will react only with the nonexpressed allele. Furthermore, the message of only one H chain is being read. Translation will stop at the terminus of this message. With these assumptions, a model could be constructed for the reading of the linear message in pieces (12) and excision of nontranslated information (Fig. 1-4).

The interspacing of nonexpressed *introns* with expressed *exons* in the genome (12) increases the variability of peptides that can be coded by translated mRNA. If the whole genone were read linearly, that is, if only one gene would form one polypeptide, the number of polypeptides that can be expressed would be limited

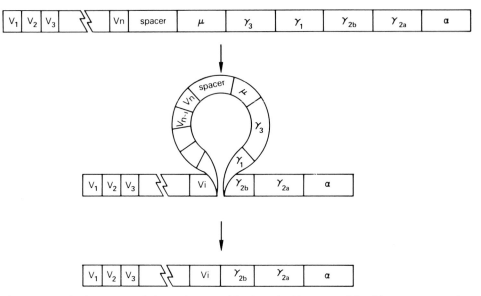

Figure 1-4. The bottom panel shows the recombination of a V segment (Vi) with γ_{2b} to express immunoglobulin of Vi idiotype and γ_{2b} isotype. The Vi-γ_{2b} recombination has occurred as a result of excision of all V segments from Vi to Vn and of all μ, γ_3 and γ_1 from the expressed allele of the genome (only $\frac{1}{2}$ copy of γ_3 and γ_1 is labeled by hybridization with the γ_{2b}, cDNA probe) (middle panel). Determination of the eliminated H chain alleles in the expression of mRNA for γ_3, γ_1, γ_{2b}, and γ_{2a}, and α has allowed the alignment of the sequence of H chain constant determinants in the undifferentiated genome (top) [From Honjo and Kataoka (4)].

by the size of the chromosome. This situation, indeed, prevails in the genomic expression of bacteria. In eukaryocytes, a similar mass of DNA can produce a much larger number of polypeptides. This is accomplished by excision at variable intron sites and realignment of scrambled exons in the formation of mRNA.

The earlier excision in the V region genome than in the C region genome is responsible for selection of specific receptors expressed on the surface of lymphocytes, which in the case of B cells (but not of T cells) are themselves immunoglobulins of the IgM isotype. The cell is committed as to its idiotype. As excision in the C region genome occurs only after antigenic stimulation, an *isotype shift* occurs as an event in immunization. Since selection of variable region genes is made early, a single antibody-producing cell yields only a single idiotype. However, malignant cells, depending on the stage of their maturation, may secrete two isotypes of immunoglobulin, such as IgM and IgA, even though they secrete only one idiotype (13,14). This phenomenon is important in the immunocytochemical determination of the degree of malignancy in lympho-proliferative disorders (page 293).

The single constant-region domain of L chains and the three constant-region domains of H chains express considerable homology. They have sequences with many identical amino acids and those substituted are usually due to single base changes in triplet codons. The homologous regions have changed little during evolution from shark to human. The regions are more similar in mouse and human immunoglobulin than corresponding domains in different H chain isotypes of the same species. The structural homology suggests that the multichain immunoglobulin molecule has evolved through gene duplication (and chromosome transfer) from a single gene coding for about 115 amino acids. As shown by Gottlieb et al. (15), the homologous sequence also appears in $\gamma 3$ microglobulin, a protein participating in cellular interaction during antibody formation and apparently present in species that have not yet evolved to form specific antibodies. Immunoglobulins appeared only later in evolution, being absent in invertebrates and primitive fish, and becoming abundant only in birds and mammals. However, the four-gene basic structure and the divergence of isotypes of immunoglobulin have appeared early along with the capability to produce antibodies. This is reflected by the fact that interspecies and interdomain constant-region homologies are greater than those of different isotypes of H chains in the same species.

The permutation of mRNA sequences that increases heterogeneity of assembled peptides through gene splicing and variability of reassembly, is not restricted to the heterogeneity of antibodies and their resulting specificities. Peptide hormones have been inherited more conservatively than homologous regions of immunoglobulins. Gene duplications are found in many sequences coding for preprohormones. Different patterns of intron excision and exon reassembly provide for a variability of preprohormones and the coexistence of different peptide cleavage products in different cells, despite widespread homologies of each individually cleaved peptide. While the heterogeneity of antibody variable regions has originally been detected by the specificities of reaction with antigens, detection of the heterogeneity of peptide hormone coexistence has mainly been dependent on immunocytochemistry (page 397).

Heterogeneity may be a widespread phenomenon, as it must be if the expression of genes in pieces is a general principle. Indeed, proteins that hitherto have been considered mainly structural components, such as neurofilaments, have been shown to be immunocytochemically heterogeneous, suggesting a function more specific than that implied by the name "cytoskeleton" for the filament-forming proteins to which neurofilaments belong.

Even the number of variable chains, excised and reassembled, may be insufficient to explain the diversity of antibodies. This is especially true for the mouse λ chain which possesses only two variable region genes, yet can express eight different amino acid sequences (16). The possibility of somatic mutation during antibody formation must, therefore, be considered as an additional contribution to immunoglobulin heterogeneity. Gaerhart et al. (17) have reinforced this notion by the sequence analysis of the L chains of IgM and IgG antiphosphoryl choline monoclonal antibodies produced by fusion of immune spleen cells with myeloma cells (page 247). Eleven out of twelve IgM L chains were identical with the antiphosphoryl choline prototype sequence. In contrast, five out of nine IgG L chains differed from the prototype. Since cells shift to IgG production only after antigenic stimulation and IgM formation, and since V region selection occurs before V and C region joining, the greater variability of IgG V_2 regions must arise late in cellular differentiation, again possibly a result of somatic mutation.

Somatic mutation may not be the only mechanism that increases diversity in nature beyond that determined by the germ line, although it may be the only one operating in antibody diversity. Bioactive peptides differ from immunoglobulins in that most of the biologic activity resides in cleavage products rather than in the assembled protein. Cleavage is enzymatic and different enzymes yield different hormonal products in different cells (page 364). Other forms of post-translational variability is the possible heterogeneity of phosphorylation that may occur in neurofilaments (page 448). Detection of these forms of heterogeneity has been dependent largely on immunocytochemistry.

ALLOTYPY

We have seen that a single gene determines only a segment of the immunoglobulin polypeptides. Many genes can be selected for variable regions, but only few for the constant regions. For instance, there is a single structural gene for the formation of the human constant κ chain region (C_κ). However, small allelic variations can occur in any of the immunoglobulin genes. An allele refers to a change in base substitution that can occur in two different forms in a gene. An individual who, in each of two corresponding chromosomes, has the same allele is homozygous with respect to the participating allele. An individual who possesses two different alleles is heterozygous. Both alleles are codominantly expressed in immunoglobulin structure, albeit not in the same cell (allelic exclusion). However, since serum immunoglobulins are the result of the secretion by many cells, both alleles are expressed in the heterozygous individual, although not necessarily in equal amounts.

Allelic genes determine the substitution of only one or two amino acids in the total peptide sequence. Allotypy was first detected by immunologic means (immunodiffusion, page 20), attesting to the high degree of specificity of antibodies.

IDIOTYPY

When we immunize mice of one strain with an immunoglobulin of another strain, we obtain antibodies against allotypic determinants. However, if we immunize mice with immunoglobulin obtained from the same strain, we usually do not obtain antibodies because animals are normally immune-tolerant of their own antigenic determinants (pages 283 and 475). A homogeneous immunoglobulin, such as BALB/c myeloma IgA S63, possesses a unique sequence in its hypervariable region. Normal BALB/c mice at best contain only a trace of this particular hypervariable sequence among all their heterogeneous immunoglobulins. The amount of this sequence may well be below the threshold for induction of immune tolerance. Thus when normal BALB/c mice are immunized with protein S63, tolerance is broken and antibodies form. These antibodies are specific to the hypervariable region of protein S63. Antibodies to hypervariable regions of immunoglobulin are known as *anti-idiotypes* and the specificities of the hypervariable region producing them, as *idiotypes* (18).

IgA S63 possesses antibody specificity for phosphoryl choline. If antisera are produced by this protein in an allogenic strain of mice, anti-idiotypes can be identified after absorption with insolubilized protein S129, a myeloma IgA from BALB/c mice with antidinitrophenol reactivity.

Anti-idiotypes can also be produced in heterologous species. Protein 315 is a mouse myeloma IgA with anti-2,4-dinitrophenol specificity. To obtain anti-idiotypes from rabbits immunized with protein 315, the antiserum is first absorbed with a mouse myeloma IgA of different specificity. The antiserum is reabsorbed with protein 315 that has been reacted with N-bromacetyl-N'-2,4-dinitrophenylethylenediamine. This compound is an *affinity label* that reacts immunospecifically with the combining sites of protein 315 and covalently with lysine groups in or near the combining sites and, thus, masks these sites. Absorption of the rabbit antiserum with the affinity-labeled protein 315 removes, therefore, antibodies to all its antigenic determinants except some of those that are in or near the specific combining sites. The absorbed antiserum becomes anti-idiotypic. The reaction of anti-idiotype with protein 315 is inhibited by 2,4-dinitrophenol and analogous ligands, indicating that the anti-idiotype is, indeed, specific for the specific combining site of protein 315.

Sher et al. (19) have shown that protein 107 (a BALB/c mouse myeloma antiphosphoryl choline IgA) reacts with the anti-idiotype produced with protein S63. In this case, however, the reaction is not altered by the presence of phosphoryl choline. Conceivably the antibodies are not truly anti-idiotypic but specific to a rare subgroup of IgA that is expressed in tumors S63 and 107 and is not abundant in normal BALB/c mice.

Anti-idiotypes have been considered important in the regulation of the immune response, and indeed, under experimental conditions injection of anti-idiotype will suppress or enhance an immune response. To assess this function of anti-idiotypes, it is necessary, in the production of anti-idiotypes, to use genetically matched animals, for otherwise the effects of the antibodies may be due to allotypic rather than idiotypic markers. Moreover, it has been shown that the anti-idiotype repetoire of an animal is also genetically determined. Anti-idiotypes reactive with a specific mouse myeloma globulin cross-react to a *lesser extent* with myeloma globulin specific to the same antigen from mice of different strains. The results indicate that idiotypic specificity may provide genetic markers for the variable regions of immunoglobulin polypeptide chains. Thus, one strain of mice may possess a different set of idiotypic sequences in its antidinitrophenyl hapten (page 16) antibody than another strain, so that again immunization would result in antibodies to allotypic markers within the V region, rather than idiotypic markers. The argument is important, for only if an animal can produce anti-idiotypic markers to its *own* idiotype, would they have physiologic importance in regulation of the immune response. Reth et al. (20) provided a partial answer to this problem by producing anti-idiotypes in (C57B/6 × CBA)F$_1$ mice with a monoclonal antibody against the 4-hydroxy-3-nitrophenylazyl hapten produced by fusion of immune spleen cells of C57BL/6 mice (page 247). These strains are histocompatible (page 282), that is, the F$_1$ offspring cannot form antibodies to antigens produced by the parental C57BL/6 strain. Two isotypes of anti-idiotypes were examined, IgG$_1$ and IgG$_{2a}$. The immune response to the hapten was enhanced by low doses of the IgG$_1$ anti-idiotype but suppressed by high doses. With IgG_{2a}, only suppression was observed. Furthermore, minute amounts of anti-idiotype, weeks before immunization, elicited suppression, indicating that the effect was exerted at the antigen receptor level.

One problem with the validity of the theory that incriminates anti-idiotypes as the main factor that regulates the immune response lies in the manner in which anti-idiotypes are produced for experimental work. Powerful immunizing procedures, using Freund's adjuvants, are needed to elicit in a strain of animals antisera to an antigen derived from the same strain. Under these conditions, high affinity antibodies are produced including autoimmune antibodies to antigens of the injected host (page 487). The immunosuppressive effects ascribed to anti-idiotypes may conceivably be due to such other autoimmune antibodies. Studies with monoclonal anti-idiotypes may conceivably provide an answer to this alternative explanation.

Yet even the effects of monoclonal anti-idiotypes may be subject to an explanation other than direct neutralization of idiotype-bearing receptors. The combination of anti-idiotype with idiotype-bearing receptors may provide a new epitope that abrogates the normal "self" tolerance of the cell (page 477). A limited immune response to normal cell-surface constituents may occur with the production of antibodies that stimulate cellular proliferation which stops short of immunoglobulin production, and may, thereby, cause a suppression of antibody formation that is only indirectly related to idiotype-anti-idiotype interaction (21). The suppression would be especially marked if administration of the anti-idiotype *preceded* immunization. If administration of the anti-idiotype were concurrent with immunization, the latter would stimulate accessory factors (page 283) that permit the proliferative phase of the immune response to progress toward antibody formation. If this were indeed the case, anti-idiotypes would play no significant role in the regulation of the normal, postimmunization immune response.

THE PRIMARY FUNCTION OF ANTIBODIES: AFFINITY FOR ANTIGEN

A *hapten* is a substance that is not immunogenic but can react with specific antibody. An epitope is the simplest unit in an antigen or hapten capable of reacting with antibody.

When a *hapten,* such as a small peptide of known amino acid sequence, is coupled with a *carrier,* such as a large protein molecule, immunization yields in most instances antibodies reactive with the hapten and antibodies reactive with the carrier. Even the antihaptenic antibodies consist of a heterogeneous group, most of them specific for the terminal amino acid, many for the terminal and penultimate amino acid, and a lesser and lesser proportion for an increasingly larger sequence of amino acids. Few antibodies react with a sequence larger than four to seven amino acids away from the terminal amino acid. The larger the number of amino acids with which the antihapten antibody reacts, the stronger the binding, and the higher the affinity of binding. High affinity means close fit with the respective amino acid sequence. Hence, high affinity for an antigen means high specificity and low *cross-reactivity* with antigenic determinants of different amino acid sequences. Although with purified antibodies (page 27) not more than four amino acids were found to contribute to binding, the limiting size of an antigenic determinant is probably closer to a sequence of seven amino acid, monosaccharide, or nucleotide residues. Purification of antibodies usually selects those with low binding affinities, apparently leaving antibodies reactive with more than four amino acids in the nonpurified residue. This is good reason to avoid specifically purified antibodies in immunocytochemistry. Monoclonal antibodies (page 245) provide better idiotypic purity and usually higher affinity.

Even though the epitope with which a single antibody may react at any one time is relatively small, the hypervariable region is large enough to express specificity to several unrelated epitopes. Thus, the mouse IgA plasmacytoma protein 460 binds both ε-dinitrophenyl-lysine and 2-methyl-1,4-napthoquinone (menadione) (22). The antigen combining site of protein 460 contains a hidden sulfhydryl group, which can only be inactivated with a sulfhydryl reagent that is a derivative of dinitrophenol [5,5′-dithiobis(2,4-dinitrophenyl)]. The derivative is an *affinity label* in which the dinitrophenol permits access to the otherwise hidden site. After inactivation of the hidden sulhydryl group, the plasmacytoma protein no longer reacts with menadione, but still reacts with dinitrophenyllysine. Therefore, the dinitrophenyl and menadione binding sites in the plasmacytoma antibody are distinct.

The reaction of antibody and antigen is reversible. High affinity implies low reversibility. In the development and application of immunocytochemical methods, we must be aware of reversibility because in immunocytochemical staining one usually applies a small volume of antibody-containing reagent and then washes with a large volume of buffer. This causes some dissociation even though with most good antibodies the binding reaction is much faster than the dissociation reaction. Antibodies of satisfactory affinity have association constants in the range of 10^5 to 10^9 per mole. Occasional antibodies have higher affinities. We have prepared monoclonal antibodies to LHRH with association constants of 10^{10} per mole (23).

Each epitope-binding site in antibody reacts independently. To measure this reaction, it is necessary to carry it out entirely in solution. This is only ensured if either the antigen or the antibody has only one binding site. If the antigen possesses several, although not necessarily identical epitopes, and the antibodies are heterogeneous (such as serum antibodies), multivalent reaction permits formation of large lattices that are difficult to dissociate, even if no visible precipitate ensues (page 234). The apparent (overall) affinity is thus increased. If each epitope is on a small hapten, such as a decapeptide, and the antiserum happens to possess only antibodies reactive with the C-terminal sequence of this peptide, the largest aggregates that can form consist of two haptens and one bivalent antibody. As each hapten reacts independently with the antibody binding site, the system is suitable for measurement of affinity.

With monoclonal antibodies, lattices cannot form even with large antigens that possess multiple, but different, epitopes. This has sometimes led to the erroneous assumption that monoclonal antibodies have low affinities. In fact, reaction with monoclonal antibodies measures true affinities, rather than the apparently increased affinity resulting from lattice formation.

Moyle et al. (24) have produced monoclonal antibodies that react with two different sites of human chorionic gonadotropin and found that the apparent affinity is greatly increased when both antibodies are allowed to react with the antigen rather than one alone. The increased affinity was explained by the formation of circular complexes containing less than 12 molecules of antibody and gonadotropin. Formation of circular complexes also appears to be important in the development of sensitive, low-reversibility immunocytochemical techniques (pages 100 and 200).

The most reliable analytical tool in nonprecipitating hapten-antibody systems is *equilibrium dialysis,* in which an antibody solution is allowed to equilibrate across a semipermeable membrane against buffer in the presence of labeled hapten. Increase in label on the antibody side versus the buffer side reflects antibody affinity, since no secondary reactions were performed to disturb this all liquid system. In such a system, given amounts of antibody saturation, say 30%, can be accomplished with low concentrations of hapten in the case of high-affinity antibodies. The same degree of binding requires high concentration of hapten with low-affinity antibodies, but except for solubility problems, a concentration can always be found that leads to 30% binding.

This, however, is not the case in solid-phase immunoassays. These widely used systems consist of solid-phase radioimmunoassay, immunocytochemistry, and enzyme-linked immunosorbent assay (ELISA). In *solid-phase radioimmunoassay,* antigen is adsorbed to a polystyrene plate. This is followed by antibody (first antibody) and a radiolabeled anti-antibody (second antibody). Alternatively, the first antibody is used in excess and its binding analyzed by judicious addition of radiolabeled antigen. Concentrations of unknown, unlabeled antigens added to the system can be evaluated by inhibition of radioactivity. In *immunocytochemistry,* insoluble antigen is presented by the tissue section examined. The antibodies are analyzed by suitable markers which may be fluorescent, electro-opaque, or enzymatic. *ELISA* is an adaptation of immunocytochemistry to antigens insolubilized on polystyrene plates. Reaction with antibody is developed by a series of second antibodies resembling those of immunocytochemical techniques. Antibody binding is evaluated by the concentration of first antibodies yielding a given optical density of enzyme reaction product. Unknown antigens are evaluated by inhibition of this reaction upon admixture with the first antibody. While liquid-phase systems are widely used for measurement of antigen concentration, solid-phase systems are more suitable for measurement of concentration of antibodies. However, Peterfy et al. (25) have shown that these systems fail with low-affinity antibodies. In a solid-phase radioimmunoassay system, increasing concentrations of high-affinity monoclonal antibodies rapidly reached the point of 50% of maximal binding (Fig. 1-5). The binding curves were steep, permitting evaluation of affinity, and they rapidly reached the plateau of maximal binding. With low-affinity antibodies, on the other hand, the curves were flat, that is, increasing concentrations of antibody had only a minimal effect and 50% binding points were never reached. The low levels of counts and the flatness of the curves made it difficult to measure antibody concentrations and also gave unfavorable signal-to-background count ratios. Similar curves were obtained in the ELISA assay.

If these systems were single-phase systems, one would expect that even with low-affinity antibodies a concentration could be found, albeit a high one, with which binding of antigen would be 50% of the maximum achievable with the high-affinity antibodies, provided the antibodies are monoclonal. However, these are solid-phase systems, in which unbound material must be washed away

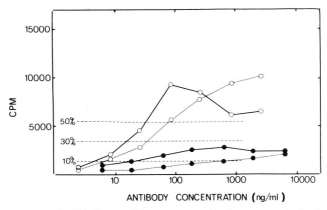

Figure 1-5. Comparison of solid-phase radioimmunoassay binding curves obtained with high-affinity (open circles) and low-affinity (closed circles) monoclonal antibodies when the solid-phase antigen bore 9 (solid line) or 1.5 (dotted line) mol of hapten per mole of bovine serum albumin carrier. Maximal binding of the radioactivity was 10,500 counts (100%). [Reproduced with permission from Peterfy F, Kuusela P, Makela O: Affinity requirements for antibody assays mapped by monoclonal antibodies *J Immunol* **130:**1809, 1983, Am. Assoc. of Immunologists. (25)].

from the solid surface. During washes, dissociation can occur, which increases in degree the more extensive the washing. With high-affinity antibodies, the amounts of bound reagents lost on washing are minimal (page 200), but with low-affinity antibodies these amounts are substantial. In the latter case, counts remaining on the surface will be low, independently of whether prior to washing the bound radioactivity was low, in the case of low concentrations of added antibody, or high, in the case of high concentrations.

THE PRECIPITIN REACTION

Monomeric immunoglobulin has two antigen binding sites. Most antigens possess multiple determinants. Hence, under suitable proportions antigen and antibody form large aggregates that precipitate out of solution. The size of the aggregates does not only depend on the number of determinants in the antigen and binding sites in the antibody but also on binding affinity. If affinity is high, aggregates form rapidly, and dissociation of aggregates becomes negligible. However, if an antibody preparation contains a large proportion of antibodies of very low affinity, polymer formation is slow and not all antigen or antibody in solution may precipitate, irrespective of proportion. Furthermore, immune precipitates obtained with antibodies with low affinity may have high solubilities. It follows that estimation of protein contents of an immune precipitate does not necessarily evaluate all the antibody in solution.

Three zones can be distinguished in the precipitin reaction of antigen and antibody: an *antibody excess* zone in which no free antigen remains in solution; an *equivalence* zone in which neither free antigen nor free antibody are detected in solution; and an *antigen excess* zone in which free antigen as well as soluble antigen-antibody complexes are in solution. Complexes of antibody and excess antigen are soluble because in excess many antigen molecules combine with antibody by one epitope only and thus prevent excessive growth of chains of alternating antigen and antibody. Soluble complexes can be obtained in pure form by precipitating antibody with antigen in equivalence and dissolving the precipitate in excess antigen. As this requires the breaking of multiple antigen-antibody bonds, it is a slow reaction that is only partially complete even when large excesses of antigen are used with continuous agitation. Much denaturation of protein ensues. To obtain good yields of antigen-antibody complex with little excess of antigen, as needed in some immunocytochemical applications, more efficient methods of preparation have been developed (page 95).

Immunodiffusion is a precipitin reaction in semisolid media. As a solution of antigen diffuses against a solution of antibody, a line of precipitation forms at a point of contact where optimal proportions for precipitation have been established (page 228). If the antigen solution consists of a variety of components that evoke different serum antibodies, a number of lines is likely to form as the rate of diffusion of each antigen component is different. A comparison of two or more different antigen preparations against a single antibody solution establishes antigenic identity or diversity depending on whether the antigen preparations form a common line with the antibody preparation (*line of identity*) or whether they form independent lines that cross over at their point of contact (*lines of diversity*). *Spur formation* at the point of contact means partial identity: the spur is due to unshared epitopes in one of the antigens in addition to those shared with the other antigen. Because of its relatively low sensitivity, immunodiffusion is of limited value in immunocytochemistry.

ELECTROBLOT IMMUNOCYTOCHEMISTRY

In the single-dimension electroblot technique of Towbin (26), antigen is separated according to size by electrophoresis into sodium dodecyl sulphate (SDS)-containing acrylamide gels, using either constant concentrations of acrylamide, or gradients to obtain better separation in given molecular weight regions. The separated proteins are electrophoretically transferred onto cellulose nitrate sheets, which are then cut into strips for immunocytochemical staining. Some strips as well as molecular weight standards coelectrophoresed and transferred, may be stained with Coomassie blue. In the double-dimension mode, proteins are first separated according to charge by electrophoretic focusing (27). The gel is then placed in a horizontal position over an SDS gel slab, and separation in the second dimension is carried out according to size. Following electrophoretic transfer onto cellulose nitrate sheets, analysis is again by immunocytochemistry. Electroblot methods have found special applications in correlating anatomic data obtained by immunocytochemistry of tissue sections with biochemical data obtained from materials in solution (pages 241 and 449).

RADIOIMMUNOASSAY

Radiolabeled antigen is added to antiserum, allowing time for completion of the reaction (28). Antibody immunoglobulin, containing the bound antigen, is then separated from the free antigen. This separation is usually effected by addition of anti-immunoglobulin (a *second antibody* specific to the immunoglobulin of the first antibody). For instance, sheep antiserum to rabbit immunoglobulin may be used as second antibody, if the first antibody that has reacted with the labeled antigen, is from a rabbit. The ensuing precipitate contains the bound antigen. Normal rabbit immunoglobulin is added as a carrier to the reaction with second antibody to ensure sufficient bulk of the precipitate when high dilutions of first antibody are used. The precipitate must be in excess of the solubility product of the first immunoglobulin and the second anti-immunoglobulin. Staphylococcal protein A combines specifically with the Fc portion of IgG and may be used instead of a second antibody. However, different IgG subclasses among isotypes in the same species and immunoglobulins of different species bind protein A with different affinities (29–31). Activated dextran-coated charcoal may be used as a further alternative. With dextran in a molecular range of 10,000 to 250,000, a matrix is formed that allows only absorption of unbound antigen, leaving the antibody and bound antigens in solution. The method is restricted to antigens smaller than immunoglobulins.

When using a second antibody, bound antigen can be estimated from the radioactivity of the precipitate. It is not desirable to wash the precipitate to rid it of occluded free antigen, because washing may dissociate antigen, especially when binding has been of low affinity, or when the binding reaction has been carried out, as usual, in slight antigen excess. Therefore, in general practice, the amount of free antigen occluded in the unwashed precipitate is considered background. For critical studies, it is possible to add tritiated water to a system in which radioiodinated antigen is used. The tritium label will be a tracer for the amount of solution, and thus free antigen occluded in the unwashed precipitate.

Some of the difficulties with analysis of precipitates could be avoided by measuring free antigen in the supernate and estimating bound antigen by the difference of free and added antigen. However, other difficulties arise here from the fact that radioimmunoassay analysis depends on partial binding of antigen, and the evaluation of the ratio of free to bound antigen, and that some of the most important points are obtained under conditions of a low degree of binding. Estimation of low degrees of binding from measurements on super- nates would depend on differences between similar magnitudes, thus being subject to large errors.

The dextran-coated charcoal absorption method has the advantage that bound antigen is measured in the supernate. However, the charcoal method is restricted to those systems in which the efficiency of differential absorption has been accurately evaluated.

Radioimmunoassay is primarily a method for measuring concentrations of antigen. Some of its advantages over other immunologic methods come from the fact that standard and unknown are reacted in the same tube. This can be done because the standard antigen is radiolabeled and the unknown unlabeled and, thus, both can be distinguished from each other. Since, of course, only the binding of the label is measurable, the unknown is estimated by its interference with the binding of the standard: It is a *competitive* assay of unknown with stan- dard. It follows that the more diluted a standard is, the less unknown is required for inhibition. As radiolabeling permits measurement of highly diluted antigens, the method has become the most sensitive tool available for the measurement of an unknown solute. It is applicable to any solute that possesses a functional epitope. Naturally, the applications of radioimmunoassay have spread to nearly every field of diagnostic medicine, but have become especially important in the development of modern endocrinology. Radioimmunoassay is to the detection of solutes what immunocytochemistry is to the detection of tissue constituents: both methods use immunologic tools, but deal with applications that are beyond the realm of immunology proper.

There are two basic requirements for the development of a successful radioimmunoassay:

1.   The antigen must be available in pure form. The assay will suffer in specificity to the extent that the antigen may be contaminated.

2.   The antigen must possess high specific radioactivity. The high activity is needed to permit use of the antigen at high dilution. Only a highly diluted, labeled antigen can be effectively competed with by a low concentration of unknown, unlabeled antigen. ^{125}Iodine and ^{131}iodine are the only isotopes that possess half-lives short enough to yield sufficient radioactivity for the determination of circulating or extractable hormones. This requirement implies that the antigen possesses groups that can be iodinated. Most proteins have such groups in tyrosine and histidine. Iodination should be carried out with carrier-free materials to the maximum possible extent that does not interfere with antigenic reactivity. For most large-molecular proteins, such conditions can be found. For a small peptide, such as luteinizing hormone-releasing hormone (LHRH) (page 384), which possesses only one tyrosine and one histidine, conditions are more critical, since apparently full substitution of both amino acids destroys much of its immunoreactivity. In the case of peptides or other substances that lack iodinable groups, such as somatostatin (page 367), immunoreactive derivatives possessing tyrosine must be used. Since a large protein antigen contains more groups that can be reacted with iodine than a small hapten, the sensitivity of radioimmunoassay is relatively higher with larger antigens and relatively lower with haptens. This is one of the factors that determines the relative sensitivities of radioimmunoassay and immunocytochemistry with different antigens (page 240).

The quality of antibody is less a requirement for successful radioimmunoassay than that of antigen. The antibody used does not have to be purified, since it is the purity of the antigen and not that of the antibody that determines the specificity of the reaction. Antibodies to contaminants are not relevant if the antigen is pure. High-affinity antibodies are desirable to obtain sensitivity and specificity. With high-affinity antibodies, lower amounts of iodinated antigen will yield 50% inhibition. Hence, lower amounts of competing, unknown antigen can be detected. High affinity is an expression of the fit of an epitope with the antibody. Therefore, high affinity implies high specificity. Low affinity is an expression of poor fit of an epitope with antibody, and implies that other, unrelated, epitopes may fit equally well or better. This may affect the specificity of the radioimmunoassay in that other factors than the antigen in the unknown sample may *cross-react* with the antibody during competition with the labeled antigen.

Antibodies of very low titer or affinity should be avoided for another reason.

The concentration of antiserum used should be appreciably lower than that of the carrier immunoglobulin. If the concentration is higher, the second antibody may no longer be in antibody excess (page 19) and, consequently, precipitation of the first antibody may be incomplete. In addition, a concentration of antiserum immunoglobulin close to that of the carrier immunoglobulin or in excess of it increases the bulk of the precipitate and, therefore, the radioactive background.

Radioimmunoassay tests are performed by measuring the effect of an unlabeled unknown on the binding of diluted labeled antigen with diluted antiserum. Standard curves are constructed by varying the amount of unlabeled antigen (X) added to fixed amounts of labeled antigen and diluted antiserum. The measured response (Y) is the ratio of labeled antigen bound in the presence of unlabeled antigens to that bound in the absence of unlabeled antigens (Figs. 1-6, 1-7). Straight plots are obtained if logit Y or $\log[Y/(1 - \alpha Y)]$ is plotted against log X, that is,

$$\text{logit } Y = a + b \log X$$

where b is the slope and a, the Y intercept.

If plotting of varying concentrations of an unknown yields a curve parallel to that obtained in plotting varying concentrations of standards, it is likely that the unknown reacts with the same antibody as the standard. Therefore, the unknown probably contains the same antigen. Relative concentrations of antigen can then be estimated by comparing its effect on Y with that of standard. An

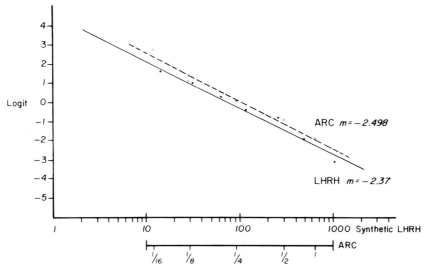

Figure 1-6. —●—●—●, a straight line with a slope of $m = -2.37$, is obtained in radioimmunoassay upon plotting logit of the ratio of labeled luteinizing hormone-releasing hormone (LHRH) bound in the presence to that bound in the absence of unlabeled LHRH against log of the concentration of unlabeled LHRH. —○—○—○, a straight line with a similar slope, is obtained when increasing concentrations of extract of arcuate nucleus (ARC) are substituted for unlabeled LHRH, suggesting the presence in the extract of a substance similar or identical in structure to LHRH. (From the work of Shirley Joseph.)

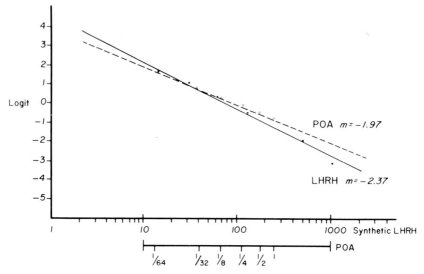

Figure 1-7. When in the plot of Fig. 1-6, hypothalamic extract is used (—O—O—O, POA), a nonparallel line with a slope of $m = -1.97$ is obtained, suggesting that the principle in the preoptic area is crossreactive with, but not identical to, LHRH (see also page 368). (From the work of Shirley Joseph.)

unknown antigen that reacts with the same antibody, but at different affinity, will not yield a parallel curve. Difference in affinity for a single antibody between one epitope and another is called *cross-reactivity*. It means that the epitopes are similar, but not identical. Lack of parallelism suggests, therefore, measurement of an antigen other than the specific antigen under investigation.

Parallelism of curves between a known and unknown antigen only means identity of the antigens. It does not suggest, as it has occasionally been done, monospecificity of the antiserum. For instance, if an antiserum to mutorotase stains renal distal convoluted tubules immunocytochemically, and if this antiserum yields parallel curves on radioimmunoassay with labeled mutorotase and unlabeled kidney extracts, one cannot conclude that the immunocytochemical stain is due to mutorotase. One could conclude that renal extract contains mutorotase, provided the labeled mutorotase was pure. However, it is quite possible for the antiserum used to contain antibodies to renal constituents other than mutorotase. In the radioimmunoassay, only antibodies to mutorotase are detected, while antibodies to other renal constituents do not participate in the reaction. However, they may well stain distal convoluted tubules immunocytochemically.

Lack of parallelism, such as that revealing at least partial nonidentity of LHRH with cross-reactive hypothalamic factors (Fig. 1-7), is due to heterogeneity of antibodies in the antisera. The affinities of at least some of these antibodies for the extracted factors differs from those for LHRH. If monoclonal antibody is used (23), parallel lines are obtained (32).

Radioimmunoassay is not a test for specificity of antibodies used in immunocytochemistry (pages 240 and 251).

IMMUNOGLOBULIN ISOTYPES AND THE SECONDARY, BIOLOGIC FUNCTIONS OF ANTIBODIES

The primary binding of antibodies with antigen is responsible for only a few of their biologic functions. Antibodies may bind with the surface of a virus and prevent its cellular attachment and infectivity. Antibodies may cause pernicious anemia by reacting with intrinsic factor and preventing its binding of vitamin B12. An antibody may prevent tetanus by combining with tetanus toxin. In general, however, the primary reaction of antibody with antigen in itself neither causes the immune elimination of an antigen nor the immune destruction of a cell. These are secondary phenomena that are mediated by properties of the constant regions of the H chains and are characteristic for the isotype involved.

All isotypes of immunoglobulins possess a basic four-chain structure similar to that of the IgG monomer. The molecular weights of these four-chain units differ slightly because of different lengths of H chains and because of different carbohydrate contents. The L chains and the variable portions of the H chains are not isotype-specific. In IgA, monomers or dimers of the basic four-chain structure occur. *IgM* consists of pentamers of the basic four-chain structure. The heavy chain of IgM (μ chain) possesses about 500 amino acid residues and contains oligosaccharides attached at five sites. The molecular weight of the pentameric IgM molecule is about 1,000,000. Each of the two μ chains in the monomer is joined to an adjacent monomer covalently via attachment to a *junction* (J) *chain* through a single sulfhydryl bond (33). The Fcμ fragment obtained by papain digestion is an annular structure still joined by sulfhydryl bonds that form the central disk of the pentameric molecule. Of the 10 idiotypic sites of IgM, five are functionally available.

Matthew and Reichardt (34) used tryptic digestion along with mild reduction to convert the 10^6 dalton IgM of a monoclonal antibody reactive with synaptic fractions to fragments less than 2×10^5 dalton. These fragments possess intact κ chains and nearly intact μ chains and apparently represent a four-chain monomer derived from the naturally occurring pentamer. Immunocytochemical localization of synaptic areas in cerebellum was much more efficient with the 2×10^5 dalton fragment than with intact IgM, apparently because of better penetration of frozen sections by the smaller fragment.

A monomeric four-chain IgM occurs in nature as the membrane-bound receptor on cells destined to become immunoglobulin secretors (B cells, page 285). Since it is difficult to solubilize this membrane-bound monomer, its amino acid composition had to be deduced from the base sequence of the DNA produced by plasmid insertion of the double stranded cDNA complementary to the IgM-coding mRNA. The membrane-bound IgM differs in the C-terminus of the μ chain, in that the last 20 residues of the μ chain of soluble IgM are replaced by a hydrophobic 41 amino acid sequence. Apparently this hydrophobic end is responsible for insertion of IgM into the cell membrane.

Transport of immunoglobulin through membranes, such as placental membranes, is an active process almost uniquely characteristic for *IgG*. IgM is essentially intravascular, but IgG is also found in extravascular fluids.

The constant regions of IgG and IgM contain binding sites for the first component of *complement*. This binding may initiate a cascade of enzymatic reactions that eventually lead to lysis of a cell with which the IgG or IgM antibody may have reacted. Some autoimmune diseases may be mediated by this mechanism (page 478). In the absence of complement, reaction of antibody with cells does not progress to lysis.

Many cells, especially lymphocytes and macrophages, contain receptors for Fcγ. Some lymphocytes contain receptors for Fcμ (35). Fcγ receptors are important in one form of cytotoxicity (page 284). The Fc receptor reactivity of antibodies must be considered as source of nonspecificity in immunocytochemistry of unfixed or frozen tissues (page 51 and 145).

IgA is the main immunoglobulin of human secretions, such as colostrum, milk, nasal secretions, saliva, and gastrointestinal secretions. Two subclasses among isotypes are determined by an α1 and α2 chain. In most cases, the α2 chains are bound to the L chains without disulfide linkages. Alpha chains and IgA possess a tendency toward spontaneous polymerization. Most of the circulating IgA, however, is monomeric. The bulk of the secreted IgA is dimeric. Dimerization is mediated via a J chain. The dimer is associated with a *secretory component,* a carbohydrate-containing β globulin. Some of the secretory component is also free in secretions. The secretory component confers upon IgA an increased resistance against proteolytic enzymes, such as found in secretions. Bloth and Svehag (36) have shown by electron microscopy that dimeric IgA has great flexibility about the point where both Fc regions are joined. The IgA found in secretions is produced locally as monomers by the lymphoid cell aggregates usually present in large quantities in submucosal areas and beneath the epithelial surface of exocrine glands. Dimerization is a function of the epithelium.

Hsu and Hsu (37) revealed by immunocytochemistry IgA and secretory component in selected periportal liver cells (Fig. 1-8). Apparently IgA is capable of intracytoplasmic transport from blood serum into the bile. The secretory component may act as a receptor for IgA.

IgE, discovered by K. and T. Ishizaka (38) is found in very small quantities in human and animal sera and carries the unique property of sensitizing *species-*

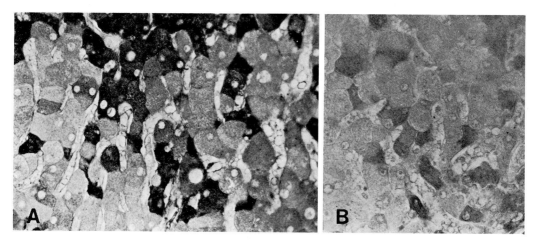

Figure 1-8.   Human liver, paraffin section, stained for IgA (A) and secretory component (B). PAP method (page 90). ×600 [From Hsu and Hsu (37)].

homologous tissue toward allergic reactions (reaginic antibody in man, homocytotropic antibody in animals). IgE myeloma protein is a carbohydrate-containing four-chain immunoglobulin with a molecular weight of about 190,000. IgE binds specifically with the surface of basophils in circulation and mast cells in tissues, and acts as receptor for specific antigens. Upon reaction with antigen, the cells degranulate, histamine and other substances are released, and the typical effects of reaginic hypersensitivity ensue. The binding of these cells can be studied by radioautography if degranulation and histamine release are prevented by ethylene diamine tetra-acetate, thus permitting cellular identification. Using radioiodinated anti-ε with preparations of human cells or tissues and developing the reaction with a sensitive photographic emulsion, silver grains are found only on basophils and mast cells, thus identifying these cells as the only cells that have bound IgE from the serum of their donor.

When serum from a ragweed-sensitive patient is added to normal leukocytes, exposure to ragweed allergen releases histamine from the basophils in the preparation. If myeloma IgE is added to normal leukocytes, exposure to anti-IgE also releases histamine. This shows that it is the IgE moiety in both reactions that is responsible for the specific attachment at basophils and the release of histamine. IgE may be a predisposing factor in immune complex disease (page 481).

IgD is found in small concentrations in serum but acts, along with IgM, as an antigen receptor in cells bound to become immunoglobulin-secreting. Apparently these cells, as they mature, acquire first the ability to form IgM, then IgD, and finally that of secreting immunoglobulin isotypes other than IgM or IgD. This isotype shift is not accompanied by change in V regions (page 11).

IgD possesses an extremely long and flexible hinge region and is highly susceptible to proteolytic digestion. In contrast, IgM possesses no demonstrable hinge region at all. The flexibility of IgD may make the receptor more susceptible to antigen-stimulated aggregation and the receptor internalization prior to proliferation and immunoglobulin secretion (page 277). Immune tolerance (page 281) is more difficult to induce in IgD than IgM-bearing cells.

AFFINITY PURIFICATION OF ANTIBODIES

Antibodies can be purified from serum by precipitation with specific antigen. The washed precipitate is dissociated at low pH, and antigen separated from antibody at this pH by gradient sedimentation. Alternatively, the precipitate can be dissociated by certain salts, such as magnesium chloride or potassium thiocyanate. At '2.5 *M* concentration, solution of immune precipitates is only partial, while at higher concentrations denaturation of antibody is extensive. Salt-dissociated antibodies and antigens can be separated by gel filtration columns equilibrated with the dissociating ions. Antibodies to individual epitopes, such as 2,4-dinitrophenol (DNP), can be purified by (1) precipitation with DNP-conjugated ovalbumin, (2) dissociation of the precipitate with DNP-lysine, (3) separation of antigen (DNP-ovalbumin) from antibody by gel filtration in the presence of DNP-lysine, and (4) removal of DNP-lysine by dialysis, first against buffered DNP, and finally against buffered saline. The DNP-lysine-antibody complex is soluble because of the monovalence (single binding site) of the DNP epitope.

Immunoabsorption may be employed instead of immune precipitation. An *immunoabsorbent* is an insolubilized antigen. Antigen may be insolubilized by polymerization, as for instance with glutaraldehyde, or by reaction with cyanogen bromide-activated cellulose, or other insoluble matrices, such as bromacetyl cellulose, or by entrapment in cross-linked microporous polyacrylamide gel (39). Elution is carried out under conditions resembling those of dissociation of immune precipitates. Immunoabsorbents have the advantage that only antibody and not antigen is eluted, thus bypassing the need of lengthy separation procedures. However, immunoabsorbents require more antigen than immune precipitates.

In general, affinity purification recovers only part of the antibodies removed from serum. The better the affinity of antibody, the poorer the yield. The antibodies of highest affinities, which often comprise only a small fraction of total antibody, are usually not dissociated from immune precipitates or immunoabsorbents.

The yields in protein, but not in average affinity, are usually higher with immunoabsorbents than with immune precipitates. In immunoabsorption, both low- and high-affinity antibodies are bound, and low-affinity antibodies are recovered in high yield. In immune precipitation, the antibodies with low affinity usually remain in solution. The selection of higher-affinity antibodies in the immune precipitate diminishes recovery in terms of antibody protein, although the average binding affinity of the recovered antibody is probably higher than with immunoabsorbents.

Immune precipitates selecting for antibodies with high affinity can be obtained by precipitation in antibody excess: high-affinity antibodies bind antigen rapidly and leave a large proportion of low-affinity antibodies in solution. Presumably, for this reason Ternyck and Avrameas (40) obtained especially low yields of antibodies purified from immune precipitates prepared in antibody excess. The question of high affinity of purified antibodies is important in several immunocytochemical methods.

Immunoabsorbents are more efficient if spacers are inserted between the epitope and the backbone of the matrix. Such an immunoabsorbent has been prepared by Varga et al. (41) by activating nylon disks with hydrochloric acid and reacting them with poly-L-serine (41 residues). The free amino groups of the poly-L-serine were then reacted with one arm of glutaraldehyde. Finally, the second arm was allowed to react with a protein antigen. Immunoabsorption was carried out by filtration through the disk. It was found that this immunoabsorbent was especially useful for removal of low-affinity antibodies. An RNAse spacer was used by us in the immunoabsorption of anti-LHRH (42).

When antibodies are removed from serum by an affinity column and purification is carried out by elution with a gradient of increasing acidity, it is found that antibodies will be solubilized over a wide range of pHs. Apparently the antibodies of lower affinities are recovered first, while those of higher affinities require lower pH. The yields are not always good. Antibodies of highest affinity cannot always be recovered from the column. For this reason, affinity-purified antibodies are generally not recommended for immunocytochemistry. Exceptions are cases in which a large contamination of interfering antibodies must be eliminated, as, for instance, in the removal of antioxytocin from antiserum to vasopressin. However, in this case it is better to employ an oxytocin matrix to remove the antioxytocin and use the remaining antiserum for immunocytochemistry, rather than passing the serum through an antivasopressin column, discarding the effluent serum, and using acid-eluted purified antivasopressin. Absorption with solid oxytocin was employed by Van Leeuwen and Swaab (43) in their immunocytochemical differentiation of vasopressin and oxytocin-producing cells using antigens attached to cyanogen bromide-activated sepharose beads as absorbent.

The low affinity of antibodies recovered from serum by affinity purification is reflected in data that gave the maximum size of glucogen epitopes recognized by purified antibody as a length of four amino acids, with the majority of antibodies recognizing only two to three amino acids. If antibodies would recognize only such short sequences, cross-reactions would be extremely extensive, considering the multitude of antigens produced by a host. In fact, however, we found that cross-reactions of monoclonal antibodies to specific neuronal constituents were extremely few (44). Apparently, with serum antibodies, affinity purification eliminates those of high affinity.

Data with nonpurified serum antibodies that attribute to antibodies a capability of recognizing up to seven amino acids, seem to be more valid than those obtained with purified antibodies. When monoclonal antibodies are affinity-purified, elution will occur in a narrow band with a characteristic pH, rather than in a broad band over a wide range of pHs as observed with antisera. This, of course, is a reflection of the homogeneous idiotype characteristic of monoclonal antibodies. We have taken advantage of this phenomenon for the isolation of a luteinizing hormone-releasing hormone (LHRH) prohormone by affinity purification with a column containing insolubilized monoclonal anti-LHRH (32). The pH gradient position was determined at which absorbed LHRH is released from the column. This point was assumed to be the same as that for release of the immunocytochemically cross-reactive LHRH prohormone. The prohormone was, indeed, recovered from the column at the predetermined pH point after adsorption to the column of LHRH-free hypothalamic extract.

REFERENCES

1. Flaster MS, Schley C, Zipser B: Generating monoclonal antibodies against excised bands to correlate immunocytochemical and biochemical data. *Brain Res* **177**:196, 1983.

2. Sims J, Rabbitts TH, Estess P, Slaughter C, Tucker PW, Capra JD: Somatic mutation in genes for the variable portion of the immunoglobulin heavy chain. *Science* **216**:309, 1952.

3. Rodwell JD, Karush F: Restriction in IgM expression. I. The V_H region of equine antilactose antibodies. *Mol Immunol* **17**:1553, 1980.

4. Honjo T, Katoaka T: Organization of immunoglobulin heavy genes and allelic deletion model. *Proc Natl Acad Sci USA* **75**:2140, 1978.

5. Kehoe JM, Capra JD: Localization of two additional hypervariable regions in immunoglobulin heavy chains. *Proc Natl Acad Sci USA* **68**:2019, 1971.

6. Capra JP, Winchester RW, Kunkel HG: Hypergammaglobulinemic purpura. Studies on the unusual anti-γ-globulins characteristic of the sera of these patients. *Medicine* **50**:125, 1971.

7. Edelman GM, Cunningham BA, Gall WE, Gottlieb PD, Rutisha U, Waxdal MJ: The covalent structure of an entire γG immunoglobulin molecule. *Proc Natl Acad Sci USA* **63**:78, 1969.

8. Putnam FW, Shinizu A, Paul C, Shinoda T: Variation and homology in immunoglobulin heavy chains. *Fed Proc* **31**:193, 1972.

9. Labaw LW, Davies DR: The molecular outline of human γG1 immunoglobulin from an EM study of crystals. *J Ultrastruct Res* **40**:349, 1972.

10. Sarma VR, Davis DR, Labaw LW, Silverton EW, Terry WD: Crystal structure of an immunoglobulin molecule by X-ray diffraction and electron microscopy. *Cold Spring Harbor Symp Quant Biol* **36**:413, 1971.

11. Hozumi N, Tonegawa S: Evidence for somati rearrangement of immunoglobulin genes coding for variable and constant regions. *Proc Natl Acad Sci USA* **73**:3628, 1976.

12. Gilbert W: Why genes in pieces. *Nature* **271**:501, 1978.

13. Wang AC, Fudenberg HH, Goldrosen MH, Freedman MH: Chemical studies of heavy chains of two IgG1-λ myeloma proteins from a single patient. *Immunocytochemistry* **A**:473, 1972.

14. Fair DS, Krueger RG, Gleich GJ, Dyle RA: Studies on IgA and IgG monoclonal proteins derived from a single patient. I. Evidence for shared individually specific antigenic determinants. *J Immunol* **107**:1226, 1971.

15. Gottlieb AB, Engelhard M, Kunkel H, Tanigaki N, Pressman D: A cross reaction between B2 microglobulin and kappa light chains. *J Immunol* **9**:2001, 1977.

16. Estess P, Otani F, Milner ECB, Capra JD, Tucker PW: Gene rearrangements in monoclonal A/J anti-arsonate antibodies. *J Immunol* **129**:2319, 1983.

17. Gearhart PJ, Johnson ND, Douglass RD, Hood L: IgG antibodies to phosphorylcholine exhibit more diversity than their IgM counterparts. *Nature* **291**:29, 1981.

18. Slater RJ, Ward SM, Kunkel HG: Immunologic relation among the myeloma proteins. *J Exp Med* **101**:85, 1955.

19. Sher A, Lord E, Cohn M: Reconstitution from subunits of the hapten binding sites and idiotypic determinants of mouse antiphosphorylcholine myeloma proteins. *J Immunol* **107**:1226, 1971.

20. Reth M, Kelsoe G, Rajensky K: Idiotypic reaction by isologous monoclonal anti-idiotype antibodies. *Nature* **290**:257, 1981.

21. Subbarno B, Mosier B: Induction of B-lymphocyte proliferation by monoclonal anti-Lyb2 antibody. *J Immunol* **130**:2033, 1983.

22. Richards FF, Konigsberg WH, Rosenstein RW, Vaugn JM: On the specificity of antibodies. Biochemical and biophysical evidence indicates the existence of polyfunctional antibody combining regions. *Science* **187**:30, 1975.

23. Knapp R, Harwell L, Sternberger LA: A monoclonal antibody to luteinizing hormone-releasing hormone. Preparation and binding studies. *J Neuroimmunol,* **6**:361, 1984.

24. Moyle WR, Lin C, Corson RL, Erlich PH: Quantitative explanation for increased affinity of monoclonal antibodies: Importance of a circular complex. *Mol Immunol* **20**:439, 1983.

25. Péterfy F, Kuusela P, Makela O: Affinity requirements for antibody assays mapped by monoclonal antibodies. *J Immunol* **130**:1809, 1983.

26. Towbin H, Straeblin T, Gordon J: Electrophoretic transfer of proteins from polyacrylamide gels to nitrocellulose sheets: Procedure and some applications. *Proc Natl Acad Sci USA* **76**:4350, 1979.

27. Laemmli UK: Cleavage of structural proteins during assembly of the head of bacteriophage Ty. *Nature* **227**:680, 1970.

28. Skelly DS, Brown LP, Besch PK: Radioimmunoassay. *Clin Chem* **19**:146, 1973.

29. MacKenzie M, Warner NL, Michell GF: The binding of murine immunoglobulins to staphylococcal protein A. *J Immunol* **120**:1493, 1978.

30. Chalon MP, Milne RW, Vaerman J-P: Interactions between mouse immunoglobulins and staphylococcal protein A. *Scand J Immunol* **9**:359, 1979.

31. Vidal MA, Conde F: Studies of the IgM and IgA contamination obtained by eluting IgG from protein A-sepharose columns with pH steps. *J Immunol Meth* **35**:169, 1980.

32. Knapp RJ, Sternberger LA: Heterogeneity of luteinizing hormone-releasing hormone studied with a monoclonal antibody. *Soc Neurosci Abst* **16**:138, 1983.

33. Inman FP, Ricardo Jr MJ: The association of J chain with the Fc region of human IgM. *J Immunol* **112**:229, 1974.

34. Matthew WD, Reichardt LF: Development and application of an efficient procedure for converting mouse IgM into small, active fragments. *J Immunol Meth* **50**:239, 1982.

35. Moretta L, Ferrarini M, Mingari MC, Moretta A, Webb SR: Subpopulations of human T cells identified by receptors for immunoglobulin and mitogen responsiveness. *J Immunol* **117**:2171, 1976.

36. Bloth B, Svehag SE: Further studies on the ultrastructure of dimeric IgA of human origin. *J Exp Med* **133**:1035, 1971.

37. Hsu S-M, Hsu P-L: Demonstration of IgA and secretory component in human hepatocytes. *Gut* **21**:985, 1980.

38. Ishizaka K, Tomioko H, Ishizaka T: Mechanisms of passive sensitization. I. Presence of IgE and IgG molecules on human leukocytes. *J Immunol* **105**:1459, 1970.

39. Carrel S, Barandum S: Protein-containing polyacrylamide gels: their use as immunoabsorbents of high capacity. *Immunocytochemistry* **8**:39, 1971.

40. Ternyck T, Avrameas S: Effects of electrolytes and distilled water on antigen-antibody complexes. *Biochem J* **125**:297, 1971.

41. Varga JM, Lande S, Richards F: Immunoglobulins with multiple binding functions. II. The use of nylon-polyserine whisker discs in screening myeloma immunoglobulins for binding activity. *J Immunol* **112**:1565, 1974.

42. Sternberger LA, Petrali JP, Joseph SA, Mills KM: Specificity of the immunocytochemical LHRH receptor reaction. *Endocrinology* **102**:63, 1978.

43. VanLeeuwen FW, Swaab DF: Specific immune electron-microscopic localization of vasopressin and oxytocin in neurohypophsis of the rat. *Cell Tiss Res* **177**:493, 1977.

44. Ostermann E, Sternberger NH, Sternberger LA: Immunocytochemistry of brain-reactive antibodies in peripheral tissues. *Cell Tiss Res* **228**:459, 1983.

Chapter Two

Conjugated Antibody Methods

We have seen in the preceding chapter that the specificity of high-affinity antibodies not only permits the distinction of innumerable, different antigen molecules, but also the dissection of different epitopes within given antigens. Immunocytochemistry utilizes the antibody specificity of immunoglobulins to detect specific constituents within tissue sections prepared for microscopy. Common analytic methods used in biochemistry require isolation of a tissue constituent prior to examination. In immunocytochemistry, the tissue constituent is examined in situ. There are other methods, besides immunocytochemistry, that permit examination of constituents in situ. These methods include enzyme histochemistry, in which a substrate analog is reacted with enzyme in situ to produce a visible reaction product. However, modern immunocytochemistry has been shown to be, in general, more specific than enzyme histochemistry (page 165). Other nonimmunocytochemical methods include autoradiography, in which a labeled substance is administered in vivo, and its distribution, as well as that of its metabolites, is examined in tissue sections after prolonged exposure on a photographic plate. Alternatively, a labeled ligand may be applied in vitro to a receptor-containing tissue section. These methods are restricted to synthetic or at least highly purified, well-defined substances. They often complement immunocytochemical data and can be carried out simultaneously with immunocytochemistry on the same tissue section. Radioactive tracers permit examination of physiologic and metabolic processes, which at least until recently, were beyond the realm of immunocytochemistry.

Immunocytochemistry requires specific antibodies. High-affinity antibodies increase reaction specificity and reliability and decrease background as well as cross-reactions with undesired antigens. This leads to the main problem that has besieged immunocytochemistry for a long time. What is an undesired antigen? Immunocytochemistry has required isolated antigens for production of specific antibodies. Therefore, to the extent that we need prior knowledge of the antigen, immunocytochemistry of the tissue, in itself, tells us little on the nature of the antigen. The information obtained by immunocytochemistry, in general, has been limited to histologic distribution of antigens in situ, provided the nature of the antigen itself has been determined separately by biochemical methods. By itself, immunocytochemistry told us little about the biochemical processes the antigen was undergoing at the time the tissue was obtained. Only recently, with the use of sensitive immunocytochemical technique in conjunction with monoclonal antibodies, has it been possible to liberate immunocytochemistry from the need of biochemically defining an antigen prior to immunization. With monoclonal antibodies, different forms of given antigens, not previously isolated, have been detected immunocytochemically in situ. Immunocytochemistry has now matured and is no longer restricted to be a purely histologic method, but may become a biochemical method by its own rights (page 427).

USE OF MARKERS

At high-resolution electron microscopy, immunoglobulin molecules are visible, and hence, their reaction with antigens is discernible. However, isolated antigen is required, free of surrounding tissue. The isolated antigen, if reacted at high dilution with purified antibody, will be "decorated" by the antibody, and if sprayed on grids for electron microscopy, this reaction can be visualized. However, if antibody is reacted with antigens in tissue, surrounding structures mask this decorating effect. Furthermore, tissue sections, even if of the thinness required of electron microscopy, do not permit the resolution necessary for detection of antibody molecules attached to antigen.

In order to reveal reaction of antibody with antigens in tissue sections in which a given antigen is surrounded by other nonimmunoreactive substances, it is necessary to mark the antibody with labels that provide for its visualization either by light or electron microscopy. There exist a great number of possible compounds that can be attached to antibody covalently or noncovalently. Covalent attachment is either via lysine and ε-amino groups of immunoglobulin (used commonly) or via tyrosine or histidine groups (not generally used) and occasionally via sulfhydryl groups. Other forms of attachment utilize chelation or colloidal sol formation. Finally, noncovalent labeling may be achieved by immunologic bonds only.

Many labels are not intense enough for most immunocytochemical applications. For instance, the color of the colloidal gold-protein A complex can be used for light microscopy (1) only at high concentrations of antibody or high densities of antigen. The electron opacity provided by conjugation of up to 200 atoms of uranium per molecule of antibody under specific protection of the antibody idiotypic sites (2), is not as good as that available from other markers.

The markers that survived staining intensity tests are, for light microscopy, highly fluorescent compounds (fluorescein and rhodamine) and certain enzymes for which substrate analogues exist that yield visible reaction products at high efficiency. These enzymes include horseradish peroxidase, *Aspergillus niger* glucose oxidase, and intestinal alkaline phosphatase. Staining intensities achieved by any of these markers is about equal. The only way to improve sensitivity of immunocytochemical methods is by the manner in which these markers are linked to the antigen via antibodies. The mode of this linkage determines sensitivity by affecting both staining intensity and background. Hence, much of immunocytochemical methodology deals with this linkage problem, irrespective of which marker happens to be chosen.

Markers for transmission electron microscopy incorporate electron density in the form of heavy metals. The markers include ferritin, colloidal gold, and enzyme reaction products that are able to precipitate upon them reduced osmium tetroxide. All these markers are detectable at the level of a single antibody molecule. As in light microscopy, sensitivity of immunocytochemistry does not depend upon the kind of marker used. Again, sensitivity differs with the manner in which the marker is linked to tissue antigen.

IMMUNOFLUORESCENCE

In the early forties, immunology had established itself as a science. The word immunochemistry had been coined; quantitation of immunologic techniques had become the requirement of the day, and Kabat and Mayer were writing their first edition of *Experimental Immunochemistry*. Massugi had produced experimental glomerulonephritis by injection into rats of duck antirat kidney serum, and Kay had shown that the lesion was produced by an autoimmune mechanism. Rheumatic fever was an enigma, and the question was timely whether its characteristic lesion, the Aschoff nodule, contained a specific antigen, perhaps a streptococcal product, or whether it was an expression of autoimmune hypersensitivity, or both. These were the days when two pages in the *Proceedings of the Society of Experimental Biology and Medicine* and 11 pages in the *Journal of Immunology* brought the first communication on the labeling of antibodies with fluorescent groups and the detection by fluorescent microscopy of pneumococcal antigens in sections of pneumococcus-infected tissue.

When these first reports of Coons appeared, immunology was already contributing a large proportion of articles in the *Journal of Experimental Medicine*. Yet, little was on the horizon to anticipate the far-reaching role that immunology would play in areas of biology and medicine beyond immunity and allergy. For as long as 10 years, Coons' first communication found no followers. Use of fluorescein-conjugated antibodies was considered a difficult technique. Indeed, the technique did not become easier when nonspecific staining was discovered by Coons in the early fifties in a report that also gave more details about preparation of fluorescein isocyanate, conjugation with antibodies, and preparation of microtome sections for staining with fluorescein-conjugated antibodies (3). The necessity of low ratios of fluorescein to protein had become apparent, and the removal of nonspecific staining by absorption with liver powder had become an empirical practice. More importantly, however, by then science had progressed to a point that the genius of Albert Coons found appropriate recognition. It must have been Coons' conviction in the ultimate importance of his work that made him persist in following his original discovery with further work 10 years later, thereby initiating immunocytochemistry as that subdiscipline of immunology that was primarily responsible for bringing immunology into pathology and for bringing from the category of unknown to that of defined etiology a greater number of diseases than any other advance in medical sciences. As a result, nowadays 45% of articles in a general medical journal, such as the *Lancet,* rely on immunology as compared to 5% in the preimmunofluorescence days.

In the preimmunofluorescence days, most immunology dealt primarily with serum factors. It is largely due to immunofluorescence that the main expression of modern immunology is in cellular immunology. Even though in the course of time immunocytochemical methods other than immunofluorescence have been developed, immunofluorescence is still the major tool in the study of the cells participating in the immune response, in the study of antigens in tissue culture, in the rapid detection of microorganisms in tissue, and in the visualization of interactions on the cell surface. Immunofluorescence is the only method that permits a cell to remain viable after immunocytochemical examination.

When tissues are stained with routine, nonspecific stains for histology and pathology, such as eosin and hematoxylin, the color contrast is sufficient that bright red and deep blue can easily be seen in the light microscope despite the thinness of a 2- to 7-μm section. Offhand it appears conceivable, therefore, to dye antibodies in solution and use, in turn, the colored antibody for specific localization of tissue antigens in microscopy. Indeed, antibodies can react with dyes just as well as tissue constituents do. Azo-dyes give some of the strongest colors. They react with the tyrosine groups in the protein molecule. The reaction of antibody with azo-dye must be restricted to less than 10 molecules of dye per molecule of antibody because increasing extent of reaction progressively destroys antibody activity and, in many cases, also interferes with antibody solubility. When only a small number of dye molecules has reacted with antibody and antibody activity has been largely retained, the resulting solution of antibody immunoglobulin is nonetheless deeply colored at the high immunoglobulin concentration viewed in a test tube. However, the color is insufficient to be recognized through the microscope in a 2- to 15-μm-thick section used for examination of tissue, even if an abundant antigen, such as a viral inclusion body, has reacted with specific antibody. The microscopist would have to distinguish unstained tissue that has full transmission, say 100%, from weakly stained tissue whose transmission is impaired by say 3%. The difference between 100% and 97% transmission cannot be discerned by the observer. If one makes an antibody fluorescent by conjugation with a single fluorescent group, choosing a strongly absorbing molecule, such as fluorescein isocyanate, a conjugated antibody solution is obtained that absorbs much less light energy than the antibody labeled with 10 azo-dye molecules. However, the fluorescent antibody confers bright green fluorescence to specific antigen in tissue sections. The brightness is due to the method of observation. In fluorescence microscopy, the light absorbed is of shorter wavelength than the light emitted. Since the light from the light source is partially beyond the visible range and since filters and epifluorescence microscopy are employed to eliminate the light originating from the light source, the microscopic field is dark except for the specifically stained fluorescent component. Even though the fluorescent tissue component may emit only 1% as much light as is seen in light microscopy under full transmission, this 1% is viewed in a surrounding field having practically 0% transmission and can, therefore, easily be discerned. In light microscopy when detectability of a colored component is limited by a small difference between two high-light intensities, increasing the total light intensity will yield little gain in proportional visibility. In fluorescence microscopy, on the other hand, increase of intensity of the light source does increase the sensitivity because it increases fluorescent emission against a background that still remains dark. Hence, strong light sources and good optics are essential in fluorescence microscopy.

Every organic substance absorbs light at least in the far ultraviolet and dissipates the absorbed energy either in the form of a chemical reaction, or as heat, or as visible light. We may decide, therefore, that a molecule suitable for immunofluorescence will have to possess at least two properties: (1) it must be efficient in absorbing light; (2) it must dissipate the absorbed light largely in the form of emitted light rather than as rotational and vibrational energy. We may want to add that the fluorescent molecule chosen should not be able to absorb at the wavelength at which it emits light; the fluorescence produced should not be internally quenched. Aliphatic, saturated compounds are not fluorescent. Their electrons are firmly bound and, hence, they absorb light only over a narrow spectral range in the far ultraviolet. Most bonds in these molecules are freely rotating and, hence, their absorbed energy is rapidly dissipated as rotational energy.

Absorbence of light is aided by the addition of loosely bound electrons, especially when they are dissipated over the entire molecule as resonance electrons. One condition leading to this situation is the presence of conjugated double bonds. A second condition is the presence of polar substituents that give the molecule electron-donating and electron-accepting centers. An example is a quinoline compound with a substituted pyridinium group. Of further aid is resonance dissipation of ions, such as in pseudocyanine (Fig. 2-1) or of electrons if there exist several equivalents of electron distribution (hybridization).

In order for a molecule to *emit* its absorbed light as fluorescence, that part of the molecule that is responsible for light absorption must possess a structural rigidity sufficient to prevent dissipation of the energy by rotation. These condi-

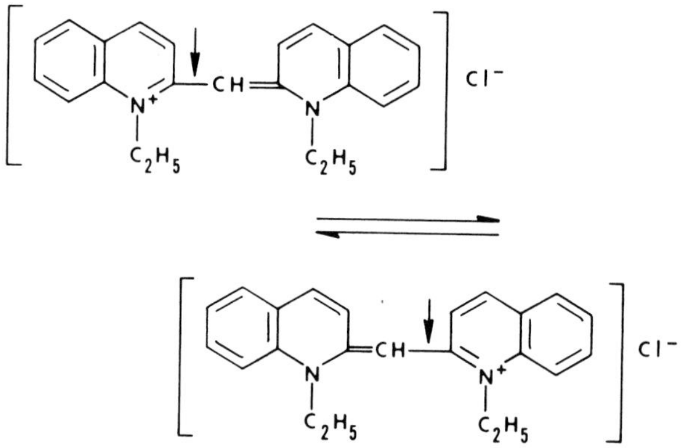

Figure 2-1. Pseudocyanine. This molecule absorbs light over a wide range of wavelengths. It possesses loosely bound electrons dissipated over the molecule through the conjugated double-bond system and through hybridization effected by the two equivalent ion-distribution states shown. The compound absorbs light strongly. It is a yellow-red dye. The molecule can rotate in the position of the arrows. Absorbed energy is thus dissipated. Hence, the compound is *not* fluorescent.

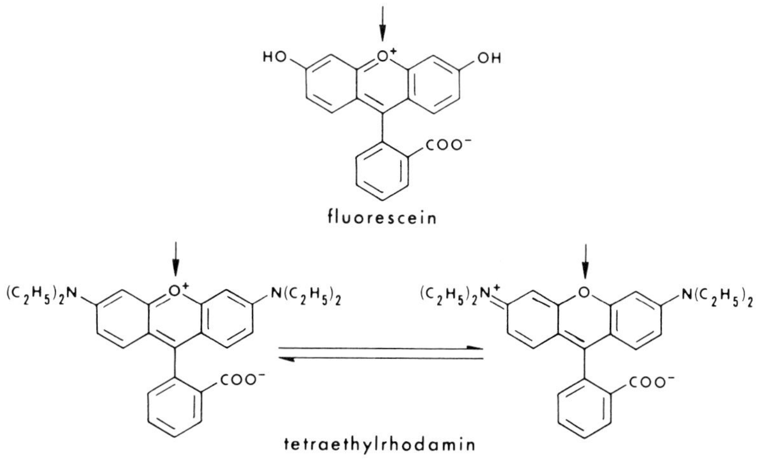

Figure 2-2. Fluorescein and its bisdialkylamino derivative, tetraethylrhodamin, absorb light efficiently because of the distribution of π-electrons over the resonating system of three conjugated rings, because of the polarity contributed by the positive and negative charges in the molecule, and because of the dispersion of electrons (loose bonds) contributed by ionic hybridization (two of the resonating forms of rhodamine are shown). The molecules are fluorescent because the light absorbing part of their structures possesses planar rigidity effected in their synthesis by the ring closure at the positions of the arrows.

tions are fulfilled by the structures of fluorescein and rhodamine (Fig. 2-2). Another reason for the choice of these markers in immunofluorescence is their greenish and reddish color of emission, respectively, which makes them distinguishable from the bluish autofluorescence of nucleic acids, and protein tryptophane and tyrosine in tissues. The two markers can also be easily distinguished from one another. This permits the simultaneous demonstration of two antigens in the same tissue section by means of two appropriate antibodies, one coupled to fluorescein and the other to rhodamine.

Fluorescein, rhodamine, and other fluorochromes must be converted to molecules capable of reacting with antibodies under conditions that do not abolish specific antibody activity: the minimal conditions are reaction in aqueous solution at or below room temperature.;

To obtain a fluorescein derivative that can be conjugated into protein, nitrofluorescein is synthesized, starting from resorcinol and 4-nitrophthalein anhydride. Via nitrophenolphthalein as an intermediate, abstraction of one molecule of water and ring closure yields nitrofluorescein (Fig. 2-3). Two isomers are obtained depending upon which of the two carboxy groups of nitrophthalein condenses with two resorcinol molecules. The isomers are separated, and one of them is reduced to fluorescein amine.

Amines, especially aromatic amines, are convenient starting materials for the preparation of highly reactive derivatives that conjugate with proteins in the cold and in pH ranges (5–9.5) at which denaturation of proteins is minimized. These derivatives include isocyanates and the more soluble isothiocyanates, diazonium salts, and azides. Alternatively, the amines can be reacted directly with protein via carbodiimide.

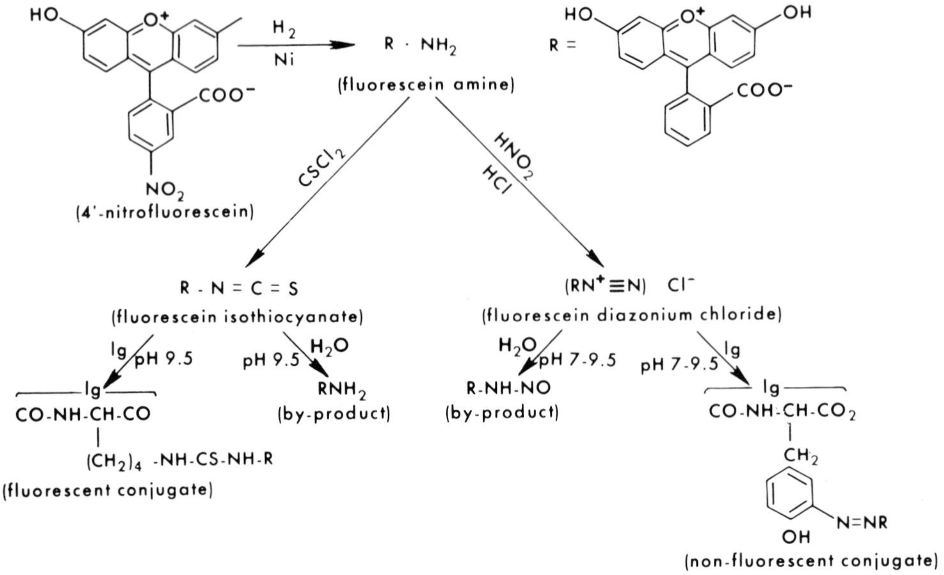

Figure 2-3. Nitrofluorescein is reduced to the amino compound. To conjugate fluorescein with protein, the isothiocyanate reaction is chosen. Conjugation occurs with the free amino groups of immunoglobulin in aqueous solution (the amino groups of lysine, as shown, or terminal amines on each L and H chain). Side reactions with the solvent lead to hydrolysis of the fluorescein isothiocyanate. Diazotization of the amine would lead to the diazonium salt that can be coupled into tyrosine of immunoglobulin. This reaction is not useful for immunofluorescence with fluorescein because the azo-dye quenches the fluorescence. A side reaction during coupling at slightly alkaline pH is formation of nitrozamine from the diazonium compound.

For use in immunofluorescence, fluorescein amine (or tetramethylrhodamine amine) is condensed with thiophosgene to form the isothiocyanate. Isothiocyanates react with amines (such as primary amino groups in protein) to form thiourea derivatives and with water at alkaline pH to reconstitute the amine from which the isothiocyanate was made. For efficient coupling of fluorescein isothiocyanate with antibody-amine, the pH should not be lower than 9.5. Some of the fluorescein isothiocyanate will be lost because of reaction with water. The resulting fluorescein amine is one of the products that must be separated from the fluorescein-conjugated antibody after conjugation.

Diazonium compounds have been used extensively for labeling of proteins since coupling proceeds rapidly and efficiently in the cold. The reaction leads to formation of azotyrosine and azohistidine bonds. The compounds are usually deep red in color; that is, they absorb blue and green light. It is for this reason that the azo-linkage is not suitable for conjugation of fluorescein with antibody: the greenish fluorescence of fluorescein is quenched by the azo-coupling. However, rhodamine analogues of fluorescein yield fluorescent conjugates via azo-linkage, because the fluorescence emission is in the orange-red range and is only partially quenched by the azo-bond. It is a weaker fluorescence than that obtained with rhodamine isothiocyanate conjugation.

For the preparation of orange-red fluorescein conjugates, rhodamine disulphonic acid is the preferred starting material. The sulfonyl chloride (prepared by reaction with phosphorus pentachloride) reacts with amino groups in the protein.

CONJUGATION OF ANTIBODY WITH FLUORESCEIN ISOTHIOCYANATE: PRINCIPLES

When reagents containing fluorescein-conjugated antibodies are used for staining of specific antigen in tissue, ideally only the specific antibody should react while the remaining constituents of the reagent are removed by washing. Fortunately, the bulk of the nonspecific constituents of the conjugate are, indeed, so removed. Therefore, it is, in general, not necessary to use purified antibodies (page 27) for reaction with fluorescein isothiocyanate. An immunoglobulin fraction containing specific antibody is quite satisfactory.

Electron hybridization makes strong fluorochromes highly polar substances. In fluorescein, two readily ionizable, aromatic hydroxyl groups and one carboxyl group contribute to polarity. Polar groups in an otherwise hydrophobic molecule further nonspecific attachment to tissue constituents, that is, "method nonspecificity" (page 47). Furthermore reaction of isothiocyanate with amino groups of proteins increases the negative charge of the conjugate and thus invites nonspecific staining, especially with positively charged proteins such as lysozyme and histones. For these reasons, two precautions are essential in the preparation of satisfactory conjugates: removal of all nonconjugated fluorescein (isothiocyanate hydrolysis products, Fig. 2-3) and avoidance of immunoglobulin conjugated with an excessive amount of fluorescein. In serum proteins, several amino groups are readily available for reaction with isothiocyanate, but others are buried and less available for reaction. The heterogeneity of immunoglobulins and the multiplicity of isothiocyanate-reactive sites in individual immunoglobulins preclude more than an approximate degree of prediction of the extent of conjugation. In any single preparation, a wide spectrum in extent of conjugation is obtained requiring separation of the more extensively and less extensively reacted portions of conjugate.

Serum albumin reacts with isothiocyanate faster than immunoglobulin. Consequently, it is not possible to even approximately predict the fluorescein-antibody ratio when isothiocyanate is added to unfractionated antisera. It is essential, therefore, to obtain at least a crude globulin fraction from serum by ammonium or sodium sulfate precipitation. For careful work, IgG should be isolated chromatographically. The isolation of IgG, at least IgG_2, from crude serum globulin, is a simple procedure (page 6). Nonspecific binding of fluorescein isothiocyanate (FITC)-conjugated immunoglobulin with tissue is minimized without greatly affecting the brightness of staining if the molar ratio of FITC to protein (expressed as IgG, molecular weight 150,000) is limited to 1 : 1 or 2 : 1. Since in the conjugation of protein with FITC most of the FITC is hydrolyzed, only a portion of the FITC actually couples with the protein. This is another reason why the extent of coupling can be predicted only approximately. Crystalline FITC should be used for a reasonably predictable reaction, or at least a reaction in which the fraction of conjugate possessing one to two fluorescein groups per 150,000 molecular weight unit comprises a high proportion of total conjugate. To this end, one uses 15 to 25 μg FITC per mg of IgG, or 6 to 8 moles of FITC per mole of immunoglobulin. Following conjugation, two separations are indicated, one of which is essential and the other desirable. Essential is the separation from the conjugate of unconjugated fluorescein (consisting of hydrolysis products, which bind nonspecifically, and conceivably even unreacted FITC that could react covalently with tissue, especially when the conjugation is carried out in the cold and staining at room temperature). The separation is best carried out by passage through a column of Sephadex G25 (4,5).

When most molecules of IgG contain either one or two molecules of fluorescein, Gaussian distribution requires that many molecules of IgG contain no fluorescein. That fraction of total conjugate that possesses fluorescein/protein (Fl/P) ratios in excess of two will increase nonspecific staining. FITC-IgG conjugates of varying Fl/P ratios can be separated on DEAE cellulose. At low ionic strength, near neutrality, unreacted IgG does not bind to the column. Conjugated protein, because of conversion of amino groups to carbamido groups and because of the charge on fluorescein is more negatively charged than unconjugated IgG. Consequently, it becomes bound on the DEAE cellulose column. Binding affinity increases with extent of conjugation. Hence, when the ionic strength of the starting buffer is increased, the unconjugated IgG will be followed, in turn, with weakly conjugated (Fl/P mole ratio of 1 to 2) and strongly conjugated protein.

It is necessary to monitor the effluent of the column for fluorescein and protein contents in order to identify the fractions with Fl/P ratios of 1 to 2. Protein concentration is monitored by absorbence at 280 nm and fluorescein concentration of 495 nm. Fluorescein diacetate is conveniently, though somewhat arbitrarily, used as a standard for estimation of conjugated FITC.

PREPARATION OF FLUORESCEIN ISOTHIOCYANATE-IMMUNOGLOBULIN CONJUGATE (FITC-IG): PROCEDURE

Except when noted otherwise, the procedure is carried out between 0 and 5°C. Antiserum is diluted with an equal volume of saline, and saturated ammonium sulfate solution is added dropwise under agitation to 37% saturation. Stirring is continued for 20 minutes and the suspension is centrifuged at 14,000 rpm for 15 minutes (Sorvall Rotor SS-34). The precipitate is redissolved in the smallest possible volume of water and dialyzed against three changes of 15 liters each of 0.01 M phosphate buffer, pH 7.5. It is of advantage to record the osmolarity or conductivity of the buffer. Completeness of dialysis may be ascertained by assuring that the osmolarity or conductivity of the last dialysis resembles that of the original buffer or by absence of ammonium ion as determined with the Nessler reagent.

For isolation of IgG (which usually comprises the bulk of antibodies in high-titered sera) as well as for purification of the conjugate, about 2 gm of DEAE-cellulose (minimum capacity: 0.14 mEq/gm) are used for each milliliter of dialyzed protein. The DEAE-cellulose is treated with 0.5N sodium hydroxide solution at room temperature. When the bulk of cellulose has settled, the supernatant suspension containing some "fines" is decanted and the sediment resuspended in water. Decantation and resuspension in water are continued until the pH of the supernate is approximately 9.0. The sediment is then resuspended in 0.1 M phosphate buffer, pH 7.5, until the pH of the supernate is 7.5. Again the sediment is washed in water until osmolarity or conductivity of the supernate is less than that of 0.01 M phosphate buffer, pH 7.5, and the suspension, as well as the remainder of the buffer to be washed, are deaerated at 1 to 5°C overnight. Continuing work at 0 to 5°C, a column is poured through a wide funnel with approximately half of the suspension, taking care to stir the suspension in the funnel in order to avoid banding. The column is then equilibrated with 0.01 M phosphate buffer, pH 7.5, and osmolarity and conductivity of the effluent buffer are again checked. The dialyzed protein, cleared by centrifugation at 35,000 rpm for 10 minutes, is applied to the column and elution is carried out with 0.01 M phosphate buffer, pH 7.5. The absorbance of the effluent is monitored at 280 nm and the eluate fractions with optical densities (OD) above 0.1 are pooled. An amount of 1.5 M sodium chloride solution is added to bring the sodium chloride concentration to 0.15 M and the material is concentrated by pressure dialysis. Protein concentration is measured by absorbence at 280 nm and adjusted to 2% in protein, 0.05 M in carbonate, and approximately 0.15N in sodium chloride by dilution with 0.5 M carbonate buffer, pH 9.5 (1/10th of the final volume) and 0.15N sodium chloride solution. Under agitation, 15 to 20 μg of dry crystalline FITC are added per milligram of IgG, and the pH is kept at 9.5 with 0.05 M sodium carbonate solution. After 1 hour, the mixture is centrifuged at 17,500 rpm for 10 minutes, and the reaction is terminated by buffer exchange and removal of unreacted FITC with a Sephadex G25 column, which has been equilibrated with phosphate-buffered saline (PBS). The crude conjugate is placed onto the column and elution is done with PBS. Two fluorochrome-containing bands separate visibly. The leading band consists of fluorescein-protein conjugate and of unconjugated protein and is obtained in the void volume. This material is collected. The trailing band contains unreacted fluorescent material (as well as the carbonate buffer). It is discarded. The collected conjugate is concentrated by pressure dialysis.

The column can be kept indefinitely if slowly but continually flushed with a deaerated solution of 0.01% sodium azide and equilibrated prior to reuse with PBS devoid of sodium azide.

At this stage, the conjugate has been freed of unreacted FITC, but it still consists of a mixture of unreacted immunoglobulin and immunoglobulin reacted with varying amounts of FITC. It is advisable to isolate from this mixture the fraction that contains one or two FITC groups per molecule of immunoglobulin. The conjugate is placed on a DEAE-cellulose column similar to that described above. Elution is carried out by a continuous gradient established between the starting buffer and the same buffer in 1N sodium chloride solution. Optical density of the effluent is monitored at 280 and 440 nm. The corresponding fluorescein/protein (Fl/P) ratio is approximately

$$\frac{(OD_{490} \text{ of conjugate}) \cdot 0.244 \cdot 150,000}{\left[(OD_{280} \text{ of conjugate}) - \frac{(OD_{490} \text{ of conjugate}) \cdot (OD_{280} \text{ of fluorescein diacetate})}{(OD_{490} \text{ of fluorescein diacetate})} \right] \cdot 0.62 \cdot 374}$$

using a molecular weight of 374 for fluorescein and 150,000 for IgG. Fractions possessing ratios between 1 and 2 are pooled, concentrated by pressure dialysis, dialyzed against PBS, and, following redetermination of the Fl/P ratio, passed through sterile Millipore filters and stored at 1 to 5°C under protection from light.

Although the measured Fl/P ratio does not reflect the accurate proportion of *conjugated* FITC to protein, it is under these conditions of measurement that the apparent ratios of 1.0 to 1.5 have been established as optimal for immunofluorescence staining.

CONJUGATION OF PURIFIED ANTIBODIES

When FITC-conjugated IgG fractions are used for staining, there is generally some nonspecific background. If the antigen concentration in tissue is high, as is usually the case with most specimens in immunofluorescence localization, this background may be unimportant, since optimal sensitivity is not necessary. Only a portion of a conjugated IgG fraction consists of specific antibody, while the bulk of protein consists of IgG with irrelevant specificities. Only the specific antibody contributes to specific staining, while specific as well as irrelevant antibodies contribute to background staining. Part of this background is due to the hydrophobic FITC groups in the IgG. It is for this reason that we had to use conjugates of fluorescein/protein ratios of less than 2 when conjugating IgG.

Where higher-than-usual sensitivity of immunofluorescence was needed, such as in the localization of individual nerve fibers containing dopamine-β-hydroxylase first accomplished by Hartman (6), specifically purified antibody (page 27) was one of the essential technical improvements. Use of purified antibody decreased the background due to nonspecific attachment of immunoglobulin as it decreased the total amount of immunoglobulin necessary for specific staining (the specific antibody/total IgG ratio is close to 1 in purified antibody, while it is usually less than 0.15 in IgG fractions). With purified antibody, it was no longer necessary to employ conjugates with a 1 : 2 fluorescein/protein ratio. Instead, the purified antibody was conjugated under conditions that yielded ratios of 4 : 1, and thus greater specific staining intensities.

Following conjugation with purified antibody, unconjugated FITC was removed by Sephadex G50 chromatography. However, it was not necessary to use a DEAE column, since with purified antibody more extensively conjugated material did not interfere.

Conditions established for purified antibodies can also be applied to monoclonal antibodies (page 245). Immunoglobulin is isolated from ascites fluid. The specific antibody/total immunoglobulin ratio is expected to range from 0.5 to 1.0.

DIRECT AND INDIRECT STAINING MODES

The simplest way of staining with conjugated antibodies is by the *direct mode* in which the labeled antibody of desired specificity is applied to the tissue section.

Unlabeled reagent is washed off, and in the case of immunofluorescence, the tissue is examined without further processing. Available quantities of specific antibodies are, however, often too limited to risk the loss in yield from partial destruction of antibody reactivity during conjugation and from purification necessary after conjugation. For this reason, it is common practice to use *indirect* methodology, in which in the first step tissue antigen is localized by unlabeled antibody from a given species, commonly applied in the form of rabbit antiserum (*first antibody*). In the second step, this reaction is visualized by a conjugated antibody to the immunoglobulin of the first antibody, such as fluorescein-labeled goat-antirabbit immunoglobulin G (*second antibody*). The indirect method, although requiring two steps in staining, is more convenient, because a single labeled antirabbit immunoglobulin is useful for visualizing reaction of tissue with any rabbit antibody.

It has been claimed that the signal from the label (whether fluorescence in fluorochrome-conjugated antibodies or darkness of the reaction product in the case of enzyme-labeled antibodies) is stronger in the indirect than in the direct method. It was felt that a second antibody provides signal amplification, since in solution a number of anti-IgGs can react with a single IgG in antibody excess (page 19). In practice, it does not appear that on the surface of a tissue section much more than one anti-immunoglobulin reacts with a single immunoglobulin bound to tissue antigen. It is more likely that the increased staining intensity observed by indirect methodology is due to availability of high titered anti-immunoglobulins for labeling, compared to the relative scarcity of hyperimmune first antibodies. Purified antigens of interest often are of limited availability and, therefore, most immunizations are carried out with less than 1 mg per rabbit, resulting in relatively low amounts of antibodies. However, production of anti-immunoglobulin can be carried out by hyperimmunization with large quantities of immunoglobulin, thus yielding routinely antibody concentrations of 2 to 6 mg/ml.

The restrictions of availability of large quantities of high-affinity antibodies and of necessity of quantities of immunizing antigen, whether purified or not, do not apply when monoclonal antibodies are used (page 260). Therefore, the direct method deserves consideration, when quantities of monoclonal antibodies are readily available.

Increase of signal strength alone is of questionable desirability in immunocytochemistry. Sensitivity of a method is expressed by the ratio of signal to background. Thus, if the staining intensity of a structure to be localized immunocytochemically is only twice that of background, the method is less sensitive then if it is 10 times background. In the indirect method, the second antibody is the main factor in low-method specificity. Anti-immunoglobulins contain contaminants that react directly with tissue, even in the absence of first antibody. For this reason, it is desirable in any chemical conjugation to use affinity-purified antibodies. However, affinity purification of a second antibody alone is no guarantee of method specificity since the immunoglobulin used for affinity purification itself may not be more free of impurities than the antigen originally used for immunization of the donor of the second antibody. Direct methods are more specific than indirect, conjugated antibody methods, since direct methods do not use conjugated second antibodies.

Monoclonal antibodies can only be used as second antibodies if it has been established that, indeed, they react with the particular first antibody used, and not merely with a component of the immunoglobulin employed in their original selection (page 250).

Antibody reactivity is adversely affected by chemical conjugation. This is one reason for producing, in immunofluorescence, antibodies conjugated with only one to two fluorescent groups. It is also the reason for using relatively mild procedures in the other conjugations described below. Antibody activity is less adversely affected if a small, rather than a large, molecule is covalently attached. Therefore, more antibody reactivity is retained upon conjugation with fluorescein, rhodamine, or biotin (page 67) than upon conjugation with proteins such as enzymes (page 56) or ferritin (page 72). Since avoidance of excessive loss of antibody reactivity is critical in direct methods, in which the total amount of available antibody is often limited, immunofluorescence is more adaptable to direct methodology than methods employing large molecular protein markers conjugated to antibodies.

Staining intensity can be increased, according to Brandtzaeg et al. (7) if direct and indirect methods are combined by first and second antibodies conjugated with the same fluorochrome. This increase in staining intensity accomplished a true increase in sensitivity, as it permitted the use of lower concentrations of antisera and yielded better signal-to-noise ratios, that is, higher ratios of staining intensity of specifically stained structures to background (page 164).

STAINING OF LIVING CELLS

Immunofluorescence is unique among immunocytochemical methods in preserving the viability of stained cells. Certain conjugation methods for electron microscopy also preserve viability, but the cells will be destroyed during electron-microscopic observation.

Antibodies do not penetrate living cells. Immunocytochemical staining of living cells is restricted to the study of antigens found on the cell surface. It is important to ensure absence of complement during staining or, alternatively to use preparations free of Fcγ and Fcμ (pages 25 and 26), for otherwise cell lysis will occur. Directly reacting conjugates prepared from affinity-purified antibodies are unlikely to contain complement. If prepared from immunoglobulin fractions, it may be safer to interrupt the complement cascade by using conjugates heated to 56°C for 30 minutes.

If preservation of viability is desired, cells are stained in suspension and washed by centrifugation. Fluorescence microscopy is done under sterile conditions. Cells will continue growing without need for removal of the conjugate.

Because of the fluidity of the cell surface and the associated mobility of antigens held on it, an antigen with multiple determinants can be aggregated by antibodies that consist of monomers each possessing two antigen-combining sites. As a result of this aggregation, surface antigens tend to clump upon staining, often appearing on one pole of the cell (*capping*, Fig. 2-4). Capping can be prevented when staining is done at 0°C, in which case ring-shaped fluorescence more accurately reflects original average distribution of surface antigens (Fig.

Figure 2-4. Cap pattern of immunofluorescence of mouse spleen cells incubated with FITC-conjugated antimouse immunoglobulin at room temperature. ×1000. [From Taylor et al (8). Reprinted by permission from *Nature*, **233**:255, Copyright 1971 Macmillan Journals Limited.]

2-5). The antibody-mediated aggregation of surface antigens is an active process requiring an intact microfilament system of the cell: Aggregation is prevented even at room temperature by inhibitors of the contractile microfilament system, such as catalasin B or vinblastine. Sodium azide or dinitrophenol also inhibit aggregation. With Fab fragments (page 6) that possess only one antigen-combining site, aggregation does not occur. Neither does it occur in fixed cells, even with bivalent antibodies (immunoglobulin monomers possessing two identical antigen-binding sites).

Although, in general, only the cell surface of living cell accepts immunofluorescence staining, antibodies do occasionally enter living cells by pinocytosis.

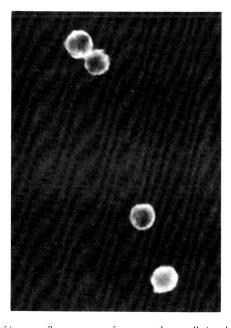

Figure 2-5. Ring pattern of immunofluorescence of mouse spleen cells incubated with FITC-conjugated antimouse immunoglobulin at 0°C. ×900 [From Taylor et al (8). Reprinted by permission from *Nature*, **233**:255, Copyright 1971 Macmillan Journals Limited.]

Conjugated immunoglobulins so imbibed will not be easily released upon washing. Hence the interior of living cells, although normally unstained, may occasionally become nonspecifically stained. In addition, the interior of unfixed, dead cells regularly stains with FITC-conjugated antibodies nonspecifically. Therefore, viability tests must be carried out prior to staining living cells.

If the reaction of antibodies on the cell surface leads to patch formation, it often mimics events that follow stimulation of cell surface receptors by specific ligands (pages 276 and 411), or it may inhibit these events. In general, patch formation is followed by endocytosis and activation of a physiologic mechanism characteristic to the cell (9,10). If such process is initiated or inhibited by the fluorescent antibodies used to mark the cell, its original state has been altered by the staining procedure, and thus, despite preservation of viability, undesirable metabolic sequellae may have been induced. It is not possible to prevent these events by staining at 0°C, because antibodies will not be removed after microscopic observation and prior to culturing of the cells at 37°C. The problem can be averted by the use of fluorochrome-labeled Fab fragments. Furthermore, the direct technique must be used unless the second antibody is also an Fab fragment specific to Fab of the first antibody. If undigested second antibody would be used, aggregation and patch formation would be promoted, despite use of Fab as first antibody.

FLUORESCENT CELL SORTING

Free floating cells labeled with fluorescent antibodies can be counted automatically in a flow microfluorometer (11). Thus, in a heterogeneous cell population, the proportion of cells containing a given surface marker can be evaluated. It is also possible to use the instrument in a preparative way, if the microfluorometer is expanded to an automated cell sorter. For instance, it is possible to label B cells with a fluorescent antibody against surface IgM, isolate automatically the labeled cells from the remaining mononuclear cell population (T cells and macrophages), and then fuse the labeled cells with myeloma cells for production of monoclonal antibodies (page 247). Direct technique is preferred here, because indirect technique may lead to agglutination and interfere, thereby, with proper cell separation and size analysis.

In the flow microfluorometer, cells are passed under pressure through a nozzle which produces an effluent jet, 50 μm in diameter. The coaxial flow system so created confines the cells to the center of the stream. Onto this stream are focused two light beams at divergent angles. One beam of incident light comes from a helium-neon laser and produces a scatter image, yielding a single impulse per cell. The degree of scattering is proportional to the size of the cell and is plotted via an analyzer on the y axis of a recorder. The second light source is an argon-ion laser that excites only the cells labeled with FITC-conjugated antibodies. Emitted light from these cells is passed through appropriate filters to exclude scattered light, and the intensity of each pulse is plotted via an analyzer on the x axis. This arrangement permits obtainment of a size-fluorescence distribution plot of the proportion of labeled cells in the total cell population.

The microfluorometer can be expanded into an automated *cell sorter* if the jet is vibrated at 4×10^4 cycles per second to produce an equal number of droplets of uniform size in such a way that the jet breaks up after it has passed through the laser beams. When the analyzer indicates a cell that gives a fluorescent signal beyond a certain threshold on the *x* axis, a negative charge is applied. If a drop produces no signal, no charge is applied. An electrostatic field separates the negative and positive droplets and thus the fluorescent from the nonfluorescent cells.

The cell sorter may also be used to separate cell populations, labeled by dual color immunofluorescence (page 194). For instance, one may study the interaction of T suppressor and T helper cells (page 283) with other cells in the immune response after their isolation in the fluorescent cell sorter from a mononuclear cell suspension of a given donor. Fluorescein-conjugated monoclonal OKT-8 antibody would label T suppressor cells green, and rhodamine-conjugated monoclonal OKT-4 antibody would label T helper cells orange-red. In this mode of use of the fluorescent cell sorters, two light scattering angles and two fluorescent wavelengths are needed (12).

Cram and Forsland (13) used the flow microfluorometer to compare quantitatively the efficiency of conjugates used in the diagnosis of hog cholera virus infection. Fluorescent distributions of infected and noninfected cells were compared. These distributions became more distinct from each other when number of cells was plotted against fluorescence/cell volume ratios rather than absolute fluorescence values, and overlap of infected and noninfected cell curves became virtually obliterated. This finding indicated that larger, more mature cells contained more virus and that nonspecific fluorescence was partly dependent on cell size. The analysis permitted both evaluation of absolute staining efficiency of different conjugates as well as evaluation of signal-to-noise ratios. One result of this technique indicated that batches of conjugate judged to be superior on their ability to yield bright fluorescence were in fact not better than poorly staining conjugates when judged on the basis of signal-to-noise ratio.

If cell sizing or survival of unaltered cells are unimportant, the fluorescence-activated cell sorter may also be used in the indirect technique. Derby et al. (14) obtained monoclonal antibodies to a retinal glycoprotein that labeled preferentially cell surface antigens in the plexiform layer of the chick neural retina. The antigen was present in 50 to 60% of cells from neural retinal cells maintained in monolayer cultures, as determined by indirect immunofluorescence with the monoclonal antibody, followed by the dissociation of the cells in calcium and magnesium-free medium and analysis in the fluorescence-activated cell sorter.

SPECIFICITY

Immunocytochemistry requires twofold specificity: the antibodies used must be specific for the antigens under investigation, and the immunocytochemical reagents should not stain tissues by mechanisms other than immunologic reactions. We will call specificity of the former class *antibody specificity* and specificity of the latter class *method specificity*.

Different controls are used for method or antibody specificity. In the indirect method, control of method specificity simply involves substitution of buffer for the first antiserum. Ideally, this should abolish all background.

In the direct method, there are two ways for determining method specificity:

1.   Application of conjugate to tissue known not to contain the antigen under investigation. For instance, fluorescent antibodies to the malaria organism *P. falciparum,* should not stain normal tissue. Fluorescent antibodies to mouse allotypic markers should not stain surface immunoglobulin-bearing cells in cytocentrifuge-prepared smears from the blood of the mouse that donated the immunoglobulin for immunization.

2.   Absorption of the antibody. For instance, if antiserum to luteinizing hormone-releasing hormone (LHRH) stains fibers in the median eminence of the hypothalamus, treatment of the serum with LHRH should remove all staining. This is merely a test for method specificity. It has been shown that it is not necessarily a test for antibody specificity (pages 237 and 386).

Appropriate antibody controls are more difficult to accomplish and greatly depend on the degree of our knowledge of the antigen investigated. In general, antibody specificity can be made plausible, even without extensive additional studies, but proof of identity of a localized antigen with the immunizing antigen is at times an involved procedure. Antibody specificity in immunocytochemistry is more difficult to establish with serum antibodies than with monoclonal antibodies, and hence we will discuss this subject in separate chapters under the headings of "Specificity of Antisera" and "Specificity of Monoclonal Antibodies."

Immunofluorescence is the only light microscopic method in which a detectable marker is directly attached to the antibody used. Impairment of antibody reactivity by conjugation is less when the marker is a relatively small molecule. Loss of antibody reactivity is more evident in the direct method in which the amount of initial antibody is often limited. For this reason, only immunofluorescence is extensively used in the direct mode. Other methods of conjugation maybe too destructive of scarce antibody. In the direct method, background due to cross-reactivity of the conjugated antibody with a relevant antigen is a function of antibody specificity and requires the same precaution as those necessary for the first antibody in indirect or unlabeled immunocytochemical methods (pages 43 and 90). Background due to changes resulting from the conjugation process itself and due to the possible presence of unreacted fluorescent tracer is a problem of method specificity.

IMMUNOFLUORESCENCE METHOD SPECIFICITY

The factors that affect method specificity are somewhat different in immunofluorescence than in other conjugated antibody methods. We will discuss here method specificity from the point of view of immunofluorescence. A general discussion of method specificity will be found on page 83.

Six factors affect method specificity in immunofluorescence:

1.   Autofluorescence of tissue.
2.   Reaction of unconjugated fluorochrome.

3. Electrostatic and hydrophobic bonding of conjugate.
4. Aggregation of conjugate.
5. Fc receptors.
6. In the indirect method, nonspecific reaction of the second antibody and
of conjugated proteins that contaminate the second antibody solution.

Of these factors, the first three are characteristic of immunofluorescence. The sources of the fourth factor, aggregation, are somewhat different in immuno-fluorescence and other conjugated antibody methods and so are methods of its avoidance.

Appropriate conjugation and staining procedures offer solutions or partial solutions to the first five factors. Factor 6 can only be solved by the use of direct fluorescence or the unlabeled antibody method (page 142).

Autofluorescence

Autofluorescence is of a yellow or bluish color and can readily be distinguished if specific greenish fluorescence is strong. However, in weakly stained prepara-tions, distinction of specific fluorescence from autofluorescent background may be difficult. Much of the problem of autofluorescence can be solved by epi-fluorescence microscopy and appropriate filters (page 54). Especially with the direct method, clean, background-free fluorescence may generally be obtained. Avoidance of autofluorescence increases the signal-to-noise ratio and thus pro-vides for high sensitivity.

Some unstained tissue components possess green autofluorescence of similar wavelengths as that of the emission of FITC. Certain fluorescent counterstains change the color of this background so that it contrasts with that of FITC. In addition, such counterstains enhance the background, which otherwise is practi-cally invisible in fluorescence dark-field microscopy. Many of the counterstains, however, reduce specific staining intensity. Those that reduce intensity the least, and provide the best elimination of green-background fluorescence, were in the hands of Schenk and Charukian (15): lissamin-rhodamine bovine serum al-bumin when the specific immunofluorescence was in the nuclei, and methyl green when it was in the cytoplasm.

Unconjugated Fluorochrome

Impurities in fluorescein or tetramethylrhodamine isothyocyanate, or nonconju-gated hydrolysis products of these reagents, seem to bind noncovalently to im-munoglobulin and, therefore, are not removed by dialysis or diethylaminoethyl-cellulose chromatography in the preparation of conjugate. These weakly bound fluorescent materials will be partially removed from the conjugate by nonspecific tissue components that bind them stronger or equally strong. Thus, nonspecific background staining will be increased. It has already been recognized by Coons (3) that this sort of nonspecificity can often be reduced by absorption with acetone-dried liver powder. However, liver powder may release into solution compounds that react with a second antibody solution, if indirect method is used, either by specific reaction or by reaction with nonspecific components of the second antibody, forming soluble aggregates that bind to tissue nonspecifically. Gailbraith and Gailbraith (16) eliminated this problem by using, instead of liver powder, solid-phase absorption with normal serum from the same species as that of the tissue to be stained.

Electrostatic and Hydrophobic Bonding of Conjugate

Conjugation with fluorescein or tetramethylrhodamine isothiocyanate replaces positively charged N-terminal or lysine amino groups with highly hydrophobic molecules. As investigated by Von Mayersbach (4,5), the increased negative charge promotes nonspecific binding to positively charged tissue components, especially in unfixed tissues. Acidophilic cytoplasm exhibits varying degrees of nonspecific staining, while basophilic nuclei do not. Eosinophil granules are especially prone to nonspecific staining, so are necrotic tissues or dead cells. Formaldehyde fixation decreases nonspecific binding by the electrostatic mechanism because it, too, increases the negative charge of tissue. However, formaldehyde fixation also increases tissue hydrophobicity, thereby promoting hydrophobic bonding. For this reason, immunofluorescence has found, until recently (page 110), limited use in staining of aldehyde-fixed tissue, dehydrated and embedded in paraffin. Immunofluorescence is mainly used on living cells, in tissue monolayers, and in frozen sections.

Fortunately, the nonspecific reaction is rarely of similar order of magnitude as the specific reaction. Thus, in rabbits infected with *Treponema pallidum*, the specific indirect immunofluorescence titers range usually between 1 : 320 to 1 : 1280 in dilution of first antibody (17). The nonspecific titer with normal serum is about 1 : 10. If the conjugated anti-immunoglobulin is of low titer, the specific titer decreases, but the nonspecific titer still is 1 : 10. For this reason, it is important to use conjugates with high antibody activity. In immunofluorescence, the conjugation reaction is a single-step reaction between conjugant and protein that can be controlled to yield products of low conjugant-protein ratio. Also, FITC is a small molecule compared to immunoglobulin and, therefore, upon mild conjugation, the probability of inhibiting antibody activity by steric hindrance remains low.

Aggregation of Conjugate

Hydrophobic bonding may not only take place between conjugate and tissue, but also among individual conjugate molecules, thus leading to multimolecular aggregates. Protein aggregation reduces solubility, and thus, aggregated conjugate is even more prone to nonspecific localization than nonaggregated material. Since hydrophobicity increases with increasing extent of fluorochrome conjugation, routine procedures of conjugation are carried out in such a way as to limit the number of fluorescent groups per antibody molecule. However, the less the number of fluorescent groups, the less, of course, is also the staining intensity. In evaluating the sensitivity of a conjugate, it is necessary to take into consideration nonspecific background rather than merely the staining intensity. This is generally done by expressing sensitivity as signal-to-noise ratio. In doing so, Brandzaeg et al. (7) found with a highly active antibody that the sensitivity was decreased one-third when the fluorescein/protein ratio was raised from 0.8 to 5. However, the sensitivity was increased 20-fold for a low-activity antibody, when the fluorescein/protein ratio was changed from 0.8 to 3.6. It suggested that in the direct method a number of conjugation ratios are tried with each antibody before adopting it for use in immunocytochemistry. The requirement detracts somewhat from the use of direct methodology, in which the amount of available antibody is often limited. Alternatively, one may have to restrict the use of direct methodology to antibodies of proven high activity. In the indirect method, this requirement is less stringent, because high-activity second antibody is easy to produce in quantity.

Aggregation of conjugates as a source of poor specificity is more of a problem with protein-protein conjugates (page 60) than with fluorochrome conjugates, because in protein-protein reactions the extent of aggregation is more difficult to control.

Fc Receptors

Fc receptors are found on the surface of macrophages and certain T-lymphocytes (page 272). They may also exist in other cells and in solid tissue. Fcγ receptors react with constant regions of γ chains and Fcμ receptors with the constant regions of μ chains. Fc receptors may contribute, therefore, to nonspecific binding (11).

In general, Fc receptors have low affinities. Good reagents for Fc receptors are provided by aggregated or circular antigen-antibody complex (pages 50 and 101) that can react with multiple receptor sites simultaneously (page 236) and thus will not dissociate easily on washing. Nonspecific reactions due to Fc receptors are, therefore, more pronounced with aggregated immunoglobulins, such as those resulting from conjugation with immunocytochemical tracers, than with native, nonaggregated immunoglobulins.

Fc receptors are mainly a problem in living cells or frozen sections. Perhaps for this reason, immunocytochemical reagents that are highly aggregated such as protein-protein conjugates (page 56) are not as extensively used on living cells as immunofluorescence.

Fc receptors seem to be quite sensitive to fixation and embedding. They pose no major problem in the staining of paraffin sections. However, embedding seems to destroy components of the cell membrane as indicated by failure of immunocytochemical localization of membrane antigens. Fc receptors seem to be removed along with other membrane components.

The best method to eliminate Fc receptor nonspecificity in immunocytochemistry of cell surfaces is the use of antibodies free of Fc. Pepsin digestion (page 10) removes the Fc regions from immunoglobulin monomers, leaving F(ab')$_2$ bivalent fragments, still bound by a hinge region. The direct method is preferred for detection of antigens on mononuclear blood cells in suspension or in frozen sections, because only one antibody, the conjugate, has to be in F(ab')$_2$

form. In the indirect method, both the first and the second antibodies must be F(ab')$_2$. Human Fc receptors react with rabbit immunoglobulin, but as shown by Alexander and Sanders (18) not with goat immunoglobulin. Therefore, F(ab')$_2$ reagents are not needed if goat antibodies are used. With the use of F(ab')$_2$, Lazarus and Poole (19) greatly reduced the nonspecific staining in the immuno-cytochemical localization of cathepsin D in frozen sections of rabbit skin. The extensive background obtained with complete antibodies alludes to the wide distribution of Fc receptors in tissues.

Blocking of Fc regions in immunoglobulin is another way to prevent nonspe-cific interaction with Fc receptors. Bacteria covered with antibodies become sen-sitive to phagocytosis by macrophages (opsonization). Macrophages are one of the groups of circulating mononuclear cells that have Fc receptors. Opsonization requires affinity of bacterial cells for the macrophages as well as participation of complement (page 25). Bacteria acquire this affinity upon reaction with specific antibodies which, in turn, react with the Fc receptors. Staphylococci of strains that produce protein A become resistant to opsonization. The resistance is due to the ability of the protein to bind with Fc, thus blocking it in the reaction of Fc with its receptors on the macrophages. In addition, the protein aggregates circu-lating IgG. The aggregated IgG depletes circulating complement and thus fur-ther inhibits opsonization. Because of its ability to bind onto Fc, staphylococcal protein A can be used as a reagent for IgG. When conjugated with FITC, it can be substituted for the second antibody in the indirect method (page 21).

Specific antibodies are used to identify various classes and subclasses of lym-phocytes. To avoid nonspecific interaction of such antibodies with Fc receptor-bearing T-lymphocytes, Ades et al. (20) stained cells with soluble complexes resulting from reaction of FITC-labeled protein A with antithymocyte serum under special conditions. In this reaction sequence, the staphylococcal protein A bound with IgG Fc of the specific antibodies in the serum, thus yielding an FITC-marked specific staining reagent. In addition, the labeled staphylococcal protein A complexed with nonspecific IgG in the antiserum, thus blocking its Fc domains and preventing the nonspecific reaction with Fc receptors on the cells. As a result, a smaller number of mononuclear cells became stained than by direct immunofluorescence.

Nonspecific Reaction of the Second Antibody

When immunoglobulin isolated from serum and used as a second antibody is conjugated with fluorochrome or any other marker, four components become labeled:

1. Specific anti-immunoglobulin.
2. Antibodies to contaminants in the immunizing antigen.
3. Other immunoglobulins found in the circulation of the serum donor.
4. Nonimmunoglobulin proteins.

These additional components are capable of reacting with a tissue even in the absence of the first antibody. The reaction may be a specific interaction appar-ently due to tissue constituents other than immunoglobulin (components 2 and

3) or due to nonspecific hydrophobic bonding (components 2, 3, and 4). Since the contaminating components are labeled, background will ensue.

Some of these contaminants can be eliminated by affinity purification of the second antibody prior to conjugation. For this reason, specifically purified antibodies are recommended in all indirect methods that use labeled antibodies. Affinity purification will not, however, abolish the phenomenon, because the affinity column IgG is not likely to be freer of contaminant than the immunizing IgG, and hence antibodies to contaminants will be co-purified.

Nevertheless, while specific purification of first antibodies in immunocytochemistry provides no advantage in most cases (page 226), that of the second antibody is important if the second antibody is to be conjugated with an immunocytochemical tracer.

QUANTITATIVE IMMUNOFLUORESCENCE

Many attempts have been made to quantify immunofluorescence observations, often with the aim of comparing data from one laboratory with those of another. Such quantification would permit evaluation of the amount of antigen in a given specimen. Similarly it would permit comparison of antibody titers and extend the diagnostic use of immunofluorescence in situations where a standard antigen is used to evaluate titers of unknown antisera, such as in immunofluorescence of standard suspensions of treponemes in the diagnosis of syphilis (17), or in the immunofluorescence of standard nuclear preparations in the diagnosis of lupus erythematosus (page 482). Standardization has been difficult because of biologic variations of antigens and antisera. Variations in antisera can be overcome by distributing batches of antiserum from a single large pool to a variety of laboratories. In the usual two-stage method, both first and second antisera must be available in large pools. It is not practical to have a large pool of fluorescent second antibody immunoglobulin, because the lifetime of the conjugate is not indefinite. Instead, attempts have been made to standardize the efficiency of varying preparations. The degree of conjugation differs from one FITC preparation to the other, even if carried out under seemingly identical conditions, and the preservation of antigen-combining reactivity of the resulting conjugate varies equally. However, the efficiency of staining can be compared among comparable dilutions of varying second antibodies with identical amounts of first antibodies in comparable tissue specimens. *Microfluorometers* have been used for such quantification. However, these instruments suffer from limitations due to variability of intensity of the light source. This difficulty was overcome by the use of an *eyepiece comparator,* with which Haskill and Raymond (21) were able to simultaneously observe the fluorescence of a single cell and that of a standard reference. The comparator uses glass fiber optics to illuminate a reference slit directly from the dark-field condensor. Rotation of a continuously variable neutral-density filter in the light path of the comparator alters the brightness of the reference slit so that the reference can be adjusted until it is equal to that of the observed cell. At this point, the degree of rotation is a direct estimate of the degree of fluorescence of the cell.

Absolute brightness of staining is an insufficient criterion for evaluating

FITC-conjugated antibodies because it neglects the degree of background staining. Instead, an image-to-background (signal-to-noise) ratio appears to be more appropriate. An additional problem in quantification is the rapid fading of FITC fluorescence during illumination.

IMMUNOFLUORESCENCE MICROSCOPY AND PHOTOGRAPHY

Specific fluorescence emission is relatively weak compared to the total light necessary for illumination. Therefore, high-intensity light as provided by the mercury arc high-vacuum lamp is a minimum requirement to obtain bright immunofluorescence.

Although fluorescein and rhodamine absorb strongly below 300 nm, optical difficulties in condensing light in this range preclude its routine use. A second absorption maximum for the fluorochromes is too near the emission peak: fluorescence microscopy is sensitive because the emitted light is seen and not the illuminating light. Since only part of the illuminating light becomes absorbed, the unabsorbed part must be separated from the emitted light. This separation cannot be accomplished if both illuminating and emitted light have close peaks. Hence, for immunofluorescence with rhodamine and fluorescein, illuminating light in the near-ultraviolet and short-wave blue are commonly used. In this range, both fluorescein and rhodamine absorb, although not as efficiently as at shorter or longer wavelengths. Filters are used between the illuminating light and the specimen to provide this range and to cause only minimal tissue autofluorescence.

Secondary filters are placed between specimen and ocular to retain the fluorescence emission light and to cut off any exciting light. Therefore, the secondary filters should cut off the light passed by the primary filter (22,23).

Use of narrow-pass interference primary filters and epi-illumination gives superior results over broad-band excitation and transmitted dark-field illumination. For fluorescein isothiocyanate immunocytochemistry, a 100-watt high-power mercury lamp is used in combination with a red suppression filter and fluorescein isothiocyanate excitation module (24). This equipment will reduce autofluorescence background and improve sensitivity.

If it is decided to differentiate in the same section between the green fluorescence of fluorescein and the orange-red fluorescence of tetraethylrhodamine conjugates (page 194), it is better to excite simultaneously at two wavelengths instead of one, thus being able to independently vary the intensity of the optimal exciting light for fluorescein and rhodamine. A Ploem-type vertical illuminator is recommended that allows switching of mirrors and filters and permits repeated observations of individual cells under different light conditions. This procedure permits separate photography of the contributions to staining of one antibody labeled with fluorescein and another labeled with rhodamine, either in the same cell or in different cells (Fig. 2-6). It is recommended that the fluorescein fluorescence be photographed before the tetramethylrhodamine fluorescence, because of the more rapid fading of the former.

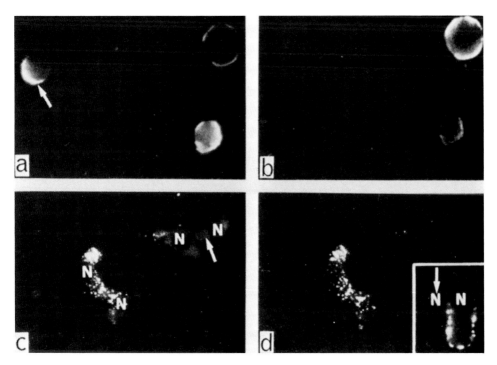

Figure 2-6. Paired direct immunofluorescence tracing of immunoglobulin components on human cells stained in viable suspensions. Left column: green fluorescein emission. Right column: red rhodamine emission. (a,b) Paired staining for IgD (green) and IgM (red) on peripheral blood lymphocytes observed in suspension: this field contains one cell bearing only IgD in a cap (arrow) and two cells bearing IgD and IgM in various proportions. (c,d) Paired staining for IgA (green) and secretory component (red) on isolated colon epithelial cells observed in smear: in this field there is one columnar cell with numerous membrane patches containing both components, two cells with only few patches, and one completely negative cell (arrow). Insert in (d) shows membrane patches with secretory component on a cell from the same suspension before smearing. Arrow indicates a negative cell. N, nucleus. (a,b) ×920, (c,d) ×650. [Reproduced with permission from Brandtzaeg et al. (7).]

Photography is essential, as fluorescence wanes on storage of specimens. This decrease in fluorescence intensity is also an important factor in the technique of photography itself: total light intensity is often low in dark-field microscopy, especially when only a small part of the section is immunofluorescent. Hence, exposure times tend to be long. However, during long exposure times, fluorescence intensity itself fades. Consequently, attempts should be made to use shortest possible exposure times; therefore, films with high ASA ratings are recommended. Furthermore, a well standardized automatic exposure meter is necessary because light measurement is synchronized with the exposure, and any decrease of fluorescence during exposure is automatically compensated for.

In attempts to preserve FITC fluorescence, it is quite common practice to photograph tissue before observing details. When one returns to the tissue after photography, most of the staining may have disappeared, and evaluation will depend entirely on the dark-field photograph.

ENZYME-CONJUGATED ANTIBODIES

We have seen that fluorescence against a dark background provides sufficient sensitivity to visualize antigens with antibodies, if the latter possessed as little as one suitable fluorochrome group. We have also seen that color absorption is insufficient were we to use, in the visible light range antibodies conjugated with strongly colored compounds. Even if antibody solubility and reactivity were not affected, there are not enough reactive groups in the antibody to permit an extent of conjugation sufficient for microscopic examination. However, if an enzyme were covalently conjugated to antibody [or attached to antibody by natural bonds (page 90)] and then visualized by a histochemical method for detection of the enzyme, a large number of colored product molecules would be deposited and the reaction would be visualized. We should recognize, however, that the number of visible product molecules obtainable is not infinite. Many reactions, especially those detectable in histochemistry, are product inhibited. It is for this reason that the enzymatic detectors, which we will describe, do not provide a signal intensity higher than that of fluorescent markers. The detectors that have survived the test of time produce signal strengths about equal to that of fluorescence. The sensitivity of the methods in the detection of antigen depends more on the manner in which the labeling enzyme is attached to the antibody than on the detectability of the enzyme itself.

In the choice of an enzyme for the use of immunocytochemistry, two requirements are essential: First, the enzyme reaction product must be light or electron-opaque, or at least must be able to react specifically with a substance that confers upon it these properties. Second, the product must be insoluble, so as not to diffuse from the site of formation and thus efface histologic localization. Most natural enzyme substrates do not fulfill either requirement. For instance, acetylcholinesterase with acetylcholine as its natural substrate forms choline and acetate as products. Neither are visible or electron opaque, and both are highly soluble. Therefore, enzyme histochemistry generally tries to develop analogs that can be substituted for the natural substrates, but produce light or electron-opaque products. These analogs should possess specificity for the enzyme similar to that of the natural substrate. Only in some cases have substrates been found and often they have less than the desired specificity. An example is the use of a diazonium group-bearing thioester instead of acetylcholine as substrate for acetylcholinesterase (Fig. 2-7). Enzyme hydrolysis liberates a diazonium-bearing thiol. The interaction of the diazonium groups with thiol results in a polymer, and a dark precipitate forms. The essential requirement in this reaction is that the substrate is soluble and the product insoluble. An enzyme used in immunocytochemistry that follows this principle of detection is β-galactosidase.

More commonly in enzyme histochemistry a substrate is chosen that develops a product which is *captured* by another reagent to form an insoluble, opaque compound. Thus, phosphatases hydrolyze certain naphtyl phosphates, yielding naphthols as one of their products. If the reaction is carried out in the presence of a suitable diazonium compound, coupling of the naphthol will form a colored product, which depending on the compound chosen may be sufficiently insoluble for histochemistry. Alkaline phosphatase has found use in immunocytochemistry.

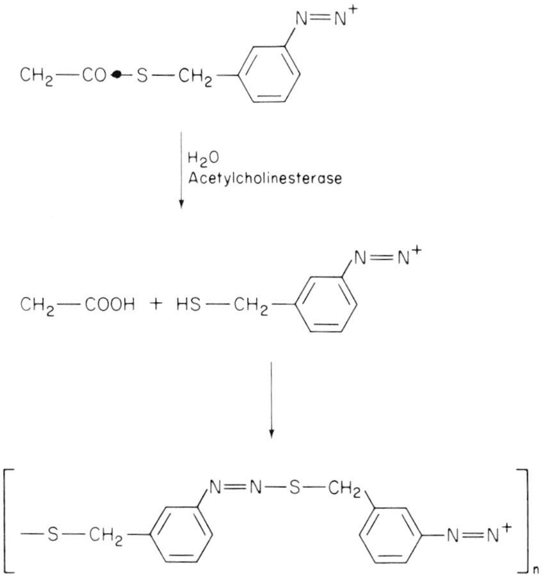

Figure 2-7. Histochemical detection of an enzyme with a substrate that forms an insoluble, visible product (25).

Many enzymes require, besides substrate, a third component to "drive" the reaction. For instance, peroxidase, the enzyme with which we will deal with extensively, reacts with its specific substrate, hydrogen peroxide, to form a primary complex accompanied by oxidation of the heme prosthetic group of the enzyme. In the absence of a third substance, an electron donor, the reaction will stop at this stage. In the presence of an electron donor, a second complex forms at a measurable rate. In the third step of the reaction, this complex dissociates, regenerating the enzyme to its reduced state and releasing the oxidized electron donor. While the first stage is substrate specific, the second stage can be mediated by a variety of easily reducible electron donors, such as amines. By utilizing the electron donor rather than the specific substrate as our histochemically demonstrable material, we have available a large number of substances to choose from for optimal detectability. This enabled Graham and Karnovsky (26) to choose for the histochemical detection of peroxidase, 3,3'-diaminobenzine (Fig. 2-8) as electron donor among a large number of amines that give colored oxidation products. Diaminobenzidine has exceptionally favorable properties, as oxidation forms a polymer, which because of extensive electron resonance (page 36) is not only intensely colored (it is also moderately fluorescent), but because of polymerization, is highly insoluble. For this reason, it diffuses less from its site of formation than most other substrates used in histochemistry, and thus detection of peroxidase is one of the most reliable methods of enzyme histochemistry. Finally, the polymer is capable of chelating with osmium tetroxide, thus becoming electron opaque for use in electron microscopy.

Several other substrates, besides diaminobenzidine, are useful for histochemistry of peroxidase. 3-Amino-9-ethyl carbazol forms a red reaction product

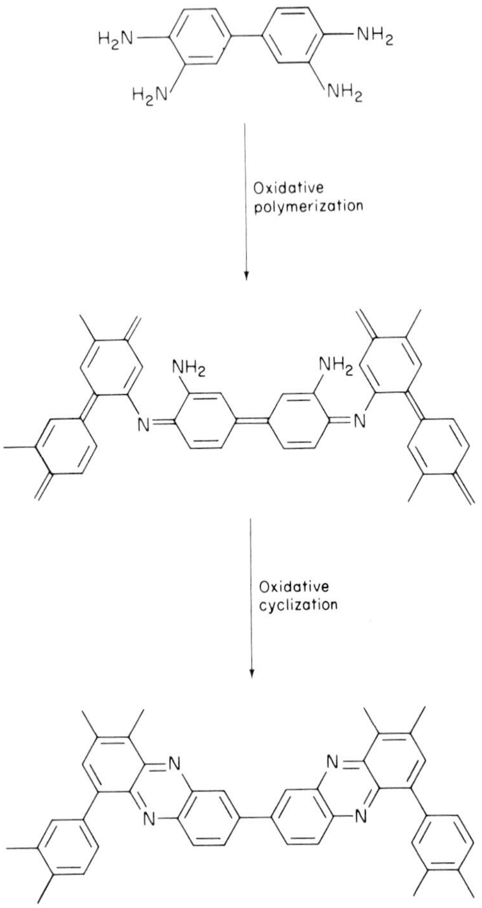

Figure 2-8. Diaminobenzidine is an electron donor to the peroxidase-hydrogen peroxide complex. In this reaction, the free bonds of the oxidation product of diaminobenzidine react with each other to form, presumably, an insoluble phenazine polymer (27).

(28,29), while 4-chloro-1-naphthol forms a blue reaction product (28) that contrasts with the brown product of diaminobenzidine in double-staining techniques (page 195). However, neither the amino carbazol nor the chloronaphthol oxidation products are as insoluble as the polymeric products of the diaminobenzidine reaction. Consequently, there is some diffusion of the products from their sites of liberation, requiring in the case of chloronaphthol, immediate photography after reaction. Furthermore, sections cannot be mounted in Permount, because the reaction products of chloronaphthol and amino carbazol are lipid-soluble. Other electron donors for peroxidase that yield colored reaction products, such as benzidine, 3,3′,5,5′-tetramethylbenzidine, or dianisidine are useful for the spectrophotometric measurement of peroxidase in solution. They cannot be employed in immunocytochemistry because of the solubility of the reaction products. However, they can be employed (30) for tracing injected peroxidase within axons and neuronal cell bodies (page 186).

The amino acids and enzymes that can be used for covalent linkage to antibody are lysine, N-terminal amino acids, reduced cysteine, tyrosine, and histidine. Only the first three have been used in immunocytochemistry. There are a number of reagents for these amino acids. To be suitable for immunocytochemical conjugation, they must react at or below room temperature, must be soluble in buffer or buffer-formamide mixtures, and they must have two functional groups: one for attachment to the enzyme, and the other for attachment to the antibody, so as to cross-link enzyme to antibody.

There are two variants of this basic procedure. In one of them (page 64), carbohydrate instead of protein is used for linkage, and in the other, a specific, bioactive marker is covalently introduced into antibody and enzyme, and both are linked via noncovalent, physiologic reactions (page 67). Most enzyme immunocytochemistry has been done with horseradish peroxidase. In horseradishes, the substance responsible for the tear-promoting effect, an allylisocyanate, reacts with peroxidase and blocks most of its available amino groups. For conjugation with immunoglobulin, bifunctional amino acid reagents are used. Modesto and Pesce (31) have shown that not more than 1.7 amino groups per molecule are available for this binding, even when excess bifunctional reagent is used. The limited extent of reaction assures that enzyme activity is not abolished as a result of exposure to conjugating agent.

Originally, peroxidase or alkaline phosphatase have been conjugated to immunoglobulin in a single-stage reaction. Enzyme was mixed with immunoglobulin and cross-linked by a bifunctional reagent, such as 4,4'-difluoro-3,3' dinitrophenylsulfone (32), or glutaraldehyde (33). Not each reactive group in enzyme or immunoglobulin is bound at the same rate, and therefore, the reaction is difficult to control even in systems consisting of only one protein. Inconsistency of reaction rates is magnified when two proteins of different reactivities are interacting with the conjugating agent simultaneously. For this reason, results of conjugation in single stages have been variable, often leading to poor conjugation (poor reaction with enzyme), too extensive conjugation (blocking of antibody reactivity), and always to polymeric conjugates consisting of many immunoglobulin and enzyme molecules, with only little antibody reactivity retained. Polymeric conjugates are an important source of poor method specificity (high background). Poorly conjugated material consists mostly of unconjugated antibody, which competes for conjugate in reaction with antigen in tissue sections, and thus reduces signal intensity.

For these reasons, conjugation in one stage has now been almost entirely superseded by conjugation in two stages. In the first stage, enzyme is conjugated with an excess of bifunctional reagent, so that one combining site reacts with the enzyme and the other is left free. In the second stage, the conjugate is reacted with immunoglobulin. In a variation of this procedure, the first stage is carried out with the antibody, the second stage with the enzyme.

Even under these precautions, reactions are variable. In contrast to immunofluorescence where only one to two groups in protein, presumably the most reactive ones, are conjugated, in the enzyme antibody cross-linkage, many groups interact. Reaction rates are still difficult to control, even in the two-stage procedure, and hence uniform products remain somewhat difficult to obtain.

Several precautions help to minimize these effects:

1. *Use of affinity-purified antibody.* In the usual two-stage conjugation procedure, in which enzyme is first reacted with bifunctional reagent, enzyme becomes rapidly conjugated. However, the second stage, in which conjugated enzyme interacts with unconjugated immunoglobulin, is inefficient. Clyne et al. (34) found that 5% of conjugated peroxidase reacts with immunoglobulin. If we assume that about 10% of the total immunoglobulin used for conjugation is specific antibody (a common proportion for a second antibody used in indirect techniques) and if 50% of antibody was inactivated during conjugation, then about 0.25% of the peroxidase used enters usable antibody. However, if purified antibody (page 27) is used for conjugation as recommended by Avrameas (33), we may expect to find 2.5% of the peroxidase on the conjugated, immunologically active antibody.

Enzyme-conjugated antibody methods have nearly always been used in the indirect method. The conjugated antibody is, therefore, generally anti-immunoglobulin. It would be convenient to use monoclonal antibody instead of affinity-purified antibody. One must ascertain, however, that the monoclonal conjugated antibody reacts with an epitope available in the first antibody used.

Antibody, affinity-purified from serum, still remains the immunoglobulin source of choice for enzyme-conjugated antibody methods. In contrast, the first antibody, which is not conjugated, should in general not be affinity-purified (page 226).

2. *Separation of polymeric conjugate.* The amount and degree of polymer formation differs with different bifunctional reagents, different enzymes, different antibody products, and finally may differ within the same procedure carried out at different times (Fig. 2-9). In general, procedures that result in largely monomeric conjugates are low in yield and leave much interfering nonconjugated antibody in solution. Procedures that are high in yield also result in extensive polymer formation. Some of the enzyme and some of the antibody reactivity may be sterically hindered in the interior of polymers.

Enzyme-antibody polymers contain more enzyme than enzyme-antibody monomers. As a consequence, the signal intensity is higher upon staining with polymeric conjugate. However, polymers also attach nonspecifically to tissue. The increase in nonspecific reactivity with polymers exceeds the increase in staining intensity. Hence, the signal-to-noise ratio decreases with polymerization and the sensitivity of the method is impaired (35,36). Consequently, polymers must be removed before a conjugate can be useful for immunocytochemistry on tissue sections. For separation, Boorsma and Streefkert (36) found gel filtration with Ultragel AcA44 better than Sephadex G-200 (Fig. 2-10).

3. *Separation of unconjugated antibody.* Unconjugated antibody competes with conjugate by blocking tissue epitopes. Furthermore, unconjugated antibody may have a higher affinity than most of the conjugate. Inhibition of antibody reactivity, as a result of mild conjugation (1 to 2 peroxidase molecules per antibody), rarely affects both combining sites. However, steric inhibition of one combining site is common. The resulting conjugate still binds antigen, but only via one site. Binding via two combining sites greatly increases overall affinity (pages 236 and 403), and therefore, tissue will react preferentially with nonconjugated antibody fractions.

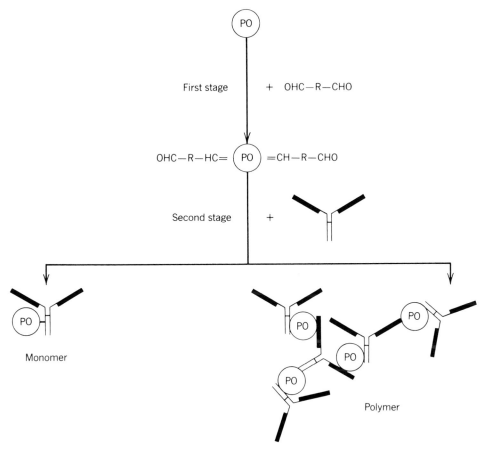

Figure 2-9. Two-stage conjugation of peroxidase (PO) and IgG with the double-armed aldehyde, glutaraldehyde. In the first stage, peroxidase is reacted with excess glutaraldehyde. About two amino groups in the peroxidase react, each with one arm of glutaraldehyde. In the second stage, conjugated peroxidase still possessing one reactive aldehyde group on each of its two reaction sites is mixed with IgG. Ideally, monomeric products consisting of conjugates of one PO and one IgG are formed. Polymeric by-products interfere. If, instead of peroxidase, other enzymes that usually possess more reactive amino groups are used for conjugation, a higher number of aldehyde groups are available for the second stage and polymer formation is increased. Also, if instead of glutaraldehyde, the aldehyde formed by oxidation of the carbohydrate moiety of PO is used, the second step of the reaction will be more effective, and again the amount of interfering polymer will be increased.

Both immunoglobulin as well as peroxidase contain carbohydrate, but the proportion of carbohydrate to protein is six to nine times higher in peroxidase. The lectin, concanavalin A, binds these proteins, and therefore, a concanavalin A sepharose affinity column removes peroxidase-conjugated antibody, as well as unconjugated antibody and peroxidase from solution. Arends (37) made use of differential desorption of these proteins from the column by elution with 0.1 M methyl-alpha-D-glucopyranoside, which competes with the absorbed proteins for carbohydrate-binding sites on the lectin. The low-carbohydrate unconjugated immunoglobulin was released from the column first and good separation was obtained from the enzyme-conjugated immunoglobulin and the trailing unconjugated peroxidase.

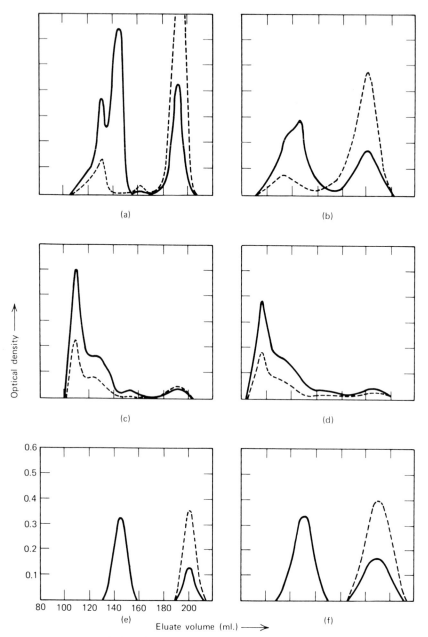

Figure 2-10. Comparison of Ultragel AcA44 (a,c,e) and Sephadex G-200 (b,d,f) chromatography for the separation of unconjugated peroxidase, unconjugated immunoglobulin, and peroxidase-conjugated immunoglobulin prepared in two stages either with glutaraldehyde (a,b) or by the periodate method (c,d). OD_{280} (——) measures protein contents, OD_{403} (– – – –) peroxidase contents. For standardization of the columns, unconjugated immunoglobulin and unconjugated peroxidase were applied in (e) and (f). Ultragel resolved the glutaraldehyde conjugate into distinct peaks, consisting apparently of monomeric conjugate (1), unconjugated immunoglobulin (2), polymeric peroxidase (3), and unconjugated peroxidase (4). With Sephadex (b), the first three peaks could not be resolved. Periodate conjugation led to polymers that left the columns in the void volume and could not be resolved either with Ultragel (c) or with Sephadex (d). [Reprinted by permission of Elsevier Science Publishing Co. Inc. from Isolation of conjugates prepared with glutaraldehyde or periodate using polyacrylamide-agarose gel (by D. M. Boorsma and J. G. Streefkerk, *Journal of Histochemistry and Cytochemistry* **21**:481, Copyright 1976 by the Histochemical Society, Inc.) (36).]

62

There are many two-stage conjugation procedures. Each of these procedures permits varying degrees of retention of enzyme and antibody reactivity. Allowing for differences from batch to batch, in general each of these procedures retains 30 to 100% of enzyme activity or 30 to 100% of antibody reactivity. These data are obtained by subjecting the conjugate to enzymatic and immunologic analysis. The size of a monomeric conjugate consisting of a single immunoglobulin and a single peroxidase is not sufficiently different from that of an oligomer consisting of a single immunoglobulin and two or three peroxidases to permit effective separation by gel filtration. These monomers and oligomers will coexist in conjugates freed of polymers. The oligomer of one IgG and two or three peroxidases will have more enzyme activity than a monomer of one immunoglobulin and one peroxidase. It will contribute more heavily to the total enzymatic activity of the purified conjugate. However, the oligomer is more likely to be sterically hindered in its antibody reactivity than the monomer. Hence, it is less likely to react with tissue in immunocytochemical staining. Therefore, the peroxidase reactivity of that fraction of the conjugate mixture which actually participates in the immunocytochemical reaction is apt to be less than that derived from measurement of total enzymatic activity in solution.

CONJUGATION OF PEROXIDASE TO IMMUNOGLOBULIN WITH GLUTARALDEHYDE

The two-stage procedure of Avrameas and Ternyck (38) results in a largely monomeric conjugate. However, the conjugation procedure is inefficient, so that much unconjugated antibody remains which is difficult to separate from the monomeric conjugate. In this procedure, about equimolar quantities of peroxidase and antibody are used. Using sodium dodecyl sulfate polyacrylamide electrophoresis, Nygren et al. (39) found that with increasing ratios of peroxidase to immunoglobulin, free immunoglobulin in the conjugate preparation disappears, but dispersity of the conjugate increases. With a 20 M excess, three bands appeared in positions between those representing unconjugated and dimeric IgG. These bands reflect complexes consisting of one, two, or three peroxidase molecules, respectively, and a single IgG molecule.

In a procedure adapted from that of Nygren et al. (39), a 16 M excess of peroxidase over antibody can be attained if in the first stage 80 mg peroxidase are dissolved in 1.0 ml of 0.05 M carbonate buffer, pH 9.5, containing 0.25% glutaraldehyde. After 2 hours at room temperature, excess glutaraldehyde is separated from the glutaraldehyde-conjugated peroxidase with a Sephadex G-25 column (0.7 × 12 cm) equilibrated with 0.15 M sodium chloride. The void volume glutaraldehyde-conjugated peroxidase is admixed for about 24 hours at room temperature with 20 mg affinity-purified antibody/0.05 M carbonate buffer, pH 9.5/0.15 M sodium chloride. The reaction is stopped by the addition of lysine to a final concentration of 0.02 M.

Modifications of this basic procedure include substitution of benzoquinone for glutaraldehyde as conjugating reagent (40,41) or substitution of protein A for immunoglobulin (41,42). No fundamental advantages or disadvantages of these modifications have been established. However, lesser excesses of peroxidase over protein A are needed to obtain conjugates relatively free of unconjugated protein A.

THE PERIODATE CONJUGATION TECHNIQUE

Realizing that conjugation of peroxidase with immunoglobulin via protein amino groups is inefficient because of the small number of available amino groups in peroxidase, and that bifunctional reagents for other amino acids in peroxidase, such as bisdiazotized benzidine, would be fairly destructive of enzymatic activity, Nakane and Kawaoi (43) have utilized the carbohydrate with which peroxidase is associated as a starting point for a two-stage conjugation. The carbohydrate moiety of peroxidase is apparently not needed for enzymatic activity. In the first stage, the carbohydrate is oxidized to aldehydes. In the second stage, the aldehyde groups are allowed to react with immunoglobulin. Most of the second-stage reaction apparently involves Schiff base formation with amino groups in immunoglobulin. In order to avoid self-coupling of peroxidase by reaction of its carbohydrate aldehyde with its protein amine, the amino groups are blocked with fluorodinitrobenzene prior to the first stage. However, this step may be unnecessary if oxidation is carried out at low pH. At the end of the second stage, sodium borohydrate is used to stabilize the Schiff base.

In the conjugation procedure of Wilson and Nakane (44), 0.2 ml of 0.1 M sodium periodate are added under stirring for 20 minutes to 4 ml peroxidase dissolved in 1.0 ml of distilled water. Following dialysis against 0.001 M sodium acetate buffer, pH 4.4 at 4°C, 20 ml of sodium carbonate buffer, pH 9.5, are added and the pH is further raised to 9.0 to 9.5. The solution is added to 8 mg affinity-purified antibody in 0.01 M sodium carbonate buffer, pH 9.5. After stirring for 2 hours at room temperature, the reaction is stopped with 0.01 ml of freshly prepared sodium borohydrate (4 mg/ml) and the mixture is left at 4°C for 2 hours.

Boorsma and Streefkerk (35) found this coupling procedure progressed more extensively than glutaraldehyde conjugation. Most of the conjugate was polymeric and consequently stained immunocytochemically with heavy background and muddy appearance. Even after chromatographic separation of polymeric conjugate (Fig. 2-10), the glutaraldehyde conjugate appeared to be somewhat more satisfactory in immunocytochemistry than the periodate conjugate. Polydispersity of the polymeric conjugate prevented complete separation from the monomeric periodate conjugate.

USE OF ANTIBODY FRAGMENTS IN CONJUGATION

We have seen that immunoglobulin-peroxidase conjugates require a twofold purification prior to use. Polymeric conjugate must be separated from the monomer. Monomeric conjugate must be separated from unconjugated antibody. The latter step is difficult, if carried out by gel filtration, because of the similarity in size of unconjugated antibody (146,000 daltons) and a 1-peroxidase-1 antibody monomeric conjugate (186,000 daltons). However, if the papain digest of antibody, Fab, which has a molecular weight of 50,000, were conjugated, it would be easy to separate a 90,000-dalton monomeric conjugate from unconjugated material.

The antibody activity of the Fab fragments is more likely to be altered by conjugation than that of whole IgG because of greater likelihood of steric hindrance in the smaller antibody fragment.

Sometimes Fab of $F(ab')_2$ fragments are preferred over whole immunoglobulins on the assumption that smaller fragments encounter less barriers to penetration of frozen or fixed tissue sections than conjugates of whole IgG. It is true that molecules smaller than 40,000 daltons penetrate such tissues easier than larger molecules. All proteins 90,000 daltons or larger in size encounter difficulties, but it remains to be established if this difficulty increases continuously with size. So far, it appears that some of the larger proteins do not penetrate well once the 40,000-dalton barrier is exceeded and that it makes little difference whether their size is 80,000 or 400,000 daltons.

CONJUGATION OF PEROXIDASE TO Fab HINGE REGIONS WITH MALEIMIDE

Imagawa et al. (45) have introduced a procedure that yields conjugates in which antibody reactivity is not compromised and polymerization of immunoglobulin is minimized even if peroxidase is reacted with bifunctional reagents extensively. In this procedure, a single peroxidase still may conjugate with more than one IgG fragment, but no fragment can react with more than one peroxidase. This is accomplished by the use of N-hydroxy-succinimide ester of N-(4-carboxycyclo-hexylmethyl)maleimide as conjugating agent. This compound is capable of reacting with amino groups via one arm and thiol via the other arm. The first reaction stage is carried out in the conventional way by reaction of the amino groups of peroxidase. The result is peroxidase possessing a conjugating reagent capable of reacting with sulfhydryl groups. For the second stage, the antibody is reduced in such a way that only one sulfhydryl group of the hinge region of rabbit IgG is exposed to the peroxidase product obtained in the first stage of conjugation.

Immunoglobulins possess a number of SS linkages (Fig. 1-1), but no free sulfhydryl groups. One of these disulfide linkages, in the case of rabbit IgG, and two in the case of human IgG links the two H chains.

We have seen earlier (page 10) that digestion of IgG with pepsin degrades the bulk of the Fc region into dialyzable fragments but leaves the hinge region intact. At least one of the interchain disulfide bonds at the hinge region is maintained and, therefore, the Fab fragments do not fall apart. The antibody fragment $F(ab')_2$ is still bivalent and precipitates with multivalent antigens. The inter-H-chain disulfide bond is, however, unusually exposed and more susceptible to reduction than the intrachain disulfide bonds and the single L-H chain interchain disulfide bond in each Fab portion of the antibody fragment. Consequently, mild reduction cleaves the divalent fragment, $F(ab')_2$, into two identical monovalent fragments, Fab'. These fragments combine with specific antigen and inhibit precipitation of the antigen with undigested, homoidiotypic antibody.

Rabbit Fab′ possesses, thus, a single, reduced sulfhydryl group which is in the hinge region. The maleimide-conjugated peroxidase will react, therefore, only with this site of Fab′. The site is on the opposite end from the variable region and, therefore, the conjugation leaves antibody reactivity unaffected (lack of steric hindrance). Also, there is only one sulfhydryl group available for conjugation in rabbit IgG, and, therefore, the degree of polymer formation of Fab′ is limited by the number of Fab′ that can react with each peroxidase. However, not more than one peroxidase can react with a single Fab′. In immunoglobulins that have two sulfhydryl groups in the hinge region, steric hindrance probably prevents attachment of more than one peroxidase. Since the size of any polymers that can form in this method is limited, conjugates do not have to be separated from polymers. Therefore, the conjugates are apt to react more specifically, and if excess of conjugating peroxidase is used, they will be largely free of unconjugated Fab′.

For conjugation with maleimide, 6 mg peroxidase are dissolved in 1.0 ml of sodium phosphate buffer, pH 7.0, and incubated at 30°C for 1 hour under stirring with 4 mg of N-hydroxysuccinimide ester of N-(4-carboxycyclohexylmethyl)maleimide dissolved in 0.05 ml of N,N-dimethylformamide. A precipitate is removed by centrifugation and the supernate is passed through a 1.0×45 cm Sephadex G-25 column equilibrated with 0.1 M phosphate buffer, pH 6.0. The protein-containing fractions are concentrated.

For the second reaction stage, maleimide-peroxidase (1.8 mg) is incubated with 2 mg rabbit Fab′ in 0.1 M sodium phosphate buffer, pH 6.0/5 mM ethylene diaminotetraacetate/4°C/20 hour (the free sulfhydryl group of the Fab′ has been protected for storage against oxidation by reversible blocking with sodium monoiodoacetate). The reaction mixture is subjected to gel filtration with a column (1.5×45 cm) of Ultragel AcA44.

NONPEROXIDASE ENZYMES FOR CONJUGATION WITH ANTIBODIES

Glucose oxidase has been a useful enzyme for immunocytochemistry since the development of a substrate that gives a stable, insoluble reaction product (46). Paranitroblue tetrazolium chloride as capturing agent for the oxidized glucose yields a stable, insoluble reaction product of blue color. Glucose oxidase is about four times the size of peroxidase and possesses many more amino groups. Consequently, in the two-stage procedure, it is liable to lead to more extensive polymerization than peroxidase, even if glutaraldehyde is used for conjugation. Also, enzyme reactivity may be more easily affected in the first stage than in the case of peroxidase in which most of the reactive amino groups are blocked by the allylisocyanate occurring in horseradishes (page 59).

Another suitable enzyme is β-galactosidase used by Bondi et al. (47). The enzyme has a high turnover number for the substrate analog, 5-bromo-4-chloro-3-indolyl-β-D-galactoside which yields an insoluble indigo reaction product.

Finally, alkaline phosphatase conjugates enjoyed a revival in the work of Bulman and Heydermann (48). Naphthol phosphate was used as substrate and the naphthol was captured by suitable diazonium salts to give insoluble, colored products.

SIGNAL INTENSIFICATION FOR LIGHT MICROSCOPY IN CONJUGATED ANTIBODY METHODS

In immunofluorescence, the signal can be intensified by strong light sources. Such intensification alone is of no benefit, because background and tissue autoimmunofluorescence are intensified also. However, epifluorescence and narrow band illumination reduce much of the autofluorescence, and hence improved instrumentation also increases sensitivity.

The reaction product in enzyme-labeled antibody methods can be intensified if the enzyme reaction is allowed to continue for longer times. This will increase the signal intensity and the background intensity in case the reaction product is soluble, as is with 4-chloronaphthol as electron donor for peroxidase. Indeed, increased incubation times with this substrate convert the grayish-blue reaction product to a deep black. Background staining is also increased and hence sensitivity is not materially affected by prolonged incubation.

In cases in which reaction leads to an insoluble polymer, such as 3,3'-diaminobenzidine tetrahydrochloride as electron donor for peroxidase, the enzyme reaction will stop with continuing incubation by virtue of product inhibition. The rise in signal intensification will decrease with time. Background staining, which is weaker and hence is subject to slower accumulation of enzyme product, will be inhibited to a lesser extent. Thus, background intensity will still increase while signal intensity remains largely constant. The signal-to-noise ratio will decrease, and the sensitivity will suffer with increased reaction time.

The diaminobenzidine reaction product possesses the ability to catalyze the reduction of silver halides to metallic silver by thioglycolic acid (49). The deposited silver converts the brown reaction product to a black deposit which is more intense in absorbence. Sensitivity is not increased, because background is similarly affected.

Experience with signal intensification of markers for light microscopy suggests that the sensitivity of most methods cannot be improved by this approach. Improvement of sensitivity requires reduction of background, which involves methods that differ in principle from indirect methods that employ conjugated second antibodies, whatever the method of conjugation may be.

CONJUGATION OF BIOTINYLATED PEROXIDASE AND ANTIBODY WITH AVIDIN

The biotin-avidin mode of conjugation employs principles of image intensification that depart radically from those established in methods in which peroxidase is conjugated to antibody covalently with bifunctional reagents. While in the conjugated antibody methods that we have discussed so far, every effort was made to eliminate polymers, in the avidin-biotin method the use of polymers has been attempted intentionally.

Biotin is a vitamin that functions as a prosthetic group to a number of transcarboxylases. By itself, biotin is no marker for visualization of antibodies. Its attraction for use in immunocytochemistry derives from the high-affinity binding (dissociation constant about $10^{-14} M$) with which biotin interacts with avidin, a 68,000-dalton basic protein from egg white. Avidin possesses four binding sites for biotin.

The N-hydroxysuccinimide derivative of biotin reacts with protein amino groups without impairing the avidin-binding capacity of the conjugated biotin (50).

In theory, the biotin-avidin interaction provides an important advantage over the previously discussed conjugation methods. Except in the case of the maleimide method, both arms of the bifunctional, conjugating reagents discussed so far were identical. As a consequence, it had been difficult to control the conjugation reaction: moderate reaction led to contamination with unreacted antibodies, extensive reaction led to polymer formation. Hypothetically, one could avoid this complication if antibody-peroxidase conjugates were made on the section rather than being preformed. One could label antibody with an excess of glutaraldehyde, and after the antibody has reacted on the tissue section, one could apply peroxidase to react with the antibody. There are three obvious reasons why this procedure would fail:

1.   Extensive reaction of antibody with glutaraldehyde will abolish antibody reactivity. In this case, most glutaraldehyde will react via one arm while the other arm would remain free.

2.   Less than extensive reaction would lead to polymerization of the antibody and relatively few arms of glutaraldehyde remain unreacted.

3.   Most importantly, glutaraldehyde being a reagent for any available protein amine, will react nonspecifically with the protein on the section.

The specificity (high affinity) of biotin for avidin avoids this complication. Biotinylated antibody does not exhibit a serious nonspecific reactivity for tissue sections, and hence, its biotin groups will be available for binding with subsequently applied avidin reagents.

In the direct biotin-avidin procedure, the first antibody is labeled with biotin, in the indirect procedure, the first antibody is unlabeled and a second antibody (which is specific for the first antibody) is labeled. As the direct method has not been used much, we will discuss only the indirect method.

There are three sequences of attaching peroxidase, or for that matter any other enzyme or marker protein, to antigen sites in tissue sections via avidin-biotin bonds:

1.   In the *bridge avidin-biotin sequence* of Guesdon et al. (51), four reaction steps involve unlabeled first antibody, biotinylated, affinity-purified second antibody, avidin, and biotinylated peroxidase. The method depends on linking biotinylated second antibody to biotinylated peroxidase via the four combining sites of avidin. The procedure avoids polymer formation, since no two reagents are permitted to interact in solution.

2.   In the *labeled avidin-biotin sequence* of Guesdon et al. (51), three reaction steps involve unlabeled first antibody, biotinylated, affinity-purified second antibody, and avidin conjugated to peroxidase with glutaraldehyde. In this procedure, conjugation of avidin to peroxidase with a bifunctional reagent encounters problems similar to those of conjugation of antibody to peroxidase.

3.   In the *avidin-biotin complex sequence* of Hsu et al. (52), three reaction steps involve unlabeled first antibody, biotinylated, affinity-purified second antibody,

and a complex of biotinylated peroxidase with avidin. The complex used as the third step is prepared 30 minutes before use by mixing avidin with biotinylated peroxidase. The reaction is fast because of the high affinity of avidin for biotin. Large aggregates form because of the multiplicity of biotin groups in the peroxidase and of biotin-binding sites in the avidin. The peroxidatic activity of a large aggregate is higher than that of the monomeric peroxidase-avidin or peroxidase-antibody complex. Therefore, the avidin-biotin complex sequence leads to higher staining intensity than the avidin-biotin sequence 1 and 2 and also higher intensity than methods using antibody directly conjugated to peroxidase. However, increase in staining intensity does not necessarily provide increase in sensitivity. In the avidin-biotin complex method, we form polymeric complexes between proteins, something we went into great length of avoiding with enzyme-antibody conjugates (page 60). These complexes are an invitation to background staining. Intensification of the signal provided by the avidin-biotin complex method does not necessarily increase sensitivity.

Comparisons of the avidin-biotin complex method with enzyme-conjugated antibody methods usually suggest that the former is more sensitive. However, it should be considered that in these comparisons antibody-enzyme conjugates have often been used that have not been freed of unconjugated antibody or polymeric conjugate.

A few comparisons have been made between the avidin-biotin complex method and the unlabeled antibody method. Only two of these studies evaluated the sensitivity rather than signal intensity and found the avidin-biotin complex method less sensitive (page 172).

Because of the high affinity of biotin for avidin, the reaction of biotinylated peroxidase with avidin and of biotinylated second antibody with avidin-biotin complex can be considered practically as irreversible as the covalent bonds in the peroxidase-antibody conjugates produced with bifunctional reagents. The most significant and limiting factor for loss of reagents by dissociation in the total immunocytochemical staining sequence is not dissociation of links between avidin and biotin, but those between tissue antigen and the first antibody and those between the first antibody and biotinylated, affinity-purified second antibody (page 200).

Considering the dissociation constant of $10^{-14} M$, we expect that the reaction of biotinylated peroxidase with conjugate should have been nearly completed during the 30 minutes allowed for its preparation. Apparently this is not the case. If a useful product would be attainable by allowing the reaction to go to completion, there would be no reason to mix the reagents just 30 minutes prior to use. One could mix them beforehand and store the resulting complex. However, it seems that the reaction is not complete in 30 minutes but proceeds until the aggregates of biotinylated peroxidase and avidin are so big that nonspecific precipitation on the section would preclude immunocytochemical staining. Even after 30 minutes, the complex obtained is large and as a result stains many structures nonspecifically. For instance, the complex appears to be an excellent stain for myelinated axons in the absence of any antibodies (page 172).

The proportions of biotinylated peroxidase and avidin are chosen so that a complex obtained after 30 minutes of admixture will be excess in avidin, in order to assure that free avidin sites are available for reaction with the biotinylated

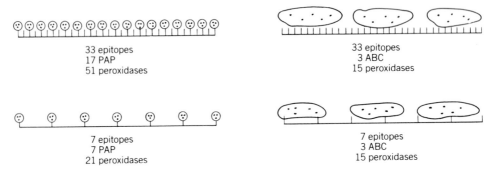

Figure 2-11. These diagrams illustrate a number of peroxidase molecules that can be deposited to antigen in tissue by the unlabeled antibody peroxidase antiperoxidase (PAP) method (page 90) and the avidin-biotin complex (ABC) method. The model is based on the quantitative immunocytochemical comparison discussed on page 172. At high density of antigen (as, for instance, 33 epitopes) steric hindrance may limit the number of PAP complexes deposited to 17 (left upper frame). If ClonoPAP is used, this will result in deposition of 51 noninhibited peroxidase molecules (dots). The avidin-biotin complex is polymeric. Steric hindrance may permit deposition of only three ABC complexes to 33 epitopes (right upper frame). Each complex contains many peroxidase molecules, but steric hindrance within the complex may reduce the number of enzymatically active molecules [we have illustrated (dots) five active peroxidases per complex]. Consequently the staining will be carried out by 15 peroxidase molecules. This corresponds to the greatly reduced signal strength actually observed with the ABC method at high antigen concentration when compared to the PAP method. When the antigen concentration is low, as, for instance, seven epitopes, there is no steric hindrance in the PAP method. Seven PAP complexes and 21 peroxidases are deposited (left lower frame). In the ABC method, steric hindrance of the larger avidin peroxidase complex still occurs permitting the deposition of perhaps only three complexes and 15 peroxidases (right lower frame). Because of steric factors, the amount of complex deposited is similar to that reacting with 33 epitopes at high density. The staining intensity at low epitope density is only slightly less than that of PAP. Background staining, which is the most important factor in sensitivity, is not taken into account in this diagram on comparison of staining intensities.

second antibody on the tissue section. In such an avidin-peroxidase complex, many peroxidase sites are buried. Even if monomeric, biotinylated peroxidase possessed as much enzyme activity as native peroxidase, we expect that in the deep of polymeric complex, some peroxidase enzyme sites are sterically hindered. The size of the complex leads by steric hindrance to a relative inhibition of staining intensity with increase in antigen concentration (Fig. 2-11).

ELECTRON MICROSCOPY WITH PEROXIDASE-CONJUGATED ANTIBODIES

The polymeric oxidation product of diaminobenzidine, which is deposited at the site of immunocytochemical localization of peroxidase-antibody conjugates, is still capable of reducing osmium tetroxide to insoluble osmium black. Thus, the reaction product does become electron-opaque.

Immunocytochemical staining for electron microscopy can be carried out either on the plastic ultrathin section (postembedding staining) or on a thick section of tissue prior to plastic embedding for electron microscopy (pre-embedding staining). In postembedding staining, much of the structure and antigenic

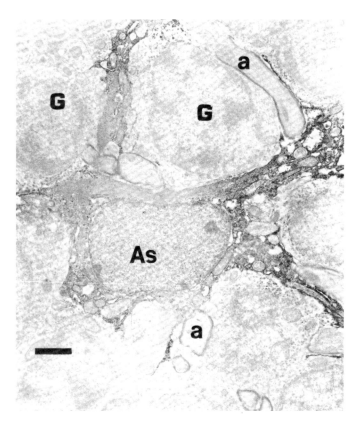

Figure 2-12. S-100 protein in the cytoplasm of astrocytes (As) among numerous unstained granule cells of the rat cerebellum. The filaments in the glial cell cytoplasm are 10 to 12 nm in diameter. Vibratome sections stained prior to embedding with peroxidase-labeled antibodies (periodate conjugate). Marker is 1 μm. [Reproduced with permission from Eng and Bigbee (53).]

reactivity of tissue is jeopardized. In general, peroxidase conjugates do not provide sufficient sensitivity for postembedding localization. Exceptions are provided by sections very rich in antigens, such as the polysaccharide capsule of some bacteria.

Conjugates have been useful for the preembedding localization of antigens. The main problem in pre-embedding localization is penetration of immunocytochemical reagents into the tissue. Special procedures for opening tissue to penetration are sometimes recommended (page 78), yet are not necessary as shown by the excellent localization of S-100 protein (Fig. 2-12) accomplished by Eng and Bigbee (53) in cerebellum in which routine fixation was the only pretreatment. Neither is the size of conjugate a crucial factor. It is not necessary to use conjugates of peroxidase with Fab or protein A to reduce the size. In the work of Eng and Bigbee (53), staining was with conjugate prepared by the periodate method, in which the product is more polymerized than that of other antibody conjugations (page 64).

THE IMMUNOFERRITIN METHOD

We have seen that labeling of antibodies with dyes does not yield sufficient absorbence for light microscopic visualization. A few light-absorbing groups distributed over the whole immunoglobulin molecule dilute the absorption capacity excessively. To visualize antibodies under ordinary light microscopy, we require a high concentration of many absorbing molecules within a confined area. This is provided by histochemical reaction products built up at an enzyme-specific site.

Similar principles hold for visualization under the electron microscope. Instead of light-absorbing labels, we need electron-opaque labels. We can label antibodies with up to 200 atoms of uranium, provided the antibody-combining sites are affinity-protected during the labeling process (2). However, the uranium is distributed over the whole of the remainder of the immunoglobulin surface. This distribution dilutes the electron-absorbing capacity of the 200 atoms and the method is, therefore, not sufficiently sensitive for modern electron-microscopic immunocytochemistry. Even more so than in light microscopy, an effective electron-opaque label must be concentrated onto a limited site. We have already seen that one way to accomplish this is to convert a light-absorbing enzyme reaction product to an electron-opaque product (page 70). Another way is to utilize the naturally occurring macromolecular ferritin, isolated from horse spleen. Ferritin is a spherical, 650,000-dalton protein with an iron content of 23% by weight. As we will see below, the molecule is discernible in the electron microscope only because the iron is concentrated in characteristic micelles in the center of the molecule that forms tetrads with diameters of 5 nm. Ferritin-labeled antibodies, introduced by Singer and Schick (54), have provided the first immunocytochemical method for the electron microscope.

There is a third way of concentrating electron opacity to a limited area. It can be accomplished by stabilizing colloidal gold particles in suspension with a shell of immunoglobulin or protein A.

An explanation for the loss of contrast when an immunoglobulin is diffusely labeled with even as many as 200 atoms of uranium has been provided by Tanaka (55). In order to give distinct contrast with surrounding areas, the value of $NZ^{4/3}/S$ for a specifically stained area should be greater than $4700/nm^2$, where N is the number of heavy metal atoms of atomic number Z added as a label to an area of size S. If we assume the area of a single antibody molecule to be $76/nm^2$, the value of $NZ^{4/3}/S$ is $45/nm^2$ for a molecule of antibody labeled with 10 mercury atoms, $134/nm^2$ for a molecule labeled with 30 mercury atoms, $944/nm^2$ if labeled with 200 uranium atoms, and $1935/nm^2$ if the uranium is bridged to osmium via thiocarbohydrazide at a ratio of one osmium to one uranium atom. Even the value for osmium-bridged uranium antibody is too low for distinction of single molecules at high resolution. Useful contrast can only be obtained at lower resolution when the concentration of antigen is high, so that several antibody molecules are packed close to each other, thus increasing N in $NZ^{4/3}/S$.

If in ferritin, the iron were distributed uniformly, the electron contrast, $NZ^{4/5}/S$, would only be $1030/nm^2$, and single molecules could not be distinguished from surrounding structures. Fortunately, the iron-containing micelles afford a high concentration of iron and characteristic structure at single-molecule resolution. $NZ^{4/3}/S$ for the tetrad is 6000/nm, well above the value needed for good differential contrast. When ferritin is conjugated to antibody covalently, the point of electron opacity is seen at a distance of about 8 nm from the point of attachment of the ferritin with the antibody (Fig. 2-13).

Ferritin is conjugated to immunoglobulin with bifunctional reagents in two stages (Fig. 2-14) using toluene-2,4-diisocyanate (54) or glutaraldehyde (57).

In the *first stage*, ferritin is reacted with an excess of bifunctional conjugant. The conjugant meets one of three fates under these conditions: One functional group reacts with ferritin and the other remains free, or both or none of the functional groups react. When both functional groups have reacted, aggregates of ferritin with ferritin may form.

In the second stage, the products of this reaction are admixed with immunoglobulin. Ferritin reacted with one arm of the bifunctional conjugant will be available for binding immunoglobulin via the second arm. It is desirable to separate unconjugated bifunctional reagent between the first and second stage in order to prevent formation of intermolecular bonds in immunoglobulin.

The final conjugate does not only consist of dimers of one ferritin and one immunoglobulin molecule. Polymerization of ferritin can occur in the first stage, by virtue of bifunctional reagent reacting with both functional groups. To the extent that such polymers also carry conjugant with one of its functional groups

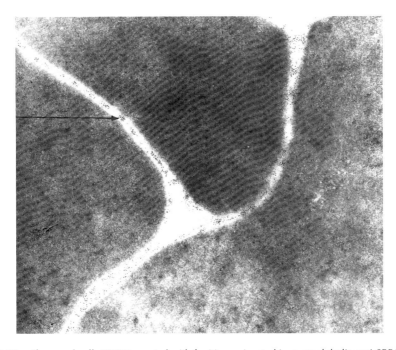

Figure 2-13.   Sheep red cells (SRBC) reacted with ferritin-conjugated immunoglobulin anti-SRBC diluted 1 : 10 (agglutinin titer was 1 : 40). Individual ferritin molecules can always be discerned in the immunoferitin method because the iron micelles in the core of the molecule are surrounded by the electron-translucent sheet of the bulk of the ferritin molecule. Although the distribution of antigen on the erythrocyte membrane is continuous (page 200), localization of ferritin appears in clusters suggesting that the localized material does not only consist of monomeric but also of polymeric aggregates of ferritin with immunoglobulin. Arrow shows intercellular immunoglobulin bridge. [From Schäfer (56).]

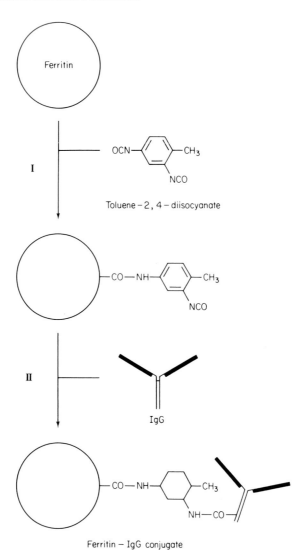

Figure 2-14. Conjugation of ferritin with toluene-2,4-diisocyanate. In the first stage, a number of toluene diisocyanate molecules reacts with each ferritin molecule, forming carbamido bonds between the 4-isocyanate groups and the free amino groups in ferritin. In the second stage, the conjugated ferritin reacts with immunoglobulin forming carbamido bonds between the 2-isocyanate groups and the free amino groups of immunoglobulin. Limitation of reaction in the first stage ensures that most reacting components in the second stage yield only dimers.

free, it can react with immunoglobulin in the second stage, leading to complexes of immunoglobulin with polymeric ferritin. To the extent that a ferritin molecule or aggregate possesses more than one conjugant with free reactive groups, it can react with more than one immunoglobulin, thus leading in the second stage to aggregates containing multiple immunoglobulin groups.

Conditions have been chosen, therefore, to minimize aggregation. Otto et al. (57) recommend diluted ferritin and a limited excess of glutaraldehyde for use in the first stage. High concentrations of ferritin make aggregation so extensive that it becomes visible to the naked eye in the form of a precipitate. For the second stage, they recommend a 5:1 weight excess of ferritin over immuno-globulin (molar ratio of approximately 1) in order to reduce the binding of multiple immunoglobulins with a single ferritin.

In the *second stage*, the initial reaction is between ferritin and immunoglobulin (Fig. 2-15). As the reaction is allowed to proceed, products of polymeric im-munoglobulin will form. For this reason, it is necessary to limit the reaction in the second stage, and when glutaraldehyde is the conjugant, to terminate the action by addition of lysine. With such limitation of the second stage reaction, the expected yield of conjugate is 20% to 30%, with the remainder of the protein being unconjugated ferritin and unconjugated immunoglobulin.

When one ferritin molecule has reacted with one immunoglobulin molecule, only one and never both of the antibody-combining sites can be affected by steric hindrance. At worst, antibody would become monovalent (unable to precipitate with antigen), but in any event would still be able to combine with antigen and, hence, would still be useful for immunocytochemical localization. In fact, even hindrance of one specific combining site in an immunoglobulin molecule is not necessarily the rule upon reaction with a single ferritin molecule. However, if the reaction is permitted to proceed to large aggregates, steric hindrance becomes likely by conjugation onto additional ferritin molecules or ferritin-immunoglob-

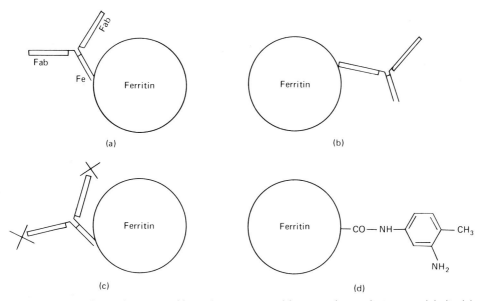

Figure 2-15. Products of reaction of limited conjugation of ferritin with specific immunoglobulin fol-lowed by purification of conjugates. (a) Ferritin-specific antibody conjugate, combining sites unaffected. (b) Ferritin-specific antibody conjugate, one combining site hindered. (c) Ferritin-nonspecific IgG conju-gate. (d) Unconjugated, diisocyanate-reacted ferritin (only one of many unreacted diisocyanate groups is shown). (a,b) Specifically reacting constituents of the conjugate. (c,d) Do not react specifically and may contribute to nonspecific staining. Nonspecific immunoglobulin is marked by × at the N-terminal portion of the Fab fragments (page 7). Ferritin (Fe) may be monomeric or polymeric, but only monomers are shown.

ulin complexes. Since in IgG preparations only a relatively small proportion of molecules is specific antibody, chances are high that polymerization with additional IgG will only add bulk but not specific reactivity to a specific antibody-ferritin conjugate.

Unconjugated immunoglobulin must be separated because it competes with ferritin-conjugated immunoglobulin for localization of antigen. Since much of the antibody activity in the conjugate has been inactivated in the process of conjugation, and most of the remaining active conjugate consists of monovalent antibody (Fig. 2-15), the relative amount of antibody-binding activity in unconjugated immunoglobulin is higher than that in conjugated immunoglobulin. In addition, an antibody binding with two combining sites on properly spaced antigen determinants in tissue is held with higher affinity than one possessing only one binding site (page 236). For these reasons, unconjugated antibody is bound preferentially over conjugated antibody and, therefore, inhibits staining disproportionally.

Separation of unconjugated and conjugated immunoglobulin is carried out on continuous sucrose density gradients (58).

Measurement of antibody activity in conjugates by tests that depend on precipitation, agglutination, or other secondary phenomena in the antigen-antibody reaction may give erroneously high or low estimates. Ferritin, especially isocyanate-conjugated ferritin, possesses a tendency to adsorb nonspecifically on surfaces. This tendency may increase nonspecifically the amount of precipitate obtained upon reaction of conjugate with specific antigen. On the other hand, steric hindrance of one of the combining sites of IgG by conjugation with ferritin results in monovalent antibody that not only fails to precipitate with antigen but also interferes with the precipitation of divalent antibody and antigen. In general, if the conjugation reaction is not limited to below 30% yield, specific precipitation or agglutination of isolated conjugate (free of unconjugated antibody) is entirely abolished or severely reduced (59).

The unreliability of agglutination for estimating retention of antibody activity upon conjugation can be illustrated by the localization of specific conjugate on the sheep erythrocyte (SRBC) surface in the studies of Schafer (56) (Fig. 2-13). The localization of conjugate was patchy even though used at a concentration four times in excess of that required for cell agglutination. In contrast, unlabeled antibody (page 200) gives patchy localization only when diluted to its agglutination titer or beyond. Apparently, conjugation enhances agglutination by nonspecific forces.

Otto et al. (57) compared by hemolytic titers the antibody activity of ferritin with antisheep erythrocyte immunoglobulin conjugates made in one and two stages. For the one-stage preparation, glutaraldehyde was added to a mixture of ferritin and immunoglobulin. Only 3% of hemolytic activity was maintained in the one-stage procedure, while 17% were preserved in the two-stage procedure. However, these data may give erroneous values for conjugated antibody activity. Hemolysis is dependent on complement fixation, which in turn requires aggregated immunoglobulin. The polymerization of immunoglobulin as a result of conjugation may favor complement fixation relative to that of unconjugated antibody, thus requiring less specific antibody for an equal amount of hemolytic activity. On the other hand, it is possible that conjugation interferes with some of the binding sites for C'q component of complement. Indeed, the interference of glutaraldehyde with determinants of immunoglobulin is extensive. Thus Goldin et al. (58) found that conjugate of ferritin with antidinitrophenyl immunoglobulin lost most of its epitopic reactivity with anti-immunoglobulin while maintaining considerable idiotypic reactivity for dinitrophenol (see also page 185).

For the conjugation of ferritin with immunoglobulin, it is important to use ferritin devoid of contaminating apoferritin that lacks heme and iron. Conjugation by the procedure of Otto et al. (57) is done at 37°C with the reagents containing 0.02% sodium azide. To 50 to 80 mg of ferritin, add glutaraldehyde in 0.1 M phosphate buffer, pH 7.0, to a final concentration of 0.02% to 0.2% in a total volume of 1.0 ml. After 2 hours, pass the solution through a Sephadex G25 column (25 × 1.6 cm). Monitor protein concentration of effluent and collect only the middle peak fraction to avoid undue dilution. Add 3 mg of affinity-purified serum antibody (monoclonal antibodies cannot be recommended for general use as second antibodies) in phosphate buffer to each 15 mg of ferritin, and let the mixture stand overnight without stirring. Add lysine to a final concentration of 0.01 M, keeping the mixture for another few hours before further processing.

Prepare a 5% to 45% w/w sucrose gradient in an exponential gradient pouring apparatus according to the recommendations of Goldin et al. (58). Use a mixing volume of 23.5 ml for the 5% sucrose. Pour the gradient to a volume of 30 to 35 ml. Place the conjugate on one or more gradients, depending on its volume, and spin at 4°C for 2 hours at 24,000 rpm (Beckman SW27 rotor). Collect the ferritin band as visualized by its brown color (ferritin-immunoglobulin conjugate plus unconjugated ferritin, free of unconjugated immunoglobulin).

Protein concentration can be determined by absorbence at 280 nm and ferritin by the Prussian blue reaction (54).

Ferritin-antibody conjugates cannot be used for postembedding staining electron microscopy (page 114) on ultrathin, plastic sections. Apparently, ferritin conjugates exhibit such strong hydrophobic bonding that they react intensively with the plastic section even when devoid of tissue.

Ferritin-antibody conjugates can be used on 50 to 100 nm thick frozen sections, cut at −70°C and picked up on Formver-coated cover grids. Nascent mouse immunoglobulin was localized by Slot and Geuze (60) on ultrathin, frozen sections of gelatin-embedded MOPC 195 myeloma cells by rabbit antimouse IgG, and ferritin-conjugated goat antirabbit IgG and nascent IgA in human duodenal mucosa (Fig. 2-16) by anti-IgA and immunogold technique (page 79). The observed localizations illustrate the usual pathway of immunoglobulin secretion that starts by peptide formation in the rough endoplastic reticulum, proceeds to protein assembly as well as glycosylation in the Golgi stacks, and leads to secretion via exocytosis. In contrast to older immunocytochemical data, the free ribosomes did not seem to be significantly involved in immunoglobulin synthesis. Also in contrast to prior notions on immunoglobulin secretion by plasma cells, but in agreement with secretion of endocrine or exocrine principles, immunoglobulins are exteriorized by transport in secretion vesicles and fusion of the vesicle wall with that of the cell membrane (page 411).

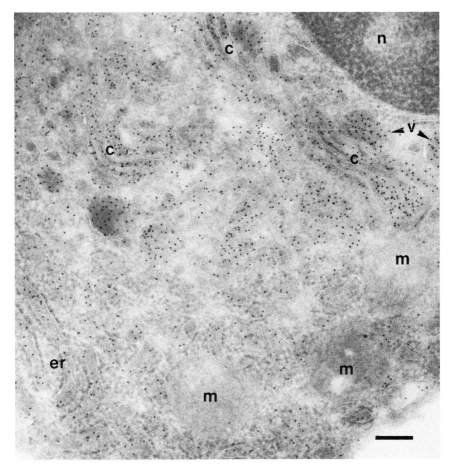

Figure 2-16. Nascent IgA in a plasma cell of lamina propria of human duodenum is in rough endoplasmic reticulum (er), Golgi cysternae (c) and significantly, in secretory vesicles (v). Low background in nucleolus (n) and mitochondria (m). Paraformaldehyde fixation. Postembedding staining on frozen section. Immunogold method. Essentially similar results can be obtained by immunoferritin method. Bar is 0.2 μm. (From the work of Jan Slot.)

Pre-embedding staining with ferritin antibodies also encountered difficulties. Even isolated cells can only be stained in their interior if membranes are disrupted to permit access of the conjugate. Disruption is usually accomplished by freezing and thawing, fixation, and membrane-lytic agents such as saponin, digitonin, or dimethyl sulfoxide. The difficulty of penetration is not due to the size of the ferritin-immunoglobulin dimer (646,000 daltons). This dimer is not appreciably larger than the peroxidase-antiperoxidase complex (420,000 daltons), which penetrates reasonably well in fixed tissue without necessity of visibly destroying cell membranes (pages 127 and 314).

The usefulness of the immunoferritin technique is mainly in the localization of antigens on cell surfaces (pages 186 and 280) and in intercellular spaces.

IMMUNOGOLD TECHNIQUES

Ferritin is a marker for electron microscopy because its iron contents are concentrated in characteristic micelles. Other metal may also give sufficient contrast, provided a large number of heavy atoms can be concentrated into a restricted domain and the resulting particle conjugated to immunoglobulin as a whole. Such particles are provided by colloidal gold in water. The negative charge of the particles repels them from each other and thus maintains their stability. However, the stability of the resulting *sols* is variable. Addition of electrolytes precipitates the particles immediately. The particles can, however, be stabilized, even in electrolytes, provided the sol is pretreated by addition of macromolecules, including proteins and carbohydrates. Such macromolecules are adsorbed on the surface of the gold particles, thus preventing access of a subsequently added electrolyte, and maintaining the gold particles in solution for varying periods of time. Faulk and Taylor (61) stabilized gold particles with antibodies against Salmonella and obtained, thereby, an immunocytochemical label for the surface of the organism. The electron opacity of gold particles is much higher than that of ferritin, because of the size of the particles, because gold is heavier than iron, and because the whole diameter of the particle with exception of a surrounding monolayer of immunoglobulin is filled with gold, in contrast to ferritin in which only the inner micelle contains iron.

However, Romano and co-workers (62) found that gold sols protected by most antibodies were not sufficiently stable in isotonic saline to be useful for immunocytochemistry. Only horse antibody was able to yield solutions stable enough to immunostain human erythrocyte surface antigens. Horisberger and Rosset (63) found that 93% of gold sol particles, 50 nm in diameter, stabilized with specifically purified antimannan could be agglutinated by addition of mannan. This suggests that nearly every particle surrounded by absorbed antibody possessed at least one antibody with an active binding site. An important aspect of the colloidal gold method is the regulation of particle size and the preparation of colloidal gold as delineated by Frens (64). Colloidal gold is prepared by reduction of an aqueous solution of chlorauric acid. Phosphorus-saturated ether is used as reducing agent for 3 to 5 nm, sodium ascorbate for 10 to 15 nm, and sodium citrate for 15 to 120 nm particles. The use of gold particles of different sizes in conjugation with different antibodies permits the postembedding localization of two antigens on the same section (page 193). Stability of protein-colloidal gold suspension is best with proteins that are soluble at their isolectic points in low salt concentrations. This condition can be met better with protein A than with IgG which indeed is characterized by low solubility at its isolectic point (page 6). The amount of protein necessary for stabilizing gold particles has to be determined in each case. Adsorption of protein onto colloidal gold particles should not be carried out in salt concentrations in excess of $0.005\ M$ sodium chloride.

In the adsorption procedure of DeWaele et al. (65), 1 mg of affinity-purified anti-IgG is dialyzed against $0.002\ M$ borate buffer, pH 9.0. After removal of aggregate by centrifugation at 100,000 g/1 hour/4°C, the optimum amount of protein for stabilization of the gold sol is determined by finding the minimum amount of salt necessary to destabilize varying proportions of protein to gold sol.

Twenty percent excess over this proportion of protein is added to the gold sol adjusted to pH 9.0 with sodium carbonate. After 2 minutes of stirring, bovine serum albumin is added to 10 mg/ml. Unstable gold complexes are removed by three cycles of centrifugation at 12,000 g/4°C/1 hour and resuspension in 0.02 M Tris-buffered saline, pH 8.2/10 mg/ml bovine serum albumin/0.02 M sodium azide. Such suspensions are reported to be stable for several weeks at 4°C (66).

The difference which proteins exhibit in their ability to stabilize gold particles suggests that the bonds between the charged gold particles and the protective macromolecules are labile. It is, therefore, quite possible that antibodies adsorbed on colloid particles may be replaced with proteins that possess stronger positive charge than immunoglobulin. Such proteins could be easily encountered in tissues when colloidal gold antibodies are used for immunocytochemical staining of intracellular antigens. The antibodies would be released and the gold particles would bind to positively charged tissue constituents nonspecifically.

Indirect immunogold technique is suitable for postembedding staining electron microscopy. An example is the study of Roth et al. (67) on the renal tubular distribution of the soluble 28,000-dalton calcium-binding protein stimulated by metabolites of vitamin D. These metabolites act as steroid hormones (their receptors are cytosolic and nuclear). The calcium-binding protein stimulated by vitamin D has been proposed to be involved in the mechanism of tubular reabsorption of calcium. Tubular segments that were positive for calcium-binding protein by immunofluorescence and protein gold (Fig. 2-17) included those that are rich in nuclear receptors for vitamin D active metabolite. However, other regions containing receptor were devoid of the binding protein.

Postembedding staining techniques have been quantified (page 148). This quantification is usually carried out by optical density measurements. In the case of immunogold technique, it might be tempting to quantify by enumeration of gold particles. When this is done, it becomes evident that gold particles do not only deposit on specifically stained structures. There is background. Quantitatively, sensitivity of staining is expressed by the ratio of specific-to-background staining. Qualitatively, specificity is generally expressed by statements alluding to numerous particles in the specifically stained areas and few in other areas.

In the study on calcium-binding protein, Roth et al. (67) were able to reveal cytosolic localization with immunogold by postembedding technique. In general, postembedding electron-microscopic staining has been restricted to antigens associated with secretion granules when the unlabeled antibody or immunogold techniques were used (page 124). It is conceivable that immunogold is able to localize antigens by postembedding technique in additional locations as well.

There is, however, a distinct difference in localization of antigens in secretion granules by protein A gold and the unlabeled antibody method. The number of antigen sites in secretion granules as visualized by unlabeled antibodies is so high as to blacken the granule in its entirety (page 118). Extensive dilution of antibody is required to discern individual epitopic sites in the granule. With immunogold, however, only a discrete number of epitopic sites become marked by the gold particles. It appears that many sites are missed. A correlate to this low binding efficiency is the need of relatively high concentrations of first antibodies in the immunogold technique.

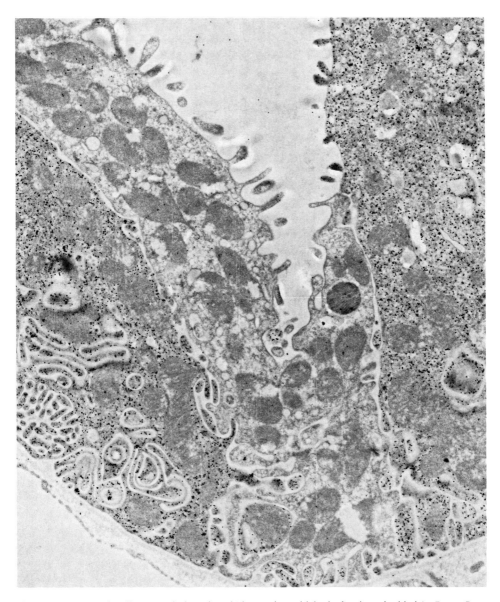

Figure 2-17. Initial collecting tubules of rat kidney, glutaraldehyde fixed, embedded in Epon. Post-embedding staining for calcium-binding protein by indirect protein A gold technique. Apical cytoplasm of the principal cell on the right and left is labeled with numerous gold particles in cytoplasmic matrix and in the nucleus (not shown). Mitochondria and lysosomes are not labeled. Gold particles in the mitochondria-rich cell in the middle are not above background. Use of low-temperature embedding with Lo-acryl K4M (instead of Epon embedding) resulted in intensified labeling. (From the work of Jurgen Roth.)

The relatively sparse distribution of gold particles permits, however, the evaluation of ultrastructural details. In the unlabeled antibody enzyme technique, the strong reaction product masks ultrastructural details. High dilutions of antisera that give only partial staining and relatively low incubation times of enzyme with substrate are needed to permit evaluation of structural detail by the unlabeled antibody enzyme method.

The immunogold method has not been found suitable for pre-embedding staining immunocytochemistry (page 126).

Immunogold provides excellent markers for the cell surface. Monoclonal antibodies exist that differentiate subcells of T-lymphocytes (page 272). Thus, OKT3 is a monoclonal antibody specific for mature T-cells. Combination of immunogold surface labeling with histology for intracellular enzymes has en-

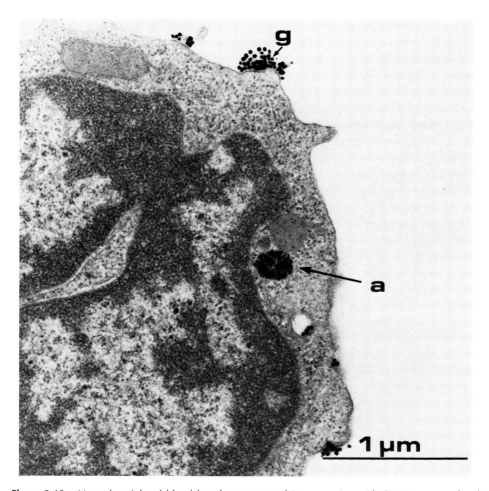

Figure 2-18. Normal peripheral blood lymphocyte reacted in suspension with OKT3, a monoclonal antibody specific for mature T cells, followed by protein A gold, then cytocentrifuged and stained on the smear for acid phosphatase activity. OKT3 reacts on the surface (g) and phosphatase activity (a) is found in lysosomes. [Reprinted by permission of Elsevier Science Publishing Co., Inc. from Cytochemical profile of immunoregulatory T-lymphocyte subsets defined by monoclonal antibodies, by M. DeWaele, J. Demey, M. Moeremans, L. Smet, L. Broodtaerts, B. van Camp, *Journal of Histochemistry and Cytochemistry* **31:**471, Copyright 1983 by the Histochemical Society, Inc. (65)]

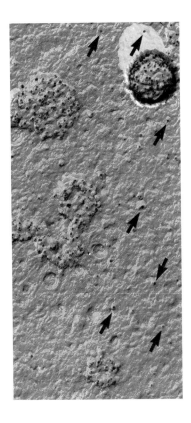

Figure 2-19. Surface replica of measles-infected HeLa cell, labeled for virus-specific surface antigen with rabbit antimeasles antibody and protein A gold. Aggregated gold particles on virus specific structures. Arrows denote isolated gold particles deposited nonspecifically. [From Mannweiler et al. (66).]

abled DeWaele et al. (65) to add to the data that show that T-lymphocytes cannot be classified on the basis of single markers, that is, if OKT antibodies are used for classification, other markers, such as enzymes or Fc receptors, do not necessarily exist only in cells characterized by a single OKT antibody (Fig. 2-18).

Immunogold technique seems to be especially suitable as specific label in high-resolution surface replica electron microscopy. Virus-specific surface antigen has been demonstrated at high resolution by Mannweiler et al. (66) on cell surfaces of HeLa cells chronically infected with measles virus (Fig. 2-19). Cell surface replication was carried out after critical point drying. The labeling occurred predominantly over stack and band-like aggregates of fine corpuscular structures at the plasma membrane of the cell surface, as well as on spherical, virus-like particles. These structures are considered to be the morphologic alterations of the cell surface resulting from virus infection. The electron density of the gold particles was that strong that particles were not masked in the evaporation shadow of large structures. Thus, particle enumeration may become meaningful.

METHOD SPECIFICITY OF CONJUGATES OF ANTIBODIES WITH ENZYMES OR OTHER PROTEINS

The problem of method specificity encountered with conjugates of antibodies and enzymes or other proteins bear a superficial resemblance to the problems encountered with immunofluorescence. Some of these problems are magnified because of the complexity of cross-linking proteins relative to that of introducing a few, small fluorescent groups into a single protein. The solutions and partial solutions of these problems differ, and for that reason we have discussed method specificity derived from immunofluorescence separately (page 48). One of the problems shared by immunofluorescence and other conjugate methods is reaction of conjugates for first antibodies with Fc receptors. However, since Fc receptors are mainly a problem in living cells and in frozen sections and since living cells and frozen sections are mainly the province of immunofluorescence, discussion of Fc receptors will not be repeated here. We will concentrate on the remaining problems of method specificity.

An indirect immunocytochemical method is specific, if no background is obtained when all the reagents except the first antibody are applied to the tissue section. This is not an idealistic requirement. Modern immunocytochemistry leaves no background when the method is carried out on paraffin or plastic sections of well-fixed tissue. Under these circumstances, the section remains invisible unless special optics, such as Nomarski differential interference optics or darkfield illumination, are used. On quantification of absorbence, there will be no difference in optical density of those sections to which all immunocytochemical agents, except the first antibody, have been applied and those which received no treatment at all.

If there are problems with method specificity, the section treated with an immunocytochemical staining sequence that is complete except for omission of the first antibody, will be stained to varying extents. The stain is the contribution of the method to nonspecific background. Poor specificity of the first antibody may also contribute to background, but this background is independent of the immunocytochemical method used and will be discussed under the heading of "Antibody Specificity" (Chapters Five and Six).

The causes of poor method specificity with protein-antibody conjugates in paraffin or plastic sections of fixed tissue are:

1. Aggregated reagents.
2. Unconjugated antibody.
3. Peculiarities of the label.
4. Contamination of labeled antibody with substances directly binding to tissue.

The first three factors can be eliminated in most cases by judicious use of conjugated antibody methods. The last factor requires different methodology (page 90).

Aggregated Reagents

Aggregation is a problem when different proteins are linked by bifunctional reagents. Monomers, consisting of one molecule of each of the two proteins, are usually specific. Polymers consisting of more than one molecule of the two proteins have a tendency to attach nonspecifically at the interface between solution and section surface. Aggregation of protein also occurs, but to the lesser extent, when a small, monofunctional label, such as a fluorochrome or biotin is introduced into a protein. Polymer formation in cross-linked proteins is more extensive the more efficient the conjugation procedure, and the more it attempts to avoid retention of unconjugated antibody.

Polymerized proteins are encountered in the conjugated ferritin and enzyme methods, in the immunogold method, and in the avidin-biotin complex method. Whenever possible, they must be eliminated before a conjugate is used.

Polymers can be removed, at least partially, from peroxidase-antibody conjugates by suitable gel filtration. Removal of polymers from ferritin-antibody conjugates is more involved because even the monomer is too large to be retained on most of the commonly available gel filtration columns. Instead it is recommended to produce conjugates under mild conditions in which polymer formation is minimized. Polymeric absorption of antibody or protein A on colloidal gold is essential for stabilization of the colloidal gold sol in physiologic solution. Therefore, avoidance of polymers is not indicated. It is possible that the large size of the protein-covered gold particle is responsible for nonspecific deposition on sections encountered with the colloidal gold method. Neither can background due to polymers be eliminated from the avidin-biotin complex method, since formation of polymeric avidin-biotinylated peroxidase complex is essential to the signal amplification intended by the method. Hsu et al. (68) have introduced a method that employs antibody to avidin and avidin-biotinylated peroxidase complex in which all biotin receptors on avidin are blocked by excess of biotinylated peroxidase. It is likely in this method that the avidin-biotinylated peroxidase complexes are smaller than in the usual avidin-biotin complex method.

Unconjugated Antibodies

Unconjugated antibody in itself does not affect method specificity. Its effects are indirect. Unconjugated antibody competes with conjugate and thus reduces signal intensity. Background may not be decreased concomitantly, and thus the sensitivity may also be decreased. This requires use of first antibody at lesser dilutions with incumbent reduction in specificity. Thus, contaminating unlabeled antibodies may become a methodologic cause of lessened antibody specificity.

In the immunoferritin method and the immunogold method, it is easy to eliminate unconjugated antibody by ultracentrifugation (pages 77 and 80). In peroxidase conjugate methods, separation of unlabeled antibody can be accomplished by differential desorption from concanavalin A columns (page 61). In immunofluorescence, unconjugated antibody is eliminated by diethylaminoethyl sepharose chromatography (page 41). It is unlikely that the extensively biotinylated first antibody in the avidin-biotin complex method contains significant amounts of unlabeled antibody. It is also unlikely that polymerized avidin-biotin complex contains significant quantities of unlabeled avidin.

Peculiarities of the Label

Fluorochrome labeling of antibodies increases their negative charge and hydrophobicity. Resulting problems are being minimized by moderate degrees of conjugation. Tissues possess autofluorescence which is minimized by narrow-band epi-illumination (pages 49 and 54).

Ferritin conjugates react nonspecifically with plastic sections. Their use is restricted, therefore, to cell surface staining and to staining on ultrathin frozen sections.

The products of diaminobenzidine oxidation creep along the surfaces on which they are liberated. This may result in nonspecific staining of structures adjacent to specifically localized structures at high resolution pre-embedding staining electron microscopy (page 129). The problem can be alleviated by lessening incubation times and lower concentrations of diaminobenzidine and hydrogen peroxide. Frozen or poorly fixed tissues sometimes oxidize diaminobenzidine in the presence of hydrogen peroxide without addition of peroxidase. This activity is sometimes called "endogenous peroxidase." It can be eliminated in most cases by pretreatment of sections with methanolic hydrogen peroxide (page 113).

Contamination of Labeled Antibodies with Substances Directly Binding to Tissue

Anti-immunoglobulin, even if affinity-purified, contains antibodies to contaminants in the immunoglobulin used for immunization. Some of these antibody contaminants react directly with tissue even in the absence of first antibody (page 142). Since these contaminating antibodies are labeled, background staining will result. This background staining is intrinsic to conjugated antibody methods. It cannot be remedied without departure from the principle of conjugation.

REFERENCES

1. DeMey J, Lambert AM, Bajen AS, Moermans M, DeBrabander M: Visualization of microtubules in interphase of mitotic plant cells of *Haemanthus* endosperm with the immunogold staining (IGS) method. *Proc Natl Acad Sci USA* **79:**1878, 1981.

2. Sternberger LA, Hanker JS, Donati EJ, Petrali JP, Seligman AM: Method for enhancement of electron-microscopic visualization of embedded antigen by bridging osmium to uranium-antibody via thiocarbohydrazide. *J Histochem Cytochem* **14:**711, 1966.

3. Coons AH, Kaplan MH: Localization of antigens in tissue cells. II. Improvement in a method for the detection of antigen by means of fluorescent antibody. *J Exp Med* **91:**1, 1950.

4. Von Mayersbach H (ed): Immunohistochemistry. *Acta Histochem (Jena) Suppl* 7, 1967.

5. Von Mayersbach H: Immunohistology, in Grauman W, Neumann K (eds): *Handbook of Histochemistry*. I. General Methodology, pt 2. Stuttgart, Gustav Fischer Verlag, 1966.

6. Hartman BK: Immunofluorescence of dopamine-β-hydroxylase. Application of improved methodology to the localization of the peripheral and central noradrenergic nervous system. *J Histochem Cytochem* **21:**312, 1973.

7. Brandtzaeg P, Purvis K, Hansson V: Methodology of immunofluorescent cell surface staining with special reference on Leydig cells and membrane immunoglobulins. *Int J Andrology Suppl* **2:**287, 1978.

8. Taylor RB, Duffus PH, Raff MC, DePetris S: Redistribution and pinocytosis of lymphocyte surface immunoglobulin molecules induced by anti-immunoglobulin antibody. *Nature (New Biol)* **233**:255, 1971.

9. Joseph KC, Stieber A, Gonatas NK: Endocytosis of cholera toxin in GERL-like structures of murine neuroblastoma cells pretreated with GM_1 ganglioside cholera toxin internalization into neuroblastoma GERL. *J Cell Biol* **81**:543, 1979.

10. Farquar MH: Multiple pathways of exocytosis, endocytosis and membrane recycling: validity of Golgi reaction. *Fed Proc* **42**:2407, 1983.

11. Jones P, Cebra JJ, Herzenberg LA: Immunoglobulin (Ig) allotype markers on rabbit lymphocytes: Separation of cells bearing different allotypes and demonstration of the binding of Ig to lymphoid cell membranes. *J Immunol* **111**:1334, 1973.

12. Kirchanski SJ, Price PJ, Daviderits G, Hoffman R: Flow cytometry measurement of membrane C3b modulation during phagocytosis. *Biotechniques* **1**:66, 1983.

13. Cram LS, Forsland JC: A quantitative method for evaluating fluorescent antibodies and the conjugation process. *Immunochemistry* **II**:667, 1974.

14. Derby MA, Dyer SA, Glaser L: Monoclonal antibodies against a differentiated retinal cell population. *Der Brain Res* **7**:317, 1983.

15. Schenk EA, Charukian CJ: Immunofluorescence counterstains. *J Histochem Cytochem* **22**:962, 1974.

16. Gailbraith RM, Gailbraith GM: Recent progress in immunohistology. *Ann Clin Lab Sci* **10**:1, 1980.

17. Hardy PH, Nell EE: Characteristics of fluorescein labeled antiglobulin preparations that may affect the fluorescent treponemal antibody-absorption test. *Am J Clin Pathol* **56**:181, 1971.

18. Alexander EL, Sanders SK: F(ab')₂ reagents are not required if goat, rather than rabbit, antibodies are used to detect human surface immunoglobulin. *J Immunol* **119**:1084, 1977.

19. Lazarus GS, Poole AR: Immunocytochemical localization of cathespin D in rabbit skin. *Arch Dermatol* **III**:1150, 1975.

20. Ades EW, Philips DJ, Shore SL, Gordon DS, LaVia MF, Black CM, Reimer CB: Analysis of mononuclear cell surfaces with fluoresceinated staphylococcal protein A complexed with IgG antibody or heat aggregated γ-globulin. *J Immunol* **117**:2119, 1976.

21. Haskill JS, Raymond MJ: New method for the rapid quantification of immunofluorescence. *J Natl Cancer Inst* **51**:159, 1973.

22. Ploem JS: A study of filters and light sources in immunofluorescence. *Ann NY Acad Sci* **177**:144, 1971.

23. Ploem JS: Immunofluorescence microscopy. Comparisons of conventional systems with interference filters and epi-illumination, in Buetner EH, Chorzelski TP, Bean SF, Jorhan RE (eds): *Immunopathology of the Skin*. Stroudsburg, Douden, Hutchinson and Row, Inc. 1973, p. 248.

24. Brinkley BR, Fistel SH, Mariam JM, Perdue RL: Microtubules in cultured cells; indirect immunofluorescent staining with tubulin antibody. *Int Rev Cytol* **63**:59, 1980.

25. Mednick ML, Petrali JP, Thomas NC, Sternberger LA, Plapinger RF, Davis DA, Wasserkrug HL, Seligman AM: Localization of acetylcholinesterase via production of osmiophilic polymers: new benzenediazonium salts with thiolacetate functions. *J Histochem Cytochem* **19**:155, 1971.

26. Graham RC Jr, Karnovsky MJ: The early stages of absorption of injected horseradish peroxidase in the proximal tubules of mouse kidney: ultrastructural cytochemistry by a new technique. *J Histochem Cytochem* **14**:291, 1966.

27. Seligman AM, Karnovsky MJ, Wasserkrug HL, Hanker JS: Non-droplet ultrastructural demonstration of cytochrome oxidase activity with a polymerizing osmiophilic reagent, diaminobenzidine (DAB). *J Cell Biol* **38**:1, 1968.

28. Nakane PK: Simultaneous localization of multiple tissue antigens using the peroxidase-labeled antibody method: a study on pituitary glands of the rat. *J Histochem Cytochem* **16**:557, 1968.

29. Rojas-Espinosa O, Dannenberg AM Jr, Sternberger LA: Role of cathepsin D in the pathogenesis of tuberculosis. A histochemical study with the unlabeled antibody enzyme technique. *Am J Pathol* **74**:1, 1974.

30. Mesulam MM, Rosene DL: Sensitivity in horseradish peroxidase neurohistochemistry: a comparative and quantitative study of nine methods. *J Histochem Cytochem* **27**:763, 1979.

31. Modesto RR, Pesce AJ: The reaction of 4,4′-difluoro-3,3-γ-globulin and horseradish peroxidase. *Biochem Biophys Acta* **229**:384, 1971.

32. Nakane PK, Pierce GB Jr: Enzyme-labeled antibodies: preparation and application for the localization of antigens. *J Histochem Cytochem* **14**:929, 1966.

33. Avrameas S: Coupling of enzymes to proteins with glutaraldehyde. Use of the conjugates for the detection of antigens and antibodies. *Immunochemistry* **6**:43, 1969.

34. Clyne DH, Norris SH, Modesto RR, Pesce AJ, Pollak VE: Antibody enzyme conjugates. The preparation of intermolecular conjugates of horseradish peroxidase and antibody and their use in immunochemistry or renal cortex. *J Histochem Cytochem* **21**:233, 1973.

35. Boorsma DM, Streefkerk JG: Periodate or glutaraldehyde for preparing peroxidase conjugates? *J Immunol Meth* **30**:245, 1979.

36. Boorsma DM, Streefkerk JG: Peroxidase conjugate chromatography. Isolation of conjugates prepared with glutaraldehyde or periodate using polyacrylamide-agarose gel. *J Histochem Cytochem* **21**:481, 1976.

37. Arends J: Purification of peroxidase-conjugated antibody for enzyme immunoassay by affinity chromatography on concanavalin A. *J Immunol Meth* **25**:171, 1979.

38. Avrameas S, Ternyck T: Peroxidase labeled antibody and Fab conjugates with enhanced intracellular penetration. *Immunochemistry* **8**:1175, 1971.

39. Nygren H, Hansson H-A, Lange S: Studies on the conjugation of horseradish peroxidase to immunoglobulin via glutaraldehyde. *Med Biol* **57**:187, 1979.

40. Ternyck T, Avrameas S: A new method using *p*-benzoquinone for coupling antigens and antibodies to marker proteins. *Ann Immunol (Inst Pasteur)* **127C**:197, 1976.

41. Nygren H, Hansson H-A: Conjugation of horseradish peroxidase to staphylococcal protein A with benzoquinone, glutaraldehyde or periodate as iron-linking reagents. *J Histochem Cytochem* **29**:266, 1981.

42. Trost TH, Weil HP, Noack M, Pullman H, Steigleder A: A new immunoenzymatic technique for localization of antibodies in immunohistology: Peroxidase-labeled protein A. *J Cat Path* **7**:727, 1980.

43. Nakane PK, Kawaoi A: Peroxidase-labeled antibody. A new method of conjugation. *J Histochem Cytochem* **22**:1084, 1974.

44. Wilson M, Nakane P: Recent developments in the periodate method of conjugating horseradish peroxidase to antibodies, in Knapp W, Holubar K, Wisk G (eds) *Immunofluorescence and Related Staining Techniques.* Amsterdam, Elsevier/North Holland, 1978, p. 215.

45. Imagawa M, Yoskitaka S, Hamagachi Y, Ishikawa E, Niitsu Y, Urushizaka I, Kanazana R, Rachibana S, Nakazawa N, Ogawa H. Characterization and evaluation of antibody-horseradish peroxidase conjugate prepared by using maleimide compound, glutaraldehyde and periodate. *J Appl Biochem* **4**:41: 1982.

46. Suffin SC, Muck KB, Young JC, Leuin L, Porter DD: Improvement of the glucose oxidase immunoenzyme technique. Use of a tetrazolium whose formazan is stable without heavy metal chelation. *Am J Clin Path* **71**:492, 1979.

47. Bondi A, Chieregatti G, Eusebi V, Fulcheri E, Bussolati G: Use of β-galactoxidase as a tracer in immunocytochemistry. *Histochemistry* **76**:153, 1982.

48. Bulman AS, Heydermann E: Alkaline phosphatase for immunocytochemical labelling problems with endogenous enzyme activity. *J Clin Path* **34**:1349, 1981.

49. Gallyas F, Gores T, Merchenthaler I: High grade intensification of the end product of the diaminobenzidine reaction for peroxidase histology. *J Histochem Cytochem* **30**:183, 1982.

50. Jasiewisz ML, Schoenberg DR, Mueller GC: Selective retrieval of biotin-labelled cells using immobilized avidin. *Exp Cell Res* **100**:213, 1976.

51. Guesdin J-C, Ternynck T, Avrameas S: The use of biotin-avidin interaction in immunoenzymatic techniques. *J Histochem Cytochem* **27**:1131, 1979.

52. Hsu SM, Raine L, Fanger H: Use of avidin-biotin-peroxidase complex (ABC) in immunoperox-

idase techniques. A comparison between ABC and unlabeled antibody (PAP) procedures. *J Histochem Cytochem* **59**:777, 1981.

53. Eng LF, Bigbee JW: Ultrastructural localization of apolipoprotein in human aortic and coronary atherosclerotic plaques. *Exp Mol Pathol* **26**:214, 1977.

54. Singer SJ, Schick AF: The properties of specific stains for electron microscopy prepared by conjugation of antibody molecules with ferritin. *J Biophys Biochem Cytol* **9**:519, 1961.

55. Tanaka H: The ferritin-labeled antibody method: its advantages and disadvantages. A methodological review. *Acta Haematol Jap* **31**:125, 1968.

56. Schafer H: *Immunoelectron Microscopy*. Stuttgart, Gustav Fischer Verlag, 1971.

57. Otto H, Takamiya H, Vogt A: A two stage method for cross-linking antibody globulin to ferritin by glutaraldehyde. Comparison between the one-stage and the two-stage method. *J Immunol Meth* **3**:137, 1973.

58. Goldin EM, Curry PM, Granatik CH: Separation of ferritin-labeled antibody from free antibody. *J Immunol Meth* **13**:299, 1976.

59. Fresen KO, Vogt A: The hemolytic activity of ferritin-labeled antibodies against sheep erythrocytes. *Med Biol Immunol* **157**:24, 1971.

60. Slot JW, Geuze HS: Sizing of protein A-colloidal gold probes for immune electron microscopy. *J Cell Biol* **90**:533, 1981.

61. Faulk WP, Taylor GM: The immunocolloid method for the electron microscope. *Immunochemistry* **8**:1081, 1971.

62. Romano RL, Stolinski C, Hughes-Jones NC: An antiglobulin reagent labelled with colloidal gold for use in electron microscopy. *Immunochemistry* **11**:251, 1974.

63. Horisberger M, Rosset J: Colloidal gold, a useful marker for transmission and scanning electron microscopy. *J Histochem Cytochem* **25**:295, 1977.

64. Frens G: Controlled nucleation for the regulation of particle size in monodisperse gold solutions. *Nature* **241**:20, 1973.

65. DeWaele M, DeMey J, Moeremans M, Smet L, Broodtaerts L, van Camp B: Cytochemical profile of immunoregulatory T-lymphocyte subsets defined by monoclonal antibodies. *J Histochem Cytochem* **31**:471, 1983.

66. Mannweiler K, Hohenberg H, Bohn W, Rutter G: Protein A gold particles as markers in replica immunocytochemistry: High resolution electron microscopy investigation of plasma membrane surfaces. *J Microsc* **126**:145, 1982.

67. Roth J, Brown D, Norman A, Orci L: Location of the vitamin D-dependent calcium-binding protein in mammalian kidney. *Am J Physiol* **243**:F24, 1982.

68. Hsu S-M, Raine L, Fanger H: The use of antiavidin antibody and avidin-biotin-peroxidase complex in immunoperoxidase techniques. *Am J Clin Path* **75**:816, 1981.

Chapter Three

The Unlabeled Antibody Peroxidase-Antiperoxidase (PAP) Method

Several factors that affect the specificity of indirect labeled antibody methods can be controlled to varying degrees by precautions in the conjugation procedure and by careful purification of the conjugate. However, the background resulting from reaction of the second antibody preparation with tissue in the absence of first antibody cannot be adequately controlled, even when purified second antibody is used. In the conjugated antibody method, the immunoreactivity of the second antibody is used only for attachment to the first antibody. Specific antibody will, indeed, do so (Fig. 3-1c), but contaminating antibodies specific to other epitopes than those of the first antibody (Fig. 3-1d) may react with tissue constituents nonspecifically.

In the development of the unlabeled antibody method, we had in mind to avoid the technical difficulties of adequate control of the labeling process itself, as well as the physiologically inherent poor specificity of the second antibodies that derives from heterogeneity of serum antibodies. This was done by permitting the second antibody to function immunologically during the staining reaction, not only for attachment to the first antibody but also for undergoing a second immunological reaction in a third staining step. By recognizing that despite heterogeneity of serum antibodies, each individual antibody possesses two identical combining sites (page 6), and by allowing only one of the combining sites to react with the first antibody, we can use the second combining site for an additional reaction in a third step of the staining sequence. We must use a third step that will discriminate between the specifically attached and nonspecifically attached second antibody. Reagents prepared for the third step of the unlabeled antibody method and its modifications accomplish specificity selection by virtue of two reasons:

90

1. They are affinity-purified reagents.
2. They have reacted with a marker by immunologic bonds.

This principle can only be successful if neither the second antibody nor the third layer of the reaction sequence are chemically labeled. If the second antibody preparation were labeled, its nonspecifically reacting components would deposit label to background. If the third layer preparation were chemically labeled, specificity would depend only on its affinity purification. However, if instead of chemically labeling, we would allow the third layer reagent to react with a marker only immunologically, we would eliminate by this requirement any constituents that could have escaped affinity purification, for such constituents would not be able to react with the marker.

Avoidance of chemical labeling, particularly that of the second antibody, is thus essential to the unlabeled antibody method. Avoidance of labeling has the added advantage that the technical complications of chemical conjugation are

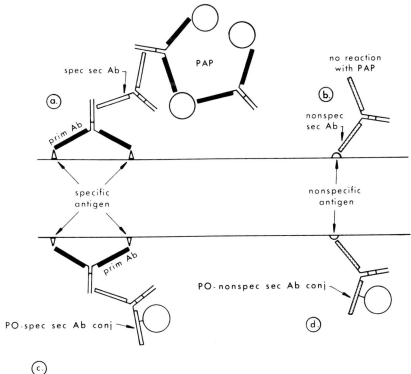

Figure 3-1. Nonspecific background with PAP and peroxidase-labeled antibodies. (a) In the PAP method, specific anti-IgG in the second antiserum (spec sec Ab) links PAP to specific first antibodies (prim Ab). (b) The second (link) antibody also contains contaminants, including possible antibodies, that react directly with nonspecific tissue antigen. Since both antigen binding sites in any antibody are identical, the contaminating antibodies cannot react with PAP. (c) In the peroxidase-labeled antibody method, specific, labeled anti-IgG (PO-spec sec Ab conj) reacts with the first antibody. (d) Nonspecific components in the second antibody (PO-nonspec sec Ab conj) react directly with tissue and since they are labeled, background staining results. [Reprinted by permission of Elsevier Science Publishing Co., Inc., from The unlabeled antibody enzyme method, by L.A. Sternberger and J.P. Petrali, *Journal of Histochemistry and Cytochemistry* 25:1036, Copyright 1977 by the Histochemical Society, Inc. (1).]

eliminated. As we have seen in the preceding chapter, these complications involve loss of immunoreactivity of the reagent, contamination with unlabeled antibodies, and polymerization of the conjugate.

The nature of the marker in the unlabeled antibody method is unimportant. Peroxidase has been used most frequently, but any other markers we have discussed in the preceding chapter can be substituted for peroxidase, provided they are immunologically linked to the first antibody. In fact, we have used ferritin in the unlabeled antibody method before use of peroxidase (2). We will return to these markers under the heading of "Variations of the Unlabeled Antibody Method" (page 180).

Our first use of peroxidase as a marker in the unlabeled antibody method was in the four-layer staining technique. To illustrate its feasibility (2), we immunostained spirochetes (*T. pallidum*) on glass slides. In the first step of the technique, we used as *first antiserum* diluted rabbit antisyphilitic serum (Fig. 3-2). Antibody in this antiserum may combine with the spirochetes via one or both antibody combining sites. This was followed by a *second antiserum (link antibody)*, such as sheep antiserum to rabbit immunoglobulin G, used in excess. Under these conditions, one of the combining sites of the second antibody reacted with the first

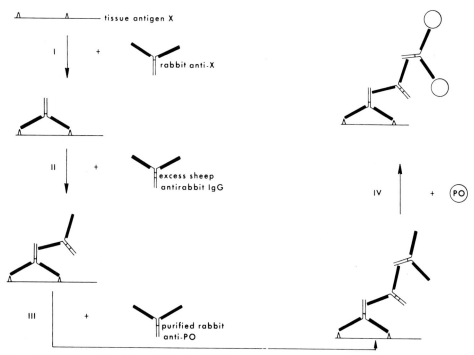

Figure 3-2.   Schematics of the unlabeled antibody enzyme method using purified antiperoxidase. Tissue antigen is localized by the sequential application of antiserum produced in species A (I), antiserum to IgG of species A produced in species B (II), affinity-purified antiperoxidase from species A (III) and peroxidase (IV), followed by staining with 4,4'-diaminobenzidine tetrahydrochloride and hydrogen peroxide (not shown). The heavy lines in the diagram of the IgG molecule represent its two Fab portions, each containing one L chain and the N-terminal part of one γ chain. The two fine lines in each molecule represent the Fc portion consisting of the C-terminal parts of both γ chains. PO: peroxidase. [From Sternberger (3).]

antibody on the spirochetes and the second combining site remained free. As a third step, we applied affinity-purified rabbit antibody to horseradish peroxidase, which acted in this step as an antigen reactive with the free antibody site of the second antibody. In the fourth step, horseradish peroxidase was added which combined with the antibody combining sites of the third-step antibody. The reaction was then developed with hydrogen peroxide as substrate and 3,3'-diaminobenzidine hydrochloride (DAB) as electron donor, yielding a brown, insoluble product.

Thus, while in labeled antibody methods, unlabeled antibodies interfere with immunocytochemical localization, in the unlabeled antibody method they mediate the specific localization.

To satisfy the specificity principle of the unlabeled antibody method, it is important that the third layer reagent of this sequence consists only of immunoglobulin and not of other proteins, and in addition, it is important that all the immunoglobulin must be antibody to peroxidase and not other antibodies. For this reason, we have used immunoabsorbent-purified antiperoxidase in the third step of this technique (2). Use of whole antiserum to peroxidase or an IgG fraction from such antiserum violates this principle and may provide, in the third step, antigenic determinants shared with tissue antigens with which the link antibody may react nonspecifically. In addition, of course, the bulk of an IgG fraction is not antibody to peroxidase and will react with link antibody in the third step without reacting with peroxidase in the fourth step.

The unlabeled antibody method as described proved sensitive on its first trial (2). Nevertheless, there remained two nagging problems in its use. The first had to do with antibody affinity. An immunocytochemical reaction is not only a forward reaction in which antibody binds antigen. A reverse reaction in which bound antibody dissociates can also take place. Although the forward reaction is much faster than dissociation, we must recall that extensive washing in excess of buffer is necessary between each immunocytochemical staining step, thus providing ample opportunity for dissociation of reagents. The first antibody, however, is often used in excess, which results in preferential binding of high-affinity antibody and little loss during washing. Even if antibody is used in high dilution (4–6), it may, depending on the nature of the antigen, react with two adjacent epitopes via both of its combining sites. The simultaneous breaking of bonds with two sites during washing is unlikely. Hence, little first antibody is lost in immunocytochemical staining (page 200). The link (second step) antibody is always used in excess. This assures that only high-affinity antibody reacts in the second step and, again, none is lost during washing. Since both antibody combining sites are identical, the bond with antiperoxidase in the third step is of equal affinity as the bond with first antibody in the second step and, again, no antiperoxidase is lost. However, the third-step reaction does not select for antiperoxidase with high affinity for peroxidase and against antiperoxidase with low affinity for peroxidase. Hence, the bonds of peroxidase with antiperoxidase in the fourth step are of variable affinities. In fact, 75% of the peroxidase becomes lost during washing after the fourth step.

The second problem with the method was the difficulty of preparing purified antiperoxidase. The preparation of antiperoxidase by specific immunoabsorbents was found to be less efficient than affinity purification of most other antiprotein antibodies. The reason is an unusually low dissociability of the peroxidase-antiperoxidase bond, even at acid pH (Fig. 3-3). If treatment at pH 2.3 is carried out at 1°C, practically no antibody is recovered. Yield improves slightly with rise in temperature and increase in time of acid treatment but incumbers danger of denaturation of antibody. Upon brief dissociation at room temperature, denaturation is insignificant, but only a fraction of the total antibody is eluted from the immunoabsorbent. Unfortunately, this fraction consists of the antibodies with the lowest affinities (page 28) for peroxidase, leaving those species of antibodies with stronger affinities on the immunoabsorbent.

Much of our effort during 1969 dealt with finding ways of improving the dissociation of peroxidase from antiperoxidase in immunoabsorbents or im-

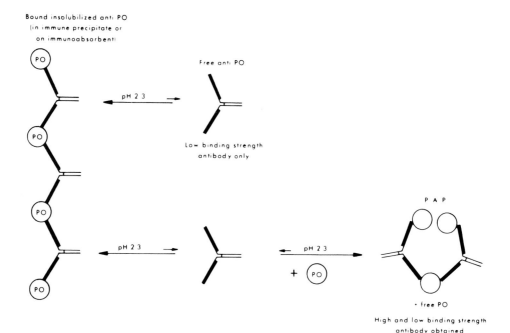

Figure 3-3.   Solubilization by acid dissociation of antiperoxidase from a peroxidase-antiperoxidase precipitate or peroxidase immunoabsorbent. At pH 2.3, the equilibrium of bound and free antiperoxidase tends toward the bound state (upper part of figure). Yield of free antiperoxidase (purified antibody) increases with increase in temperature and dilution. In general, only that fraction of antibody is obtained in solution that possesses the poorest affinity for peroxidase. If, however, free peroxidase is added to the acid dissociation mixture, the free antiperoxidase is bound with peroxidase in solution, forming peroxidase-antiperoxidase complex (PAP) solubilized by excess peroxidase (lower part of the figure). Just as the equilibrium of reaction favors the immune precipitate or absorbent-bound form of antiperoxidase at pH 2.3, so does it favor its binding with added peroxidase as soluble peroxidase-antiperoxidase complex. The formation of peroxidase-antiperoxidase complex removes the free form of antiperoxidase from the solubilization reaction equilibrium, so that more free peroxidase can dissociate from the precipitate or immunoabsorbent. The yield-limiting factor in this reaction is the degree of excess of added peroxidase. However, even a small amount of free peroxidase yields some soluble PAP complex, since even a small amount is excess to the very small amount of antiperoxidase that is free in solution at any time. Since the binding of antiperoxidase with free peroxidase is of equal affinity as that in the immune precipiate or absorbent, the proportion of high- and low-affinity antiperoxidase in PAP is the same as that of the original peroxidase-antiperoxidase precipitate or absorbent. (From the work of L.A. Sternberger.)

mune precipitates, all without avail. During one of these frustrating experiments, we asked ourselves, why not aid the dissociation of a peroxidase-antiperoxidase immune precipitate by addition of further peroxidase. We know, of course, that antibody precipitates with antigen under suitable proportions, and that when antigen is in excess, only soluble complexes of antigen and antibody form. It was also known that immune precipitates can be dissolved by addition of excess of antigen, but an extremely large excess is needed and even then the procedure requires shaking of precipitates at room or elevated temperature for about a week, yielding, thereby, largely denatured, soluble products.

The failure of peroxidase-antiperoxidase precipitates to dissolve in acid was unique, as most other protein antigen-antibody precipitates dissolve instantaneously. The specific attraction of an epitope and an antibody idiotypic site is mediated by ionic interactions, hydrogen bonding, and van der Waals forces. The solubility of immune precipitates at acid pH is due to weakening of the ionic forces. The nonionic forces apparently are insufficient to hold antigen and antibody together. When an epitope is acidic, the idiotypic region of antibody is usually rich in basic amino acids, such as arginine or lysine. When the epitope is basic, the idiotypic region is rich in acidic amino acids, such as glutamic or aspartic acids.

Apparently, the antigenic determinants of peroxidase are neither acidic nor basic so that the nonionic forces of interaction with specific antibody predominate over the ionic ones. When during acidification ionic interaction becomes obliterated, the effect will only weaken the bonds between peroxidase and antiperoxidase without affecting actual separation of the molecules. However, it was reasoned that addition of a small excess of peroxidase *during* acidification might help the dissociation. The peroxidase added to the solution would have equal affinity for antiperoxidase as the peroxidase in the immune precipitate, and since the added peroxidase is in excess, it may drive the dissociation reaction to completion. In fact, when a moderate excess of peroxidase was added to an acidified peroxidase-antiperoxidase precipitate, solution was instantaneous (4). Upon neutralization, the material remained soluble. Apparently, during acidification the antigen-antibody bonds have been weakened sufficiently to equilibrate instantaneously with the added peroxidase. Thus, the formation of soluble antigen-antibody complex became instantaneous and complete, while in the case of a neutral peroxidase-antiperoxidase precipitate, a large amount of peroxidase would have been required for a slow and incomplete formation of the complex.

The addition of peroxidase to an acidified peroxidase-antiperoxidase precipitate yielded, of course, no longer the originally desired purified antiperoxidase, but resulted, instead, in a purified *peroxidase-antiperoxidase* (PAP) *complex*. This did not matter, however, because in the staining procedure (Fig. 3-2) we added antiperoxidase to the section in step III and peroxidase in step IV, thus forming a complex between peroxidase and antiperoxidase on the section. With the new preparation, the only change was formation of the complex in solution rather than on the section. The staining procedure required the only modification that instead of applying antiperoxidase and peroxidase separately, they were now to be applied in a single step in the form of PAP (Fig. 3-4). It turned out, however, that this reaction sequence was four times more sensitive than the *sequential* application of purified antiperoxidase followed by peroxidase (page 149).

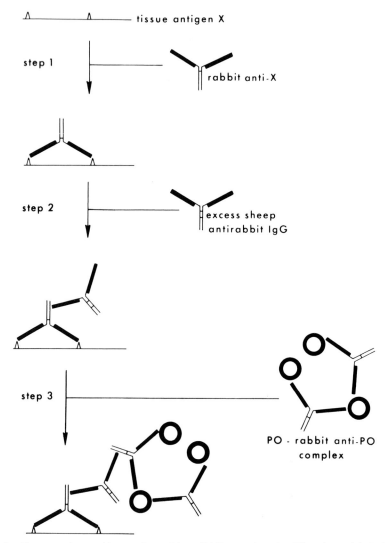

Figure 3-4. The use of peroxidase-antiperoxidase (PAP) complex simplifies the unlabeled antibody method from a five-step (four immunoreagent layer) to a four-step (three immunoreagent layer) procedure. The cyclic nature of PAP assures retention of peroxidase during washing and thus increases sensitivity. Step 1: Diluted antiserum from species A specific to tissue constituent X. Step 2: Excess of antiserum to IgG of species A, produced in species B. Step 3: PAP prepared with antiperoxidase from species A. Step 4: Diaminobenzidine tetrahydrochloride and hydrogen peroxide. For electron microscopy, this is followed by osmication. (From the work of L.A. Sternberger.)

PREPARATION OF SOLUBLE PAP COMPLEX

Principle

Immune precipitates are obtained from antiserum by addition of peroxidase (Fig. 3-5). The washed precipitates are resuspended in saline containing four times the amount of peroxidase used for precipitation, and the suspension is

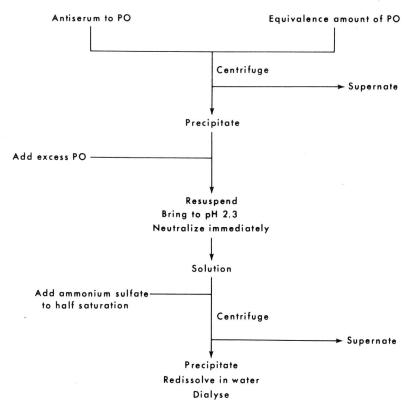

Figure 3-5. Preparation of immunospecifically purified soluble PAP complex. [Reprinted by permission of Elsevier Science Publishing Co., Inc. from The unlabeled antibody enzyme method of immunohisto-chemistry, by L.A. Sternberger, P.H. Hardy Jr., J.J.cuculis, H.G. Meyer, *Journal of Histochemistry and Cytochemistry* **18**:315, Copyright 1970 by the Histochemical Society, Inc. (4).]

brought to pH 2.3. Following fairly immediate neutralization and removal of any undissociated precipitate, the soluble PAP complex is separated from free peroxidase by precipitation with ammonium sulfate.

When the original precipitation of antiperoxidase from antiserum is carried out with an amount of peroxidase that precipitates at the antigen excess end of the equivalence zone (amount of peroxidase that precipitates all precipitating antibody from the antiserum and leaves a barely detectable amount of free peroxidase in solution), then the yield of PAP will be about 30% in antibody and 30% in peroxidase. The average molecular ratio of peroxidase to antiperoxidase in PAP will be 3 : 2. If the original precipitation is done further in antibody excess (and, again, four times the added amount of peroxidase is used for resuspension), the yield of PAP will be lower in antibody and higher in peroxidase (approximately 100% in peroxidase). The average composition still will be 3 : 2. If the original precipitation is done further in antigen excess, the yield will be higher in antiperoxidase (approximately 100% in antiperoxidase) and lower in peroxidase. The average composition of PAP will still be 3 : 2.

For practical reasons, we have adjusted the proportion of peroxidase in the precipitation of antiperoxidase from antiserum in such a way that the yield of both peroxidase and antibody in PAP are 30%. The lost peroxidase is largely in the ammonium sulfate supernate and can be recycled. The lost antibody is largely in the precipitate that forms upon dialysis of the redissolved ammonium sulfate-separated PAP. This precipitate can also be recycled by repeating the preparation procedure. This contrasts with the peroxidase-labeled antibody procedure, in which the yields in peroxidase and in antibody are low (page 60) and in which the unconjugated peroxidase as well as the lost antibody are irreversibly inactivated and can, therefore, not be recycled.

The relatively low variance of composition of PAP, the possibility of obtaining it with relatively low excesses of antigen, and a number of other properties discussed on page 100 are the result of unusually stable antigen-antibody bonds. The stability of the complex is a fortunate property that has contributed to the sensitivity of the unlabeled antibody method (5,6) and has facilitated its quantification (5,7).

Procedural Details

In a preliminary test, determine qualitatively the equivalence zone of the antiperoxidase serum used [prepared by immunization of rabbits with peroxidase (RZ = 3.0) and Freund's adjuvants]. Place into a series of 10 tubes 0.2 ml saline containing amounts of peroxidase varying from 0.05 to 0.5 mg/ml. Add to each tube 0.2 ml of antiperoxidase serum. Leave tubes at 1 to 5°C overnight. Centrifuge. Collect supernates into a second set of tubes and transfer 0.15 ml of each supernate from the second set into a third set of tubes. Add to each tube of the second set 0.1 ml of the antiperoxidase serum and observe excess of antigen by qualitatively reading precipitation after 1 hour at room temperature. Add to each tube of the third set 0.1 ml of a solution of peroxidase (0.1 mg/ml) and observe excess of antibody by qualitatively reading precipitation after 1 hour. Three zones will be observed: supernates in the zone of excess antibody, supernates in the equivalence zone that show neither excess antibody nor excess antigen, and supernates in the antigen excess zone. Record the concentration of peroxidase *per milliliter* used in that tube of the equivalence zone that is nearest to the antigen excess zone (AgX equivalence proportion).

Good yields of PAP (in peroxidase as well as in antiperoxidase) are obtained if antiperoxidase is precipitated from antiserum with about 1.5 times AgX equivalence proportion. It is convenient to use 24 mg of peroxidase for this initial precipitation. We now have to determine how much antiserum to use. If 24 mg is 1.5 times AgX equivalence proportion, then 16 mg is AgX equivalence proportion. Assume that in the preliminary test AgX equivalence proportion was recorded in the tube in which 0.4 mg peroxidase per milliliter (0.08 mg per tube) had been added to antiserum. Then a total of 40 ml antiperoxidase will be needed to precipitate 16 mg peroxidase at the AgX equivalence proportion or 24 mg at 1.5 times AgX equivalence proportion.

Therefore, place in a 250-ml centrifuge bottle 6.0 ml of a 0.4% solution of peroxidase freshly prepared by dissolving 125 mg of lyophylized peroxidase (RZ = 3.0) in 32 ml of saline. Add 40 ml antiperoxidase serum. Mix. Allow to stand at room temperature for 1 hour. Centrifuge at about 2000 rpm (International rotor 259) for 20 minutes at 1 to 5°C. Remove supernate by suction. Resuspend precipitate in a small volume of cold saline by forcing it several times through a 10-ml pipette. Then wash by adding approximately 200 ml of saline. Centrifuge. Carry out a total of three such washes. Thoroughly resuspend precipitate (by forcing it through a pipette) in 24 ml of the 0.4% solution of peroxidase. Under mild stirring, bring to pH 2.3 at room temperature with 1.0, 0.1, and 0.01N hydrochloric acid (2 drops of 1.0N hydrochloric acid followed by sufficient amounts of the more dilute solutions for fine adjustment). Neutralize fairly immediately to approximately pH 7.4, using sodium hydroxide solutions (1.0, 0.1, and 0.01N). Add 2.4 ml of a solution containing 0.08N sodium acetate and 0.15N ammonium acetate. Chill solution on an ice bath. Centrifuge at approximately 17,500 rpm for 10 minutes at 1°C (Sorvall rotor SS-34). Carry out all subsequent steps in refrigerated containers at 0 to 2°C or in a cold room at 0 to 5°C. Under stirring, add slowly to the supernate an equal volume of a solution of ammonium sulfate saturated at 0 to 5°C. Wash precipitate once in half-saturated ammonium sulfate solution. Dissolve precipitate in 24 ml of water and dialyze under protection from light against three changes of 15 liter each of sodium ammonium acetate saline (13.5 liter saline, 1.5 liter water, 75 ml of 1.5N sodium acetate, and 75 ml of 3N ammonium acetate solution). Remove precipitate by centrifugation at 17,000 rpm for 15 minutes.

The peroxidase and antiperoxidase contents of PAP are determined by absorbance at 400 and 280 nm of samples diluted 1 : 10.

$$\text{Peroxidase (PO) contents of PAP per ml} = \text{OD}_{400} \cdot 0.413 \cdot 10 \text{ mg}$$

Anti-PO contents of PAP per ml
$$= \left[(\text{OD}_{280} \text{ of PAP}) - \frac{(\text{OD}_{400} \text{ of PAP}) \cdot (\text{OD}_{280} \text{ of PO})}{(\text{OD}_{400} \text{ of PO})} \right] \cdot 0.620 \cdot 10 \text{ mg}$$

$$\text{PO/anti-PO mole ratio} = \frac{\text{mg PO} \cdot 156{,}000}{\text{mg anti-PO} \cdot 39{,}800}$$

In general, during preparation of PAP, dissolution of the immune precipitate upon acidification in the presence of excess peroxidase is instantaneous. Rarely, the precipitate does not dissolve completely. In this event, proceed anyway with the procedure described above, without modification. The quality of PAP is not affected.

PAP in the liquid form is stable to storage and shipping for several days provided 0.015 M sodium azide is added. For prolonged storage, we place PAP in a $-85°C$ freezer or quick freeze it in dry ice-acetone and place it in a $-20°C$ freezer. Once one of these samples is thawed, it is divided into small aliquots, 100 μl each, and placed in tightly stoppered vials. These vials are again quick frozen as above. They can be stored for at least 14 years without detectable loss of activity. The contents of one vial can be thawed and frozen several times. Therefore, it is possible to dilute only part of a 100-μl vial for a given experiment and store the remainder for a number of additional experiments. PAP should be diluted on the day of each experiment and kept at 0 to 5°C until used. Diluted PAP is not stable on storage, whether in liquid or frozen form. Lyophilization of PAP is not recommended because of aggregate and polymer formation, loss of sensitivity, and lack of sufficient experimental data that examined the properties of lyophilized PAP.

Sodium azide, at 0.015 M concentration, partially and reversibly inhibits peroxidase activity in PAP. No inhibition is measurable once PAP has been diluted 1 : 40 or higher. Undiluted PAP is, by virtue of its preparation, near the limit of its solubility (4.3 mg total protein per milliliter for rabbit PAP). Solutions containing more protein are, therefore, not purified PAP.

PAP is preferably prepared from the same species as that which donates the first antibody in the staining sequence. However, Marucci and Dougherty (8,9) found that these requirements do not always have to be adhered to strictly (page 180). PAP of essentially identical molecular ratios of peroxidase to antiperoxidase has been prepared from sera of rabbits (4), goats (10), baboon (8), mice (11), and hamsters (12), as well as from monoclonal antibodies. The preparations most commonly used are those from rabbit and goat sera and from monoclonal mouse or rat antiperoxidase (ClonoPAP).

PROPERTIES OF PAP

Two unexpected phenomena took place when PAP was first prepared (4). We were surprised that a relatively small excess of peroxidase produced good yields of complex, while other antigen-antibody complexes required large excesses. Furthermore, the composition of different preparations of PAP generally were three peroxidase to two antiperoxidase subunits and the composition was largely independent of the amount of peroxidase used in the preparation. This finding, again, was in distinction to the observation with other antigen-antibody complexes prepared by conventional means and known to consist of mixtures of heterogeneous composition, depending largely on the amount of antigen used in their preparation.

These observations required further examination. The unique properties of PAP could have been due to the new manner of preparation of antigen-antibody complex or it could have been a characteristic feature derived from properties of peroxidase. We, therefore, prepared soluble complexes of other antigens and antibodies in the same manner as PAP—that is, by acidification of immune precipitate in excess antigen. We made complexes of ferritin and antiferritin and of apoperoxidase and antiperoxidase. Apoperoxidase is peroxidase devoid of its heme group. It cross-reacts completely with antiperoxidase. For the preparation of both complexes, larger excesses of antigen were needed than for the preparation of PAP, indicating that they behaved as conventional antigen-antibody complexes despite the acidification procedure. Therefore, the uniqueness of PAP must be due to properties of peroxidase itself.

We studied PAP by zonal and boundary sedimentation and by diffusion in liquid and solid media and found it to be of fairly homogeneous composition, with a sedimentation peak at 11.5 S, corresponding to a molecular weight of 400,000 to 430,000 (4). Therefore, PAP consists mainly of three peroxidase and two antiperoxidase subunits. From theoretical considerations, one must assume that traces of other complexes as well as free peroxidase also should be present, but apparently the 3 : 2 form is so unusually stable that complexes of other composition are of low concentration. The finding is in distinction to other soluble antigen-antibody complexes, which in extreme antigen excess consist mainly of free antigen, followed in lesser amounts by complexes of two antigens to one antibody, and by linear complexes of three antigens to two antibodies, five antigens to three antibodies, and perhaps some circular complexes of two antigens and two antibodies and some complexes with free antibody sites, such as one antigen to one antibody. When lesser excesses of antigens are used, only low yields of complex are obtained consisting of relatively large aggregates of antigen and antibody.

Electron microscopy of PAP, on negative staining, or after staining with DAB and hydrogen peroxide, provided an explanation for its composition, for on electron microscopy, PAP complexes were cyclic (Fig. 3-6). Most of these cycles were pentagonal or occasional ones were hexagonal or quadrangular. The diameter of these particles averaged 21 nm. This size and the pentagonal conformation is indeed attained when three molecules peroxidase are placed upon two combining sites of two molecules of antibody (Fig. 3-7), while occasional hexago-

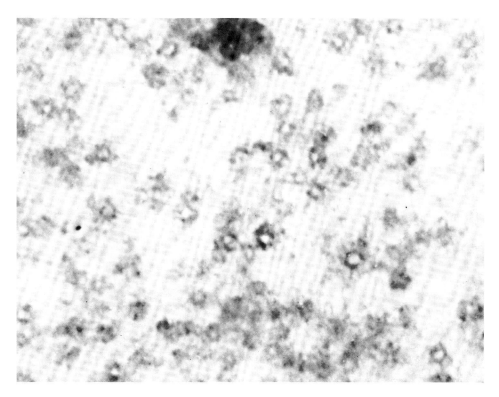

Figure 3-6. The unique cyclic, pentagonal conformation of PAP complexes is revelaed by spraying them on electron microscopy grids and staining with diaminobenzidine and hydrogen peroxide. ×250,000. [Reprinted by permission of Elsevier Science Publishing Co., Inc. from The unlabeled antibody enzyme method of immunohistochemistry, by L.A. Sternberger, P.H. Hardy Jr., J.J.cuculis, H.G. Meyer, *Journal of Histochemistry and Cytochemistry* **18**:315, Copyright 1970 by the Histochemical Society, Inc. (4).]

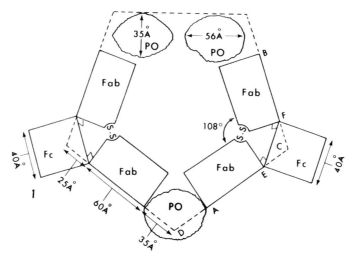

Figure 3-7. Peroxidase-antiperoxidase complex (PAP) is largely a pentagonal complex of three peroxidase and two antiperoxidase subunits. [Reprinted by permission of Elsevier Science Publishing Co., Inc. from The unlabeled antibody enzyme method of immunohistochemistry, by L.A. Sternberger, P.H. Hardy Jr., J.J.cuculis, H.G. Meyer, *Journal of Histochemistry and Cytochemistry* **18**:315, Copyright 1970 by the Histochemical Society, Inc. (4).]

nal forms might consist of four peroxidases and two antibodies and quadrangular forms of two peroxidases and two antibodies. One of the peroxidase molecules in the pentagonal form has bound two antibodies while each of the other two peroxidases has bound only one antibody. It is not known what effects ring closure between these two peroxidases. We did find that peroxidase dimerizes on acidification, but this is rapidly reversed on neutralization. Perhaps the presence of antibody and the greater stability of ring structures favors the equilibrium between monomeric and dimeric peroxidase toward dimerization also at neutrality. In any event, the circular structure must have unusual stability, because it is formed to the near exclusion of all other possible forms. Moreover, it is obtained readily and in high yields with small excesses of peroxidase. In other antigen-antibody systems, such small excesses of antigen yield little soluble complex. Stabilization by ring formation has recently been confirmed with monoclonal antibodies (page 17).

The cyclicity of PAP is responsible for two features of the unlabeled antibody method when used with PAP. First, the sensitivity is increased beyond that obtained upon the use of antiperoxidase followed by peroxidase, because now the peroxidase is stabilized and no longer lost on washing. Second, the cyclicity gives the complex characteristic structure, discernable in electron microscopy (pages 118 and 120). The structural identity of PAP is important in electron microscopy in addition to the deposition of electron-opaque reaction products because PAP complexes afford closer resolution of antigen sites and distinguish the sites at which diaminobenzidine is polymerized from possible other sites toward which it might diffuse nonspecifically. Finally, identification of PAP as a single unit permits localization of a single epitope.

STAINING FOR LIGHT MICROSCOPY

It has been traditional, in the early days of immunocytochemistry, to avoid strong fixatives and embedding procedures, such as paraffin embedding, that include dehydration and heating of tissue. These procedures at best permitted poor staining and usually resulted in no staining at all because they adversely affected most epitopes.

Soon after the introduction of the PAP method and after realization of its high sensitivity, Di Stefano et al. (9), Halmi et al. (10), and Burns (11) independently reported the efficient staining of paraffin-embedded tissue. Antisera contain many antibodies, most of which may well be to epitopes destroyed by fixation and embedding. However, few of the antibodies, their number depending on the nature of the antigen, may be specific to resistant epitopes. When the immunocytochemical technique is sensitive, these remaining antibodies may suffice for detection of antigens where older methods fail. It is in the routine use of paraffin sections that the sensitivity of the PAP method has found most of its applications. Once the use of the PAP method with paraffin section has been established, Halmi and Duello (12) discovered that routinely processed autopsy material could be examined decades after storage in paraffin, and even old slides stained by hematoxylin and eosin could be rediagnosed immunocytochemically for identification of hormone-secreting tumors, after destaining and immunocytochemical processing. In fact, even slides previously stained with aldehyde thionin-periodic acid Schiff-orange-G could be restained immunocytochemically, which was quite surprising inasmuch as these slides had been subject to permanganate oxidation prior to the initial staining.

For these reasons, the strategy of staining an unknown antigen differs in the PAP method from that of labeled antibody methods. In labeled methods, frozen sections are always included, along with a fairly large battery of fixatives. A number of dilutions of first antiserum are used. In the PAP method, it is usually most practical to use initially only one fixative: either buffered formalin, or Bouin's fixative (75 ml saturated aqueous picric acid, 25 ml formalin, 5 ml glacial acetic acid) or formalin-mercury bichloride (13) (76 ml of mercuric chloride, saturated at 0°C, and 20 ml of 37% formaldehyde). Osmium tetroxide, either alone or in combination with above solutions, is sometimes used as a superior fixative for the PAP method (page 217). If nothing is known about an antiserum, a dilution of 1 : 1,000 should be used. Concentrations higher than 1 : 500 should be avoided because of participation of nonspecific antibodies. A good initial concentration for affinity-purified antibody is 2 μg/ml. Ascites fluids containing monoclonal antibodies are best used at dilutions 1 : 2000 on a first trial.

The *basic staining procedure* by the PAP method involves paraffin sections placed on carefully cleaned chromealum or gelatin-covered slides. Sections are deparaffinized and held in a moist chamber such as provided by a pad of filter paper in a Petri dish. A wooden applicator, broken to fit into the Petri dish, is used to separate the slide from the pad. Reagents are applied with pipettes in 0.050 to 0.125 ml amounts, depending on the size of the section. Following incubation with each reagent, slides are rinsed with buffer from a spray bottle, then washed under stirring in three changes of buffer, 5 minutes each in dishes equipped with magnetic stirring bars.

The literature occasionally espouses one buffer as better than another. This is usually based on experience with a single antibody system. In the choice of buffers, we should realize that buffers are used in high concentrations relative to those of first antibodies, thus conceivably providing haptenic inhibitors. For instance, with the use of monoclonal antibodies against phosphorylated epitopes of neurofilaments (14), we found strong inhibition with relative low concentrations of phosphoserine and phosphothreonine admixed to the antibody. It stands to reason that inorganic phosphate would also inhibit, but poorly so. Effective cross-reaction with phosphorylated epitopes would require, therefore, high concentrations of phosphate. Such concentrations were, indeed, obtained with 0.2 M phosphate buffer. When this buffer was substituted for Tris buffer in the immunocytochemical reaction with the first antibody, staining was inhibited. Phosphate buffer did not inhibit the staining with monoclonal antibodies to nonphosphorylated epitopes. Therefore, if a buffer is found to inhibit in a given system, it may not be very helpful to state that such buffer is unsuitable for immunocytochemistry. Instead, it may be more productive to use the information to gain some insight in the nature of the epitope that participates in the staining. The effect of buffers is apt to be more dramatic with monoclonal antibodies than with serum antibodies (page 453).

It would be impractical, however, to use every buffer that has been described for every antigen one attempts to stain. With antisera containing polyclonal antibodies, most buffers will give some staining. We feel that 0.05 M Tris buffer, pH 7.6, containing 1.5% sodium chloride gives good staining with most antigens. The high concentration of sodium chloride appears to reduce the effect of low affinity cross-reacting antibodies and thereby gives better antiserum specificity. If it is suspected that a specific antibody used as first antibody in the staining procedure, is of low affinity, it may be better to use 0.05 M Tris buffer, pH 7.6, containing 0.85% sodium chloride. To prevent, in the staining procedure, reagents from running of the sections, a dry rim around the section is established by suction from an obliquely cut disposable plastic pipette tip.

Basic staining procedure for paraffin sections consists of the following five steps:

1. Normal serum of the species that donates the link antibody in step 3, diluted to 3% in buffer, for 30 minutes. Excess serum is shaken off, but the section is not washed. It is rimmed by suction.

2. First antiserum, diluted 1 : 1000, in buffer containing 1% normal serum, for 30 minutes to 24 hours at room temperature, followed by spray rinse and washing.

3. Link antiserum (second antibody), diluted 1 : 20 in buffer for 30 minutes, followed by spray rinse and washing.

4. PAP, diluted 1 : 100 in buffer containing 1% normal serum, for 30 minutes, followed by spray rinse and washing.

5. Diaminobenzidine-hydrogen peroxide for 8 minutes, followed by washing in distilled water. The solution is made up freshly by diluting 1.0 ml of a 0.5% solution of diaminobenzidine tetrahydrochloride to 10 ml in buffer and adding 3 μl of 30% hydrogen peroxide.

If rabbit serum is the first antibody and goat antirabbit IgG the link antibody, the normal serum should be goat serum and rabbit PAP should be used in step 4. If monoclonal antibodies from mouse ascites are the first antibodies and goat antimouse IgG the link antibody, again the normal serum should be goat serum and ClonoPAP should be used in step 4.

Burns (15) found that at least with abundant antigens, steps 1, 3, and 4 in the staining process could be reduced to 5 minutes without much loss in sensitivity.

Normal Serum

Potentially, immunoglobulins could bind nonspecifically to the section by hydrophobic bonding. This bonding is extremely strong on a plastic section such as that used in postembedding staining electron microscopy. We found that once a protein is bound nonspecifically on a plastic section, it will prevent a second protein from binding. On the chance that some nonspecific binding might also occur on paraffin sections and also because of the possibility of retention of some Fc receptors on the section, we have practiced pretreatment of paraffin sections with normal serum of the species that donates the link antiserum. This serum was chosen on the assumption that the donor of the link antiserum will not, in all likelihood, possess many circulating antibodies against a serum of its own species. Hence, the normal serum, when applied to the section, will not become visible in the PAP procedure. It is possible that normal serum pretreatment is not always necessary.

Normal serum is also incorporated in the diluants for first antiserum or monoclonal antibodies and for PAP or ClonoPAP. Normal serum is important to prevent loss of the highly diluted reagents from adsorption to the walls of their containers.

First Antibody

It is always advantageous to try a number of dilutions of antiserum or monoclonal antibodies. However, if this is impractical, we feel that a 1 : 1000 dilution of antiserum or a 1 : 2000 dilution of monoclonal antibody usually gives good staining. If a titration of the first antibody is carried out, it is advisable to use a dilution range of 1 : 500 to about 1 : 100,000 for antisera and 1 : 500 to 1 : 1,000,000 for monoclonal antibodies. One will find, in general, that with initial dilutions staining intensity will not decrease (it will remain maximal). On further dilution, a point will be reached from which all staining intensity will decrease. The optimal dilution of first antibody is the highest dilution at which staining still is maximal. The curve of staining intensity against antibody dilution beyond this point is sigmoidal. Except for special applications in which inhibition or intensification are studied, we are interested in immunocytochemistry in the dilution that yields optimal or maximal staining. In radioimmunoassay, on the other hand, one always uses dilutions that give partial binding, such as 50% or 30%. Of course, if titers for radioimmunoassay or immunocytochemistry are compared, dilutions will be used that give similar degrees of binding.

Determination of the 50% binding point with monoclonal antibodies or affinity-purified serum antibodies of known antibody protein concentration would appear to be a good way to estimate the dissociation constant of an antibody. Unfortunately this method might give falsley lower affinities, because it fails to consider any dissociation during washing in excess buffer that follows the first antibody reaction and subsequent steps in the immunocytochemical staining procedure.

The necessary *incubation time* in the first antibody is a function of its affinity. It is an intrinsic property of the first antibody and has nothing to do with the immunocytochemical method. With high concentrations, even reaction with low-affinity antibodies may reach 95% equilibrium within 30 minutes. This includes reaction of low-affinity cross-reacting and normal antibodies which we want to minimize as much as possible. For this reason, we use high dilutions of first antibody. With many high affinity antibodies, reaction, even at high dilution, will be nearly complete within 30 minutes. With other antibodies, reaction will be stronger after 24 hours than after 30 minutes. For this reason, we use 24 hours with all antibodies unless we have tested their efficiency in 30 minutes' incubation. However, all our monoclonal antibodies have originally been selected by immunocytochemistry with incubation times of 1 hour, even though the dilution of antibodies when examined in their original monoclonal cultures was very high (page 252). The shorter incubation time was dictated by the need of fast results as well as by the fact that we were mainly interested in detecting high-, rather than low-affinity monoclonal antibodies.

Because of a *prozone* phenomenon, the staining of frozen sections with the PAP method is often more difficult than that of paraffin sections. Bigbee et al. (16) localized glial fibrillar acidic protein on frozen sections of rat cerebellum and optic nerve with immunofluorescence and peroxidase-labeled antibodies, while adjacent sections processed by the PAP procedure yielded only nonspecific background, suggesting that the failure of staining was an inherent property of the PAP procedure. On further investigation, it was found that excessive concentrations of first antiserum were responsible for the negative results. Once the dilution of the first antiserum had been increased from 1:50 to 1:1000, staining became positive by the PAP method and the background had disappeared. Apparently, an excess of first antiserum in the PAP method inhibited the bifunctional reactivity of the link antibody. Bigbee et al. (16) suggested that if the concentration of the first antibody is too high, the second antibody will preferentially react with the first antibody via both of its idiotypic sites, irrespective of excess of second antibody used, so that nothing would be available to cross-link it to PAP.

Because of the destruction of many epitopes during fixation and embedding, the prozone phenomenon is less likely to be encountered with paraffin sections. Nevertheless, it has occasionally been observed. Vandesande (17) examined the antidiuretic hormone, vasopressin, in magnocellular nuclei of the hypothalamus and found intense localization with relatively high concentrations of antivasopressin serum. The vasopressin system is activated by dehydration; and, if transport of vasopressin is blocked, one may expect an increased concentration of vasopressin in magnocellular nuclei. With the same concentration of antiserum, however, the cells remained unstained in dehydrated animals. Progressive dilution of antiserum led to intense staining and to the correct results of higher staining intensities at higher dilutions of antiserum in the dehydrated than in the normal animals.

A prozone phenomenon was also observed by Linder and Miettinen (18) with indirect immunofluorescence, using antirenal basement membrane antigen on frozen sections of kidney tubules, bile canaliculi, and intestinal villi. These are reactions of a profuse antigen with an unusually potent antiserum.

PAP

An excess of PAP is recommended for optimal staining. This is accomplished with a 1 : 100 dilution even when tissue antigen is sparse or the first antibody is weak or its dilution high. For more abundant antigens and with the use of potent first antibodies, much higher dilutions of PAP can be used without decrease in sensitivity. Stilman et al. (19) and Sundler et al. (20) used PAP at dilutions of 1 : 1000. However, when nothing is known of a tissue antigen or the first antibody, we recommend dilutions of PAP or ClonoPAP of 1 : 100. For immunoblots (pages 241 and 449), we use ClonoPAP diluted 1 : 200.

Diaminobenzidine

In accordance with stability tests for diaminobenzidine tetrahydrochloride performed by Pelliniemi et al. (21), it is most convenient to make a 0.5% solution of diaminobenzidine tetrahydrochloride in 0.05N Tris buffer, pH 7.6, which may or may not contain 1.5% sodium chloride, and store these at $-20°C$ or $-85°C$ until dilution and addition of hydrogen peroxide just prior to use.

Diaminobenzidine is slowly oxidized by hydrogen peroxide even in the absence of peroxidase. A solution of diaminobenzidine tetrahydrochloride starts to become brownish about 20 minutes after the addition of hydrogen peroxide. This reaction is accelerated by lower pH. For the same reason, measured activity of peroxidase is higher at pH 5.4 than at pH 7.6. A stronger signal can be obtained, if the immunocytochemical staining reaction is carried out at pH 5.4. However, the pH of 7.6 was chosen on purpose to minimize sporadic oxidation of diaminobenzidine with hydrogen peroxide and, thus, to eliminate this potential source of background.

After staining with diaminobenzidine, sections may be counterstained with hematoxylin or Nissl stain or any other tinctorial stain. They may be dehydrated in xylene or cedar wood oil, and mounted in Permount, or alternatively they may be mounted without dehydration in glycerol according to the procedure of Webster et al. (22). 4-Chloro-1-naphthol has been used instead of diaminobenzidine by Dacheux and Dubois (23) and aminocarbazol by Rojas-Espinoza et al. (24). These reaction products are soluble in lipid-soluble mounting media.

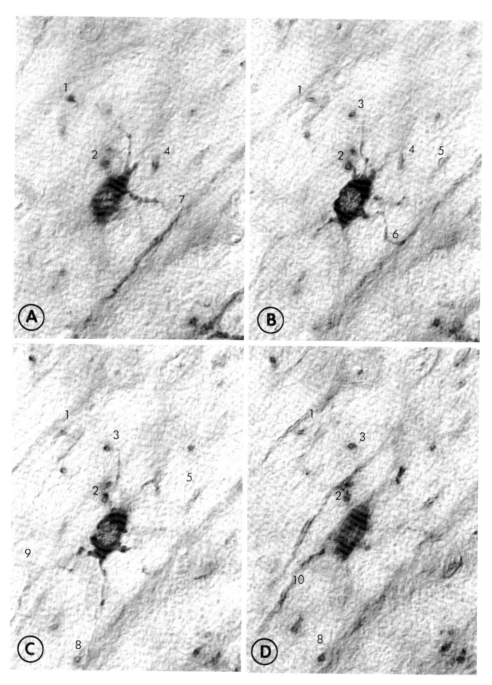

Figure 3-8. Myelin basic protein is abundant in early neonatal oligodendrocytes. Here in the same microscopic field of 5-day-old rat pons viewed at different focal depths, processes of a single obligodendrocyte are seen depositing myelin simultaneously around axons going in different directions and thus belonging to different nerve tracts. (A) Processes extend to myelin sheaths numbers 1 and 7. Attachment of the processes of sheaths 2,3,4,6 and 5,8,9, and 10 is shown in (B), (C), and (D), respectively. PAP method. Differential interference optics. ×750. [From Nancy Sternberger et al. (13).]

If sections are not counterstained, microscopy is best performed under differential interference (Nomarski) optics (22), which greatly intensifies contrast of specifically stained structures, apparently for a number of reasons:

1. The depth of focus with Normarski optics is shallow. Refractive differences are not likely to be confused with contrast differences. Therefore, unstained background which in regular microscopy may erroneously appear darkened when out of focus, will remain clear.

2. Specifically stained material appears in an illusionary relief form because Nomarski optics depends on contrast difference rather than color difference. Relief forms are illustrated by the visualization of oligodendrocytes (Figs. 3-8, 3-9) during the process of myelination in the work of Nancy Sternberger et al. (13).

Protease Pretreatment

Difficulties and inconsistencies have sometimes been encountered in the localization of immunoglobulin in paraffin sections by the PAP method. Staining can be facilitated or improved by treatment of sections with proteolytic enzymes prior to immunostaining (25). Trypsin, protease I and VII, and other proteolytic enzymes were successful. Other antigens also require proteolytic enzyme treatment. For instance, Katoh et al. (26) found treatment with trypsin essential for detection of human blood group antigens in bronchial epithelial cells and dem-

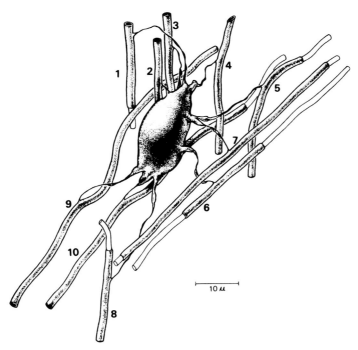

Figure 3-9. A reconstruction of the 10 myelin sheaths from Fig. 3-8 shows that six are trasversely sectioned and belong to the tectospinal tract, while the remaining four are longitudinally oriented and probably surround pontocerebellar fibers. [From Nancy Sternberger et al. (13).]

onstration of their absence in fibroblasts. It was felt that loss of blood group antigens, as well as acquisition of tumor-associated antigens (page 468), might be a marker of carcinogen-induced transformation of human bronchial epithelial cells. Similarly, McComb et al. (27) found that tryptic digestion led to a marked improvement in localization of factor VIII (von Willebrand factor), a marker of endothelial cells (Fig. 3-10). Radaskiewicz et al. (28) found that without proteolytic digestion, it was not possible to demonstrate small amounts of hepatitis B surface antigen in routine material. Protease type VII was more effective than trypsin. However, Mepham et al. (25) found trypsin to be the most effective proteolytic enzyme for demonstration of immunoglobulin in paraffin-embedded surgical specimens. Relatively high concentrations of trypsin (0.1%) were used for relatively prolonged times, up to 60 minutes.

Once it was accepted that proteolytic digestion may improve visualization of some antigens in paraffin sections by the PAP method, it was found that it had similar effects on immunofluorescence. In fact, it is because of proteolytic digestion that immunofluorescence of paraffin sections has become practical. An added advantage seems to be a reduction of autofluorescence background by proteolytic digestion.

The digestion is extensive with the concentrations of enzymes and incubation times used, especially if one considers that sections contain approximately 1 mg of protein only. Aldehyde fixation affects lysine groups. Trypsin cleaves near lysine and aginine groups. The masking of lysine amine may make fixed tissue more resistant to digestion. However, other changes that occur in fixation and embedding may increase susceptibility to trypsin.

Digestion affects the gelatin or albumin commonly used to make paraffin sections adherent to slides. Therefore, it is necessary to mount sections with a glue not affected by proteolysis. In the procedure practised at the Institut für Pathologie, Kantonspital, University of Basel, slides are acid-cleaned with Manostat Chromerge concentrated labware cleaner (sulfuric acid and chromic acid). Alternatively, small numbers of slides can be cleaned with 70% ethanol. Three milliliters of Elmer's glue are thoroughly mixed with 50 ml distilled water. A thin film of this mixture is smeared onto the surface of the slides and allowed to dry. Paraffin-embedded tissue is mounted to the coated surface of the slides in a 55–56°C distilled water bath containing 1 to 2 ml Elmer's glue per 100 ml distilled water. The sections are dried on the slides at 37°C overnight or on a warming tray set at 45°C for a few hours to overnight. Care should be taken that the water trapped under the section after mounting evaporates.

Caution is indicated about the general use of proteolytic digestion for immunocytochemistry on paraffin sections. Most antigens are well localized without digestion. It is only the exceptional antigen that brings possible difficulties. Some antigens are destroyed by proteolytic digestion. With monoclonal antibodies, we found that tryptic digestion had no effect on phosphorylated epitopes of neurofilament proteins in paraffin sections, producing neither enhancement nor reduction in staining (14). This lack of effect on immunocytochemical staining occurred despite the fact that the tryptic digestion did induce conformational changes in neurofilaments measured by susceptibility to phosphatase. On the other hand, tryptic digestion abolished staining of nonphosphorylated epitopes with monoclonal antibodies (page 450), even though only 0.05% trypsin/0.02N calcium chloride was used for 10 minutes.

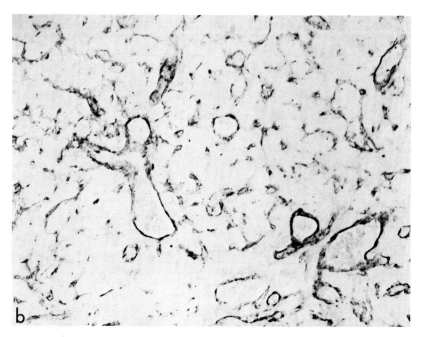

Figure 3-10. Serial section of cerebellar hemangioblastoma stained for factor VIII. PAP method. Counterstained with methylene blue. (a) Without trypsin pretreatment, staining is mostly in the large venules (arrows). Capillaries and small venules are weakly stained or not at all. (b) With trypsin, both intensity and number of stained blood vessels is greatly increased. ×170. [From McComb et al. (27).]

Martin and Voigt (29) found that vasopressin and enkephalin coexist in nerve terminals of the rat neurohypophysis, a finding that is important in the expression of a given peptide, such as enkephalin, at times in sequences in which it is known to exist (such as proopiocortin) and at times in yet unknown sequences (pages 359 and 383). However, coexistence in itself is no proof of a common precursor. Interestingly, on first attempts at immunocytochemical staining, vasopressin terminals failed to reveal reactivity for enkephalin, although oxytocin terminals did (Fig. 3-11). However, when sections were treated with trypsin, vasopressin reactivity appeared in vasopressin terminals. This suggested that enkephalin, vasopressin, and oxytocin existed in different forms in terminals. Apparently in the vasopressin terminals, enkephalin was masked by covalent incorporation in a precursor through a bond, such as Lys-Arg, that is cleaved by trypsin.

However, in other situations, trypsin may abolish immunoreactivity, and the effect may be subject to useful interpretation. The molluscan neurosecretory

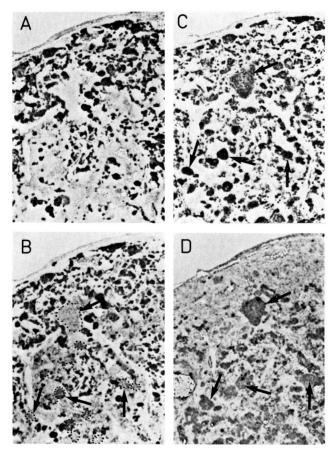

Figure 3-11. A series of four sections through the rat neurohypophysis stained with oxytocin (a), enkephalin (b,c), and vasopressin (d) immunoreactive terminals. The sections in (c) have been treated with trypsin. Oxytocin and, after tryptic cleavage, also vasopressin terminals (arrows) exhibit enkephalin immunostaining. PAP method. ×600. [From Martin and Voigt (29).]

tetrapeptide Phe-Met/Leu-Arg-PheNH$_2$ contains in it N-terminal sequence the two amino acids that constitute the C-terminal portion of enkephalin, Tyr-Gly-Gly-Phe-Met/Leu. Nerve endings in octopus vena cava react with antimolluscan peptide, but not antienkephalin. Martin and Voigt (29) found that after tryptic digestion, molluscan peptide immunoreactivity disappeared, but staining with antienkephalin became apparent. Since trypsin affects the Met/Leu-Arg bond, it could be concluded from these findings that the molluscan nerve endings, indeed, contain a hexapeptide or a precursor of it, encompassing the sequence Tyr-Gly-Gly-Phe-Met/Leu-Arg-PheNH$_2$. Here, trypsin had a specific unmasking effect. It is conceivable that in the case of localization of other proteins, such as immunoglobulin, protease digestion has similar unmasking effects. When immunizing animals with immunoglobulin, antibodies are not only produced against the injected antigen itself, but also against the proteolytic digestion product that forms in the deposit at the site of antigen inoculation. These antibodies are not necessarily reactive with native immunoglobulin, but may react with peptides unmasked upon proteolytic digestion on the slide. It follows that proteolytic digestion may be useful only in immunocytochemistry of special cases in which such new epitopes are unmasked and in which immunization produces antibodies to these new epitopes. By the same token, proteolytic digestion may abolish immunoreactivity to epitopes of the native antigen, which in some cases may be the only ones in which we are interested.

It also follows that proteolytic digestion is not indicated when monoclonal antibodies are used as first antibodies in immunocytochemistry. Monoclonal antibodies have usually been selected by immunologic reactions with a known antigen, or alternatively by a defined immunocytochemical staining pattern (page 429). By virtue of their monoclonality, they will only react significantly with epitopes available in the antigen or tissue section used for selection. No improvement of staining can occur if antigen or sections are degraded by proteolytic digestion, since the monoclonal antibodies contain no additional antibodies of specificities to different epitopes that may be so unmasked. However, proteolytic digestion may abolish the reactivity of an epitope, as it actually has occurred (14).

The controversy over which enzyme is better for unmasking antigenic reactivity, whether trypsin or protease type VII, again will have to resolve itself around the nature of the groups unmasked. Different enzymes cleave at different sites and reveal different epitopes. Because of heterogeneity of antisera with regard to contents of antibodies to such disclosed epitopes, it may even be impossible to arrive at a given enzyme that is optimal for a given antigen with all antisera. In any event, no general rule can be made whether it is advisable to use enzymatic digestion as a preliminary step to immunocytochemical staining of paraffin sections.

Endogenous Peroxidase

Red blood cells become stained when exposed to diaminobenzidine and hydrogen peroxide even in the absence of added peroxidase. This "endogenous peroxidase" activity is not abolished by paraffin embedding. Granulocytes possess a true endogenous peroxidase. Much of this activity is destroyed, however, by adequate fixation. Although red blood cell staining can easily be distinguished from staining of the remaining tissue, it is desirable to eliminate red cells from experimental material by perfusion of animals with physiologic solutions under general anesthesia, followed by perfusion with fixative.

The main purpose of perfusion is not, however, elimination of red blood cells but assurance of better fixation than that accomplished by immersion of tissues. Poor fixation is another source of "endogenous peroxidase" activity. Poorly fixed areas in tissue as well as necrotic areas help a tendency toward nonspecific staining even in the absence of first antibody, and this is also called "endogenous peroxidase" activity. Poor fixation is sometimes encountered in prospective immunocytochemistry of biopsy specimens and sometimes cannot be avoided in retrospective immunocytochemistry of autopsy material.

Burns (15) recommends that endogenous peroxidase activity be eliminated by treatment for 30 minutes in 0.5% methanolic hydrogen peroxide. This treatment is to be done prior to step 1 in the basic staining procedure outlined above and after protease treatment, if any. Destruction of "endogenous peroxidase activity" is not indicated in experimental material. Paraffin-embedded tissues from adequately perfused and fixed tissues present no nonspecific background when in the PAP method, first antibody treatment has been omitted. We found that hydrogen peroxide pretreatment may be deleterious to the immunoreactivity of some antigens.

Most routine pathologic specimens are likely to be of a quality that makes the question of "endogenous peroxidase activity" unnecessary.

POSTEMBEDDING STAINING FOR ELECTRON MICROSCOPY

Antibodies do not penetrate intact tissue. Even if tissue is fixed, penetration is unpredictable and sluggish. Therefore, it appears appropriate to stain for electron microscopy only after the tissue has been embedded and thin sections have been prepared (postembedding staining). In a 70- to 100-nm-thick section, as routinely prepared for electron microscopy, cells and subcellular organelles are cut open and accessibility of antibodies should no longer pose a problem. However, ferritin or peroxidase-labeled antibodies failed to localize antigens on thin sections prepared from routine electron microscopy embedding media. It had been concluded, therefore, that embedding destroyed all antigenic reactivity and that staining with labeled antibodies should be done before embedding (pre-embedding staining), even if difficulties were encountered in penetration (page 78). Difficulty in penetration was thought to be proportional to the size of labeled antibodies. For this reason, we had reasoned incorrectly, early in the development of the PAP method, that pre-embedding staining with PAP should not be attempted, for, after all, PAP with a molecular weight of 420,000 is bigger than monomeric peroxidase-antibody conjugates.

In the initial attempts of using PAP method for postembedding staining of ultrathin sections (30), we found the staining to be entirely nonspecific: that is, even parts of the section devoid of biologic material were covered with PAP.

To explain the causes of this nonspecific staining, we applied PAP alone to plastic sections. The whole section became opaque after treatment with diamino-benzidine and hydrogen peroxide, and osmication, indicating that the PAP had attached to the section. However, this nonspecific adsorption was abolished when the section was pretreated with diluted normal sheep serum. When normal rabbit serum was applied to the section, followed by sheep antirabbit IgG and PAP, again there was strong staining. This staining was due to nonspecific adsorption of the normal rabbit serum, since it disappeared when the sheep antirabbit IgG was omitted. Again, the nonspecific adsorption of normal rabbit serum could be blocked by pretreatment with normal sheep serum. When sheep antirabbit IgG was applied first and followed by PAP, there was no staining. Apparently, the antirabbit IgG was adsorbed nonspecifically, since otherwise the PAP would have been adsorbed nonspecifically, which would have resulted in staining. The adsorption of antirabbit IgG on the section seemed to be so strong as to distort or hinder its idiotypic sites and to prevent, thereby, binding with PAP.

These observations suggested that any protein is adsorbed to electron microscopy sections nonspecifically, and that the adsorption is strong enough to prevent adsorption of a subsequently applied protein even if the section is being washed. Serum immunoglobulins of one species prevent the adsorption of immunoglobulins of another species but not necessarily that of proteins with different net charges, such as ferritin or free peroxidase or immunoglobulins conjugated with polar or hydrophobic substituents. These considerations suggested for the unlabeled antibody method the pretreatment of thin sections with dilute, normal serum of the same species that donates the link antiserum. Thus, if the second antibody used in the staining procedure is goat antimouse immunoglobulin, normal goat serum is indicated for pretreatment. Goat antimouse immunoglobulin may react with immunoglobulins of other species, such as rat immunoglobulin. However, the antiserum will not react with goat IgG because the host goat is tolerant (immunosuppressed) toward production of antibodies to epitopes of mouse IgG shared with goat IgG. Furthermore, if antibodies to goat IgG could be produced in the goat, they would be neutralized by the excess of circulating IgG in the host. We have never observed any problems with any hypothetical cross-reacting allotypes (page 14) in the sera of rabbits, sheep, or goats with normal sera from these species when mouse, rat, or goat IgG were used as immunizing antigens.

The postembedding staining procedure is performed on silver or light gold Araldite sections. The sections are placed on 300 mesh, uncoated nickel, or gold grids. It seems to be necessary to remove part of the plastic from the section prior to staining or otherwise swell the section so as to permit interaction of antibody with embedded epitopes. Five percent hydrogen peroxide for 3 minutes is often used. Higher concentrations of hydrogen peroxide may dissolve the entire section and vitiate staining. However, if the hydrogen peroxide is not fresh or adequately preserved, higher concentrations may at times be applicable. Methanolic sodium hydroxide was successful in the hands of Rossi and Bestetti (31) when used under conditions in which removal of the plastic was partial.

In the following staining procedure, normal serum comes from the species that donates the link antiserum. Quantitative studies have shown (32) that it is slightly better to apply normal serum not only before the first antibody, but also before the link antiserum and PAP. "Tris" in this procedure is 0.05 M Tris hydrochloride, pH 7.6/1.5 M sodium chloride.

Step 1:   The sections are floated for 3 minutes at room temperature on drops of a 5% aqueous solution of hydrogen peroxide on glass slides. They are then "jet washed" by a spray of saline from a plastic spray bottle and "blotted" by holding them edgewise on filter paper.

Subsequent reagents are applied by floating the sections on drops of solutions in shallow depressions in a layer of paraffin in covered petri dishes.

Step 2:   Normal serum diluted 1 : 30 in Tris, for 5 minutes at room temperature followed by blotting, but not washing.

Step 3:   First antiserum, diluted and containing 1% normal serum, for about 48 hours at 2 to 5°C, permitting the dishes to re-equilibrate to room temperature for the last 1 to 2 hours, followed by jet washing in Tris and blotting.

Step 4:   Normal serum, diluted 1 : 30 in Tris, for 5 minutes at room temperature, followed by blotting, but no washing.

Step 5:   Link antiserum (antiimmunoglobulin), diluted 1 : 20 in 0.05 M Tris for 5 minutes at room temperature, followed by jet washing in Tris and blotting.

Step 6:   Normal serum, diluted 1 : 30 in Tris, for 5 minutes at room temperature, followed by blotting, but no washing.

Step 7:   PAP diluted to 0.066 mg antiperoxidase per millimeter in Tris, containing 1% normal serum for 5 minutes at room temperature (this concentration of antiperoxidase is usually attained by a 1 : 40 to 1 : 80 dilution of PAP). The grids are jet washed in 0.05 M Tris buffer, pH 7.6, lacking sodium chloride, but not blotted.

Step 8:   The grids are held in forceps and immersed, eight at a time, for 3 minutes at room temperature, into a beaker containing a freshly prepared solution of 0.0125% diaminobenzidine tetrahydrochloride and 0.0025% hydrogen peroxide in 0.05 M Tris buffer, pH 7.6 (32). This solution is kept under agitation over a magnetic stirrer at 50 to 80 rpm. The grids are rapidly transferred for about 30 seconds to another beaker containing water, also kept under agitation. Following removal from the water, the sections are jet washed in water, blotted, and placed on filter paper. The sections are then floated on a 4% solution of aqueous osmium tetroxide in porcelain depression dishes for 10 to 25 minutes and again washed in water.

Nickel or gold grids are necessary to avoid reaction of the grid bars with osmium. During the staining procedure up to (but not including) the osmium step, the grids are never allowed to dry completely.

All solutions are prepared from distilled, deionized, Millipore-filtered water (0.45 pore size). Undiluted sera or ascites fluids are stored at −85°C or, after freezing in dry ice and acetone at −20°C. They are thawed in a 37°C water bath. All undiluted sera are Millipore filtered either before or after storage. The normal sera are decomplemented in a water bath at 56°C for 30 minutes.

First antisera are used at dilutions ranging from 1 : 1000 to 1 : 100,000, monoclonal antibodies at dilutions of 1 : 1000 to 1 : 1,000,000. Significant staining has been obtained with many sera at even higher dilutions (4,32,33). Higher concentrations of antiserum are not recommended (page 232).

Instead of 1% and 3% normal serum, one can use 0.25% and 0.75% human serum albumin, respectively. This is important in the case of hormone receptor staining (page 403) in which binding proteins in serum may interfere.

Water-insoluble embedding media appear to have lesser tendency to react with proteins than water-soluble media. Should proteins become unfolded during embedding, the chance of refolding to the original state seems to be better with water-insoluble than water-soluble embedding media, and denaturation seems to be minimized. When water-insoluble embedding media are used, the tissue must be dehydrated prior to embedding, which is usually done with alcohols and propylene oxide.

Originally, we had felt that relatively mild fixatives are to be used for postembedding staining because fixation seemed to destroy some epitopes, while embedding may destroy others. Apparently, these procedures destroy so many epitopes that only a minor fraction of the total antibodies in an antiserum, consisting of those antibodies that react with the few preserved epitopes, participate in the staining reaction. Hence, a sensitive technique was needed, and postembedding staining could not be performed prior to the development of the PAP or immunogold (page 79) methods. Using sensitive technique, it was found, however, by Rodning et al. (34) and by Li et al. (35) that stronger fixatives, such as osmium tetroxide, give better ultrastructure and may not affect reactivity of certain epitopes (page 217). Thus, Rodning et al. (34) were able to detect, by postembedding staining technique, immunoglobulin, an antigen that has consistently escaped postembedding staining detection after treatment with mild fixatives.

The advantage of postembedding staining is simultaneous exposure of all tissue epitopes to the first antibody. Thus, if different cells or different granules contain similar amounts of antigen, they are stained at similar intensities. An example is the staining of prolactin cells in glutaraldehyde-fixed porcine pituitary by Dacheux (36) which reveals highly intense secretion granules of the specifically stained lactotropes against a background of nearly invisible cells containing other hormones (Fig. 3-12). Variations between individual cells and secretion granules can be interpreted as variations in hormone contents. In contrast, in pre-embedding staining, any variations in staining intensity are primarily affected by variations of penetration of antibody into the tissue.

Qualitative and quantitative analysis of staining is facilitated in the postembedding staining technique, not only because of assured accessibility of antibody, but also because of the possibility of staining serial sections with various antibodies, various concentrations of given antibodies as well as using them for controls. In the pre-embedding staining technique, such evaluation is impossible because different bits of tissue must be used for various antibodies and various concentrations of given antibodies, as well as for controls.

One of the many problems with postembedding technique is the generally poor preservation of structure when compared to that of standard, purely morphologic electron microscopy. There are several ways to overcome this problem. Much of the poor preservation in early postembedding work was due to the belief that mild fixatives must be used, such as Zamboni's fixative (page 214). which, however, do not preserve cellular membranes. With the use of better fixatives, such as formaldehyde-glutaraldehyde combinations followed by osmium tetroxide, or osmium tetroxide alone, membranes can be preserved at

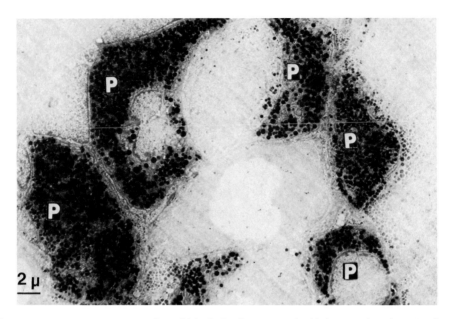

Figure 3-12. Porcine pituitary, glutaraldehyde-fixed, Epon embedded, treated with antiprolactin, 1 : 1000. PAP postembedding staining procedure. P, prolactin cells. Secretory granules of cells other than prolactin cells are only faintly visible. [From Dacheux (36).]

least with regard to their morphologic appearance. Nevertheless, in the postembedding staining procedure, membrane antigens are generally not revealed (page 403). However, for structures that are preserved antigenically, postembedding PAP procedure is sensitive and gives a strong, specific stain. This stain is demonstrated by blackening of the specific are (secretion granules in Fig. 3-12), or by identification of the pentagonal or circular PAP complexes (Fig. 3-13), or by the more diffuse, droplet-like deposition of 4-chloro-1-naphthol reaction product (Fig. 3-14). Because of the intensity of staining and the discrete morphology of the reaction product, it is possible to counterstain sections with lead citrate without masking specifically stained structure. With such counterstaining in osmium-fixed tissue, Li et al. (38) were able to observe much structural detail on postembedding staining. In a fetal pituitary (Fig. 3-14) stained for 1-24 corticotropin, it was possible not only to distinguish stained secretion granules against unstained mitochondrial membranes and cristae, endoplasmic reticulum, and plasma membrane, but also to observe exocytosis of secretion granules, a phenomenon which only rarely has been observed even with nonimmunocytochemical, purely morphologic electron microscopy.

It is not necessary to use, for morphologic evaluation, the same section as that employed in immunocytochemical staining. An advantage of the postembedding technique is the possibility of obtaining serial sections not only through the same cell but even through the same secretion granule. This procedure is especially useful if relatively mild fixatives that are not optimal for tissue preservation in electron microscopy have been used, such as picric acid-paraformaldehyde. In sections so processed, immunocytochemical localization is crisp, but the structure

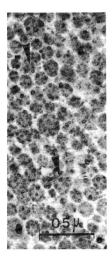

Figure 3-13. Luteinizing hormone in gonadotrophic secretory granules of frog pituitary. Postembedding staining. The cyclic or pentagonal PAP complexes identify antigenic sites of the hormone. [From Doerr-Schott (37).]

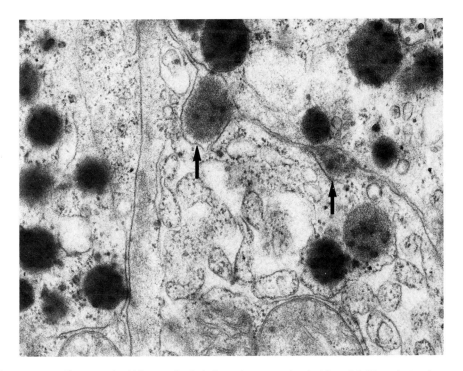

Figure 3-14. Fifteen-week-old human fetal pituitary, immunostained with anti-1-24-corticotropin, contrasted with lead citrate. PAP postembedding staining technique, using 4-chloro-1-naphthol as electron donor for peroxidase. Specific stain is identified by deposits of the globular reaction product on the secretion granules. Staining of membranes and the remainder of the secretion granules is due to uranyl acetate. Arrows point to the extruding secretory granules in the process of releasing the hormonal contents into the extracellular space. Nevertheless, a slight deposit is still seen on the extruded granules. ×43,000. [From Li et al. (38).]

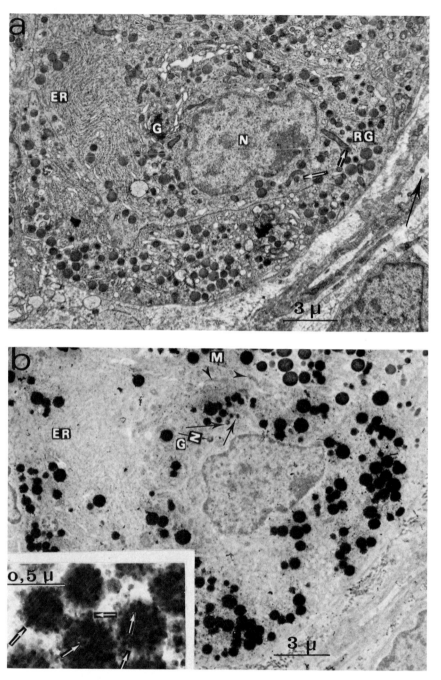

Figure 3-15. (a) A prolactin cell of picric acid paraformaldehyde-fixed cow pituitary stained with uranyl acetate. The Golgi complex (G) near the nucleus (N) is associated with vesicles and small granules. Round, secretory granules (RG) are located at the vascular pole. The mitochondria are often elongated. The well-developed endoplasmic reticulum (ER) is close to the plasma membrane at the opposite pole of the cell. Long arrow points to an exocytosed granule. (b) This adjacent immunocytochemically stained section reveals prolactin in the secretory granules of the same cell, both by the electron opacity of the reaction product and by morphologic identification of the PAP complexes. (c). Comparison with (a) permits the conclusion that the secretory granules at the vascular pole as well as the small secretory granules in the Golgi complex (G, arrow) contain prolactin, while Golgi saccules, cisternae of the endoplasmic reticulum (ER), mitochondria, and nucleus are devoid of immunoreactive material. Inset (c) shows PAP complexes at specific reaction sites. [From Dacheux and Dubois (23).]

of surrounding, unstained tissue is difficult to discern because of lack of contrast. Dacheux and Dubois (23) were able to solve this problem by staining ultrathin sections with uranyl acetate for morphology and processing adjacent sections by immunocytochemistry (Fig. 3-15). Use of slotted nickel or gold grids, which permit orientation of sections in the same direction, are a convenient aid in the search of the same cell in adjacent sections. It is also desirable to use grids with relatively wide spaces among grid bars in order to minimize the chance that a cell observed in one grid is masked by a grid bar in an adjacent grid. This may require a supporting film for the section. In general, however, when serial sections are not being made, fine mesh grids are preferable because sections can be placed on grids without supporting film.

One of the problems with post- as well as pre-embedding electron microscopic immunocytochemistry is the limited size of the tissue that can be surveyed in the electron microscope. While it is possible to obtain information on subcellular distribution, the general histologic relationship of a cell to its surrounding tissue is often difficult to establish. In addition, if one were to localize an antigen found only in a rare cell, such as somatostatin (page 370) in neurons of cerebral cortex, it would require an immense number of sections to find a cell stained in post-embedding procedure. This problem can be solved, as illustrated in the work of Heitz and Wegmann (39), by preparing serial, semithin, and thin Epon sections of tumor biopsy and surgical specimens fixed in formaldehyde and postfixed in osmium tetroxide. By light microscopy, lysozyme was identified in supranuclear cytoplasmic areas of an adenocarcinoma of the stomach (Fig. 3-16) and adjacent ultrathin sections localized the enzyme to secretion granules. The observation permitted assignment of staining to Paneth cells and showed that neoplastic

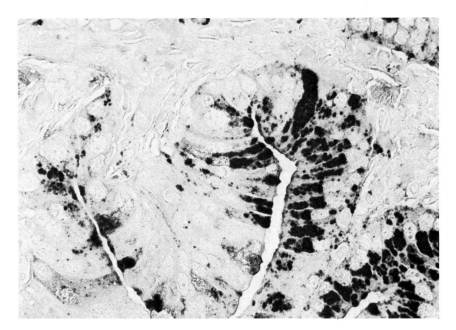

Figure 3-16. Adenocarcinoma of the stomach, formaldehyde-osmium tetroxide fixation. Semithin Epon section, stained for lysozyme. PAP technique. ×533 [From the work of Philipp Heitz.]

Paneth cells occasionally occur in tumors of the human gastrointestinal tract. Rodning et al. (40) using semithin, plastic sections with PAP staining, identified IgA and IgG in Paneth cells, suggesting a functional, antibacterial association of the secretion products of Paneth cells.

Rossi and Bestetti (31) used alcoholic sodium methoxide to *partially* remove Spurr's low viscosity medium from semithin and ultrathin sections in their studies on the mechanism of impairment of reproductive functions in diabetes. Appropriate hypothalamic areas, stained for luteinizing hormone-releasing hormone (LHRH) and pituitaries stained for luteinizing hormone were selected for light microscopy and cellular substructure was evaluated in adjacent thin sections selected for staining by electron microscopy. In light microscopy, the

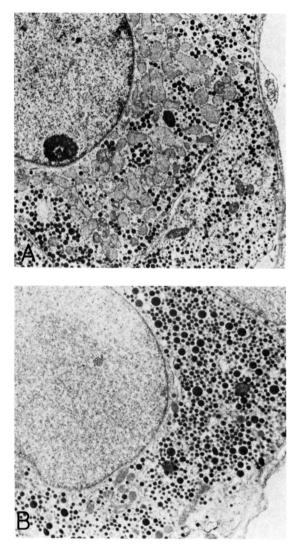

Figure 3-17. Normal (a) and diabetic (b) rat gonatrophs, not immunostained. Cells were identified immunocytochemically by staining adjacent semithin sections ×6,900. [From Rossi and Bestetti (31).]

amounts of LHRH in the hypothalamic areas examined appeared to be comparable in their experimental diabetic material and in the controls. By electron microscopy in normal animals, the LHRH was localized in axonal secretion granules. In diabetic animals, however, these secretion granules were in various stages of degeneration, some appeared to be fused, and LHRH was also found in vesicles characteristic to the diabetic axon. Electron microscopy of pituitary gonadotropes revealed cells with LH secretion granules of similar size in control and diabetic animals (Figs. 3-17 and 3-18). However, the diabetic cells were smaller, their endoplasmic reticulum was poorly developed, and the secretion granules were densely packed. These findings suggest that in diabetic animals the secretory activity of luteinizing hormones is more inhibited than its synthesis, leading to accumulation of granules, and possible short-loop feedback involvement of the endoplasmic reticulum and the Golgi system. The inhibited secretion appears to be the result of hypothalamic pathology, in which LHRH is produced, but is apparently degraded rather than secreted normally.

Postembedding staining depends on the sensitivity of the immunocytochemical method. It is assumed that many epitopes are lost during fixation and embedding, but that with sensitive technique, those that are preserved suffice for immunocytochemical localization. Reactivity with antigen, can, however, also be impaired by immobilization in the embedding medium. This may be a more important factor which limits the general applicability of postembedding staining. Indeed, light microscopy of plastic-embedded, glutaraldehyde-osmium tetroxide-fixed material may be equally good or, as shown by Nancy Sternberger et al. (41), better than paraffin-embedded paraformaldehyde-fixed material (page 221). In staining semithin sections for light microscopy, one may remove the plastic completely or partially. In the use of ultrathin sections by electron microscopy, it is not possible to remove all the plastic and still have well-structured, stainable material. Partial removal accomplished with sodium methoxide, or minimal removal or possible other effects mediated by hydrogen peroxide, are necessary to unravel epitopic sites. It seems that this is possible only with densely

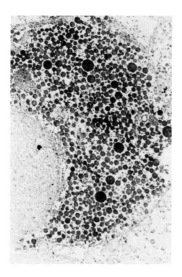

Figure 3-18. Streptotocin-induced diabetic rat gonadotroph stained for luteinizing hormone. PAP postembedding technique. ×6,900. [From Rossi and Bestetti (31).]

packed antigens or haptens that are found, at least in mammalian cells, only in secretion granules. Antigens have not been localized in bona fide identified membranes, including endoplasmic reticulum, stacks of the Golgi apparatus, and at best only poorly on receptors on cell membranes. It seems that the minimal removal of plastic from sections does not liberate most of the epitope sites immobilized by the plastic. However, if antigens are densely packed, proximity of identical epitopes may spare them from infiltration by the plastic, and leave them available for reaction with antibodies. Two-dimensional proximity over the plane of the section exists only in material accumulated in secretion granules. On membranes, only one-dimensional proximity is possible, thus providing little protection from hindrance by the plastic.

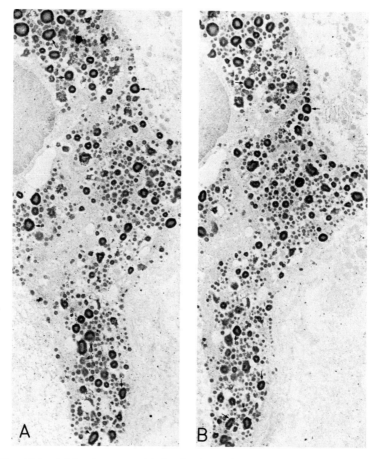

Figure 3-19.   (a) Luteinizing hormones-β is localized mainly to the periphery of the large secretion granules in this Araldite section of rat pituitary. The small secretion granules are only weakly stained. PAP postembedding staining technique. (b) Section adjacent to (a) stained for rat follicle stimulating hormone-β. Arrows denote some of the large secretion granules, indicating colocalization of follicle stimulating and luteinizing hormones in the same secretion granule. Serial section comparison of antigen localization at the subcellular level is another aspect that requires postembedding staining. $\times 12,000$. [From Tougard et al. (42).]

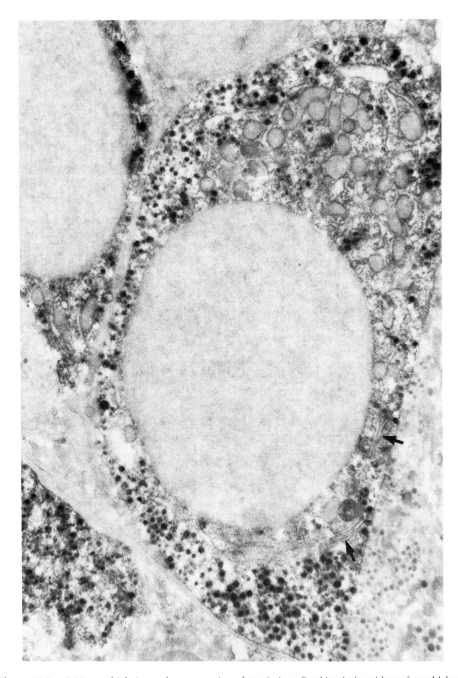

Figure 3-20. A 25-μm-thick tissue chopper section of rat pituitary fixed in picric acid paraformaldehyde was stained for luteinizing hormone-β, postfixed in osmium tetroxide and embedded in Araldyte (pre-embedding staining). Small secretion granules are well stained as illustrated here with a gonadotroph of the type that contains only small secretion granules. Cisternae of the rough endoplasmic reticulum are flattened (arrows). Peroxidase-labeled antibody method. ×12,000 [From Tougard et al. (42).]

Even the localization of secretion granules is favored to the large granules in which a relatively smaller proportion of contacts to the membrane surface is expected than in small granules. Consequently, the better localization of luteinizing hormone and follicle-stimulating hormone on postembedding staining to large than to small secretion granules, as observed by Tougard et al. (42) and Dacheux (43), may merely be the result of lesser impairment by infiltrated plastic (Fig. 3-19). The impression of preference of LHRH receptors for large granules reported by us (44) may have similar technical causes. In contrast, by pre-embedding technique, using peroxidase-labeled antibodies, the small granules are better stained than the large ones (42,43), suggesting exposure of a relatively high proportion of surface to the sluggishly penetrating antibodies (Fig. 3-20). In addition, pre-embedding technique visualized other cytoplasmic components, not revealed by postembedding staining.

Even though it is known that proteins are assembled on endoplasmic reticulum, and even though immunologic techniques are widely used to isolate nascent peptides with attached mRNA, postembedding staining has not accomplished a bona fide localization of antigen-bound endoplasmic reticulum. Occasionally, some electron opacity was seen in immunostained sections in cytoplasmic areas that could correspond to the location of endoplasmic reticulum, but morphologic identification of these spots as endoplasmic reticulum has been unconvincing.

Antigens that are not stored in large secretion granules have not been identified in postembedding staining in mammalian cells. These antigens include neurotransmitter-synthetic enzymes, such as tyrosine hydroxylase, dopamine-β-hydroxylase, and choline acetyl transferase, which are confined to small vesicular granules that have no dense core and which seem to behave in the staining procedure like antigens on membranous surfaces rather than in the interior of large granules. Other antigens that have not been localized by postembedding technique include fibrillar antigens, such as glial fibrillary acidic protein or neurofilaments or tubulin.

The restriction of localization of antigens to secretion granules limits the general utility of the postembedding staining technique in electron microscopy. In contrast, processing of semithin plastic sections for light microscopy by techniques that are similar to those used in electron microscopy seems to be a procedure of much usefulness (page 220).

PRE-EMBEDDING STAINING FOR ELECTRON MICROSCOPY

In the early phases of the use of PAP, electron microscopy was restricted to postembedding staining. We felt that pre-embedding staining would be futile, for it had been generally thought that penetration of the unsectioned tissue components by immunoreagents is dependent upon their size. If molecules of 200,000-dalton size, such as dimers of peroxidase-antibody conjugates, penetrate sluggishly, and 650,000-dalton complexes, such as ferritin-antibody dimers, not at all, it would appear unlikely that the 420,000-dalton PAP complex will be effective in pre-embedding staining. However, these considerations assume that size is the main rate-limiting factor in penetration. Indeed, it is, to the extent that molecules larger than 40,000 daltons penetrate only sluggishly. This size limitation includes all antibodies as well as conjugated antibody fragments. One may wonder, however, whether molecules exceeding in size the 40,000-dalton critical point will exhibit a continuously decreasing penetrability into fixed tissue as their size increases, or whether other factors, such as charge, influence more than mere size, the penetration through any pores artificially induced by fixation as well as by occasional treatment with Triton or digitonin.

In the 7-μm-thick, deparaffinized paraffin section, penetration is not a problem, as indicated by uniform staining of axons and dendrites that can be traced over fair distances with adequate antibodies (page 433) in pictures that resemble those of Golgi stain in much thicker sections. Moreover, Grzanna et al. (45) have shown excellent penetration of 100-μm-thick Vibratome sections, when tissue is pretreated with Triton X-100 and first antibodies are admixed with low concentrations of Triton as well (see also pages 320 and 321).

Since single epitope sites can be visualized by PAP technique on the cell surface (46), it is possible to reason that material detected by light microscopy should also be visible in electron microscopy. These considerations form the basis of the pre-embedding staining technique. In the most commonly used procedure, 25-μm-thick Vibratome sections are stained as for light microscopy. The stained sections are flat embedded in Epon, observed by light microscopy, and then selected areas are embedded for electron microscopy and thin sectioned.

Tissue is fixed most commonly in 1 to 4% paraformaldehyde containing 0.2% glutaraldehyde. The proportion of ingredients may be changed, but it is thought that too high concentrations of glutaraldehyde inhibit penetration of formaldehyde and that too low concentrations jeopardize membrane staining. Experimental animals are perfused with physiologic solutions followed by fixatives under Nembutal anesthesia. Tissues are generally, although not necessarily, postfixed in the same fixative.

Staining procedure is essentially as for light microscopy (page 104), except that sections are handled in 24-well culture dishes rather than on glass slides. About 0.5 ml of immunoreagents are used per well. Washes are done with maximal volume of buffer that can be accommodated in the wells. Solutions are removed by careful suction. As in light microscopy, we use 0.05 M Tris buffer, pH 7.6/0.3 M sodium chloride as diluant and wash solutions. Effective staining and penetration can also be obtained with buffers containing 0.15 M sodium chloride. Hypertonic buffer helps to select for high-affinity antibodies and may also aid in penetration. Sodium chloride concentration can be increased up to 0.5 M, or alternatively, 0.5 M Tris buffer devoid of sodium chloride may be used.

Penetration of antibodies into Vibratome sections is about 2 μm if isotonic buffers are used and slightly better in hypertonic buffer. Olschowka et al. (47) have shown that if the first antibody is applied in the presence of 0.2% Triton (18 hours at 5°C) and if 0.025% Triton is added to washing buffers after the first antibody step and to the second antibody, but not to subsequently applied reagents, penetration of up to 40 μm of both sides of the Vibratome section can be attained (Figs. 3-21 and 3-22). Calcium chloride (0.1 mM) was added to all solutions in this work.

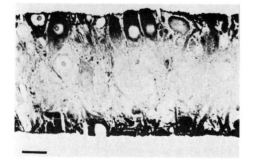

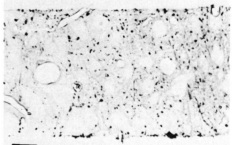

Figure 3-21.   A Vibratome section through the nucleus locus ceruleus, one of the sites of origin of noradrenergic fibers (page 320), has been stained for dopamine-β-hydroxylase in the presence of Triton X. The section was flat embedded and 3-μm plastic sections were cut perpendicular to the Vibratome section. Penetration is up to 25 μm from the surface. Neurons with cytoplasm exposed to the cut surface are permeated better than those underlying entirely beneath the surface. PAP method. Bar is 2 μm. [From Olschowka et al. (47).]

Figure 3-22.   In a field of noradrenergic terminals prepared similarly to that in Fig. 3-21, this light micrograph shows that the visualization of axons is extended to a depth of up to 45 μm. Comparison with Fig. 3-21 illustrates the variability one may expect from one tissue specimen to another when the pre-embedding staining technique is followed by electron microscopy. PAP method. Bar is 2 μm. [From Olschowka et al. (47).]

Triton pretreatment of the sections, while satisfactory for light microscopy, is disruptive to ultrastructure. The admixture of lower concentrations of Triton to the first antibody is not as damaging. Most investigators prefer to omit Triton altogether. Penetration does not only depend on the solvents used, but may vary greatly among different tissues, even if the same fixatives have been used.

If Triton is admixed with first antibodies, the normal serum pretreatment of the section may be omitted, and it is not necessary to incorporate normal serum in the diluent of the first antibody.

After the tissue has been stained immunocytochemically, it is postfixed with 0.1% osmium tetroxide for 15 minutes to confer electron opacity to the diaminobenzidine reaction product and to further stabilize cellular membranes. The sections are then dehydrated and flat embedded in Epon on a plastic slide and under a plastic coverslip. Light microscopy permits selection of suitably stained tissue. This is a great advantage over the postembedding technique, in that, in case of antigens that are found only in few cells among the total material, it is not necessary to scan a great number of thin sections until a positively stained one is found. However, there are some limitations to the light microscopic selection procedure. Strongly stained areas are sometimes unsuitable for electron microscopy, because the electron opacity is too high to permit identification of underlying ultrastructure. For this reason, it is sometimes advisable to select an area adjacent to that which appears most strongly stained in light microscopy. Furthermore, because of the higher sensitivity of electron microscopy over light microscopy, it is possible to miss ultrastructurally stained areas not apparent under light microscopic observation.

Once an area has been selected by light microscopy, it is broken away from the remainder of the slide and embedded under the tip of a Beem capsule in such a way that its flat surface is parallel with the long axis of the capsule. Consequently, thin sections for electron microscopy will be perpendicular to the surface of the light microscopy section.

The potential superiority of electron microscopy by pre-embedding staining is exemplified in the work of Altschuler et al. (48) on the synaptology of aspartate aminotransferase. Until recently, "conventional" neurotransmitters, [which include catecholamines (noradrenalin, adrenalin, dopamine, and serotonin), acetylcholine, aspartate, glutamate, γ-aminobutyrate, carnosine, and taurine)] could not be localized immunocytochemically because of lack of antibodies to the unmodified small molecular antigens. Instead, the localization of transmitters has been inferred by that of their specific, biosynthetic enzymes. The enzyme localization reflects that of the corresponding neurotransmitter, especially if we deal with an enzyme that is rate limiting in neurotransmitter synthesis. Aspartate aminotransferase exhibits high activity in auditory nerve fibers and diminished activity in the cochlear nucleus after auditory nerve lesions and may control a specific neurotransmitter system. Using no Triton for pre-embedding staining, but buffers close to isotonicity to which 1.5% sucrose was added, immunoreactive axon terminals were seen to surround spherical cells of the rostral anteroventral cochlear nucleus (Fig. 3-23). These terminals engaged in asymmetric synapses with the cell soma and were, therefore, considered primary aspartergic afferents of the auditory nerve. Other terminals failed to exhibit immunoreactivity and were identified as nonprimary afferents.

This study illustrates some of the advantages of pre-embedding staining, that makes it increasingly the technique of choice for electron microscopic immunocytochemistry. The specific localization is crisp, within a resolution corresponding approximately to that of the size of small secretion vesicles. The localization is specific: there is no stain beyond the confines of the axon terminal. There is no leaching of reaction product to adjacent cells. Mitochondrial cristae can be identified in the stained terminal as devoid of aspartate aminotransferase. Synapses are clearly seen. In contrast, synapses are not seen in postembedding staining. Also, in contrast to postembedding staining, the ultrastructure of unstained areas, the unstained axon terminals, as well as the cell body (Fig. 3-23), is excellent. Penetration of immunoreagents is satisfactory as indicated by the uniform staining of all vesicles within the positively stained terminal.

It is commonly observed that the ultrastructure in pre-embedding staining is only good in areas that are unstained. There is little structural detail in the vicinity of the stained vesicles. It seems that all membranes within this vicinity have accepted the immunostain. These include the outer mitochondrial membrane, the inner axolemmal membrane, the membranes of some large vesicular or granular structures, as well as the synaptic thickening. This is a general phenomenon in pre-embedding staining. It is difficult to ascertain whether this localization is specific or whether it is due to possible translocation of the diaminobenzidine reaction product which is known to creep along structures at which it is liberated, at least for a distance of about 50 nm, as illustrated by the outline of PAP complex sprayed on the grid (page 101). The question could be answered by the use of the unlabeled antibody method with ferritin-antiferritin

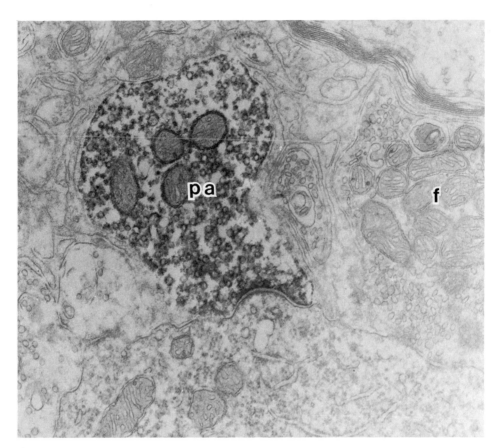

Figure 3-23. A primary aspartate amino transferase-containing afferent terminal (pa) possesses stained small, round vesicles as well as stained mitochondrial membranes. It synapses with the soma of a cochlear neuron. A terminal devoid of aspartate amino transferase (f) and presumably containing a transmitter other than aspartate, also synapses with the soma. In this particular case, the synaptic thickening of the aspartate terminal is more electron opaque than that of other terminals, perhaps suggesting that the enzyme is present not only in the small clear vesicles but also in the synaptic thickening itself. This finding may have been possible by the relatively crisp staining accomplished through omission of Triton in the staining procedure. PAP pre-embedding staining technique. ×32,000. [From Altschuler et al. (48).]

complexes instead of PAP (page 186) or by the immunogold method. With these reagents, immunocytochemical localization does not depend on buildup of an enzyme reaction product. However, none of these reagents penetrate cells in a pre-embedding staining situation.

Dopamine-β-hydroxylase is the rate-limiting enzyme for the synthesis of noradrenalin and adrenalin. Since adrenalin is absent from the central nervous system, immunocytochemistry for dopamine-β-hydroxylase is specific for noradrenalin. As in many specific neurotransmitter systems, noradrenergic fibers have their origin in limited areas but the distribution of their projections is widespread. In distinction to most other neurotransmitter systems, which are distributed along discernible nerve bundles, the noradrenergic system is distributed throughout the brain in a diffuse manner. It has been thought for a long

time that these fibers control cerebral blood flow by diffusion of the neurotransmitter to vascular elements upon release from nonspecialized terminals.
Olschowka et al. (47), in their electron microscopic studies, found that noradrenergic axons form extensively arborized branches richly endowed with varicosities that are separated by only short, intervaricose segments. In these varicosities, synapses are so frequent (Fig. 3-24) that one may surmise, that if sectioned
through all planes, no varicosity without synapses would be found. The data
indicate that noradrenergic fibers form true synapses, and any regulation of
blood flow would, therefore, have to be through interneurons rather than
through direct diffusion onto vascular elements.

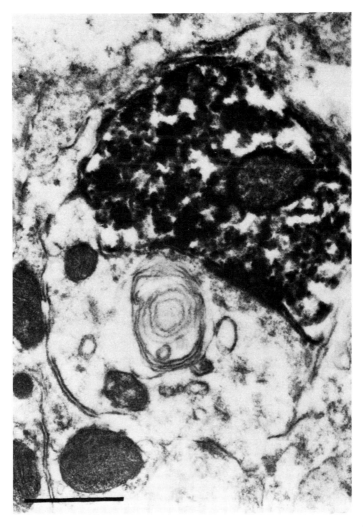

Figure 3-24. In this axonal varicosity of rat brain reacted with antidopamine-β-hydroxylase by pre-
embedding technique in the presence of Triton $\times 100$, staining of the synaptic vesicle and the outer
mitochondrial membrane is intense. PAP technique. Bar is 0.5 μm. [From Olschowka et al. (47).]

In these studies, staining was intense, probably aided by the treatment with Triton. There was some disruption of membranes (Fig. 3-24) when compared to staining in the absence of Triton (Fig. 3-23), but disruption was minimized by judicious and carefully controlled use of minimally effective concentrations of Triton.

Glutamate decarboxylase is the rate-limiting enzyme for the synthesis of γ-aminobutyric acid. A neuron can be considered γ-aminobutyrergic by immuno-cytochemical staining for glutamate decarboxylase or by autoradiography after uptake of tritiated γ-aminobutyrate (page 315). Wu et al. (49) have shown, by pre-embedding staining in the presence of Triton X-100, that rabbit amacrine

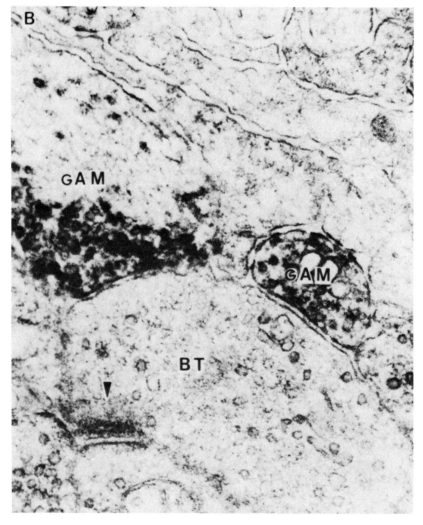

Figure 3-25. Glutamate decarboxylase-containing nerve terminal of amacrine cells (GAM) make synaptic contacts with terminals of a bipolar cell (BP) in the rat retina. Bipolar terminals can be identified by their characteristic ribbons (arrow). Protein A-PAP pre-embedding technique with added Triton. ×61,300. [From Wu et al. (49).]

cells are γ-aminobutyrergic. They were found to be presynaptic mainly to bipolar and amacrine cells (Fig. 3-25).

In general, neurotransmitters are too small to be localized by antibodies specific to the neurotransmitter hapten itself. The hapten has to be conjugated to a protein carrier (page 16) to become antigenic, but because of its small size, crucial epitopes may become altered as a result of the conjugation process. Also because of their small size, neurotransmitters may not possess groups reactive with fixatives, or, if they do, the reaction will abolish epitopic reactivity. In the former case, the neurotransmitter is lost during tissue processing; in the latter, it may no longer be detectable. Serotonin was found to be an exception. This neurotransmitter is altered by aldehyde. It can be conjugated to bovine serum albumin with aldehyde to make an immunizing antigen. It also can be conjugated to tissue in aldehyde fixation. Steinbusch et al. (50) have shown that antibodies to aldehyde-altered serotonin are useful for the detection in tissue of serotonin altered in a similar way by fixation with aldehyde.

The raphé system is richly endowed with serotonin somata and fibers. By pre-embedding electron microscopy, Pecci Saavedra et al. (51) have shown that in the raphé nucleus, serotonin terminals were dendrites (Fig. 3-26). No serotonin-

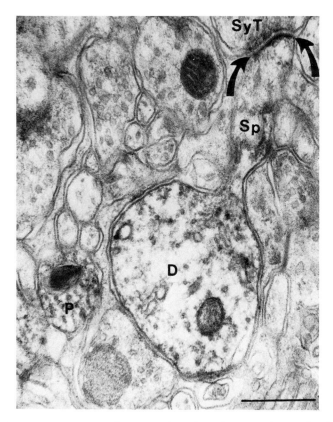

Figure 3-26. The neurotransmitter in this terminal (D) from the rat nucleus raphe dorsalis has been identified as serotonin by pre-embedding PAP staining with added Triton. The terminal is a dendrite because it has a dendritic spine (Sp). Other criteria include presence of ribosomes and smaller number of vesicles than axon terminals. The spine possesses a synaptic junction, and is, therefore, presynaptic. ×40,000. [From Pecci Saavedra et al. (51).]

containing axon terminals were seen. The findings suggest a transmitter role for dendritic spines as presynaptic units.

Vasoactive intestinal peptide is a neurosecretory peptide found, as other peptides, in the central nervous system and in the periphery. In the periphery, it is commonly found in nerve endings that innervate glands. Neurosecretory peptides should be classified as neurotransmitters if they replace classical neurotransmitters in certain terminals. They should be considered neurotransmitters of higher order if they modulate or control the action of classical neurotransmitters. In the latter case, they should be found to coexist with neurotransmitters in nerve terminals (page 397).

Using frozen sections for pre-embedding staining, Johansson and Lundberg (52) found vasoactive intestinal peptide in large dense core vesicles of nerve endings in the cat submandibular gland close to secretory acini, and in demilunes, ducts, and blood vessels (Fig. 3-27). The terminals contained a proportion of small clear vesicles to large dense core vesicles of about 9 : 1. The small vesicles were considered to contain acetylcholine, and vasoactive intestinal peptide was considered to coexist with acetylcholine as a neuromodulator.

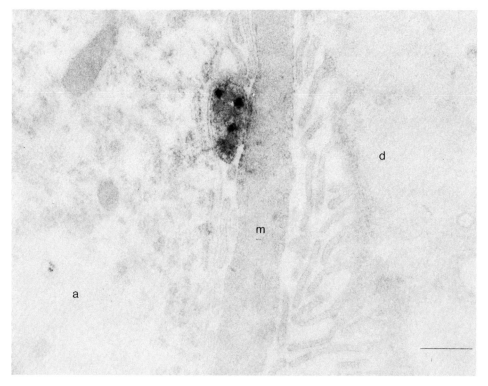

Figure 3-27. In this frozen section of rat submaxillary ganglion stained for vasoactive intestinal peptide, a bouton containing the peptide in dense core vesicles makes close contact with an acinar cell (a) inside a myoepithelial cell (m); (d) demilune cell. PAP pre-embedding technique. Bar is 0.5 μm. [Reprinted with permission from *Neuroscience* **6:**847, O. Johannson, J.M. Lundberg, Ultrastructural localization of vasoactive intestinal polypeptide-like immunoreactivity in large dense-core vesicles of "cholinergic type" nerve terminals in cat exocrine glands, Copyright 1982, Peryamon Press Ltd. (52).]

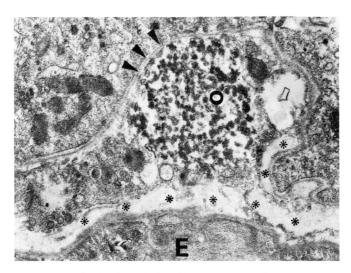

Figure 3-28. Corticotropin-releasing factor is found in 80 to 120 nm diameter secretory granules in this axon terminal (circle) that releases its contents directly, without synaptic junction, into the precapillary space (asterisk). Arrows denote the direct contact of the terminal with the limiting endothelial basement membrane. PAP pre-embedding staining technique with added Triton. ×20,500. [From Liposits et al. (55).]

The Scharrer concept (53,54) implies that bioactive peptides or neurosecretory principles are released synaptically and nonsynaptically (page 358). Liposits et al. (55) provide electron microscopic evidence for the direct release of corticotropin-releasing factor into the pituitary portal circulation (Fig. 3-28).

The sensory neurosecretory peptide, substance P, is widely distributed in the spinal cord as well as the remaining central nervous system, but its amounts are much higher in the dorsal (sensory) than the ventral (motor) regions of the spinal cord. In the ventral horn, the boutons are so small and rare that they are at the limit of resolution of light microscopy. They are best demonstrated by Vacca's double PAP method (page 186) which intensifies the immunocytochemical signal and enlarges its dimensions (56). For pre-embedding staining electron microscopy, single PAP method was used in line with the higher sensitivity of electron microscopic versus light microscopic immunocytochemistry. The fine terminals possessed few intensely labeled large, dense core vesicles and many small, clear vesicles (Fig. 3-29). The asymmetric synapse also appeared to contain substance P, suggesting that substance P directly participates in synaptic transmission. Its role in the ventral horn is supposed to be excitatory.

In their cells of origin, most neurosecretory peptides exhibit similar distribution on pre-embedding staining electron microscopy. Typical is the localization of vasopressin in neurons of the paraventricular nucleus as studied by Piekut (57). Peptide was found mainly in secretion granules, but localization in the rough endoplasmic reticulum and the rest of the cytoplasm was also apparent (Fig. 3-30).

Myelin basic protein, first isolated by Kies et al. (58) is an important constituent of myelin (page 341) and one of the antigens that can cause experimental

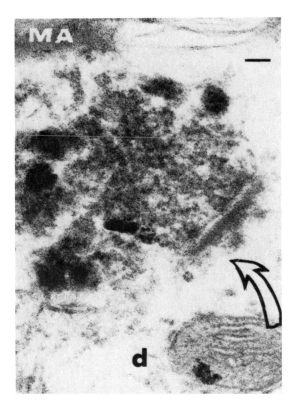

Figure 3-29. Substance P is found mainly in the large, dense core vesicles as well as in the asymmetric synapse in cells in this small terminal bouton in the ventral horn of the rat spinal cord. (MA), Myelinated axon. (d) Dendrite. PAP pre-embedding staining technique in the presence of Triton. Bar is 0.1 μm. [From Vacca et al. (56).]

autoimmune encephalitis (page 487). Nancy Sternberger et al. (59) have shown that this oligodendrocyte-borne protein appears during early development in oligodendrocytes prior to formation of myelin. As myelination proceeds, the protein is found both in the oligodendrocytes and the nascent myelin. Upon approach to adulthood, as myelination slows, an increase of myelin basic protein in myelin itself, accompanies a decrease in oligodendrocytes. In the past, no myelin could be detected in adult oligodendrocytes. However, with continued improvement in technique, myelin basic protein has also been found in adult oligodendrocytes (60), thus suggesting antimyelin basic protein as a marker for oligodendrocytes. Pre-embedding staining electron microscopy of Vibratome sections of adult brain with the use of buffer containing 0.3 M sodium chloride, but being devoid of Triton, provided extensive localization in the cytoplasm of oligodendrocytes and their processes. Avoidance of Triton in the technique improved the ultrastructural details observed by pre-embedding staining electron microscopy in unstained tissue surrounding the stained areas.

While in developing tissue myelin basic protein can be demonstrated in oligodendrocytes and myelin in sections stained in the absence of Triton, addition of Triton is necessary for visualization of components of compact myelin in adults.

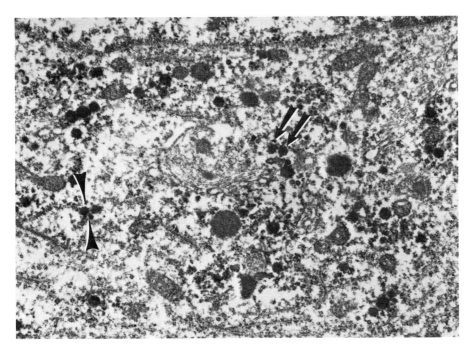

Figure 3-30. Vasopressin in the cytoplasm of a neuron from the rat paraventricular nucleus. Arrows point to neurosecretory granules. PAP complexes are seen in association with some cisternae of the rough endoplasmic reticulum (arrowhead). PAP pre-embedding procedure in the presence of Triton. ×19,200. Bar is 1.0 μm. [From Piekut (57).]

Apparently Triton, by permitting penetration of antibodies into myelin, may affect adversely the antigenic reactivity of myelin constituents. Consequently, the lower amounts of myelin basic protein in oligodendrocytes of adults were no longer detected. The avoidance of Triton has now permitted the detection of myelin basic protein in adult oligodendrocytes, but the compact myelin could not be stained in the absence of Triton.

S-100 is a calcium-binding protein found in astrocytes and other glial elements but not in oligodendrocytes. By pre-embedding electron microscopy in the absence of Triton, Rende et al. (61) were able to visualize the interaction of stained specific processes with unstained neuronal elements (Fig. 3-31). As outlined by Gröschel-Stewart (62), it is mainly through immunocytochemistry that contractile proteins, such as myosin, tropomyosin, and α-actinin, have become associated with contractile cytoplasmic elements of cells other than muscle cells. By pre-embedding staining, Drenkhahn and Gröschel-Stewart (63) found myosin along the rootlets and the microfilament networks of the terminal web of rat intestinal brush order (Fig. 3-32). In contrast, actin was concentrated along microfilament bundles of the core of the microvilli and their rootlets (Fig. 3-33). Tropomyosin had a similar distribution as myosin. On the basis of the findings, a model was proposed in which contraction might involve a simultaneous interaction of small myosin aggregates with both the terminal web filaments and the rootlet filaments. The microfilaments of the terminal web might serve as anchor-

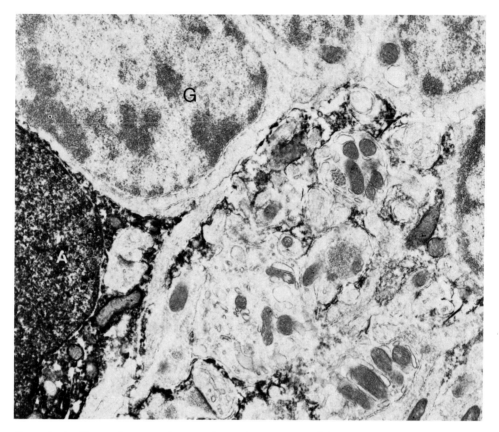

Figure 3-31. The nucleus, cytoplasm, and extensive processes of this rat cerebellar astrocyte (A) are stained for protein S-100. Stained astrocytic processes surround unstained synapses. G, granule cell. Pre-embedding PAP technique in the absence of Triton. ×20,000. [From Rende et al. (61).]

ing system for the myosin units, preventing them from sliding up the rootlet filaments. As a consequence, actin-myosin interaction within the terminal web will result in shortening of the microvillar processes.

The transformation of the chick embryo fibroblasts by avian sarcoma virus is associated by major changes in cell shape and adhesion. These changes suggest that at least one site of action of the transforming gene product, a phosphoprotein with a 65,000-dalton subunit molecular weight, may be on the cell membrane. On pre-embedding staining of saponin-permeabilized cells, the protein was localized by Willingham et al. (64) on the inner surface of the plasma membrane (Fig. 3-34) by the unlabeled antibody antiferritin-ferritin four-layer sequence (page 186). The finding illustrates that the isolated, permeabilized cell is well penetrated by antiserum and ferritin, at least when these reagents are not chemically conjugated.

We have tried to summarize here some of the most informative results that have come from pre-embedding staining technology. However, many problems remain. Tissue preservation is variable. With careful technique, ultrastructure of unstained components may be excellent. Unfortunately, the structure in stained

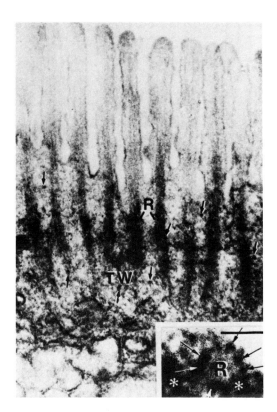

Figure 3-32. On pre-embedding staining for myosin in the presence of Triton, PAP complexes (small arrow) are located at the rootlets (R) and in the terminal web (TW) in the brush border region of rat small intestine. Bar is 0.5 μm. Insert shows a cross-sectioned rootlet which is surrounded by individual PAP complexes (arrows) and aggregates of PAP complexes (asterisk). Bar is 0.1 μm. [From Drenkhahn and Gröschel-Stewart (63).]

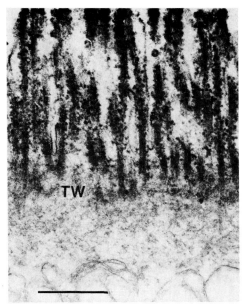

Figure 3-33. On pre-embedding staining for actin in the presence of Triton, PAP complexes are found along the core of microvilli and their rootlets. Bar is 0.5 μm. [From Drenkhahn and Gröschel-Stewart (63).]

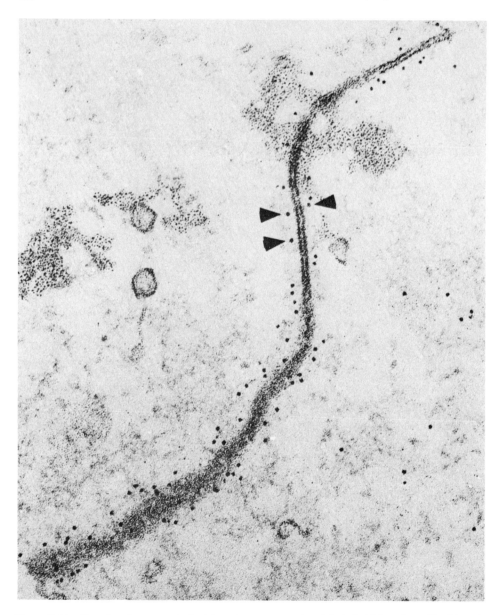

Figure 3-34. Transforming gene product in avian sarcoma virus-infected chick embryo fibroblasts is found on the inner surface of the adhering plasma membrane. Pre-embedding staining by unlabeled antibody antiferritin-ferritin four-layer technique on saponin-permeated cells. [From Willingham et al. (64).]

areas is often poor. The loss of structural detail cannot be solely attributed to masking of low-contrast structures by the electron-dense PAP complexes or any diaminobenzidine reaction products that may have creeped along surfaces within the immediate confines of their sites of formation. This problem cannot be solved by the use of nonenzymatic markers, such as ferritin or colloidal gold, since these markers have not been shown to successfully penetrate more than one cell layer, such as is found in monolayer tissue cultures, even after permeabil-ization with Triton or saponin.

For these reasons, the resolution of pre-embedding staining technique in stained areas is low when compared to that attained with purely morphologic electron microscopy. However, the resolution in unstained areas surrounding stained profiles is as good as in standard electron microscopy. For many studies, the ultrastructure of these surrounding areas is as important as that of the specifically marked areas. Ultrastructure is especially good if Triton permeabil-ization is avoided. The PAP method is sensitive enough that good specific stain-ing still can be obtained even if omission of the Triton may have limited the quantity of antibodies that reach the specifically stained areas. Use of 0.3 M sodium chloride in the dilution and wash buffers is recommended, although occasional low-affinity first antibodies do better in 0.15 M sodium chloride, and high-affinity antibodies may occasionally be used to advantage in 0.5 M sodium chloride.

The widest application of pre-embedding staining is in synaptology. Synapses cannot be identified by light microscopy, but their detection does not require the ultimate in resolution by electron microscopy. We must remain in doubt whether a neurosecretory peptide is found only in large dense core vesicles, or whether the accompanying small, lucid vesicles also contain it, albeit in lesser amounts, and whether the intense electron opacity of the synapse does not make it difficult to ascertain whether a neuropeptide is actually found in the synapse and the postsynaptic membrane. Nevertheless, the frequent groupings of synapses im-munocytochemically identified for a given peptide or neurotransmitter near morphologically well-defined terminals devoid of the antigen and, therefore, containing different transmitter principles, and the association of these synapses with morphologically well-defined postsynaptic regions, make pre-embedding staining an essential tool in discovering the wealth of impulses which even a limited, visualized region of a single neuron can obtain from a variety of profuse aborizations with different neurotransmitter contents. If we do not demand the ultimate in detail for specifically stained structures and are happy with good surrounding morphology, pre-embedding electron microscopic immunocyto-chemical staining is a rewarding technique for anyone with the patience to engage in electron microscopy.

Pre-embedding staining does not incorporate the possibility of quantification beyond that of enumerating stained nerve terminals. Comparison with controls is often difficult and must depend on different tissue specimens. Quantification by comparison with control and serial sections remains the domain of post-embedding staining. However, the restriction of postembedding staining to secretion granules, as well as to limited antigens, suggest pre-embedding staining as the technique of choice.

The most disturbing aspect of pre-embedding staining is the wide distribution of antigens within individual cell bodies. There are few, if any, exceptions in which the pre-embedding staining localization was not in the expected endoplas-mic reticulum. However, in nearly every case, localization was in other areas as well, some expected and some unexpected. These areas are nearly always the same and include vesicular membranes, nuclear membranes, mitochondrial membranes, and nearly everything structured in the cell body beyond the cristae of mitochondria. Since this pattern of localization is usually so general, irrespective of the antigen studied, one wonders to what extent it is specific. Unfortunately, fine structural elements, like microtubules, cannot be seen in specifically stained areas, even though they can be discerned in unstained surrounding tissue.

METHOD SPECIFICITY

As in conjugated antibody methods (pages 47 and 83), we can describe sources of nonspecific background as methodologic, that is, inherent in the immunocytochemical reagents, and immunologic, that is, due to unwarranted reactions of the first antibodies. Poor methodologic specificity could come from one of the following four sources:

1.   Attachment to tissue of a component of the first antiserum by nonimmunologic bonds.
2.   Direct attachment to tissue of a nonanti-IgG component of the link antiserum. Such a component may or may not be an antibody.
3.   Direct attachment to tissue of PAP.
4.   Reactivity of tissue for diaminobenzidine and hydrogen peroxide in the absence of any immunoreagents, often called "endogenous peroxidase."

We have already discussed possible problems for endogenous peroxidatic reactivity (page 113).

The principle of the PAP method avoids the first three sources of poor specificity in contrast to labeled-antibody methods where some of them contribute to background staining. The primary source of poor methodologic specificity is in the link antiserum, which contains components that react directly with tissue and conceivably also with nonantibody components of the first antiserum once they are attached to tissue. Evidence for this reaction was provided by Marucci and Dougherty (8) in their work on the immunocytochemical detection of human antibodies to herpes simplex virus (HSV) reactive with virus-infected human kidney monolayer cells. These workers have been challenged by the fact that no human PAP is available, and, therefore, they could not utilize the reaction sequence: human anti-HSV, guinea pig antihuman immunoglobulin, human PAP. Instead, they first attempted a four-layer technique in which human anti-HSV was followed by rabbit antihuman immunoglobulin, guinea pig antirabbit immunoglobulin, and rabbit PAP. With this sequence, staining occurred in infected as well as noninfected portions of the cell culture. By omission of individual components of the staining sequence, it was found that it was the second serum, rabbit antihuman immunoglobulin, that was responsible for the nonspecificity: It reacted directly with the tissue and this reaction was detected by guinea pig antirabbit immunoglobulin and rabbit PAP. Although dilution of this serum permitted some distinction of infected from noninfected areas of the culture, background staining in the noninfected areas still was formidable (Fig. 3-35).

This background staining with the four-layer technique was in contrast to their previous experience with the three-layer technique. To obviate this problem, it occurred to Marucci and Dougherty (8) to use a three-layer technique

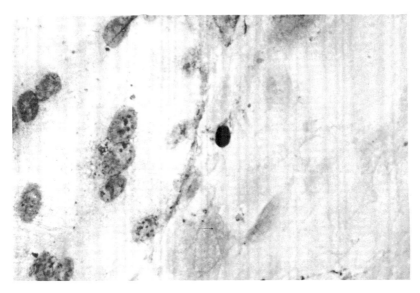

Figure 3-35. In a four-layer PAP technique for staining of kidney monolayers infected with herpes simplex virus (HSV) the sequence human anti-HSV (1 : 10), rabbit antihuman IgG (1 : 500), guinea pig antirabbit IgG (1 : 1), and rabbit PAP (1 : 5) was employed. The infected area of the cell culture is on the left. The uninfected area on the right shows background staining. [Reprinted by permission of Elsevier Science Publishing Co., Inc. from use of the unlabeled antibody histochemical technique for the detection of human antibody by A.A. Marucci and R.M. Dougherty, *Journal of Histochemistry and Cytochemistry* **23:**618, Copyright 1975 by the Histochemical Society, Inc. (8).]

with species heterologous reactions: They substituted baboon PAP for the theoretically indicated human PAP, staining by the sequence human anti-HSV, rabbit antihuman immunoglobulin, baboon PAP—and the reaction became specific (Fig. 3-36). Background disappeared, even though the same serum that was responsible for background staining when used at a 1 : 500 dilution in the four-layer technique was now used undiluted in the three-layer technique. Therefore, the rabbit antihuman immunoglobulin contained an important nonspecific factor that reacted directly with tissue even at fairly high dilution. However, this factor could not be detected in the three-layer technique, even when undiluted serum was used.

The difference in staining between the three- and four-layer techniques illustrates the basic principle of the unlabeled antibody method. The link serum in the three-layer technique reacts specifically with IgG epitopes in the first layer. Other factors, which may include antibodies to epitopes in the tissue, react nonspecifically with tissue components. The free idiotypic site of the specific anti-IgG antibody in the link serum possesses equal IgG specificity as that bound to the first antibody. Therefore, it will react with PAP (Fig. 3-1a). The free idiotypic site of an antibody attached to a nonspecific tissue epitope can only react with a similar nonspecific epitope. PAP is a purified reagent, devoid of such nonspecific components, and, therefore, the PAP cannot react with the free idiotypic site of the nonspecific antibody (Fig. 3-1b). If, by any chance, PAP, despite specific purification, contained a contaminant shared with the nonspe-

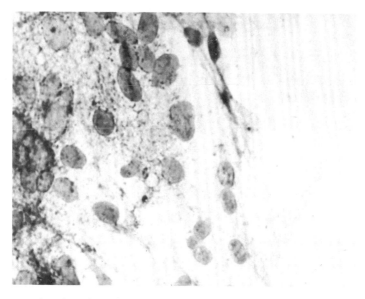

Figure 3-36. In a three-layer heterologous PAP technique for staining kidney monolayers infected with HSV, the sequence human anti-HSV (1 : 10), rabbit antihuman IgG (1 : 1), and baboon PAP (1 : 5) was employed. The infected area of the cell culture on the left is stained. The uninfected area on the right is nearly invisible. [Reprinted by permission of Elsevier Science Publishing Co., Inc. from use of the unlabeled antibody histochemical technique for the detection of human antibody by A.A. Marucci and R.M. Dougherty, *Journal of Histochemistry and Cytochemistry* **23**:618, Copyright 1975 by the Histochemical Society, Inc. (8).]

cific tissue component, the link antibody, indeed, would react with this component in PAP. However, such a contaminant would not be an antibody to peroxidase. Therefore, despite its reaction with the link antibody, the contaminant will be devoid of peroxidase and will not be detected with diaminobenzidine and hydrogen peroxide. Thus, a double amplification of specificity is built into the PAP method.

In labeled antibody methods, on the other hand, both the specific and nonspecific factors of the second antiserum are labeled (Fig. 3-1c,d). Attachment of nonspecific factors directly to tissue results, therefore, in nonspecific staining.

A second reason for methodological nonspecificity in the PAP method could conceivably be binding to tissue by nonantibody components in the first antiserum, or reaction of any antibodies with tissue by bonds other than immunologic bonds. Nonantibody components are no problem in the unlabeled antibody method because if they react with the link antiserum, the antibodies responsible for this reaction will not be able to bind PAP. First antibodies, insofar as they react nonspecifically (nonimmunologically) with the tissue will, however, be detected by the method. Antibodies do react nonspecifically with tissues that bear Fc receptors (page 272). In addition, antibodies may be absorbed nonspecifically via other poorly understood bonds. Both these reactions are minimized by pretreating sections with normal serum from the same species that donates the link antiserum. Since antiimmunoglobulin produced by immunization with immunoglobulin from a different species will not react appreciably with immunoglobulin from the immunized species, the pretreatment serum cannot be detected by the PAP method, but may mask certain nonspecific binding sites for antibodies of the first antiserum. In practice, the pretreatment may not always be necessary. The PAP method is commonly used on routinely embedded paraffin sections in light microscopy and on Araldite sections in electron microscopy. Both procedures apparently destroy Fc receptor and thus an important cause of nonspecificity. With fresh tissues or cells or with frozen tissues, nonspecificity because of Fc receptors should be borne in mind. However, nonspecific bonds, whether via Fc receptors or other mechanisms, are weaker than specific bonds. They require high concentrations of antiserum. Antisera diluted less than 1 : 1000 should be avoided in the PAP method, as high concentrations invite participation of cross-reacting antibodies (antibody specificity, page 232) or nonspecific bonding (method specificity from such factors as Fc receptors). Dilution of monoclonal antibodies less than 1 : 1000 should also be avoided, not because of background, but because of the Eng-Bigbee prozone effect (page 106) with ascites fluids containing large amounts of high-affinity antibodies.

PAP, being a complex that contains two Fc's is a better reagent for Fc receptor than monomeric immunoglobulin of the first or link antisera. In fact, PAP has been used as a reagent for Fc receptor (65). Again, the reaction does not take place in paraffin, Araldite, or Epon sections. In the studies of Mason et al. (66), even in fixed smears of human leukocytes, nonspecific uptake of the reagents of the PAP method via Fc receptor was less a problem than in immunofluorescence. Apparently, PAP and first antisera at the dilutions used did not react with these receptors. The link antiserum, goat antirabbit IgG, was used in high concentration (1 : 20 to 1 : 50). However, Alexander and Sanders (67) have shown that goat sera do not react with Fc receptors of human leukocytes. Even if antisera from other species, such as swine, are used as link antibodies, the reactivity with Fc receptors may be prevented by section pretreatment with normal serum of the respective species.

IDENTIFICATION OF BACKGROUND

As the background in the PAP method is often barely visible on paraffin sections stained for light microscopy, counterstaining is of help in establishing the relationship with surrounding tissue of a structure that has been stained brown by diaminobenzidine. Hematoxylin is a suitable counterstain for almost any tissue, while Wright-Giesma has been used for leukocyte smears, and hematoxylin, Nissl stain, and cresyl violet have been useful in nervous tissue. If black-and-white micrographs are being made, it is worthwhile preparing serial sections for staining and to counterstain only occasional sections while using the noncounterstained sections for photography.

Counterstained preparations that are photographed in black and white often fail to do justice to the immunocytochemical localization. Even in human pathology material, we prefer to omit counterstaining and use Nomarski differential interference optic instead. This is of advantage in Vibratome sections (Fig. 3-8), but becomes essential in paraffin sections stained with monoclonal antibodies. Without Nomarski optics, structures surrounding immunostained elements are so invisible that it is impossible to orient the stained structures, whether they are cell bodies, or for example, nerve projections. Nomarski optics will outline surrounding structures sufficiently to become faintly visible (pages 108 and 160).

QUANTITATIVE IMMUNOCYTOCHEMISTRY

Any immunologic reaction involves a minimum of two components: antigen and antibody. Certain secondary reactions are usually needed for physiologic effects of the antigen-antibody reaction, and other secondary reactions are generally employed to detect and measure antigen-antibody reaction. Immunocytochemistry also uses secondary reactions to detect antigen after its reaction with antibody. The secondary reactions can be quantified at low resolution in light and electron microscopy by optical density measurements (immunofluorescence, enzyme conjugated, and unlabeled antibody enzyme methods) or, at high resolution, by counting the number of deposits obtained (immunoferritin, immunogold, and unlabeled antibody enzyme methods).

Basic to immunocytochemical quantification of antigen is the bimolecular nature of the antigen-antibody reaction: To obtain a given optical density, we may increase the concentration of antigen while proportionally decreasing that of antibody, or increase the concentration of antibody while proportionally decreasing that of antigen. If we keep the concentration of antigen constant, a quantitative relationship must be obtained between the concentration of first antibody and the optical density measured. This is a minimal condition for successful quantification. To evaluate various concentrations of antibody, we need serial sections of the same tissue. Ideally, for light microscopy, all sections should be through the same cell and the concentration of antigen within its cytoplasm should be invariant. Similarly, for electron microscopy, each section should be through the same secretion granule. However, only few sections through the same cell or secretion granule can be obtained, and the concentration of antigen within these structures is not necessarily invariant. To overcome these problems, a large number of serial sections of cells or secretion granules, as the case may be, have to be analyzed statistically.

This labor intensive approach depends on the assumption that variations in number of cells or granules from section to section is random. The assumption, indeed, appears to be justified for tyrosine hydroxylase-containing cells within the core of the nucleus locus ceruleus (68–70) or for secretion granules of pituitary cells (32,71). The approach also requires that stained structures are well definable for measurement. Whole cell cytoplasm for light microscopy, or individual secretion granules for electron microscopy, are such structures. However, structures such as nerve fibers that interlace with each other and leave unstained space between them, are difficult to define individually for optical density measurement, and variation in their anatomic distribution even within few serial sections often may exceed that of the average optical density of the section. The difficulty can be obviated by plotting area variation against optical density variation (page 159).

When an epitope occurs repetitively on an antigen, such as determinants in polysaccharides, or when an antigen is small and densely structured, such as neuropeptides in secretion granules or on receptors, the density of a given epitope may exceed that of an antibody-combining site that fits onto it in antibody excess. Since the size of the cross-sectional diameter of the Fab end of antibody is about 20 nm^2, not more than one epitope under this area can be detected at saturation. Epitopic density in excess of 1 in 20 nm^2 cannot be detected with any immunocytochemical method. A further limitation is the density of first antibody that can be detected by the subsequent immunocytochemical reagents. Since PAP is larger than a single immunoglobulin molecule, not all first antibodies can be detected, even at saturation. In the enzyme-conjugated antibody method or in the immunoferritin method, the degree of steric hindrance depends on the degree of polymerization of the conjugate. In the immunogold method, the degree of hindrance does not depend as much on the size of the colloidal gold particle as on that of the shell of protein that surrounds it. In the avidin-biotin complex method, the complex is so large that saturation is already reached at low concentrations of antibody, and thus by inference, at low epitopic density (Fig. 2-11). The method is, therefore, not suitable for quantification (page 172). Since fluorescent antibodies are not significantly larger than unlabeled antibodies, the upper limit for quantitative immunocytochemistry may be higher in immunofluorescence than in the PAP method. However, other problems, such as lack of visualization of surrounding structure, make it difficult to evaluate quantitative immunofluorescence data with regard to tissue distribution of a given antigen.

Most epitopes occur only once in a given protein antigen. If the protein has a cross-sectional area equal or larger than that of an Fab end, steric hindrance of a given epitope by first antibody is not likely to occur. Globular proteins of 37,000-dalton size have about one-third of the cross-sectional area as that of Fab ends. Even under these circumstances, steric hindrance can occur if antisera are used that possess antibodies to multiple epitopes on a given protein. However, with monoclonal antibodies and large protein antigens, steric hindrance by excess first antibody becomes unlikely.

Steric hindrance can still be due to subsequently applied reagents. In the PAP method, excess first antibody could cause steric inhibition by virtue of the Eng-Bigbee effect (page 106). However, the effect is rarely seen on paraffin sections and was of no significance over a wide range of antibody dilutions in the quantitative studies on tyrosine hydroxylase by Benno et al. (69).

Quantification by Enumeration in Electron Microscopy

Under certain circumstances, the counting of deposits gives direct estimate of the number of epitopes in the tissue. When an immunocytochemical deposit on an antigen has a certain periodicity, as illustrated by the work of Furcht et al. (72), on fibernectin and procollagen on collagen fibrils, a 1 : 1 relationship of deposit to epitope sites is established. If an antigen possesses a dense or irregular distribution over a surface, immunocytochemical reaction in the PAP method gives a continuous deposit that makes enumeration impossible. However, when the antibody is diluted, discrete sites can be visualized that permit enumeration of reacting antibody molecules. Yet, antigen concentration cannot be evaluated, because under conditions of high dilution of antibody, most antigen sites remain unreactive. Continuous deposits were obtained on the red blood surface upon staining with antierythrocyte serum over a wide range of antibody concentrations. However, when the small amounts of antibody dissociated during washing in the immunocytochemical staining procedure were evaluated by reaction with a second set of red blood cells, deposits became discrete (page 200). It is important in such work to use relatively low concentrations of diaminobenzidine and hydrogen peroxide or short incubation times, in order to minimize the size of the deposits. This precaution is not necessary when immunoferritin or immunogold methods are used. With these methods, discrete deposits seem to be obtained at higher first antibody concentrations than with the PAP method, suggesting that many antigen sites remain unmarked, and imposing thereby certain restrictions to attempts at quantification.

A more practical approach to quantitative immunocytochemistry is the measurement of optical densities of reaction product. Such data permit, however, only quantification in relative terms by comparison with optical density of controls. We do not measure absolute quantity of antigen. Quantification in absolute terms would require independent measurements. For instance, Reis et al. (68) correlated change of tyrosine hydroxylase enzymatic activity in the total nucleus ceruleus after reserpine treatment with change in immunocytochemical reactivity. The purpose of quantitative immunocytochemistry is, of course, to express a given constituent in a given region. It is not impossible to extrapolate immunocytochemical measurement on selected cells of the locus ceruleus to that of all cells, calculating the total number of immunocytochemically stained cells in the region (73), and then determine the average optical density per cell. Variations of optical densities in different regions of the nucleus ceruleus from this average should help evaluating tyrosine hydroxylase in absolute terms for a given region or a given cell.

Quantification of Optical Density Measurements in Electron Microscopy

In postembedding staining, experimental and control sections are obtained from the same block. Therefore, the absorbance of stained material can be compared with that of unstained material in the same tissue and quantification is possible, at least in terms of arbitrary units. To obtain reproducible results in absorbance measurements, we found that minor variations in section thickness and in electron microscopy photometry had to be controlled. This was accomplished by expressing absorbance not in optical density units but in terms of the ratio of a stained area in a section with another area in the same section devoid of stain. For instance, if secretory granules of a cell are stained while nuclear chromatin is unstained, optical density (OD) is expressed in terms of the index

$$-\frac{OD_{secretion\ granule} - OD_{nuclear\ chromatin}}{OD_{nuclear\ chromatin}}$$

The optical density index is a dimensionless quantity, independent of section thickness and photometry within a given range. The negative sign denotes that measurements are made on the negatives obtained in electron microscopy.

When a ligand is added to a receptor, the bound ligand can often be detected immunocytochemically. Addition of varying concentrations of ligand give us an opportunity to employ quantitative immunocytochemistry under conditions in which the antigen (ligand) is the variant rather than antibody concentrations (page 403). On plotting optical densities obtained with constant amounts of first antibody and varying amounts of ligand, similar curves are obtained as those observed with constant amounts of antigen and varying amounts of antibody. These curves were sigmoidal (69–71) and reduced to straight lines upon plotting on a probability scale (Fig. 3-37).

We also used quantification to compare the sensitivity of the unlabeled antibody method when used in the *three-layer PAP sequence* (Fig. 3-4) and in the four-layer sequence where purified antibody is applied in the third reaction step and peroxidase in the fourth (Fig. 3-2) (*four-layer purified antibody sequence*). Additional comparison was made with a simplified four-layer sequence, in which antiserum to peroxidase, rather than purified antibody, is used (*four-layer antiserum sequence*) (page 183). Sensitivity was expressed as the dilution of first antiserum that gave a given degree of staining (Fig. 3-38). Plotting of optical density indices showed that the three-layer PAP sequence was four to five times more sensitive than the four-layer purified antibody sequence and 20 times more sensitive than the four-layer antiserum sequence. In fact, the antiserum sequence was generally too insensitive for postembedding staining electron microscopy. The difference in the sensitivity of the antiserum and the purified antibody four-layer sequences corresponded to the ratio of antiperoxidase to total immunoglobulin in the antiserum, indicating that the nonantiperoxidase immunoglobulin in nonpurified antiserum to peroxidase or in immunoglobulin isolated from it competes with antiperoxidase for sites on the link antibody. The higher sensitivity of the three-layer PAP sequence as compared to the four-layer

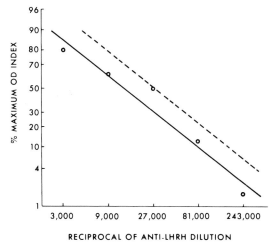

Figure 3-37. Araldite sections of pituitaries were reacted with varying amounts of luteinizing hormone-releasing hormone (LHRH) and stained immunocytochemically with anti-LHRH. Gonadotroph secretion granule-bound LHRH was evaluated by optical density measurements. Percent maximal optical density index was plotted against log dilution. [From Sternberger et al. (71).]

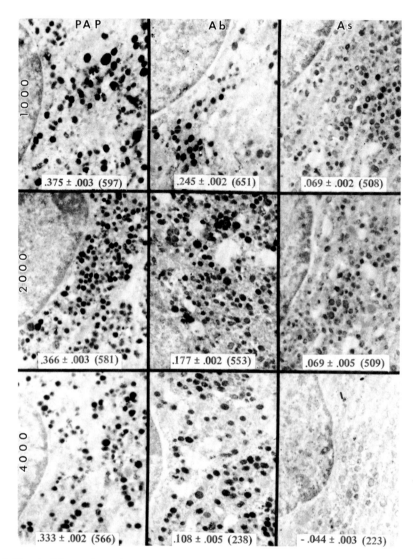

Figure 3-38. Araldite sections of rat pituitary pars intermedia stained postembedding with various dilutions of anti-17-39-ACTH as indicated on the sides of the frames and stained by three different sequences of the unlabeled antibody method as indicated on top of the frames. (PAP) Unlabeled antibody three-layer PAP sequence. (Ab) Unlabeled antibody four-layer purified antiperoxidase-peroxidase sequence. (As) Unlabeled antibody four-layer antiserum to peroxidase-peroxidase sequence. The first antiserum had been diluted in Tris saline, pH 7.2, containing 0.25% human serum albumin (reciprocal of dilution indicated on left of frames). Albumin buffer only was used instead of first antiserum for controls. Numbers underneath the frames indicate absorbance indices of the secretory granules in corticotrophs ±SEM. The number of granules examined is given in parentheses. [Reprinted by permission of Elsevier Science Publishing Co., Inc. from The unlabeled antibody enzyme method of immunocytochemistry, by J.P. Petrali, D.M. Hinton, G.C. Moriarty, L.A. Sternberger, *Journal of Histochemistry and Cytochemistry* **22**:782, Copyright 1974 by the Histochemical Society, Inc. (32).]

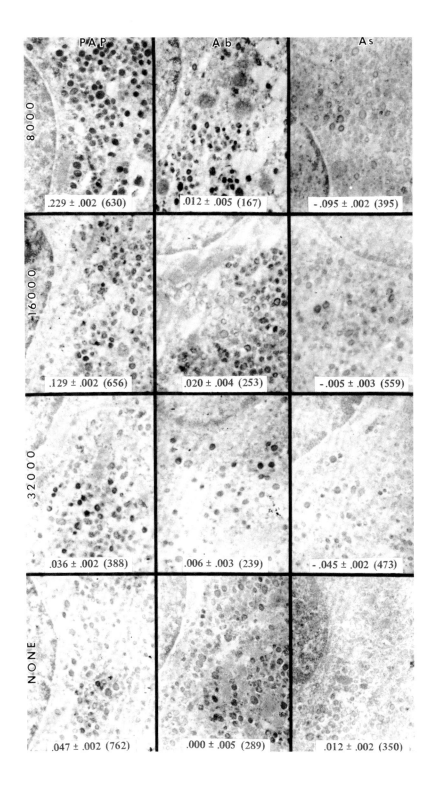

	PAP	Ab	As
8 0 0 0	.229 ± .002 (630)	.012 ± .005 (167)	-.095 ± .002 (395)
1 6 0 0 0	.129 ± .002 (656)	.020 ± .004 (253)	-.005 ± .003 (559)
3 2 0 0 0	.036 ± .002 (388)	.006 ± .003 (239)	-.045 ± .002 (473)
N O N E	.047 ± .002 (762)	.000 ± .005 (289)	.012 ± .002 (350)

151

purified antibody sequence is probably due to loss of peroxidase in the four-layer sequence. In the three-layer PAP sequence, peroxidase is apparently stabilized by the cyclicity of the PAP complex.

Quantification for Light Microscopy by Cell Counting

If it is desirable to study the proportion of cells in a given tissue that possess a given biochemical factor that can be detected immunocytochemically, it is possible to obtain quantitative data without optical density measurements. For instance, IgA in antibody-secreting cells of the ileal mucosa participates (along with lysozyme) in the secretory defense of the mucosa against bacterial invasion, and secretion of IgA varies as a function of intestinal flora. Rodning et al. (73) compared the relative contents of IgA-secreting cells in normal mucosa with those of gnodobiotically reared rats as well as of rats with a surgically induced blind ileal loop. Sections were stained with anti-IgA and the various morphologically discernible components of the ileum, which included epithelium, interstitium, and muscularis mucosa, were analyzed as to their contributions to total volume. Using micrometer stages to measure horizontal and vertical traverse of the structures and employing a large number of serial sections, the relative proportion of one component to the other could be evaluated. The procedure was then applied to each IgA-containing cell in representative serial sections, and total volume calculated by assuming spherical configurations of the cells. Whether intestinal flora was decreased by gnodobiotic environment or increased in the blind loop, the proportion of interstitium to muscularis was increased (Fig. 3-39). In the gnodobiotic animal, the proportion of IgA-containing cells was greatly decreased. However, in the blind loop, the proportion of IgA cells remained unchanged. It was felt, that perhaps immunoglobulins other than IgA are involved in the response to the increased flora in the blind loop.

The above evaluation depended on the ability to discern the unstained surrounding tissue with sufficient clarity to measure its dimensions. It also depended on the distinction of IgA-containing cells from cells devoid of IgA. Therefore, it required strong staining (Fig. 3-40). It was necessary that the staining is strong enough as to leave no ambiguously stained cells. Thus, sensitive immunocytochemistry was a prerequisite. Data obtained by this analysis revealed total participation of IgA-containing cells. They do not consider variations of IgA in individual cells. This is a logical assumption, for increases in immune response are reflected by an increasing number of clones participating, and not by an increase in the amount of immunoglobulin produced by an individual cell.

BALB/cJ mice possess greater midbrain tyrosine hydroxylase activity than CBA/J mice. Tyrosine hydroxylase is the rate-limiting enzyme in the synthesis of dopamine and noradrenalin. Baker et al. (74) found by counting of cells stained for tyrosine hydroxylase reduction of cell numbers in all dopaminergic areas in CBA/J as compared to BALB/cJ mice, in close correlation with the decrease of enzyme activity in whole midbrain. The differences in activity could not be attributed to regional differences or the differences in amounts of enzyme produced by individual cells and the finding suggested that neurons of specific transmitter class may be under genetic control.

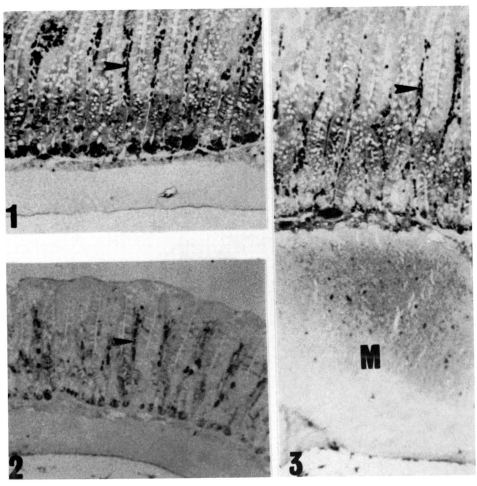

Figure 3-39. IgA in normal (1) and gnodobiotic (2) rat ileum and in a self-filling blind ileal loop (3) is found within antibody-secreting cells (arrows) of the lamina propria, within columnar epithelial cells of the crypt regions and within Paneth cells at the bases. IgG containing cells are decreased in the gnodobiotic animal, and the muscularis externa (M) is increased in the self-filling blind loop. PAP method. ×64. [From Rodning et al. (73).]

Quantification for Light Microscopy by Optical Density Measurements

Nancy Sternberger et al. (59), in their quantitative studies on the accumulation of myelin basic protein in developing oligodendrocytes (page 342), used an image analyzer that correlated light transmission (in arbitrary units) to area. The microscopic field was projected on a television screen with an optical density-sensitive (noncompensating) camera and the cell of interest outlined with a joystick. In these studies, it was found that variation in section thickness is not as important a factor as in quantification of electron microscopy sections. Therefore, data could be expressed as optical densities (signal minus background) rather than as indices.

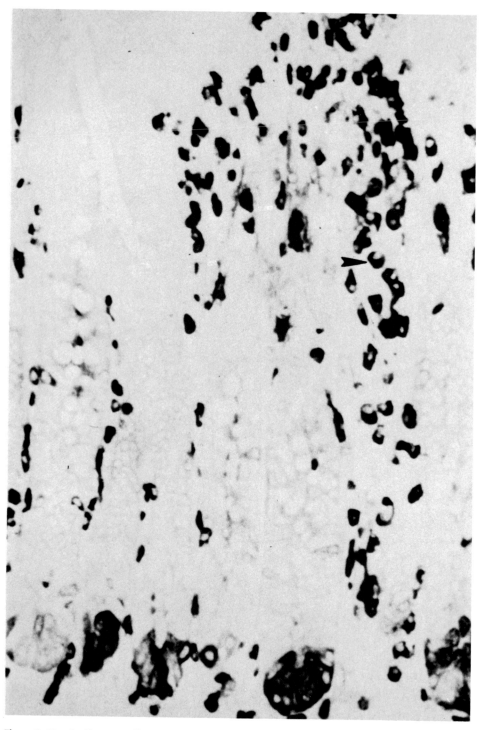

Figure 3-40. Rat ileum paraffin sections stained for IgA. PAP method. Mapping of numerical density and diameter of IgA producing cells was performed by planimetry. [From Rodning et al. (73).]

Reis et al. (68) and Benno et al. (69,70) perfected light microscopic image analysis by computerized measurement of areas of given optical densities within operator-chosen fields. In their studies on tyrosine hydroxylase in the nucleus ceruleus, the stained nucleus was outlined in serial sections by means of the joystick and its optical density determined by subtraction from that of an identically shaped adjacent unstained background area. To determine variations in individual cells, the procedure was repeated for each cell under joystick-determined instructions, recording total cell area minus nuclear area. For this work, paraffin sections were most satisfactory. Cryostat sections could vary as much as 200% in thickness. To obtain results that permitted regional evaluation of changes in tyrosine hydroxylase, constant amounts of antibody were used, as well as saturating concentrations of diaminobenzidine, but incubation times were so adjusted that the darkest element in the tissue was below maximal optical density. Variations of total density of the locus ceruleus between sections in the same animal were found insignificant when compared to variations from one animal to another. A close correlation was found between the biochemically and immunocytochemically determined total activity of the locus ceruleus. There was considerable variation of tyrosine hydroxylase in individual cells. This variation bore no relation to morphologic features of the cells. However, it did bear a strong correlation to the location of the cells within the nucleus ceruleus. Since in noradrenergic neurons the amount of tyrosine hydroxylase is directly influenced by firing rate, the results suggest that the biochemical heterogeneity of nucleus ceruleus neurons reflects differences in their functional activities. Conceivably, differences of tyrosine hydroxylase in various locations within the nucleus ceruleus may be related to heterogeneity of its wide projection field.

Whitorsch (75) found that an electrophoresis densitometer can be used to quantify immunocytochemically stained regions. The densitometer plots optical density versus linear distance over a constant bandwidth. Peak heights so obtained reflect maximal optimal density of a region, while peak widths reflect its size. Epithelial cells of the rat prostate possess intracellular binding sites for prolactin. Reaction of the ligand with the binding sites can be evaluated immunocytochemically by staining with antiprolactin after treatment of paraffin sections with prolactin. A dose dependence of densitometry signals versus ligand concentration (Fig. 3-41) as well as versus antibody concentration was found.

Rhodes et al. (76) used a microspectrophotometer to measure optical density of individual oxytocin-producing, immunocytochemically stained in the supraoptic, paraventricular and anterior commissural nuclei of rats as influenced by water deprivation and estrogen treatment. These measurements permitted construction of histograms in which percent of total cells was plotted versus optical density (Fig. 3-42). The only established physiologic action of oxytocin involves the milk letdown reflex. Its role in parturition is debatable. Oxytocin release occurs after estrogen treatment, injection of hypertonic saline, or during copulation at least in the males of some species. By quantitative immunocytochemistry, Rhodes et al. (76) found that estrogen treatment of ovariectomized rats reduced oxytocin only in the anterior commissural but not in the paraventricular or supraoptic nuclei. Water deprivation in males or females had effects similarly restricted to the anterior commissural nuclei. In females, but not in males, there was a decrease in the paraventricular nucleus as well.

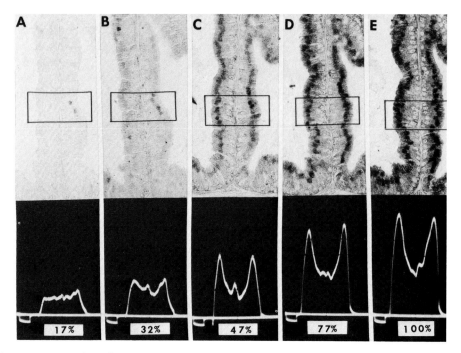

Figure 3-41.   Serial paraffin sections of rat ventral prostate were treated with buffer (A) or rat prolactin [25 ng/ml in (B), 100 ng/ml in (C), and 250 mg/ml in (D), 500 ng/ml in (E)] prior to antiprolactin and the PAP method. The enclosure represents the area scanned by an electrophoresis densitometer and plotted on the bottom of the figures. Relative absorbencies of each section are expressed as percentage under each scan. [From Witorsch (75).]

Comparison of staining intensity as a function of first antibody dilution is an effective way of obtaining insight into relative concentrations of tissue antigen. When antirenin was used at a dilution of 1 : 1000, Taugner et al. (77) observed strong localization not only in the epithelial cells of the renal afferent arteriole, the expected localization, but also in some cells of the proximal connecting or cortical collecting tubules (Fig. 3-43). Renin is the precursor of angiotensin II, which is enzymatically converted to the hypertension-producing octapeptide angiotensin I. By stepwise dilution of antiserum to 1 : 10,000, staining of the proximal tubules disappeared first, followed by disappearance of that of the connecting and cortical collecting tubules (Fig. 3-44). The staining in the afferent arteriole disappeared only at a dilution of 1 : 1,000,000. These findings suggested that tubular localization of renin is not due to primary synthesis at this unexpected site, but rather to uptake of renin secreted into the glomerular space. The suggestion was confirmed by the autoradiographic localization of intra-arterially injected ^{125}I renin in the apical region of proximal tubular cells. In this work, an important relationship was established by the mere expedience of using antibodies over a wide range of dilutions even without quantitative evaluation of optical densities in the micrographs obtained.

In all the studies discussed so far, in which optical density measurements by image analysis were used, care was taken to examine a number of serial sections

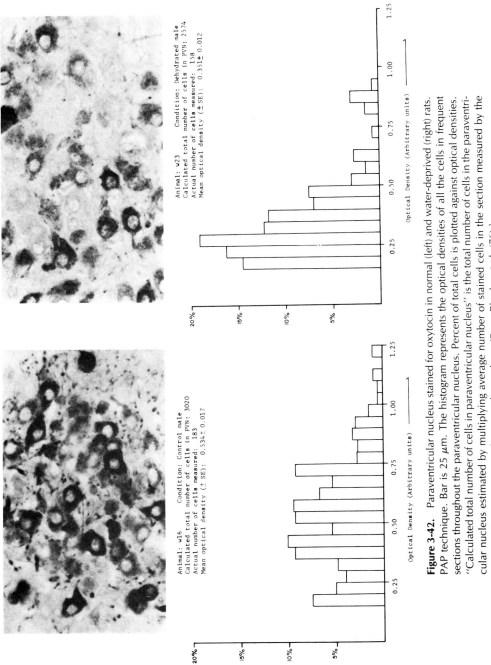

Animal: w16   Condition: Control male
Calculated total number of cells in PVN: 3020
Actual number of cells measured: 183
Mean optical density (± SE): 0.534± 0.017

Animal: w23   Condition: Dehydrated male
Calculated total number of cells in PVN: 2574
Actual number of cells measured: 158
Mean optical density (± SE): 0.351± 0.012

Figure 3-42. Paraventricular nucleus stained for oxytocin in normal (left) and water-deprived (right) rats. PAP technique. Bar is 25 μm. The histogram represents the optical densities of all the cells in frequent sections throughout the paraventricular nucleus. Percent of total cells is plotted against optical densities. "Calculated total number of cells in paraventricular nucleus" is the total number of cells in the paraventricular nucleus estimated by multiplying average number of stained cells in the section measured by the number of sections required to span the nucleus. [From Rhodes et al. (76).]

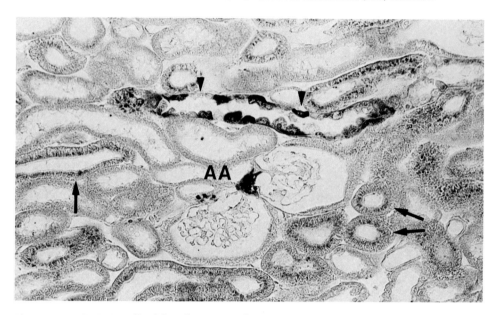

Figure 3-43. Renin in cells of the afferent arteriole (AA), proximal tubule (arrow), and connecting or cortical collecting tubules (arrowheads) of the mouse. Seven-μm paraffin section. Dilution of antiserum 1 : 1000. PAP method. ×295 [From Taugner et al. (77).]

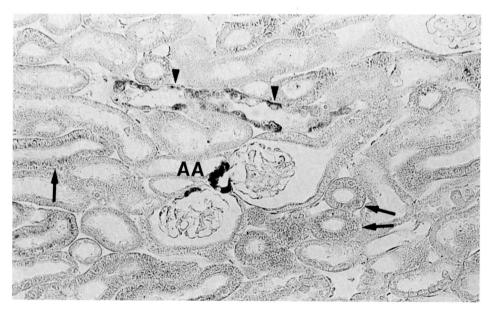

Figure 3-44. Section in series to that of Fig. 3-44. Antirenin serum, 1 : 10,000. The connecting or cortical collecting tubules are only weakly stained (arrowheads). The proximal tubules are unstained. (AA) Afferent arteriole. PAP method ×295 [From Taugner et al. (77).]

and to make sure that variations in total optical density from one serial section to the other was minimal. This is possible in relatively large structures containing abundant antigen in specifically stained cells, such as the pituitary or the nucleus locus ceruleus. In the case of the latter, special care was exercised to exclude proximal axons and dendrites from the measurement of optical density of neural cell bodies, partly because of difficulties of accurately outlining these projections with a joystick. Antigens that are only found in long axon projections and in terminal axons and are absent from cell bodies, dendrites, and proximal axons, such as neurofilament-specific phosphate epitopes (page 448), cannot be measured by outlining with a joystick. In any tissue section, only bundles of narrow neurofilaments are stained, while the bulk of intervening tissue is unstained. No big masses of concentrations of stained fibers exist that would be comparable to the accumulation of stain in perikarya of the locus ceruleus. Therefore, the total optical density of an area is determined more by the intervening unstained background than by the stain contributed by the fibers themselves, and because of variation in fibers, adjacent sections are not necessarily comparable. To quantify staining of these structures, we are required, therefore, to obtain both data on optical density and on total areas stained in the same section.

Immunocytochemical structures in a single section, whether they are cells or fibers, are never stained uniformly. Staining intensity differs from cell to cell, or from fiber to fiber. Therefore, if we were to measure area (Y-axis) as a function of optical density (X-axis), there will be a gradual decrease in area recorded when optical density is increased. If the variation of stain from fiber to fiber is little, we can expect that the curve will be rather steep. If the variation is high, we can expect it to be flat. In either case, if the variation is Gaussian, we can expect a straight line on logarithmic plotting. If the average optical density of the area is high, the line will reach the X-axis (logarithmic plot) or approach it (numerical plot) only at high optical density readings. If we were to measure area as a function of optical density in an unstained section, we expect the recorded area to decrease rapidly as the optical density is increased. There is no variation in staining (the total section is unstained) and, therefore, the curve will be steep and will cross the X-axis at low optical density in a logarithmic plot.

These considerations form the basis for optical density image analysis of neurofibrils. The section is considered to be part of two major components: a randomly distributed network of stained fibers, plus a large area of unstained material intervening between the fibers and surrounding them. If we plot stained area against optical density, we expect a biphasic curve: A steep curve that reflects background is expected to be the dominant feature at low optical density, and a flat curve that reflects stained area, the dominant part at high optical density. The entire curve reflects both, total area stained as well as optical density, and, therefore, the two independent variables, optical density of stained structures as well as change in size of the structures from section to section can be controlled.

In practice, we outline on the television screen a rectangle, considerably smaller than the total light microscopic field so as to include only the core of the microscope light beam, and instruct the analyzer to confine area measurements within this rectangle (7). We place the structure to be studied (Fig. 3-45) within

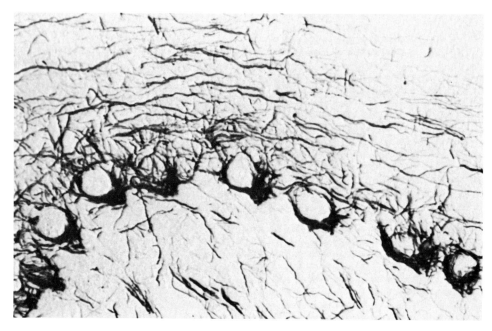

Figure 3-45. Basket cell fibers, stained with monoclonal antiphosphorylated neurofilament epitope antibody 06-17, diluted 1 : 8,000. ClonoPAP method. Nomarski optics ×320. For quantification in the following figures, regular transmission optics is used and a field from the center of a micrograph is chosen. (From the work of Sternberger and Sternberger.)

this rectangle on the television screen (Fig. 3-46) and attempt to confine ourselves to the same structure in adjacent serial sections. Differential interference optics is avoided.

There are four constants to which we can compare the measurements to be undertaken. These are:

A.   Total area in the rectangle. There will be no optical density at which the measured area is larger than this limit.

B.   Zero area in the rectangle. There will be no optical density at which the area is negative.

C.   100% transmission. This quantity is obtained by increasing the potentiometer reading of the image analyzer until the area readout reaches a maximum, when the microscope light beam passes through an area of the microscope slide devoid of tissue section. Area can be measured to five significant figures and potentiometer readings to three significant figures (Fig. 3-47).

D.   0% transmission. This quantity is obtained by turning the microscope objective lens away from the light path and decreasing the potentiometer setting until the area reading is the same as that in Figure 3-47 and does not increase any further.

Operations C and D are repeated prior to reading of each microscope slide in order to eliminate variations in microscope light intensity too subtle to be recorded on the microscope potentiometer.

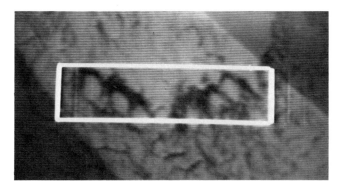

Figure 3-46. A microscope field from the center of an image such as in Figs. 3-45 or 3-54 is projected on the television screen of the image analyzer with a Chalnicon camera and the selected field placed within the rectangle outlined on the screen using the horizontal, vertical, and rotational traverses of the microscope stage. Color intensity of the tungsten microscope lamp is ketp at 9 V. Intensity for transmission on the television screen is reduced to visibility of structure by the use of neutral density filters. Area measurement as a function of instrument current is confined to that outlined by the rectangle and is kept constant throughout the experiment. Photogrph of the image analyzed on the television screen. (The oblique streaking in the photograph is due to the cathode ray sweep of the television and short photographic exposure. It is not visible to the naked eye and does not affect image analyzer measurements.) (From the work of Sternberger and Sternberger.)

Measurements of stained areas are done by stepwise increasing the potentiometer setting of the image analyzer and recording the area obliterated. The higher the optical density, the earlier the start of obliteration. The image obtained on the screen when about one-half of the stained area is obliterated is represented in Figure 3-48. The curve in Figure 3-49 is, therefore, constructed from the right to the left.

Figure 3-47. The image analyzer is standardized to 100% transmission with light through the glass slide off the section by increasing the current until the whole area is filled on the television screen, as indicated by a maximum numerical readout on the image analyzer. The analyzer is standardized to 0% transmission with the microscope objective out of the light path by decreasing the current until the whole area is filled on the television screen, as indicated again by a maximum numerical readout on the image analyzer. Photograph of the television screen. (From the work of Sternberger and Sternberger.)

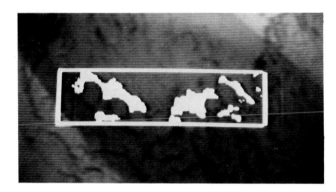

Figure 3-48.   This is the picture on the television screen when about one-half of the stained area is seemingly obliterated. Rat cerebellar cortex, basket cell fibers, 7-μm paraffin section stained with monoclonal antibody to phosphorylated neurofilament epitopes, 07-5, diluted 1 : 512,000. PAP method. In the particular setting illustrated, the area obliterated was that possessing optical densities greater than 0.3 and was 1225 arbitrary units compared to that of the total rectangle of 48,800 units. On the television screen, the area appears larger than that recorded, because the lower sensitivity of the fluorescent screen compared to that of the image analyzer does not reveal dark spaces within the white areas. (From the work of Sternberger and Sternberger.)

The optical density at any potentiometer setting (X) is:

$$\log \frac{\text{(reading at 100\% transmission} - \text{reading at 0\% transmission)}}{X - \text{(reading at 0\% transmission)}}$$

(the reading of the image analyzer potentiometer is proportional to light transmitted in arbitrary units).

When the image of a structure is strong, a curve is obtained which on a log area against optical density plot can be broken down into two linear curves (Fig. 3-49). The right arm of the curve represents variation of area of stained structure with optical density. The left arm represents variation of area of unstained background with optical density. The steeper the angle between the right arm and the left arm, the stronger is the staining intensity. With decreasing staining intensity, the angle eventually disappears. When an unstained control area adjacent to that of a stained area is positioned into the rectangle on the TV screen, only that part of the curve that represents background is obtained. It is a steep curve forming a single straight line.

The ordinates of these curves represent areas at given optical densities. The abscissae represent optical densities at given areas. When the rectangle on the TV screen is moved partially out of the field of analysis of stained fibers, so that the proportion of stained fibers in the area is decreased and the proportion of unstained background increased, the right limb of the biphasic curve is shortened and the left limb is lengthened, but the curve remains parallel to the previous curve. The slope of the lines is unaltered. The slope of the right arm of the curve is, therefore, an index of the staining intensity and is proportional to the average optical density of the stained structures, irrespective, within limits, of the total areas of these structures and the amount of unstained tissue intervening. The analysis is, therefore, suitable for staining intensity measurements of

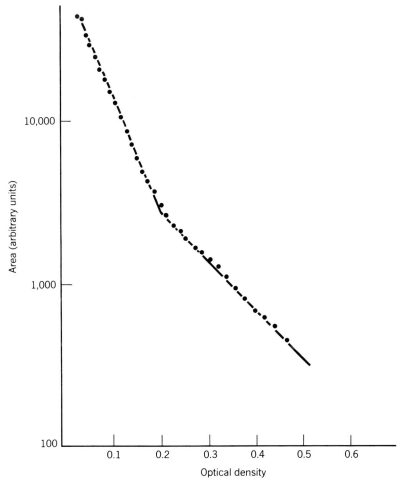

Figure 3-49. Area of stained structure as a function of optical density. Rat cerebellum paraffin section. Basket cell fibers. Section treated with monoclonal antibody to phosphorylated neurofilament epitopes, 07-5, diluted 1 : 32,000, goat antimouse IgG and PAP made from monoclonal antiperoxidase (ClonoPAP). (From the work of Sternberger and Sternberger.)

irregular structures such as neurofibrils, which cannot be outlined by a joystick at suitable resolution and which are too variable and too small to be represented in equal amounts in serial sections.

The difference between the slope of the right arm of the stained section curve from that of the control background curve is an index of the average optical density of the stained structure. Its dimensions are optical density per unit area and could be called "specific optical density." The ratio of both slopes represents the sensitivity of the immunocytochemical method. It is a dimensionless quantity.

This analysis is fairly rapid and does not require a manual outline of each structure to be fed into the image analyzer. We have used it in a comparison of the sensitivity of the unlabeled antibody PAP method with the avidin-biotin complex method.

SENSITIVITY

The sensitivity of an immunocytochemical method is the minimal amount of antigen that can be detected. Varying concentrations of antigen can be stained after spotting on nitrocellulose paper, which strongly absorbs the antigen. Sensitivity can also be determined in electrophoresis electroblots (pages 20 and 241). In tissue sections, however, sensitivity cannot be determined directly, because the concentration of antigen within a given structure of a section is unknown, whether in absolute terms or relative to the concentration in a similar structure in an adjacent section. However, the bimolecular nature of antigen-antibody reaction requires that, in immunocytochemical reactions, reactivity should decrease either with concentration of antigen or of first antibody. Therefore, if serial sections are examined in which the concentration of antigen can be presumed to be relatively constant, sensitivity can be determined by the minimal concentration of first antibody which yields a given degree of staining, that is, a given strength of specific *signal*. The strength of the signal is measured by deducting the optical density of the background (*noise*) from that of the signal.

Noise-corrected signal strength is, however, no measurement of sensitivity. A signal of 1.2 optical density units against a background of 0.4 optical density units is not a more sensitive estimate of immunocytochemical reactivity than a signal of 0.6 optical density units against a background of 0.2 optical density units. Detectability, and thus sensitivity, depends on the ratio of the signal to the noise. Thus, while the corrected signal optical density provides a relative measurement of antibody, and thus of antigen concentrations, at least in light microscopy (pages 153 and 155), the sensitivity for determining these figures is measured by signal-to-noise ratio.

Even without elaborate quantitative analysis, experience has now provided relative impressions of the sensitivity of various immunocytochemical methods. In general, these estimates depend upon whether a given antigen can or cannot be detected under given conditions of fixation by one method and not by another; or alternatively, whether one method permits the use of lower antibody concentrations for satisfactory staining than another.

Comparison of PAP with Nonimmunocytochemical Methods

Several comparisons exist between PAP and tinctorial staining. Thus, in a study of pituitary adenomas, Halmi et al. (10,12) found that more than half of the pituitary tumors that were negative on tinctorial staining with Brooke-orange-G-Carmoisin were positive for prolactin with the PAP method. Even with the four-layer sequential antiserum method, McNeill et al. (78) were able to detect extra-hypothalamic pathways containing vasopressin, while tinctorial staining with aldehyde fuchsin was only positive in neurophysin-rich areas such as magnocellular neurons, median eminence, and posterior pituitary (page 379). It is now generally recognized that PAP staining is more sensitive than tinctorial staining in differentiation of pancreatic islet cells.

The specificity of enzyme histochemistry depends on the selectivity of enzyme for the substrate analog used for staining. However, the specificity of enzymes is less than that of antibodies, as illustrated, for example, by the large number of different enzymes that hydrolyze phosphate esters. Specificity is further impaired by the need of substrate analogs for histochemical determination. Histochemical determination of carbonic anhydrase depends on base formation in the vicinity of enzyme-liberated carbon dioxide. Histochemical specificity of this reaction is usually determined by the effect of the inhibition of acetonitrile. However, Anderson et al. (79) found that enzyme histochemistry failed to visualize mucin granules on the surface mucosal cells of the glandular stomach, while PAP staining did, and this was confirmed by radioautographic uptake of ^{3}H-acetazolamide, an active site-directed method. In contrast, the enzymatic method stained many regions including articular cartilage that remained unstained with PAP. However, no carbonic anhydrase could be detected in cartilage by histochemical methods. Conceivably, other enzymes than carbonic anhydrase reacted with the substances used for enzyme histochemistry. Enzyme histochemical specificity could not be reliably deduced by blocking with acetolamide, as it seemed to interfere with both nonspecific and specific reaction product-capturing sites.

In light and electron microscopic studies, Lietz et al. (80) found alkaline phosphatase in duodenal enterocytes by enzyme histochemistry as well as with PAP. However, in goblet cells, the enzyme could only be demonstrated with PAP. By enzyme cytochemistry, alkaline phosphatase was seen on the brush border and to some extent in Golgi-associated vesicles of enterocytes. With PAP, additional phosphatase antigenic reactivity was seen in Golgi-associated endoplasmic reticulum. Within the Golgi apparatus, immunocytochemistry detected phosphatase antigenic reactivity in the secretion product and in the apical ergastroplasmic membranes. Vacca et al. (81) found detection of injected horseradish peroxidase more sensitive with PAP in paraffin sections than by peroxidatic activity in frozen sections.

One of the most important aspects of surgical tumor diagnosis is evaluation of the degree of malignancy of lesions, especially with regard to prognostication of the latency of its invasiveness. Transitional cell carcinomas of the urinary bladder lose expression of the blood group antigens A, B, and H (H antigen is characteristic of patients with blood group O). The original test for demonstrating these antigens in tissue sections depended on the adherence of blood group-specific red blood cells after treatment of the section with blood group-specific antibodies. However, Coon and Weinstein (82) found that in 34% of patients with blood group O (about one-half the patient population in North America), the cell adherence for H antigen was negative. For these reasons, they compared red cell adherence with immunocytochemistry and found (83) that among nine patients of blood group O whose tumor biopsies were negative by red cell adherence test, but positive by the PAP method, seven were free of invasion 1 to 8 years after biopsy, while two had noninvasive recurrences (Fig. 3-50). The detection of antigens A and B in this work was done by the sequence human first antibody, goat antihuman IgG, chimpanzee PAP. Detection of antigen H was found more sensitive by the use of a specific lectin rather than anti-H antibody. The novel staining sequence was Ulex europeus lectin, rabbit anti-Ulex lectin, goat antirabbit IgG, rabbit PAP.

Besides detecting blood group antigen-containing tumors and thus permitting diagnosis of low malignancy, the immunocytochemical technique also had

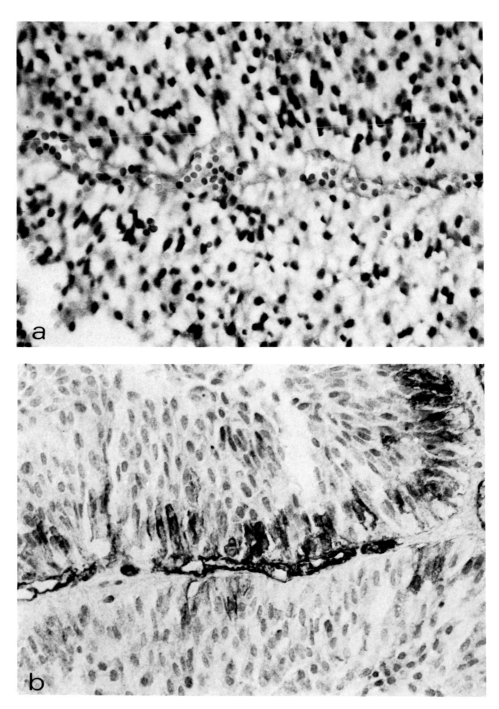

Figure 3-50. Transitional cell carcinoma of low degree of malignancy of the urinary bladder from a patient of blood group O, analyzed for the presence of antigen H. Paraffin section ×500. (a) The red cell adherence test reveals the indicator cells over the vascular endothelium, but the tumor cells are devoid of erythrocytes. Hemotoxylin and eosin. (b) A modified PAP technique revealed H antigen in the cell membranes of tumor cells near the vascular stalk. Nuclear fast red counterstain. [From Coon and Weinstein (83).]

better resolution than the red cell adherence test. Resolution is important, especially in small biopsy specimens, to distinguish tumor from surrounding normal tissue (Fig. 3-50). Also, hemorrhagic areas may mislead the interpretation of the red cell adherence test.

Comparison of PAP with Immunofluorescence

Comparison of sensitivities between both methods include detectability of given antigens, evaluation of background, and comparison of dilution of first antibody that gives satisfactory staining. Burns (11) localized hepatitis B antigen in formalin-fixed, paraffin-embedded tissue and found that the sensitivity of immunofluorescence did not compare with that of PAP. Böcker (84) compared the localization of alkaline phosphatase in various tissues and found, particularly in duodenal enterocytes and goblet cells, strong localization of PAP as compared to barely detectable immunofluorescence (80). Wachsmuth (85) employed quantitative immunocytochemistry with a microspectrophotometer (page 155) to show that PAP staining revealed 3–10 times less aminopeptidase in bile canaliculi of frozen liver sections than immunofluorescence.

Hancock (86) found Leu-enkephalin, substance P, and somatostatin-immunoreactive fibers in the spinal cord, not previously revealed by immunofluorescence. Takeuchi et al. (87) found an extensive serotonergic system in the cerebellum with PAP staining, while previous immunofluorescent studies hardly detected these systems because of low concentrations of serotonin in this area.

Woodhams et al. (88) described a gradient sedimentation procedure for obtaining a preparation enriched in Purkinje cells. The procedure was monitored by immunocytochemistry with an antiserum reacting with Purkinje cells, deep cerebellar nuclei, and large neurons of the brainstem. PAP staining was found to be more sensitive and to give less background than immunofluorescence.

Immunofluorescence of paraffin-embedded material is usually unsuccessful because of high background. Using microspectrophotometry for the evaluation of hepatitis B surface antigen in liver biopsy specimens, Radaszkiewicz et al. (89) found that background fluorescence is reduced to about 50% upon protease treatment of the sections (page 109). With the PAP method, background was negligible even without protease treatment. Signal intensity for this antigen was increased by digestion in both methods. Mason et al. (66) found that in the detection of surface immunoglobulins on human leukocytes on smears, PAP methodology gave less background than immunofluorescence.

Toxoplasma gondii infection of the central nervous system expresses itself in protean neurologic symptoms in immuno-compromised patients that often require brain biopsy for diagnosis. While the parasite cysts are easily recognized morphologically, only the proliferative forms, which are difficult to recognize, are generally found in infected brain tissue. Immunocytochemistry is needed for a proper diagnosis and the PAP technique was preferred by Conley et al. (90) because of lack of specificity and uninterpretable background with immunofluorescence.

The first staining performed with the PAP method was on spirochetes (T. pallidum) with rabbit antisyphilitic sera (4). These organisms are invisible in light

Table 3-1.   Optimal Concentrations of First Antibody

Antigen	Antibody Dilution for Immunofluorescence	Antibody Dilution for PAP	Reference
Calcitonin	1 : 80	1 : 320	Alumets et al. (91)
Vasoactive intestinal peptide	1 : 80	1 : 5600	Alm et al. (92)
Porcine vasoinhibitory peptide	1 : 80	1 : 5120	Ahrén et al. (93)
ACTH	1 : 80	1 : 640	Alumets et al. (94)
Beta-endorphin	1 : 20	1 : 240	Alumets et al. (94)
Leu-enkephalin	1 : 60	1 : 240	Alumets et al. (94)
Gastrin	1 : 640	1 : 25,000	Alumets et al. (94)
Glucogen	1 : 80	1 : 2560	Alumets et al. (94)
Neurotensin	1 : 40	1 : 640	Alumets et al. (94)
Secretin	1 : 80	1 : 2560	Alumets et al. (94)
Somatostatin	1 : 80	1 : 1280	Alumets et al. (94)

microscopy. With the PAP method, they became visualized with varying antisera in dilutions from 1 : 100,000 to 1 : 1,000,000. These titers were 100 to 1000 times higher than those obtained by indirect immunofluorescence (page 42). On the other hand, the titers of preimmune sera were usually 1 : 10, whether PAP or immunofluorescence was used. There would have been little advantage with the PAP method if the preimmunization titer relative to immunofluorescence would have increased proportionally with the postimmunization titer. This would only have indicated a greater detectability of the enzyme reaction signal as compared to fluorescence. However, the fact that the preimmunization titers remained unchanged in both methods indicates that the increase in titer in the PAP method is a reflection of a better signal-to-noise ratio rather than amplification of visualization itself: The specificity is increased because of lower background. Quite generally, optimal concentrations of first antibody in the PAP method are lower than those needed in immunofluorescence, as indicated by Table 3-1.

Comparison of PAP with Peroxidase-Conjugated Antibody Method

Baker et al. (95) found a much higher sensitivity for PAP when studying the pathways of luteinizing hormone-releasing hormone in the median eminence of the rat hypothalamus. Taylor (96) was able to diagnose a greater number of reticulosarcomas and was able to clearly establish the presence of immunoglobulin in Reed-Sternberg and mononuclear "Hodgkin" cells, a finding that had been unequivocal with peroxidase-labeled antibodies. Burns (15) has shown that the PAP method was 20 times more sensitive and that, in addition, background was greatly reduced. Sutmuller and Cowan (97) stained monolayer kidney cells infected with foot and mouth disease virus and found that the background obtained with several peroxidase-labeled antibody methods became greatly reduced when PAP was used. Pich et al. (98) obtained better results with PAP than with labeled antibodies in the detection of caseine in a large number of paraffin-embedded human tissues. Mason and Taylor (99) studied the distribution of lysozyme in various normal and pathologic human tissues and found striking positivity in the active histiocytic cells in granulomatous conditions. With the peroxidase-labeled antibody technique, several cases were equivocal, but could be decided upon when PAP was employed. Background staining was minimal with PAP, especially because the high sensitivity permitted use of first antisera at higher dilutions. King (100) investigated the postulate that the unidirectional transfer of iron from mother to fetus is mediated via binding of a maternal transferrin-iron complex to the surface of the placenta and subsequent release of iron to the fetus and return of transferrin to the maternal circulation. Upon staining of small pieces of formaldehyde-fixed tissue prior to embedding for electron microscopy, transferrin was, indeed, found on the surface of human syncytial trophoplasts lining the maternal blood spaces. When PAP was used, there was essentially no nonspecific background in contrast to noticeable and variable levels of background with peroxidase-labeled antibodies. Van Leeuwen (101) was unable to differentiate between vasopressin and oxytocin on thin sections of hypothalamus and pituitary when peroxidase-labeled antibodies were used. Intense background masked specific structure. Upon dilution of first antiserum, both background and specific staining, if any, disappeared. However, when PAP was used, dilutions of first antiserum could be employed at which background had disappeared, but specific staining remained intense (see also page 232).

Estrogen stimulation in immature chicks results in growth of the oviduct and differentiation of ciliated and goblet cells in the surface epithelium and of gland cells in the mucosa. Progesterone induces, in such estrogen-primed chicks, the production of avidin, an egg white protein that binds the vitamin, biotin. Using peroxidase-conjugated antibody method, as well as PAP method, for pre-embedding staining electron microscopy, Rantala et al. (102) confirmed the light microscopic finding of avidin in goblet cells (Fig. 3-51). The PAP method, because of higher sensitivity, was also able to detect avidin in some ciliated epithelial cells (Fig. 3-52). In addition, PAP method detected avidin in most apical portions of chicks treated with estrogen only.

Lehy and Cristina (103), in a study on the development of endocrine cells in human fetal large intestine, used antiglucogan at a dilution of 1 : 40 and antisomatostatin at a dilution of 1 : 20 in the peroxidase-conjugated antibody method, but could dilute these sera to 1 : 4000 and 1 : 1000, respectively, for the PAP method, thus bringing them into a reliable range of dilutions. With 30 minutes incubation times, Taylor (96) uses for lymphoma diagnosis with the PAP method, antisera at dilutions of 1 : 200 to 1 : 2000 while dilutions of 1 : 10 to 1 : 100 seemed to be necessary for use with peroxidase-conjugated antibodies.

We have seen (page 165) that blood group antigens are of help in grading transitional cell carcinoma of the bladder, their presence indicating low invasiveness. Conversely, carcinoembryonic antigen is often an indicator of malignancy. In the case of transitional cell carcinoma, Goldenberg and Warren (104) found carcinoembryonic antigen in only 4 out of 35 tumors despite their invasiveness,

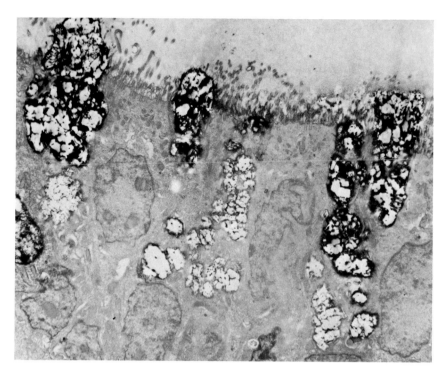

Figure 3-51. Avidin in the apical portion of goblet cells in the estrogen-primed, progesterone-treated chick oviduct. Ciliated epithelial cells are unstained. Peroxidase-conjugated antibody method. ×3,600. [From Rantala et al. (102).]

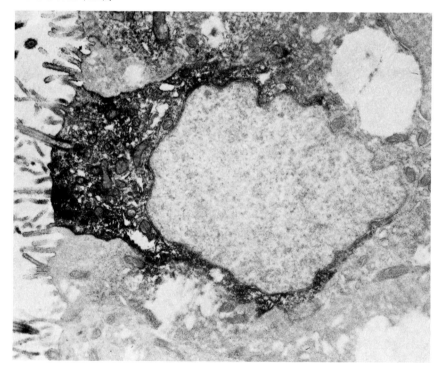

Figure 3-52. Avidin-producing ciliated epithelial cell in the estrogen-primed, progesterone-treated chick oviduct. PAP method. ×11,600. [From Rantala et al. (102).]

when peroxidase-conjugated antibodies were used. In cytologic urine preparations, there was a negative correlation of carcinoembryonic antigen immunofluorescence with malignancy. However, when the PAP method was used in the studies of Jautzke and Altanaehr (105), distribution and amounts of carcinoembryonic antigen in the tumors revealed the expected correlation with invasiveness and, thus, provided a useful test for malignancy. In these studies, a greater percentage of tumors was positive, thus showing that lack of sensitivity of previous methods was the main cause of poor correlation.

In quantitative studies, Celio et al. (106) found the PAP method more sensitive than the peroxidase-conjugated protein A method (page 52). Sensitivity was important in their studies of adrenocorticotropin (ACTH) in the human pituitary. ACTH is, along with β-lipotropin, a product of the precursor, pro-opiomelanocortin (page 359). Beta-lipotropin is further processed to γ-lipotropin and β-endorphin. In the rat, a distinction between the pituitary ACTH cells in the intermediate and anterior lobe can be made. In the intermediate lobe, but not the anterior lobe, ACTH is further processed to α-melanocyte-stimulating hormone and 18–39 ACTH (CLIP). In the human pituitary, despite anatomic differences between typical anterior lobe cells and cells intermingling with the posterior lobe, the few cells that exhibited α-melanocyte-stimulating hormone reactivity in analogy to those of the intermediate lobe of the rat, did not fall into a discrete anatomical pattern (107). The antibody to β-endorphin also localized somatotrophs. However, this reaction was shown to be a cross-reaction, possibly due to a low degree of sequence homology (one to three amino acids) that could be eliminated by using diluted antisera. Here, the PAP method was important in demonstrating the low specificity of this unexpected cross-reaction. Peroxidase-conjugated protein A, being less sensitive, does not permit the same degree of dilution of antiserum.

Soria et al. (108) have shown that the PAP method is also more sensitive in ELISA assay (page 252) than the peroxidase-conjugated antibody method. The assay can be used for the estimation of antigen in solution by competing it with antigen absorbed on a polystyrene plate for reaction with first antibody. Fibrinopeptide A levels are a sensitive indicator for the tendency to thrombosis. In the competitive ELISA assay, PAP yielded greater optical density of reaction product than peroxidase-conjugated antibodies and the dilution curves with competing antigen were steeper, thus attesting to higher sensitivity. With PAP ELISA, a range of fibrinopeptide from 0.5 ng to 25 ng/ml was found for normal subjects.

Comparison Among Unlabeled Antibody Methods

The sensitivity of the PAP method can be increased by a second application of link serum and PAP (page 185).

Comparisons have also been made in the unlabeled antibody method between the use of PAP and the sequential application of antiperoxidase and peroxidase, using antiserum to peroxidase rather than purified antibody (four-layer antiserum sequence, page 183). The titer of first antiserum that gives a given degree of staining is a better index for comparison of sensitivities than the observation that a certain tissue stains more strongly with one method than another at a constant concentration of first antiserum. By comparing first antiserum dilutions, Baker et al. (95) were able to establish that the PAP method was in excess of 200 times more sensitive than the four-layer antiserum method, which in turn was more sensitive than the use of peroxidase-labeled antibodies. Böcker (84), who found the PAP method more sensitive than immunofluorescence, found the four-layer antiserum method only equally as sensitive. Peroxidase injected as a marker for axonal pathways in the central nervous system is usually detected enzymatically in cryostat sections. Paraffin sections give better structure, but the enzymatic activity of peroxidase is lost. In order to take advantage of paraffin sections, Vacca et al. (81) used peroxidase as antigen reactive with antibody to peroxidase. In this procedure, PAP was more sensitive than the four-layer antiserum sequence.

Comparison of PAP with Avidin-Biotin Complex (ABC) Method

Hsu et al. (109) reported a lower signal intensity for the PAP method than the ABC method.

Buchan et al. (110) compared staining intensity as well as sensitivity (background) of the PAP method with immunofluorescence, peroxidase-conjugated antibodies, and the ABC method, using a monoclonal antibody to gastric inhibitory peptide (GIP 3.65H). Immunoreactive cells were found in the rat ileum as well as duodenum and jejunum. All the four methods yielded high staining intensities. Immunofluorescence and the peroxidase-conjugated method permitted in the rat dilutions up to 1 : 500,000, while in the PAP and ABC methods dilutions of 1 : 1,000,000 could be used. However, the sensitivities of the methods as evaluated by background differed greatly. Of the four methods, the PAP method consistently gave the best results, as background was negligible (Fig. 3-53). Peroxidase-conjugated antibodies and immunofluorescence gave some background. The highest background was obtained with the ABC method. These studies also employed rabbit and guinea pig antisera to gastric inhibitory peptide. The rabbit antiserum had to be used at a concentration of 1 : 1000, but again the same background relationship was observed as with the monoclonal antibody.

We compared quantitatively (Figs. 3-45,46,48,49) staining intensities and sensitivities of the PAP method with the ABC method on serial saggital sections of rat brain (7) using monoclonal antibodies to phosphorylated epitopes of neurofilaments (page 448). With antibody 07-6, staining intensity and sensitivity revealed by PAP exceeded that of ABC throughout a wide range of dilutions (Figs. 3-54,55,56,57). The staining intensity curve of the PAP method declined steeply once antibody was diluted beyond an excess. Consequently, the PAP method can be used to compare regions of high antigen concentration with regions of low antigen concentration. In contrast, the staining intensity curve of the ABC method was flat throughout the antibody dilution range. Consequently, the method is not suitable for estimating concentrations of antigen or for comparing areas of high antigen concentration with areas of low antigen concentration.

The flatness of the ABC curve is explained by the nature of the method. Signal intensity is amplified in the ABC method by building up, prior to staining,

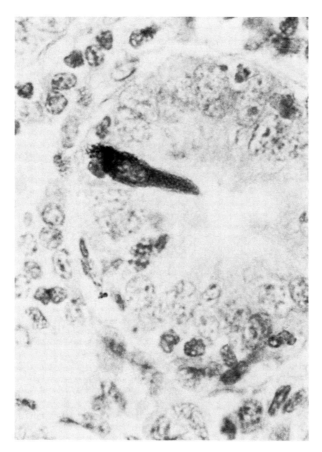

Figure 3-53.   Endoscopy specimen of human duodenum, paraffin section, stained with antigastric inhibitory peptide monoclonal antibody 3.65H, diluted 1 : 11,000. PAP method counterstained with hematoxylin. ×500. [From Buchan et al. (110).]

a large complex of avidin with biotin-labeled peroxidase. On a widely dispersed antigen (low antigen concentration) or a widely dispersed first antibody (low antibody concentration), a large deposit of peroxidase is attached to a single immunoreactive site (Fig. 2-11). With increasing concentrations of antigen or of first antibody, steric hindrance of the complex occurs and staining intensity is not significantly increased. Consequently, it is difficult to differentiate high and low concentrations of antigen. This is one reason why, in the unlabeled antibody method, we have not attempted to polymerize PAP to increase staining intensity. The second reason is background resulting from possible nonspecific localization of polymerized protein complexes.

Monoclonal antibody 04-7 also reacts with phosphorylated epitopes of neurofilaments, but it is specific for different types (neurotypes) of this heterogeneous protein. The heterogeneity is illustrated by differences of antibodies 07-5 and 04-7 in staining distribution. For instance, in the cerebellum, antibody 07-5 reacts strongly with basket cell fibers and somewhat weaker with white matter fibers (Figs. 3-54,55). In contrast, antibody 04-7 reacts weakly with basket cell

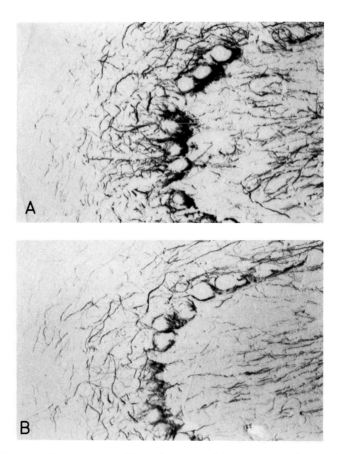

Figure 3-54. Rat cerebellum, serial paraffin sections, treated for 24 hours with monoclonal antiphos-phorylated neurofilament antibody 07-5, diluted 1 : 32,000. (a) PAP method. (b) ABC method. ×200. (From the work of Sternberger and Sternberger.)

fibers and strongly with white matter fibers (Fig. 3-58a). In addition, the total immunoreactivity of 04-7 is less than that of 07-5, which may be due to a sparse distribution of the neurofilament type with which it reacts. The reactivity can be further reduced, at least with weakly reacting antibodies such as 04-7, by incubating for 30 minutes instead of 24 hours. The ABC method was unable to clearly reveal the staining differences between basket and white matter fibers with antibody 04-7 (Fig. 3-58b). Here again, we encountered the difficulty of the ABC method to establish relative antigen densities. While both the PAP and ABC methods disclosed the weakly stained basket cell fibers, the ABC method was unable to disclose the higher epitope density in white matter fibers. Again, the inhibition seemed to be due to steric hindrance by the large, avidin-biotinylated peroxidase complex. On the other hand, in the basket cell fibers which possess only low densities of the neurofilament epitopes reactive with 04-7, the ABC method was not inhibited.

In contrast to the PAP method, the ABC method resulted in significant background in the absence of first antibody (Fig. 3-59). Thus, the ABC method

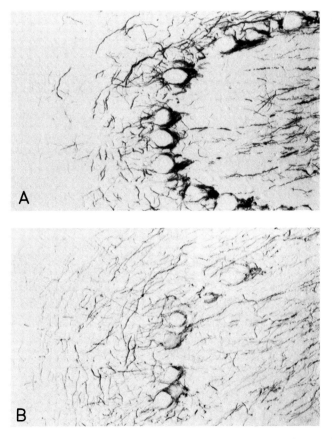

Figure 3-55. Rat cerebellum, serial paraffin sections, treated for 24 hours with monoclonal antiphosphorylated neurofilament antibody 07-5, diluted 1 : 512,000. (a) PAP method. (b) ABC method. ×200. [From the work of Sternberger and Sternberger.]

stained white matter throughout the brain, even in the absence of any antibodies. Background is probably due to polymerization of avidin with biotinylated peroxidase.

RESOLUTION

The reaction product of diaminobenzidine with hydrogen peroxide on peroxidase is insoluble. It is first deposited at or near the catalytic site of the enzyme, then creeps along the rest of the exposed surface of the peroxidase molecule, outlines the PAP complex (Fig. 3-6), covers and shelters the antibody reagents used in immunocytochemical staining, and eventually reaches adjacent surfaces until a big glob of reaction product is formed. Thus, large deposits mask ultrastructure and impair resolution. The reaction would be difficult to control were it not for inhibition of peroxidase by polymerized diaminobenzidine product. In order to obtain good resolution in staining with the PAP method, it is important

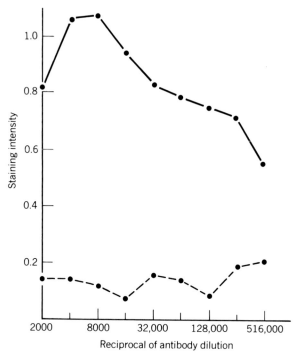

Figure 3-56. Staining intensity (signal-specific optical density minus background-specific optical density) of basket cell axons in serial cerebellar sections treated with monoclonal antibody 07-5. Solid line, PAP method. Broken line, ABC method. (From the work of Sternberger and Sternberger.)

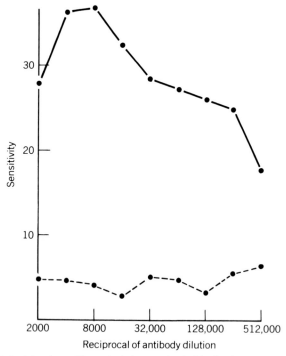

Figure 3-57. Sensitivity (signal-specific optical density divided by background-specific optical density) of basket cell axons in serial cerebellar sections treated with monoclonal antibody 07-5. Solid line, PAP method. Broken line, ABC method. (From the work of Sternberger and Sternberger.)

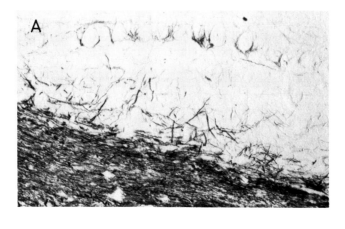

Figure 3-58.   Rat cerebellum, serial paraffin sections, treated for 30 minutes with monoclonal antiphos-phorylated neurofilament antibody 04-7, diluted 1 : 1000. (a) PAP method. (b) ABC method. ×200 (From the work of Sternberger and Sternberger.)

to limit the incubation times in diaminobenzidine and hydrogen peroxide. Satis-factory concentrations of diaminobenzidine for high-resolution immunocyto-chemistry are 0.0125% to 0.05%, and for hydrogen peroxide, 0.0025% to 0.01% with incubation times from 3 to 8 minutes.

Resolution cannot be determined if the antigen concentration is so high that immunocytochemical deposits merge, as in the peroxidase-conjugated antibody and the PAP method on pre-embedding staining, or the PAP method on post-embedding staining. Neither can resolution be measured if the antigen concentration is so high that the immunocytochemical method misses most epitopes. To some extent, this is the case with most antigens whenever an immunocytochemical method is used. However, it is more pronounced with the immunoferritin, immunogold, and ABC methods than with the peroxidase-conjugated antibody method (if polymers are not removed from the conjugate) than the PAP method.

Resolution can, however, be determined if an antigen can be demonstrated to possess a regular periodicity, as has been done with fibronectin and collagen I in the work of Furcht et al. (72). Extracellular matrix is composed of fibronectin,

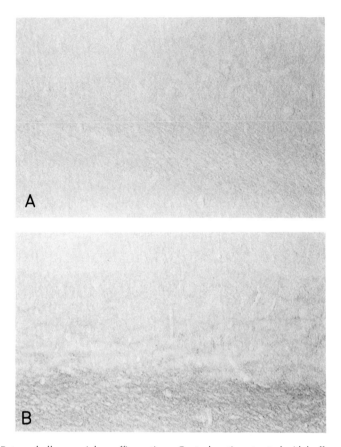

Figure 3-59.   Rat cerebellum, serial paraffin sections. Control sections treated with buffer and (a) reagents of the PAP method and (b) reagents of the ABC method. (From the work of Sternberger and Sternberger.)

collagen, and proteoglycan. Among other functions, fibronectin binds to collagen and mediates cellular adhesion to collagen. Collagen is expressed as a number of distinct genetic procollagen types that are converted post-translationally to collagen. Collagen possesses distinct epitopic regions that exhibit periodicity. In cultured human fibroblasts, fibronectin reacted in a nonperiodic manner with cell membranes and membrane-associated vesicles and with extracellular fibrils with diameters of about 10 nm (72).

Ascorbic acid is a cofactor for prolyl hydroxylase which is critical in the processing of matrix collagen. In tissue cultures after ascorbic acid treatment, a new form of fibrils with a diameter of 40 nm appears. These fibrils exhibit an axial periodicity of 70 nm for both procollagen I and fibronectin (Fig. 3-60). The periodicity was exhibited on staining with affinity-purified antifibronectin and the PAP method and established that the PAP method has a resolution of at least 70 nm. In the immunoferritin method, there frequently appeared no regular pattern, but in some sections a similar periodicity was established. The need for selected areas to establish periodicity in the immunoferritin method may have been due to formation of large complexes in the conjugation procedure, as well

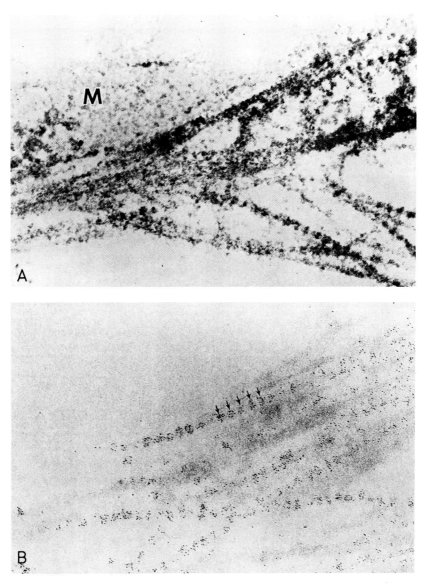

Figure 3-60. Ascorbate-treated human fibronectin in cultures was reacted with antifibronectin in pre-embedding staining. (a) PAP method reveals a 70-nm periodicity. (M) Cell membrane. ×70,000. (b) Immunoferritin method also reveals an apparent periodicity of 70 nm (arrows). However, selection of favorable fields was necessary to reveal periodicity with immunoferritin method. [Reprinted by permission of Elsevier Science Publishing Co., Inc. from Fibronectin presence in native collagen fibrils of human fibroblasts: Immunoperoxidase and immunoferritin localization by L.T. Furcht, D. Smith, G. Wendel-schafer-Crabb, D.J. Mosher, J. M. Foidaut, *Journal of Histochemistry and Cytochemistry* **28:**1319, Copyright 1980 by the Histochemical Society, Inc. (72).]

as possibly the presence of unconjugated antibody in the conjugate preparation. The similar periodicity established for fibronectin and procollagen epitopes suggests that specific segments in both fibrils mediate their interaction (72,111).

VARIATIONS OF THE UNLABELED ANTIBODY PAP METHOD

A great number of variations of the unlabeled antibody method are possible in theory, and a number of them have been tested experimentally. In principle, variations involve:

1. Modification in the second antibody.
2. Substitutions for antigen-antibody complex in the third layer.
3. Intensification of the PAP reaction.
4. Use of alternative markers.

Modification in the Second Antibody

It is desirable, in the unlabeled antibody method, to use PAP of the same species as that of the first antibody. However, Erlandsen et al. (112) and Marcucci and Dougherty (8) have shown that it is not necessary that PAP is of the same species as first antibody. Marucci and Dougherty were able to detect human first antibody with guinea pig antihuman IgG and baboon PAP, while Erlandsen et al. found that guinea pig first antibody can be detected with sheep antirabbit IgG and rabbit PAP. Although by most immunologic tests, the cross-reactivity among immunoglobulins is only partial, Erlandsen et al. found the heterologous system at least as sensitive as the homologous system. Among a variety of sheep antirabbit IgGs, only one was found to fail to cross-react with guinea pig immunoglobulin by radioimmunoassay, and this serum also failed to be useful in heterologous PAP technique. An application of the heterologous method is in the cellular distribution of hormones in islets of Langerhans of human pancreas (113). In two adjacent paraffin sections stained for insulin and glucagon, respectively, insulin was found throughout the islet in the B cells, and glucagon was located at its periphery in the A cells (Figs. 3-61a,b). When two adjacent sections were stained for gastrin and somatostatin, both were found in the same D cells (Fig. 3-62).

Erlandsen et al. (114) also found in a study of the distribution of IgA within Paneth cells of rat small intestine that rabbit antiserum to human lysozyme gave a strong immunocytochemical reaction with rat lysozyme, while such cross-reaction is uncommon when examined by immunodiffusion. Studies of antigenic differences between species as revealed by immunodiffusion have been widely used to evaluate evolution of the molecules in question, as well as taxonomic classification of the species. The increased sensitivity of immunocytochemistry is capable of detecting cross-reactions not discernible by other means and could be used, according to Erlandsen et al. (114), to facilitate the study of evolutionary patterns of IgA.

Antirabbit IgG generally does not cross-react with antimouse IgG. The failure

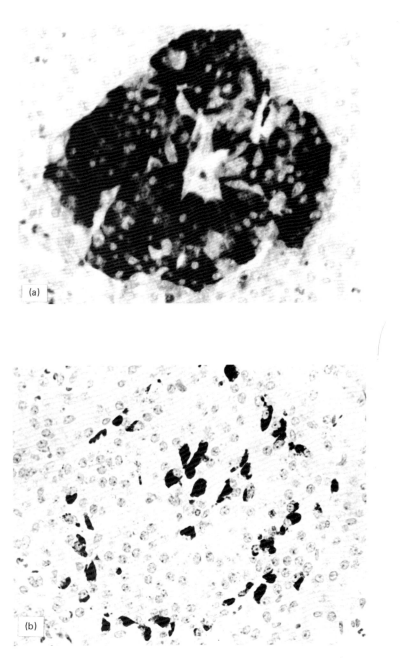

Figure 3-61. Adjacent paraffin sections of human pancreas, stained with guinea pig first antisera, sheep antirabbit IgG, and rabbit PAP. First antiserum is anti-insulin in (a) and antiglucagon in (b). Bouin's fixation. ×360. [Reprinted by permission of Elsevier Science Publishing Co., Inc. from Pancreatic islet cell hormones, by S.L. Erlandsen, O.D. Hegre, J.A. Parsons, R.C. McEvoy, *Journal of Histochemistry and Cytochemistry* **24**:883, Copyright 1976 by the Histochemistry Society, Inc. (113).]

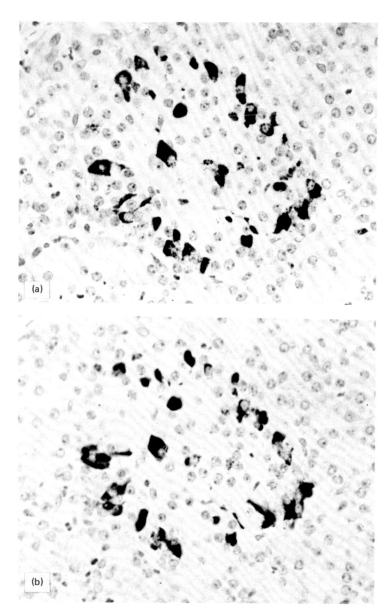

Figure 3-62. Adjacent paraffin sections of human pancreas, stained with guinea pig first antisera, sheep antirabbit IgG, and rabbit PAP. First antiserum is antigastrin in (a) and antisomatostatin in (b). The same cell is localized with both antisera. Bouin's fixation. ×260. [Reprinted by permission of Elsevier Science Publishing Co., Inc. from Pancreatic islet cell hormones, by S.L. Erlandsen, O.D. Hegre, J.A. Parsons, R.C. McEvoy, *Journal of Histochemistry and Cytochemistry* **24:**883, Copyright 1976 by the Histochemistry Society, Inc. (113).]

of cross-reaction facilitates blocking of epitopes visualized with monoclonal mouse antibody by rabbit antisera, and vice versa.

Antirabbit IgG or antimouse IgG usually exhibit no immunocytochemically detectable cross-reaction with human IgG. To stain first antibodies from patients with dengue fever, Okuno et al. (115) used the sequence: patient antiserum, rabbit antihuman serum, sheep antirabbit IgG, rabbit PAP. This four-layer sequence gives strong staining. Staining was clean (115). However, caution is needed in the general application of the four-layer technique. The second antibody may contain immunoglobulins reacting nonspecifically with some tissues. These components are specifically detected by the third layer and thus by PAP. Therefore, in the four-layer technique, some of the basic specificity amplification advantages of the PAP method (page 143) may be lost.

An alternative manner of avoiding the need of species homology in the first antibody and PAP was the substitution of protein A (page 21) for link antibody, introduced by Celio et al. (106). While this method was found to give clean staining well suited for heterologous first antibody and PAP, use of protein A yielded lower sensitivity than use of link antibody in a homologous series.

Substitution for Antigen-Antibody Complex in the Third Layer

In the original unlabeled antibody method (2), we used the sequence: rabbit antibody, sheep antirabbit IgG, affinity-purified rabbit antiperoxidase, peroxidase. Mason et al. (116) used a similar sequence, except for substitution of affinity-purified antibody by antiserum with encumbent reduction in sensitivity (page 171) due to the presence of nonantiperoxidase immunoglobulin in antiserum. Nevertheless, Petrusz et al. (117) were able to obtain good staining with this method, provided they used a hyperimmune antiserum to peroxidase, which possessed high-affinity antibodies in which the absolute amounts of specific antibody relative to total immunoglobulin were high.

El Etreby et al. (118) were able to use four to eight times higher dilutions of first antibody in the PAP than in the four-layer antiperoxidase serum technique. Our data (page 149) indicate $\frac{1}{20}$th the sensitivity of the four-layer antiserum sequence compared to PAP, when the antiperoxidase serum was the same as that which provided the source of the PAP used.

The four-layer sequence, using affinity-purified antiferritin as third layer and ferritin as fourth layer, was successful in the hands of Willingham et al. (119) to obtain intracellular penetration of ferritin in saponin-permeated tissue culture monolayer cells (Fig. 3-63).

In the three-layer technique, Ribak et al. (120) replaced PAP, affinity-purified from antiserum to peroxidase, with the smaller complex prepared from F(ab')$_2$ antiperoxidase.

PAP provides, in the three-layer technique, an antigen reactive with the link antibody. Antiserum or monoclonal antibody to peroxidase is needed for the preparation of PAP. One could reason that instead of using antiserum, one could employ normal immunoglobulin and conjugate it with peroxidase chemically. The staining sequence would be first antiserum, link antiserum, peroxidase-conjugated IgG. The method still would be an "unlabeled antibody

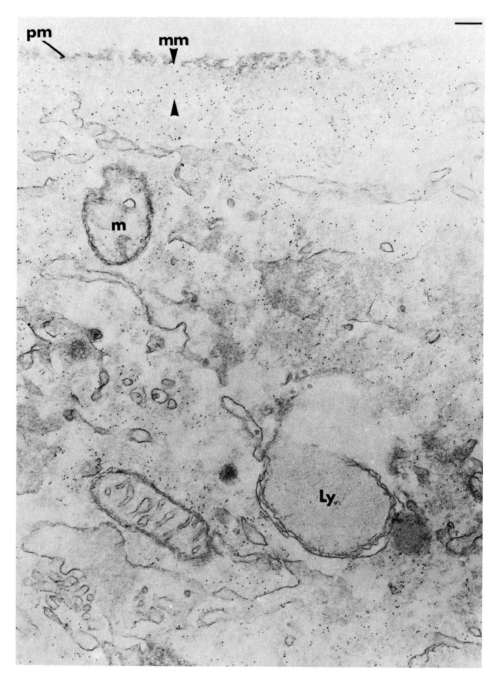

Figure 3-63. Myosin is diffusely localized in the perinuclear cytoplasm between organelles in this Swiss 3T3 cell, fixed in carbodiimide and low concentration of glutaraldehyde and permeated by saponin. Lysozomes (Ly) and mitochondria (m) are unstained. (mm) Microfilament mat (between arrows). (pm) Plasma membrane. Unlabeled antibody antiferritin-ferritin 4-layer sequence. [Reprinted by permission of Elsevier Science Publishing Co., Inc. from Ultrastructural immunocytochemistry localization of myosin in cultured fibroblastic cells, by M.C. Willingham, S.S. Yamada, P.J. Bechtel, A.V. Rutherford, I.H. Pastan, *Journal of Histochemistry and Cytochemistry* **29:**1289, Copyright 1981 by the Histochemical Society, Inc. (119).]

method" because none of the antibody has been labeled and the conjugate is used as an antigen rather than as an antibody. We (1), as well as Tougard et al. (121), have compared staining by PAP and peroxidase-conjugated immunoglobulin in the three-layer antibody sequence using equal concentrations of immunoglobulins, and found that while PAP conferred strong postembedding electron-microscopic staining of hormones in pituitary gonadotrophs, peroxidase-conjugated immunoglobulin gave no staining whatsoever. The enzymatic activity of the peroxidase bound to each IgG in the conjugate was less than the peroxidase activity per antibody in PAP. However, when quantitative comparison was made on the basis of equal enzymatic activity (rather than equal immunoglobulin concentration), the conjugate still failed to react at activity levels at which PAP gave strong staining.

Intensification of the PAP Reaction

When the PAP method is used for tracing of neuronal projections in thick Vibratome sections, a three-dimensional "transmitter-specific Golgi image" is revealed (page 320). To obtain optimal images, Johansson and Backmann (122) found it was by no means trivial to intensify the diaminobenzidine reaction product for light microscopy by mild osmication. Following completion of the PAP staining, the Vibratome sections were mounted on glass slides and immersed in ice-cold Ringer solution for at least 1 hour. Following blotting, the slides were stained with drops of 2% osmium tetroxide for 1–2 minutes and dehydrated after washing (Fig. 3-64).

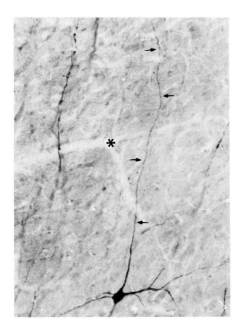

Figure 3-64. A single fiber (arrow) of a noradrenergic neuron stained with antiphenylethanolamine-N-methyltransferase can be traced throughout this Vibratome section. PAP method intensified with osmium tetroxide. Asterisk denotes blood vessel. ×165. [From Johannson and Backman (122).]

Vacca et al. (123) were able to increase the sensitivity of the PAP method by a five-layer procedure, in which the PAP was followed by a second application of link serum and a second application of PAP. Ordonneau et al. (124,125) increased the sensitivity of the four-layer sequential serum antiperoxidase procedure by the following six-layer sequence: first antibody, link antibody, antiserum to peroxidase, link antibody, antiserum to peroxidase, peroxidase.

Use of Alternative Markers

The principle of the unlabeled antibody method does not restrict it to peroxidase as a marker. Any other immunocytochemical marker can be used. We have attempted ferritin-antiferritin complexes in the unlabeled antibody method even before using peroxidase (2). The complex was prepared by reacting ferritin with Fab fragments of antiferritin. Since Fab fragments are monovalent, the complex does not precipitate. However, ultracentrifugation isolates the complex free of other serum constituents. Marucci et al. (126) prepared ferritin-antiferritin complexes in a manner similar to that of PAP. The complex was used for the serotype-specific localization of budding avian leukosis virus on the surface of infected chick embryo fibroblasts.

Clark et al. (127) introduced glucose oxidase-antiglucose oxidase as third layer in the unlabeled antibody method. The histochemical reaction for glucose oxidase yields a blue formazan product, which provides excellent contrast to the brown peroxidase reaction product and is, therefore, useful in the contrasting color staining of two antigens in the same section.

Ferritin-antiferritin and glucose oxidase-antiglucose oxidase complexes require larger excesses of antigen for preparation than does PAP. This property they share with most macromolecular antigens (page 100). Peroxidase may be among the few antigens which, because of favorable size and epitopic distribution, forms complexes in which the 3:2 (peroxidase:antiperoxidase) form predominates. Because of the stability of this complex, relatively small excesses of peroxidase are used for its preparation. Most antigen-antibody complexes are heterogeneous in antigen-antibody ratios and require relatively large excesses of antigen for maintenance in solution, and thus for stability. Because of lesser stability of the complexes, higher concentrations are needed for staining than in the case of PAP.

COMBINATION OF PAP IMMUNOCYTOCHEMISTRY WITH TRACER UPTAKE STUDIES IN THE NERVOUS SYSTEM

One of the greatest difficulties in study of connectivities in the central nervous system is due to the extent of ramifications of single neurons within the maze of intertwined pathways. Mere histologic observation of a nerve terminal in a tissue section tells us nothing about its origin. Tracing the fiber back to its origin, by serial sections stained tinctorially, again is futile because it is difficult to distinguish a given fiber from surrounding fibers. Major pathways that are concentrated in large projection bundles have been identified by degenerative changes that occur after localized lesions. However, this method is not satisfactory with pathways that are heavily intertwined with other pathways. The Golgi method (page 320) is useful to outline individual neurons and their projections, but the method is entirely nonspecific, affecting 1% to 2% of cells at random and leaving the remainder of neurons undetected. A great advance in tracing of neural projections was made by the discovery of anterograde and retrograde transport within the neuron. Protein synthesis starts in the perikaryon, and newly synthesized material will be transported within the confines of the projections belonging to a given perikaryon. Labeled amino acids will be incorporated into proteins that can be traced autoradiographically as *anterograde transport*. Certain dyes, such as lucifer yellow, will also be transported anterogradally and can be identified by fluorescence microscopy. For the identification of neurons by anterograde transport, microinjection of the marker into the cell body is necessary.

A more widely applicable marker technique is retrograde transport that has formed the basis of the fundamental work of Nauta et al. (128) on the afferents to caudoputamen. This work stimulated extensive studies that eventually have helped to delineate most major pathways in the central nervous system. The method is based on the finding that certain substances, such as horseradish peroxidase, are taken up by nerve endings and transported back to the cell body of origin. The uptake phenomenon makes it unnecessary to inject the tracer directly into the neuron. It is only necessary to inject within the confines of the terminal. Although there is also some anterograde transport, the retrograde transport is easily distinguished from the anterograde transport if nondiffusable histochemical markers, such as diaminobenzidine, are used for peroxidase. The important feature of this method is the exclusive marking of neurons that have terminals at the injection site with relatively little transsynaptic transport (see also page 190).

The peroxidase uptake method has been essential for the sharp anatomical delineation of neuronal connectivities. However, by itself, the method tells us nothing about the transmitter content of identified pathways as will be discussed in Chapter Eight, nothing about neuropeptide or neuromodulator contents that increase the diversity of neurotransmission as discussed in Chapter Nine, and nothing about specific heterogeneous intraneuronal constituents of yet unknown function as will be discussed in Chapter Ten. It is important to know which of these principles are found in a pathway identified anatomically by retrograde labeling, and it is equally important which fraction of total projections in a given pathway contains one and which another of these principles. This identification can be done by combining retrograde uptake of peroxidase or other substances, or anterograde transport of perikaryonally injected substances, with immunocytochemistry of these principles in the neurites of identified pathways. It is essential that the pathway tracer is visualized in the same section in which the immunocytochemistry is performed.

Priestley et al. (129) discovered that retrogradally transported horseradish peroxidase can be distinguished from PAP-stained neurotransmitters, even when both are detected by the same enzymatic method using hydrogen peroxide and diaminobenzidine substrates for peroxidase. The reason for this distinction lies in the mode of transport of horseradish peroxidase and its final disposition in the perikarya within multivesicular bodies. The transported peroxidase will appear in the form of discrete granules even in light microscopy, when their formation is encouraged by prolonged fixation in paraformaldehyde and when tissue sections are observed under differential interference optics (Nomarski) (Fig. 3-65). It is also important to use diaminobenzidine as electron donor for peroxidase, because substrate inhibition tends to limit the deposits to the confines of these granules. In contrast, the immunocytochemical stain is diffuse over the whole cytoplasm, and thus can be easily distinguished from the granular stain of injected peroxidase. The work of Priestley et al. (129) shows that not all cells projecting from the raphé nucleus to the striatum are serotonergic.

The injected and the PAP peroxidase may also be differentiated by the use of substrates that yield reaction products of different colors. Bouker et al. (130) used cobalt chloride to blacken the brown reaction product of diaminobenzidine and hydrogen peroxide of injected peroxidase and then performed the immunocytochemical reaction with 3-amino-9-ethyl carbazol to yield a red reaction product. The insoluble diaminobenzidine product sheltered the peroxidase en-

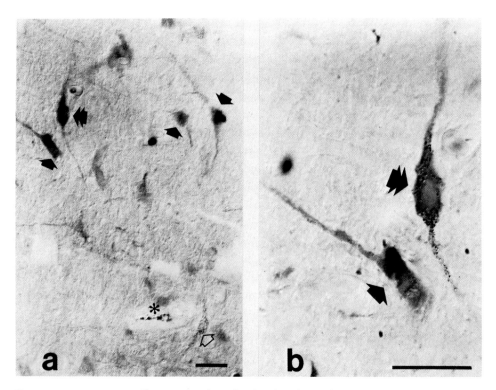

Figure 3-65. Serotonergic fibers project from the dorsal raphé nucleus to the striatum. Horseradish peroxidase has been injected into the striatum. Cryostat sections from the dorsal nucleus were stained first with diaminibenzidine and hydrogen peroxide and then, immunocytochemically, with monoclonal rat antiserotonin, rabbit antirat IgG, and rat PAP and again with diaminobenzidine and hydrogen peroxide. (a) Filled single arrowhead: serotonergic cells not labeled retrogradally. Open single arrowhead: retrogradally labeled cell devoid of serotonin. Filled double arrowhead: retrogradally labeled, serotonergic cell. This is seen better on higher magnification. (b) Filled double arrowhead revealing black dots on top of diffuse immunocytochemical staining. Asterisk: horseradish peroxidase taken up nonspecifically in an endothelial cell. Bar is 25 μm. [From Priestly et al. (129).]

zymatic site from reaction with subsequently applied aminoethylcarbazol, thus preventing mixing of colors (page 196).

In general, the blackening of the diaminobenzidine reaction product by cobalt chloride is insufficient to differentiate it from the brown reaction product of PAP with diaminobenzidine. When staining is strong, material not treated with cobalt chloride may also appear black. Beitz (131) intensified the diaminobenzidine reaction product with nickel ammonium sulfate and cobalt chloride for the detection of horseradish peroxidase and for differentiation from subsequent PAP staining. This work addressed itself to the role of the raphé magnus nucleus as a relay structure in the modulation of peripheral pain stimuli by a variety of central nuclei. Electric stimulation of the periaqueductal gray and the nucleus raphé magnus produces inhibition of nociceptive responses ascending from the dorsal horn nuclei. Since the periaqueductal gray has little connectivity with the spinal cord, it was reasonable to suspect the nucleus raphé magnus as a relay station that may modify nociceptive stimuli. Enkephalin (page 361) and substance P (page 367) are neuropeptides which inhibit and intensify, respectively, nociceptive stimuli. Many brainstem nuclei project to the nucleus raphé magnus. To establish whether these projections may modify nociceptive stimuli, horseradish peroxidase was injected into the nucleus raphé magnus and the retrogradally identified neurons of origin in the brainstem were stained immunocytochemically for enkephalin and substance P. The data revealed that many brainstem nuclei connect to the nucleus raphé magnus. However, not all of them utilize enkephalin or substance P as neuropeptides (peptidergic transmitters). The nuclei paragigantocellularis, cuneiformis, and solitarius possess high percentages of neurons which stain for enkephalin or substance P. Many of the retrogradally labeled cells in such area as the A5 group contain enkephalin, but none contain substance P. On the other hand, many of the projection neurons from the superior colliculus contain substance P, but not enkephalin. The periaqueductal gray, although being a site of electrically stimulated analgesia, and although labeled by the injected horseradish peroxidase, did not contain significant quantities of enkephalin or substance P neurons. Conceivably, other peptides modulate this pathway.

The lectin, wheat germ agglutinin, is also transported retrogradally. It can be labeled by conjugation with peroxidase (130) and provides a more sensitive tracer than horseradish peroxidase alone. Despite blackening of the diaminobenzidine reaction product, its visualization in PAP immunocytochemically counterstained material still depends on its conglutination in multivesicular bodies (Fig. 3-65), which is aided by extensive fixation in aldehydes. However, such extensive fixation, especially in glutaraldehyde, abolishes the immunoreactivity of a number of neuropeptides. For this reason, Lechan et al. (132) injected unlabeled wheat germ agglutinin for retrograde tracing. The projection sites were visualized with affinity-purified antiwheat germ agglutinin, anti-IgG and PAP, with diaminobenzidine as electron donor to yield a brown reaction product. Without removal of the bound reagents (page 196), a second antigen was visualized again by PAP method, but with 4-chloro-1-naphthol to yield a blue reaction product. The investigation addressed itself to the relatively well-defined, restricted area that exhibits catecholaminergic neurons and the extensive, long fiber ramifications which their projections undergo. Wheat germ agglutinin was injected into the median eminence and into the caudate-putamen complex and was rapidly transported over wide distances. Staining of labeled cells for tyrosine hydroxylase identified dopaminergic neurons in the substantia nigra. Wheat germ agglutinin was transported retrogradally and anterogradally from the injection site, but in comparison with horseradish peroxidase or peroxidase-labeled wheat germ agglutinin, unlabeled wheat germ agglutinin as detected by PAP method, appeared to be superior with respect to the number of retrogradally labeled neurons identified. Furthermore, a more limited diffusion at the injection site allowed for more focal injection. Transsynaptic labeling which may be encountered with horseradish peroxidase or tetanus toxin as retrograde tracers, has not been a problem with injection of unlabeled wheat germ agglutinin.

It is important to obtain physiologic data from cells visualized by immunocytochemistry. We have already seen that isolated cells can be surface labeled by immunofluorescence without affecting their viability (page 44). However, despite the innocuousness of fluorescent antibodies, this technique cannot be applied to solid tissue, because immunocytochemical observations require sections. Instead, it is necessary to obtain physiologic data first, and then study the tissues involved by immunocytochemistry. In the nervous system, it is necessary for this purpose to mark a single neuron, obtain physiologic recordings, and then fix and section the tissue and stain the marked neuron immunocytochemically. Lucifer yellow is a fluorescent dye that can be injected into neurons without affecting their physiologic activity significantly. It fills cell bodies and neurites rapidly. Kawata et al. (133) have labeled magnocellular neurons in the supraoptic nucleus with lucifer yellow and have shown that the labeling does not interfere with its subsequent staining for vasopressin by PAP method.

COMBINATION OF PAP IMMUNOCYTOCHEMISTRY WITH AUTORADIOGRAPHY

Until recently, immunocytochemistry was restricted to determining the nature of tissue constituents without being able to discriminate their metabolic states as reflected by the rate of their synthesis or degradation, or by conformational changes as a result of interaction with kinases, transferases, other enzymes, or ligands. While detection of at least kinase and transferase-dependent processes has now become possible by immunocytochemistry, studies on rate of assembly and degradation still require independent methodology.

Radioactive tracers can be detected histologically by autoradiography. In conjunction with immunocytochemistry, autoradiography can be used to study:

1. Rate of incorporation of labeled amino acids into immunocytochemically detectable proteins.
2. Rate of DNA synthesis in relation to immunocytochemically detected antigens.
3. Immunocytochemical identification of cells that possess receptors for stained hormones.
4. Simultaneous localization of two antigens by electron microscopy.

Kinase and transferase-dependent conformational changes, can, however, be studied by immunocytochemical means alone (page 448).

Labeling by radioactive tracers, while yielding time-dependent dynamic information, is nonspecific in that all substances that use the tracer as a metabolite pick it up. ^{3}H-Methionine will label any protein and ^{3}H-thymidine any DNA. Immunocytochemistry is needed to identify specific proteins. Labeling specificity is high with ^{32}P-adenosine triphosphate if mediated by a specific kinase or with ^{3}H-steroids that have specific receptors. Still immunocytochemistry of labeled proteins is more specific than the kinases and receptors involved.

For combined immunocytochemistry and autoradiography, sections are first stained immunocytochemically, washed in water, dried, and then coated with photographic emulsion of autoradiographic grade, exposed for a few days to a few months, and then developed and fixed. The intensity of labeling is evaluated by counting of silver grains.

Although there exists a corticotropin-releasing hormone, vasopressin may also participate in corticotropin release (page 382), particularly through its projections to the external zone of the median eminence which increases in vasopressin contents after adrenalectomy. Silvermann et al. (134) have shown that following adrenalectomy, ^{3}H-cytidin incorporation is increased in the perikarya of the paraventricular nucleus identified immunocytochemically as neurophysin and vasopressin neurons. No increase in incorporation of label was seen in vasopressin neurons of the supraoptic or suprachiasmic nuclei. The findings reveal a significant feedback from the adrenals on the paraventricular nucleus and specifically incriminate vasopressin neurons of this nucleus in the ACTH release function attributed to the vasopressin fibers that terminate in the external zone of the median eminence. Vasopressin itself, neurophysin, or another precursor or its fragment may be the active principle involved (page 383).

Using ^{3}H-thymidine autoradiography in conjunction with PAP immunocytochemistry for serotonin, Lauder et al. (135) were able to study in embryos of mothers injected with tracer, the relation of cell differentiation to initiation of serotonin synthesis (Fig. 3-66), and the relation of synthesizing cells to less differentiated cells in their vicinity. The latter, as indicated by silver grains in cells devoid of serotonin which surround serotonin cells devoid of silver grains, could indicate interaction of both groups of cells in development.

Although it has been widely held that secretion follows cell division, and that secreting cells do not divide, studies by Lehy (136) show that differentiated endocrine cells in the gut do divide. Upon pulse labeling, a significant proportion (as much as 1%) of mucosa cells labeled by PAP method for somatostatin, contained silver grains. After a 36-hour continuous infusion, the labeling index of somatostatin as well as gastrin cells was still low in relation to nonendocrine epithelial cells, suggesting a slow turnover of the endocrine cells. Estrogen acts on brain and pituitary to regulate reproductive cycles in most mammals and it also acts to prime targets in the brain for behavioral effects connected with reproduction. Luteinizing hormone-releasing hormone is the neuropeptide that mediates both cyclicity and behavioral effects (page 384). Shivers et al. (137) have revealed nuclear receptors for estrodiol in the anterior hypothalamus, but the estrogen-concentrating cells were distinct from those which contained luteinizing hormone-releasing hormone by PAP method. The results indicate that the estrogen effect on reproductive events associated with luteinizing hormone-releasing hormone secretion is via interneurons. Conversely, Rhodes et al. (138)

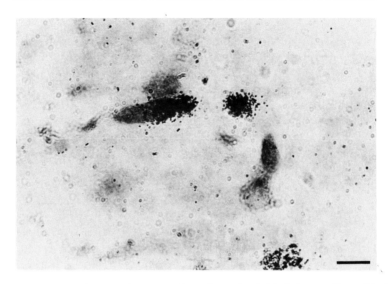

Figure 3-66. A neuron in the rat embryo at 14 days of gestation is labeled autoradiographically by ^{3}H-thymidine incorporation, and for serotonin contents by PAP method. Apparently the cell has been labeled at the end of the S-phase of its last cycle. Since no immunostained cells with mitotic figures have been observed in these embryos, it is unlikely that the double staining indicates that a cell is proliferating while synthesizing serotonin. Since the double labeling illustrated is rare in embryos, the finding can be interpreted to indicate that neurons begin to synthesize transmitter early in the G1 phase of their last cycle (survival time following injection of isotope into pregnant rats is only 4 hours, and thus, only recently dividing cells have thymidine label). Bar is 10 μm. [From Lauder et al. (135).]

did find ^{3}H-estradiol concentration in many magnocellular neurons that contained neurophysin (page 379) by PAP method. Other neurophysin-contacting neurons were devoid of estrogen receptors, but some receptor-containing cells were devoid of neurophysin. Since neurophysin cells were labeled by estradiol in both normal rats and rats congenitally unable to produce vasopressin and its respective neurophysin, but able to produce oxytocin and its respective neurophysin (page 379), it could be concluded that both oxytocin and vasopressin cells are directly affected by estradiol. The projection of both neuropeptides undergo extensive ramifications in the midbrain and brainstem and may mediate behavioral effects.

Benzodiazepines are used therapeutically as anxiolytics, hypnotics, anticonvulsants, and muscle relaxants. A specific synaptic receptor for this drug can be photoaffinity labeled by the analog ^{3}H-flunitrazepan. Mohler et al. (139) found that perfusion fixation after administration of the analog does not impair photoaffinity labeling. They were, therefore, able to investigate electron-microscopically the nature of the transmitter that enters a photoaffinity-labeled synapse (Fig. 3-67). They found that half of the photoaffinity-labeled synapses were associated with glutamate nerve endings, as revealed by immunocytochemistry for glutamate decarboxylase. The findings suggest that enhancement of γ-aminobutyrergic transmission may be a primary mechanism of benzodiazepin action.

The immunocytochemical localization of two constituents in the same specimen by pre-embedding staining electron microscopy has been difficult to

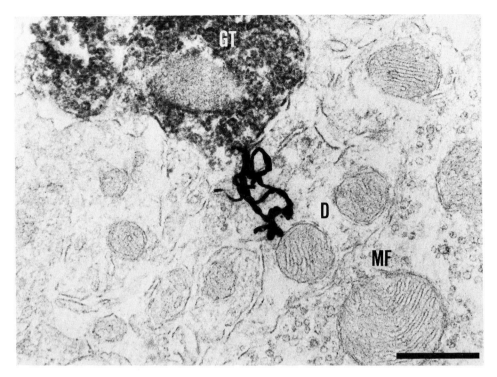

Figure 3-67. Autoradiograph of ³H-flunitrazepam photoaffinity-labeled site reveals synapses possessing benzodiazepine receptors. PAP staining for glutamate decarboxylase shows that many of these synapses are γ-aminobutyrerigic. Bar is 7.5 μm. [From Mohler et al. (139).]

achieve. However, Basbaum et al. (140) were able to localize simultaneously a neurotransmitter and neuropeptide by making use of the phenomenon that neurotransmitters (but not neuropeptides) are reutilized after release at synaptic junctions. Thus, for example, ³H-serotonin is taken up specifically at serotonergic nerve endings and can be used as a label for serotonergic endings by electron microscopic autoradiography. Animals were treated with a monoamine oxidase inhibitor before the administration of ³H-serotonin, in order to prevent excessive breakdown prior to uptake. Vibratome sections were stained for enkephalin by PAP method and embedded for electron microscopy.

STAINING OF TWO ANTIGENS IN THE SAME SECTION

The presence of two antigens in the same or similar location can be established by the use of serial sections, each stained for one of the antigens. The technique is limited by the section thickness. Adjacent, 7-μm sections do not always reveal the same cell. For visualization of two antigens in serial sections in determination of their coexistence in the same location, semithin sections are preferred. Alternatively, staining could be performed on the same section using immunocytochemical procedures that yield different colors with both antigens.

Detection of coexistence or separate existence of two substances in nerve projections is more difficult than in cell bodies. The small size of the fibers makes serial sections impractical, even if they are semithin. However, their small size also makes color discrimination difficult upon staining of two antigens in the same section.

The colors of fluorescent emission are brighter than those of transmission of reaction products used in enzyme techniques. For this reason, immunofluorescence is preferred over the PAP method in many applications of dual color staining. The method of choice is direct technique, in which one antibody is labeled with fluorescein isothiocyanate to yield a greenish emission, and the other with rhodamine isothiocyanate to yield an orange-red emission. Both antisera are applied to the section simultaneously. Brandtzaeg (141) found paired staining with direct technique useful for distinguishing monoclonal from polyclonal immunoglobulin in lymphoma diagnosis.

Several antigens can also be visualized by immunofluorescence in the same section, with only one fluorochrome and direct technique. Nash et al. (142) used sequential staining of plasma cells from mice immunized with ferritin to determine for each cell the class of immunoglobulin produced and to establish which immunoglobulin-containing cell provides immunoglobulin with specificity for ferritin. Sections were treated with ferritin followed by fluorescein-conjugated rabbit IgG antiferritin. After mounting the sections, the cells were photographed. Prints were made by projecting the negative image through a lattice of coordinates made by stretching silk screens across the masking frame of the photographic paper (Fig. 3-68, F-AF). The photographed section was kept in place in the fluorescent microscope and exposed upon removal of all filters to the full ultraviolet beam for 10 to 20 minutes. Extinction of all fluorescence is confirmed in Fig. 3-68, IR. The cover slip was removed from the slide by immersion into buffer. The reaction was then incubated with fluorescein-labeled anti-IgA and photographed. A print was made by aligning the negative in the same position over the coordinates as the previous print (Fig. 3-68, A). Without further ultraviolet irradiation, the cover slip was removed, and the section exposed to fluorescein-conjugated rabbit IgG antimouse IgM. The procedure was then repeated with anti-IgG, and anti-IgG$_2$ in sequence (Fig. 3-68, AM, AMG$_1$, and AMG$_1$G$_2$).

Instead of obliterating fluorescence between staining steps, it is also possible to remove antibodies. Hökfelt et al. (143) stained by indirect immunofluorescence cells in the ventral tegmental area with antisera specific to the C-terminals common to gastrin and cholecystokinin (first sequence), removed the antibodies with acid permanganate (144), and then restained for tyrosine hydroxylase (second sequence). This work was important in documenting coexistence in the same neuron of a neurotransmitter, such as dopamine, and a neuropeptide, such as cholecystokinin. Removal of antibodies was necessary between staining sequences, not only to remove the fluorescence, but also to remove the second antibody of the first sequence. Without complete removal, the first antibody of the second sequence might react with the second antibody of the first sequence and give false colocalization. When removal is incomplete, that is if the second antibody is removed but the first left on the section, the second antibody of the second staining sequence will react with the first antibody of the first sequence, and again yield false colocalization.

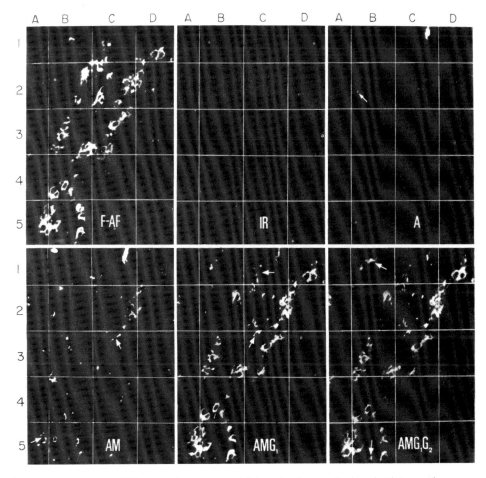

Figure 3-68. In sequential immunofluorescence staining of cells from the lymphoid tissue of a mouse immunized with ferritin, the antiferritin-producing cells are identified and located upon a grid of coordinates (F-AF). Fluorescence is then destroyed by ultraviolet irradiation (IR), and cells producing IgA are localized (A) on the same coordinates. The cell marked by the arrow does not appear in frame F-AF. Hence, this cell contains IgA of specificity other than antiferritin. After application of fluorescein-conjugated anti-IgM, the IgA-containing cell is still seen in addition to a fair number of IgG-containing cells (AM). The cells denoted by the arrows also appear in frame F-AF. Hence they contain IgM antiferritin. However, the large cells in grid location B3 and B4 do not appear in frame F-AF, and contain, therefore, IgM that is not reactive with ferritin. Most of the IgG_1-containing cells (frame AMG_1) also appear in frame F-AF, except those marked by arrows that seem to contain IgG of specificities other than antiferritin. Staining with anti-IgG_2 added only few cells (AMB_1G_2, arrows). Their IgG_2 is specific for ferritin. [From Nash et al. 142).]

Staining of two antigens by contrasting color in the peroxidase-labeled antibody method has been introduced by Nakane (145). The two antigens were stained sequentially. In the first sequence, antibody to the first antigen was followed by peroxidase-labeled second antibody and diaminobenzidine and hydrogen peroxide to yield a brown reaction product. In the second sequence, first antibody to the second antigen was again followed by peroxidase-labeled second antibody and then revealed with 4-chloro-1-naphthol and hydrogen peroxide to yield a grayish-blue reaction product. To avoid color mixing that could result from reaction of 4-chloro-1-naphthol with the peroxidase label deposited in the first sequence, or from reaction of the antibodies of the second sequence with those of the first, the protein reagents of the first sequence were removed by hydrochloric acid. Acid treatment did not remove the diaminobenzidine reaction products themselves.

In some cases, a similar protocol could be applied to the PAP method. However, often difficulties were encountered in removal of the reagents of the first sequence. Some of these difficulties were overcome in the work of Vandesande and Dierickx (146) who removed antibody by electrophoresis at 20 V/cm in a combination of glycine buffer, pH 2.2, and 30% dimethylformamide. The electrophoresis applies a continuous elution gradient to the section and may supply the added force needed to break the few bonds between antigen and antibody that remain operative, although weakened, despite acidification and dimethylformamide.

Traumu et al. (144) used a combination of acid and potassium permanganate.

The method of removing reagents of the PAP sequence has been used successfully in the hands of Ajika (147) to show that LHRH and dopamine terminals are in direct contact in the median eminence without intervening glial elements. Similar technique has been used by Larsson et al. (148) to show that antropyloric mucosal somatostatin cells send projections around nearby gastrin cells, thus providing additional evidence for the existence of *private* (54) transmitter systems of neurosecretion (page 358).

The bonds of PAP and of first antibody to second antibody can generally be broken easily by acidification. However, the reaction of epitopes that bind their specific antibodies largely by hydrophobic bonds rather than ionic bonds is not altered by acidification. One of these bonds which has been studied to some extent is that of peroxidase with antiperoxidase (page 94). Many authors had difficulties in removal of the antibody of the first staining sequence in certain systems as evidenced by mixed color staining in areas where only the first staining sequence was expected to react.

In our investigation on dual color staining by sequential PAP sequences, we stained for the same antigen (vasopressin) in both the first and second staining sequences (149,150). In this system, failure of removal of proteins of the first sequence would be indicated by brown deposits and successful removal by mixed brown and blue color. We attempted, in some experiments, to remove proteins of the first sequence by acidification, and in others to immunoblock these proteins. We also included controls in which the removal step was omitted. To our surprise, we found that only the controls gave satisfactory staining that was specific. We felt that the reaction product of diaminobenzidine, which is known to inhibit peroxidase activity when in excess and to creep along surfaces on which it is liberated (page 175), masked the reagents of the first staining sequence and sheltered them, as it was later called by Valnes and Brandtzaeg (151), from reaction with the second staining sequence. To ensure sheltering, it was necessary that the diaminobenzidine concentration was sufficient. The routine concentration of 0.05% diaminobenzidine and 0.01% hydrogen peroxide for 8 minutes was satisfactory. One-fourth of this concentration was the limiting dilution at which color mixing still could be prevented.

With this method, it has been possible to visualize separate cell bodies containing two different hormones in pituitary and magnocellular neurons. In case of coexistence in the same cell, it was necessary to avoid the staining hindrance of the first sequence toward reaction in the second sequence. This could be accomplished by dilution of first antibodies in the first sequence, and was experimentally established by progressive dilutions of antivasopressin in the first sequence and staining for antivasopressin again in the second sequence. Color mixing occurred once a critical dilution of first series antivasopressin was reached.

This method was not very satisfactory to distinguish adjacent projection fibers in the median eminence of the hypothalamus that contained two different peptides, or to visualize colocalization of two peptides in given fibers. The bluish color of the 4-chloro-1-naphthol reaction is not sufficiently different from the brown color to be readily distinguished when the stained area is small, such as fibers in contrast to perikarya, in which colors could be readily distinguished. Furthermore, the color difference is less dramatic after photographic reproduction than in the microscope.

This problem has been solved in the work of Clark et al. (127) by the use of glucose oxidase-antiglucose oxidase instead of PAP. Glucose oxidase gives a true blue reaction product, much more distinct from brown than the grayish-blue product of 4-chloro-1-naphthol. In their dual color staining procedure, Clark et al. stained the first antigen by PAP with diaminobenzidine as substrate to shelter the antibodies. Without attempts at antibody removal, they stained the second antigen by the unlabeled antibody glucose oxidase-antiglucose oxidase sequence with formazan as the blue reaction product.

Gamma trace (cystatin C) is a low molecular weight protein with 37 N-terminal amino acids that possess some homology to glucagon, but no immunologic cross-reactivity. It is a potent inhibitor of intracellular lysozomal proteinases and occurs in many neuroendocrine cells (152,153). Löfberg et al. (152) stained a glucagonoma for γ-trace and glucagon in dual color PAP sequence without antibody removal after the first sequence and found that upon progressive dilution of the antiserum of the first sequence, mixed blue and brown staining appeared. Thus, γ-trace is a constituent of glucagon-producing α-cells of pancreatic islets (Fig. 3-69). Its amino acid sequence deserves consideration as part of the sequence of a precursor that incorporates γ-trace as well as glucagon (page 359). Hereditary cerebral hemorrhage with amyloidosis is connected with abnormal metabolism of γ-trace (Fig. 3-70).

Buchan et al. (110) used monoclonal antigastric inhibitory peptide in the first reaction sequence and rabbit serum antiglucagon, antiglicentin, and antivasoactive intestinal peptide in the second reaction sequence and found consistently that in the human and rat small intestine, gastric inhibitory cells are a separate entity from glucagon, glicentin, and vasoactive intestinal peptide cells.

DePasquale et al. (154) used PAP and 4-chloro-1-naphthol in the first reaction sequence and diaminobenzidine in the second sequence to establish polyclonality or monoclonality of lymphoma cells (page 293). The first sequence stain was photographed and mapped. The reaction product was then dissolved in acetone,

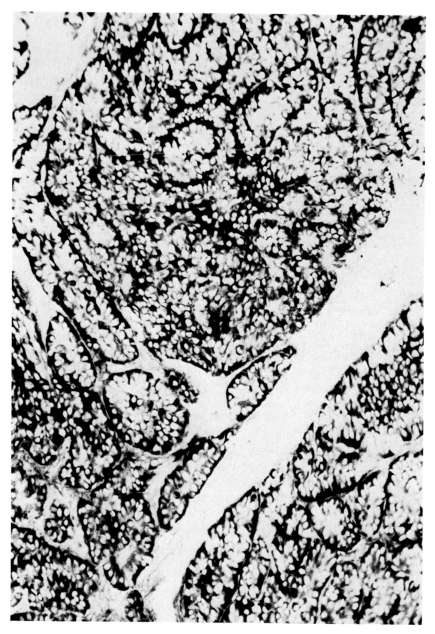

Figure 3-69. Gamma trace in α cells of a glucagon-producing pancreatic neoplasm. PAP method. ×250. [From Löfberg et al. (152).]

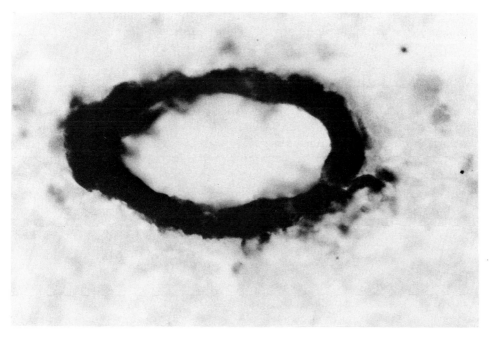

Figure 3-70. Cerebral vascular amyloid in hereditary cerebral hemorrhage with amyloidosis. Monoclonal antihuman α-trace. PAP method. ×800. [From Grubb and Löfberg (153).]

the first sequence antibodies were removed, and the second sequence was carried out with PAP and diaminobenzidine.

Mason and Sammons (155) succeeded to stain simultaneously, rather than sequentially, two antigens in the same section, brown and blue, respectively. Prerequisites for this system were:

1. Application of two first antibodies from different species.

2. Application of species-specific second antibodies that do not cross-react among the immunoglobulins of the species of the first antibody (see also page 180).

3. Application of antigen-antibody complexes in which antigen is visualized by different reactions.

An example is the staining of λ and κ chains in the same section:

First layer:	Rabbit anti-λ + goat anti-κ
Second layer:	Swine antirabbit IgG + donkey antigoat IgG
Third layer:	Rabbit antialkaline phosphatase + alkaline phosphatase + goat PAP

The reaction is developed in sequence by diaminobenzidine + hydrogen peroxide and by naphthol AS phosphate + fast blue BBN.

In the third layer, only the PAP was applied as preformed antigen-antibody complex. The simultaneous application of antiserum to phosphatase and phosphatase resembled, more or less, the sequential application of antiserum and antigen in the unlabeled antibody four-step sequence (page 183).

REVERSIBILITY OF THE IMMUNOCYTOCHEMICAL REACTION

The reaction of antigen with antibody is reversible. The binding reaction is much faster than the dissociation reaction. During each step of the immunocyto-chemical reaction, an equilibrium occurs with immunoreagent in solution and immunoreagent bound on the section. After each step, the tissue is washed with an excess of buffer. This procedure invites dissociation. Following each washing, the tissue is exposed to the immunoreagent of the next step. Again, dissociation of the preceding immunoreagent is favored. Thus, first antibodies may dissoci-ate during incubation with link antibodies because the link antibody solution contains no first antibodies in equilibrium with those found on the section.

We have examined dissociation in each step of the staining procedure by counting the number of molecules dissociated in each succeeding staining step, using sheep red blood cells (sRBC) as a model (46). The counting was accom-plished by measuring immunocytochemically the number of immunoreactive molecules transferred in each staining step from the immunocytochemically processed sRBC to freshly added sRBC used as indicator cells. The assumption was made that the binding reaction is much faster than the dissociation reac-tion—that is, that most of the immunoreagents dissociated during each staining step will, indeed, be bound by the freshly added sRBC. An excess of fresh sRBC was used to favor this equilibrium. Dissociation was measured for each incuba-tion step in the staining sequence, such as, for instance, dissociation of first antibody during incubation with link antibody. However, no attempt was made to measure dissociation during washing. This dissociation was minimized, how-ever, by washing at 2°C while incubation in immunoreagents was at 25°C.

When sRBC were stained in suspension with rabbit anti-sRBC, sheep antirab-bit IgG diluted 1:10, PAP diluted 1:50, and 0.05% diaminobenzidine with 0.01% hydrogen peroxide for 10 minutes each, deposition of reaction product was continuous on the sRBC until a 1:5000 dilution of the saturation concentra-tion of the first antiserum, used as immunoglobulin fraction, was reached. The saturation concentration was determined by the use of a radioiodinated im-munoglobulin and found to be 10^6 molecules of antibody per cell. With dilutions higher than 1:5000, localization of reaction product on the sBRC surface be-came discrete, and enumeration of the number of bound first antibodies had become possible.

To measure the dissociation of first antibody during incubation with link antibody, sRBC that had gone through the first step of the PAP method were added to link serum mixed with untreated sRBC indicator cells, and the staining reaction was completed with the mixture of cells. An average of 2,200 molecules of first antibody per cell out of a total of 10^6 had been transferred during staining, suggesting a dissociation of 0.2%. To measure dissociation of first anti-body in the third step of the PAP procedure, untreated indicator cells were added to the PAP. Again, 0.2% of antibody had dissociated. To measure dissoci-ation of first antibody during the enzymatic reaction, untreated indicator cells were added to the diaminobenzidine-hydrogen peroxide mixture; again, 0.2% of first antibody had dissociated.

To measure dissociation of link antibody, the PAP procedure was carried through the first two steps. Indicator cells reacted with a saturation level of first antibody were added to the PAP and the mixture was carried through the remainder of the staining sequence. No antibody had been transferred to the indicator cells, suggesting that dissociation of link antibody was negligible. When adding the indicator cells to the diaminobenzidine-hydrogen peroxide mixture, only 200 molecules of link antibody were transferred, again showing that dissociation was negligible.

To measure dissociation of PAP, the staining reaction was carried through the third step of the procedure. Indicator cells carried through the first two steps were added to the diaminobenzidine and hydrogen peroxide and the staining reaction was completed with the cell mixture. No reaction product was seen on the indicator cells, showing that no PAP had dissociated.

These data suggest that a total of 0.6% of first antibodies had dissociated during staining, while dissociation of link antibody and PAP was negligible. The dissociation of first antibody is minimized if the antibody reacts with tissue antigen via both of its combining sites (page 235). Such binding is favored if an identical epitope is present repetitively on tissue with a frequency corresponding to the distance between both antibody combining sites (page 6). It is more likely to occur if an antigen is small and densely packed—present in high concentrations. Large molecular antigens have a better chance for such double binding if they contain repetitive sequences, such as are found in polysaccharides.

Dissociation of first antibody is also minimized if antibodies of uniformly high affinity are used, such as monoclonal antibodies that had originally been selected by immunocytochemical assay (page 252).

Link antibody is used in excess. Since serum antibodies are heterogeneous mixtures of low and high affinities, use of link antibody in excess assures that mainly high-affinity antibodies react, while low-affinity antibodies remain in solution. Since the reacted bonds of the link antibodies are of high affinity, dissociation during washing is negligible.

Inasmuch as both antibody binding sites in any single antibody are identical, the bond between link antibody and PAP is of equally high affinity. Therefore, again, no PAP is lost upon washing.

REFERENCES

1. Sternberger LA, Petrali JP: The unlabeled antibody enzyme method. Attempted use of peroxidase-labeled antigen as the third layer in the technique. *J Histochem Cytochem* **25**:1036, 1977.

2. Sternberger LA: Some new developments in immunocytochemistry. *Mikroskopie* **25**:346, 1969.

3. Sternberger LA: Enzyme immunocytochemistry, in Hayat HM (ed): *Electron Microscopy of Enzymes: Principles and Methods*, vol I. New York, Van Nostrand Reinhold Co, 1973, p 150.

4. Sternberger LA, Hardy PH Jr, Cuculis JJ, Meyer HG: The unlabeled antibody-enzyme method of immunohistochemistry. Preparation and properties of soluble antigen-antibody

complex (horseradish peroxidase-antihorseradish peroxidase) and its use in identification of spirochetes. *J Histochem Cytochem* **18**:315, 1970.

5. Moriarty GC, Moriarty CM, Sternberger LA: Ultrastructural immunocytochemistry with unlabeled antibodies and the peroxidase-antiperoxidase complex. A technique more sensitive than radioimmunoassay. *J Histochem Cytochem* **21**:825, 1973.

6. Elias JM, Johnsen TA: The utilization of RIA antibodies for the immunohistochemical staining of polypeptide hormones on paraffin-embedded tissue. *Am J Clin Path* **71**:489, 1979.

7. Sternberger NH, Sternberger LA: The unlabeled antibody method. Comparison of sensitivity of peroxidase-antiperoxidase with avidin-biotin complex method by a new mode of quantitative immunocytochemistry. *J Histochem Cytochem*, in press.

8. Marucci AA, Dougherty RM: Use of the unlabeled antibody histochemical technique for the detection of human antibody. *J Histochem Cytochem* **23**:618, 1975.

9. DiStefano HS, Marucci AA, Dougherty RH: Immunohistochemical detection of avian leukosis virus antigens in paraffin-embedded tissue. *Proc Soc Exp Biol Med* **142**:1111, 1973.

10. Halmi NS, Parsons JA, Erlandsen SL, Duello T: Prolactin and growth hormone cells in the human hypophysis: A study with immunoenzyme histochemistry and differential staining. *Cell Tiss Res* **158**:497, 1975.

11. Burns J: Immunoperoxidase localization of hepatitis B antigen (HB) in formalin-paraffin processed liver tissue. *Histochemistry* **44**:133, 1975.

12. Halmi NS, Duello T: "Acidophilic" pituitary tumors. A reappraisal with differential staining and immunocytochemical techniques. *Arch Pathol Lab Med* **100**:346, 1976.

13. Sternberger NH, Itoyama Y, Kies MW, Webster H deF: Immunocytochemical method to identify basic protein in myelin-forming oligodendrocytes of newborn rat CNS. *J Neurocytol* **7**:251, 1978.

14. Sternberger LA, Sternberger NH: Monoclonal antibodies distinguish phosphorylated and nonphosphorylated forms of neurofilaments in situ. *Proc Natl Acad Sci USA* **80**:6126, 1983.

15. Burns J: Background staining and sensitivity of the unlabeled antibody-enzyme (PAP) method. Comparison with peroxidase labeled antibody sandwich method using formalin fixed paraffin embedded material. *Histochemistry* **43**:291, 1975.

16. Bigbee JW, Kosek JC, Eng LE: The effects of primary antisera dilution on staining of "antigen" rich tissue with the peroxidase antiperoxidase technique. *J Histochem Cytochem* **25**:443, 1977.

17. Vandesande F: An initial review of immunocytochemical methods for light microscopy. *J Neurosci Meth* **1**:3, 1979.

18. Linder E, Miettinen A: Prozone effects in indirect immunofluorescence. *Scand J Immunol* **5**:514, 1976.

19. Stilman M, Recht LD, Rosario SL, Seif SM, Robinson AG, Zimmerman EA: The effects of adrenalectomy and glucocorticoid replacement on vasopressin and vasopressin-neurophysin in the zona externa of the median eminence of the rat. *Endocrinology* **101**:42, 1977.

20. Sundler F, Hakenson R, Hammer RA, Alumets J, Carraway R, Leeman S, Zimmerman EA: Immunohistochemical localization of neurotensin in endocrine cells of the gut. *Cell Tiss Res* **178**:313, 1977.

21. Pelliniemi LJ, Dym M, Karnovsky JM: Peroxidase histochemistry using diaminobenzidine tetrahydrochloride stored as a frozen solution. *J Histochem Cytochem* **28**:191, 1980.

22. Webster H deF, Reier PJ, Kies MW, O'Connel M: A simple method for quantitative morphological studies of CNS demyelination. Whole mounts of tadpole optic nerves examined by differential-interference microscopy. *Brain Res* **79**:132, 1974.

23. Dachuex F, Dubois MP: Ultrastructural localization of prolactin, growth hormone and luteinizing hormone by immunocytochemical techniques in the bovine pituitary. *Cell Tiss Res* **178**:313, 1977.

24. Rojas-Espinosa O, Dannenberg AM, Sternberger LA, Tsuda T: The role of cathepsin D in the pathogenesis of tuberculosis. A histochemical study employing unlabeled antibodies and the peroxidase-antiperoxidase complex. *Am J Pathol* **74**:1, 1974.

25. Mepham BC, Frater W, Mitchell BSL: Use of proteolytic enzymes to improve immunoglobulin staining by the PAP technique. *Histochem J* **11**:345, 1979.

26. Katoh Y, Stoner GD, McIntire KR, Hill TA, Anthony R, McDowell E, Tramp B, Harris C: Immunologic markers of human bronchial epithelial cells in tissue sections and culture. *J Natl Cancer Inst* **62**:1177, 1979.

27. McComb RD, Jones TR, Pizzo SV, Bigner DD: Specificity and sensitivity of immunohistochemical detection of factor VIII/von Willebrand factor antigen in formalin-fixed, paraffin-embedded tissue. *J Histochem Cytochem* **30**:371, 1982.

28. Radaskiewicz T, Tragosics B, Abdelfattahged M, Denk H: Effect of protease pretreatment on immunomorphologic demonstration of hepatitis B-surface antigen in conventional paraffin-embedded liver biopsy material: quantitative evaluation. *J Immunol Meth* **29**:27, 1979.

29. Martin R, Voigt KH: Enkephalins coexist with oxytocin and vasopressin in nerve terminals of rat neurohypophysis. *Nature* **289**:502, 1983.

30. Hardy PH, Meyer HG, Cuculis JJ, Petrali JP, Sternberger LA: Postembedding staining for electron microscopy by the unlabeled antibody peroxidase method. *J Histochem Cytochem* **18**:684, 1970.

31. Rossi GL, Bestetti G: Morphologic changes in the hypothalamo-hypophyseal-gonadal axis of male rat after twelve months of streptotoxin-induced diabetes. *Diabetologia* **21**:476, 1981.

32. Petrali JP, Hinton DM, Moriarty GC, Sternberger LA: The unlabeled antibody enzyme method of immunocytochemistry. Quantitative comparison of sensitivities with and without peroxidase-antiperoxidase complex (PAP). *J Histochem Cytochem* **22**:782, 1974.

33. Moriarty GC: Immunocytochemistry of the pituitary glycoprotein hormones. *J Histochem Cytochem* **24**:846, 1976.

34. Rodning CG, Erlandsen SL, Coulter HD, Wilson ID: Localization of immunoglobulin antigens (IgA) on epoxy embedded tissue. *J Histochem Cytochem* **26**:223, 1978.

35. Li JY, Dubois MP, Dubois PM: Somatrophs in the human fetal anterior pituitary. An electron microscopic immunocytochemical study. *Cell Tiss Res* **181**:545, 1977.

36. Dacheux F: Ultrastructural immunocytochemical localization of growth hormone in the porcine pituitary. *Cell Tiss Res* **207**:277, 1980.

37. Doerr-Schott J: Localisation submicroscopique par cyto-immunoenzymologie de differents principes hormonaux de l'hypophyse de *Rana temporia* L. *J Microsc.* **20**:151, 1974.

38. Li JY, Dubois MP, Dubois PM: Ultrastructural localisation of immunoreactive corticotropin, β-lipotropin, γ and β-endorphin in cells of the human fetal anterior pituitary. *Cell Tiss Res* **204**:37, 1979.

39. Heitz PU, Wegmann W: Identification of neoplastic Paneth cells in an adenocarcinoma of the stomach using lysozyme as a marker, and electron microscopy. *Virchov Arch A Path Anat Histol* **387**:107, 1980.

40. Rodning CG, Wilson ID, Erlandsen SL: Immunoglobulins within human small intestinal Paneth cells. *Lancet* **1**:184, 1976.

41. Sternberger NH, Quarles RH, Itoyama Y, Webster H deF: Myelin-associated glycoprotein demonstrated immunocytochemically in myelin-forming cells of developing rat. *Proc Natl Acad Sci USA* **76**:1510, 1979.

42. Tougard C, Picart R, Tixier-Vidal S: Immunocytochemical localization of glycoprotein hormones in the rat anterior pituitary. A light and electron microscopy study using antiserum against rat β-subunits. A comparison between preembedding and postembedding methods. *J Histochem Cytochem* **28**:101, 1980.

43. Dacheux F: Subcellular localization of gonadotrophic hormones in the castrated porcine pituitary cells using preembedding and postembedding methods. *Cell Tiss Res* **236**:153, 1984.

44. Sternberger LH, Petrali JP: Quantitative immunocytochemistry of pituitary receptors for luteinizing hormone-releasing hormone. *Cell Tiss Res* **162**:141, 1975.

45. Grzanna R, Molliver ME, Coyle JT: Golgi-like demonstration of central noradrenergic neurons in thick sections by the unlabeled antibody method. *Proc Natl Acad Sci USA* **75**:2502, 1978.

46. Hinton DM, Petrali JP, Meyer HG, Sternberger, LA: The unlabeled antibody enzyme method of immunohistochemistry. Molecular immunocytochemistry of antibodies on the erythrocyte surface. *J Histochem Cytochem* **21**:978, 1973.

47. Olschowka JA, Molliver ME, Grzanna R, Rice FL, Coyle JT: Ultrastructural demonstration of noradrenergic synapse in the rat central nervous system by dopamine-β-hydroxylase immunocytochemistry. *J Histochem Cytochem* **29**:271, 1981.

48. Altschuler RA, Heises GR, Harmison GG, Wenthold RJ, Fey J: Immunocytochemical localization of aspartate aminotransferase immunoreactivity in cochlear nucleus of the guinea pig. *Proc Natl Acad Sci USA* **78**:6553, 1981.

49. Wu J-Y, Brandon C, Su YY, Lau DMK: Immunocytochemical and autoradiographic localization of GABA system in the vertebrate retina. *Mol Cell Biochem* **39**:229, 1981.

50. Steinbush HWN, Verhofstad AAJ, Joosten HWJ: Localization of serotonin in the central nervous system by immunohistochemistry. Description of a specific sensitive technique and some application. *Neuroscience* **3**:811, 1978.

51. Pecci Saavedra J, Brusco A, Pavessini S: Immunocytochemical study of synaptic connectivities of the raphe neurons: The possible presynaptic role of dendrites. *Communicationes Biophysicas* **1**:189, 1982.

52. Johannson O, Lundberg JM: Ultrastructural localization of vasoactive intestinal polypeptide-like immunoreactivity in large dense-core vesicles of "cholinergic type" nerve terminals in cat exocrine glands. *Neuroscience* **6**:847, 1982.

53. Scharrer E, Scharrer B: Secretory cells within the hypothalamus. *Res Publ Assn Res Nervous and Mental Diseases* **20**:1970, 1939.

54. Scharrer B: Neuroendocrinology and histochemistry, in Stoward PJ, Polak JM (eds): *Histochemistry: The Widening Horizons.* John Wiley and Sons, New York, pp 11–20.

55. Liposits Z, Gören T, Sétáló G, Langrari I, Flecko B, Vig S, Schally AV: Ultrastructural characteristics of immunolabeled corticotropin releasing factor (CRF)-synthesizing neuron in rat brain. *Cell Tiss Res* **229**:191, 1983.

56. Vacca LL, Hobbs J, Abraham S, Naftchi E: Ultrastructural localization of substance P immunoreactivity in the ventral horn of the rat spinal cord. *Histochemistry* **76**:33, 1982.

57. Piekut DT: Ultrastructural characteristics of vasopressin containing neurons in the paraventricular nucleus of the hypothalamus. *Cell Tiss Res* **234**:125, 1983.

58. Kies MW, Thompson EB, Alvord EC Jr: The relationship of myelin protein to experimental allergic encephalitis. *Ann NY Acad Sci* **122**:148, 1965.

59. Sternberger NH, Itoyama Y, Kies MW, Webster H deF: Myelin basic protein demonstrated immunocytochemically in oligodendroglia prior to myelin sheath formation. *Proc Natl Acad Sci USA* **75**:2521, 1978.

60. Sternberger NH, del Cerro C, Kies MW, Herndon RM: Immunocytochemistry of myelin basic protein in adult oligodendrocytes. *J. Neuroimmunol* **7**:355, 1985.

61. Rende M, Zucco M, Cocchia D, Michetti F: S-100 protein in the brain of hypothyroid adult rats: An immunochemical and immunocytochemical study. *Der Brain Res* **2**:590, 1982.

62. Gröschel-Stewart U: Immunochemistry of cytoplasmic contractile protein. *Int Rev Cytol* **65**:193, 1980.

63. Drenkhahn D, Gröschel-Stewart U: Localization of myosin, actin and tropomyosin in rat intestinal epithelium: Immunohistochemical studies at the light and electron microscope levels. *J Cell Biol* **86**:475, 1980.

64. Willingham MC, Jay G, Pastan I: Localization of the ASVsrc gene product to the plasma membrane of transformed cells by electron microscopic immunocytochemistry. *Cell* **18**:125, copyright 1979 by M.I.T.

65. Itoh G, Miura S, Suzuki I: Immunohistochemical detection of Fc receptor. I. Light microscopic demonstration of Fc receptor by using soluble immune complexes of peroxidase-antiperoxidase immunoglobulin G. *J Histochem Cytochem* **25**:252, 1977.

66. Mason DY, Labaume S, Preud'homme J-L: The detection of membrane and cytoplasmic immunoglobulins in human leucocytes by immunoperoxidase staining. *J Clin Pathol* **29**:413, 1977.

67. Alexander EL, Sanders SK: F(ab')₂ reagents are not required if goat, rather than rabbit, antibodies are used to detect human surface immunoglobulin. *J Immunol* **119**:1084, 1977.

68. Reis DJ, Benno RH, Tucker LW, Joh TH: Quantitative immunocytochemistry of tyrosine hydroxylase in brain, in Chan-Palay V, Palay SC (eds): *Cytochemical Methods in Neurobiology.* Alan R. Liss, New York, 1982.

69. Benno RC, Tucker LW, Joh TH, Reis DJ: Quantitative immunocytochemistry of tyrosine hydroxylase in brain. I. Development of a computer-assisted method using the peroxidase-antiperoxidase technique. *Brain Res* **246**:225, 1982.

70. Benno RC, Tucker LW, Joh TH, Reis DJ: Quantitative immunocytochemistry of tyrosine hydroxylase in brain. II. Variations in the amount of tyrosine hydroxylase among individual neurons of the locus ceruleus in relationship to neuronal morphology and topography. *Brain Res* **246**:235, 1982.

71. Sternberger LA, Petrali JP, Joseph SA, Meyer HG, Mills KR: Specificity of the immunocytochemical luteinizing hormone-releasing hormone receptor reaction. *Endocrinology* **102**:63, 1978, The Endocrine Society.

72. Furcht LT, Smith D, Wendelschafer-Crabb G, Mosher DJ, Foidaut JM: Fibronectin presence in native collagen fibrils of human fibroblasts: Immunoperoxidase and immunoferritin localization. *J Histochem Cytochem* **28**:1319, 1980.

73. Rodning CB, Erlandsen SC, Wilson D, Carpenter A-M: Light microscopic morphometric analysis of rat ileal mucosa. I. Component quantification of IgA-containing immunocytes. *Digest Dis Sci* **28**:742, 1983.

74. Baker H, Joh TH, Ruggiero DA, Reis DJ: Variations in number of dopaminergic neurons and tyrosine hydroxylase activity in hypothalamus of two mouse strains. *J Neurosci* **3**:832, 1983.

75. Witorsch RJ: Evaluation of immunoperoxidase-stained tissue section with an electrophoresis densitometer. *J Histochem Cytochem* **30**:179, 1982.

76. Rhodes CH, Morell JI, Pfaff DW: Changes in oxytocin contents in the magnocellular neurons of the rat hypothalamus following water deprivation or estrogen treatment. Quantitative immunohistochemical studies. *Cell Tiss Res* **216**:47, 1981.

77. Taugner R, Hackenthal E, Inagami T, Nobiling R, Poulsen K: Vascular and tubular renin in the kidneys of mice. *Histochemistry* **75**:473, 1982.

78. McNeill TH, Kozlowski GP, Abel JH Jr., Zimmerman EA: Neurosecretory pathways in the mallard duck (Anas platyhynchos) brain: Localization by aldehyde fuchsin and immunoperoxidase techniques for neurophysin and gonadotrophin releasing hormone. *Endocrinology* **99**:1323, 1976.

79. Anderson RE, Gay CV, Schraer H: Carbonic anhydrase localization by light and electron microscopy. A comparison of methods. *J Histochem Cytochem* **30**:1135, 1983.

80. Lietz H, Böcker W, Groblinghoff M: Immunocytochemical demonstration of alkaline phosphatase. *Histochemistry* **42**:181, 1974.

81. Vacca LL, Rosario SL, Zimmerman EA, Tomashefsky P, Ng P-Y, Hsu KC: Application of immunoperoxidase techniques to localize horseradish peroxidase trace in the central nervous system. *J Histochem Cytochem* **23**:208, 1975.

82. Coon JS, Weinstein RS: Variability in the expression of O (H) antigen in human transitional epithelium. *J Urol* **125**:301, 1981.

83. Coon JS, Weinstein RS: Detection of ABH tissue isoantigens by immunoperoxidase methods in normal and neoplastic urothelium. Comparison with the erythrocyte adherence method. *Am J Clin Path* **76**:163, 1981.

84. Böcker W: Use of a triple layer enzyme method as an alternative to immunofluorescence for the detection of tissue antigens. *Beitr Pathol* **153**:410, 1974.

85. Wachsmuth ED: A quantitative approach to efficiency and sensitivity: Enzyme histochemistry, immunofluorescence and peroxidase-antiperoxidase technique in tissue sections. *Acta Histochem* **Suppl XXV**:47, 1982.

86. Hancock MG: Leu-enkephalin, substance P and somatostatin immunocytochemistry combined with retrograde transport of horseradish peroxidase in sympathetic preganglion neurons. *J Autonom Nerv Sys* **6**:263, 1982.

87. Takeuchi Y, Kimura H, Sano Y: Immunohistochemical demonstration of serotonin-containing nerve fibers in the cerebellum. *Cell Tiss Res* **226:**1, 1982.

88. Woodhams PL, Cohen J, Mallet J, Balázs R: A preparation enriched in Purkinje cells identified by morphological and immunocytochemical criteria. *Brain Res* **199:**435, 1982.

89. Radaszkiewicz T, Dragosics B, Abdelfettahagd M, Denk H: Effect of protease pretreatment on immunomorphologic demonstration of hepatitis-B-surface antigen in conventional paraffin-embedded liver biopsy material: Quantitative evaluation. *J Immunol Meth* **29:**27, 1979.

90. Conley EK, Jenkins KA, Remington JS: Toxoplasma gondii infection of the central nervous system. Use of peroxidase-antiperoxidase method to demonstrate toxoplasma in formalized, paraffin-embedded tissue reaction. *Hum Path* **12:**690, 1981.

91. Alumets, J, Håkenson R, Lundqust G, Sundler F, Thorell J: Ontogeny and ultrastructure of somatostatin and calcitonin cells in the thyroid gland of the rat. *Cell Tiss Res* **206:**193, 1980.

92. Alm P, Alumets J, Hakenson R, Owman Ch, Sjöberg N-O, Sundler F, Walles B: Origin and distribution of VIP (vasoactive intestinal polypeptide) nerves in the genitourinary tract. *Cell Tiss Res* **205:**337, 1980.

93. Ahrén B, Håkenson R, Landquist I, Sjöland K, Sundler F: Gastric inhibitory peptide-like immunoreactivity in glucagon cells. Interaction between GIP and glucagon on insulin release. *Acta Physiol Scand* **112:**233, 1981.

94. Alumets J, Falkmer S, Grimelius L, Håkenson R, Ljundberg O, Sundler F, Wilander E: Immunocytochemical demonstration of enkephalin and β-endorphin in endocrine tumors of the rectum. *Acta Path Microbiol Scand Sect A* **88:**103, 1980.

95. Baker BL, Dermody WC, Reel JR: Distribution of gonadotropin-releasing hormone in the rat brain as observed with immunocytochemistry. *Endocrinology* **97:**125, 1975.

96. Taylor CR: Immunohistochemical studies of lymphoma: Present, past and future. *J Histochem Cytochem* **28:**777, 1980.

97. Sutmuller P, Cowan KM: The detection of foot-and-mouth disease antigens in infected cell cultures by immunoperoxidase techniques. *J Gen Virol* **22:**287, 1974.

98. Pich A, Bussolati G, Carbonara A: Immunocytochemical detection of casein and casein-like proteins in human tissue. *J Histochem Cytochem* **24:**940, 1976.

99. Mason DY, Taylor CR: The distribution of muramidase (lysozyme) in human tissues. *J Clin Path* **28:**124, 1975.

100. King B: Localization of transferrin on the surface of the human placenta by electron microscopic immunocytochemistry. *Anat Rec* **186:**151, 1976.

101. Van Leeuwen FW: Immunolocalization of vasopressin and oxytocin at the light and electron microscopic level in rats. *J Histochem Cytochem* **24:**618, 1976.

102. Rantala I, Helic H, Elu H: Immune electron-microscopic localization of a progesterone-inducible protein (avidin) in the chick oviduct mucosa. *Endocrinology* **110:**768, 1982.

103. Lehy T, Cristina ML: Ontogeny and distribution of certain endocrine cells in the human fetal large intestine. Histochemical and immunocytochemical studies. *Cell Tiss Res* **203:**415, 1979.

104. Goldenberg DM, Warren BP: Immunoperoxidase staining of carcinoembryonic antigen in urinary bladder cancer. *Urol Res* **6:**211, 1978.

105. Jautzke G, Altanaehr E: Immunohistochemical demonstration of carcinoembryonic antigen (CAE) and its correlation with grading and staging of tissue section of urinary bladder carcinomas. *Cancer* **50:**2052, 1982.

106. Celio MR, Lutz H, Binz H, Fey H: Protein A in immunoperoxidase techniques. *J Histochem Cytochem* **27:**691, 1979.

107. Celio MR, Pasi A, Burgisser E, Buetti G, Hollt V, Gramsch Ch: "Proopiocortin fragments" in normal human adult pituitary. Distribution and ultrastructural characterization of immunoreactive cells. *Acta Endocrinol* **95:**27, 1980.

108. Soria J, Soria C, Ryckewaerdt JJ: A solid phase immunoenzymologic assay for measurement of human fibrinopeptide A. *Thrombosis Res* **20:**425, 1980.

109. Hsu S-M, Raine L, Fanger H: The use of antiavidin antibody and avidin and biotin-peroxidase complex in immunoperoxidase techniques. *Am J Clin Path* **75:**816, 1981.

110. Buchan AMJ, Ingman-Baker J, Levy J, Brown JC: A comparison of the ability of renin and monoclonal antibodies to gastric inhibitory polypeptide to detect immunoreactive cells in the gastroventropancreatic system of mammals and reptiles. *Histochemistry* **76**:341, 1982.

111. Repesh LA, Fitzgerald TJ, Furcht LT: Fibronectin involvement in granulation tissue and wound healing. *J Histochem Cytochem* **30**:351, 1982.

112. Erlandsen SL, Parsons JA, Burke JP, Redick JA, Van Orden DE, Van Orden LS: A modification of the unlabeled antibody enzyme method using heterologous antisera for the light microscopic and ultrastructural localization of insulin, glucagon and growth hormone. *J Histochem Cytochem* **23**:666, 1975.

113. Erlandsen SL, Hegre OD, Parsons JA, McEvoy RC, RP: Pancreatic islet cell hormones. Distribution of cell types in the islet and evidence for the presence of somatostatin and gastrin within the same cell. *J Histochem Cytochem* **24**:883, 1976.

114. Erlandsen SL, Rodning CB, Mortero C, Parsons JA, Lewis EA, Wilson ID: Immunocytochemical identification and localization of immunoglobulin A within Paneth cells of the rat small intestine. *J Histochem Cytochem* **24**:1085, 1976.

115. Okuno Y, Fukunaga T, Srisupnlack S, Fukai K: A modified PAP staining technique using sera from patients with dengue hemorrhagic fever: Four-step PAP staining technique. *Biken J* **22**:131, 1979.

116. Mason TE, Phifer RF, Spicer SS, Swallow RA, Dreskin RB: An immunoglobulin-enzyme bridge method for localizing tissue antigens. *J Histochem Cytochem* **17**:563, 1969.

117. Petrusz P, DiMeo P, Ordranneau P, Weaver C, Keefer CA: Improved immunoglobulin-enzyme bridge method for light microscopic demonstration of hormone-containing cells of the rat adenohypophysis. *Histochemistry* **46**:9, 1975.

118. El Etreby MF, Dubois MP: The utility of antisera to different synthetic ACTH's and MSH's for immunocytochemical staining of dog pituitary glands. *Histochemistry* **66**:245, 1980.

119. Willingham MC, Yamada SS, Bechtel PJ, Rutherford AV, Pastan IH: Ultrastructural immunocytochemical localization of myosin in cultured fibroblastic cells. *J Histochem Cytochem* **29**:1289, 1981.

120. Ribak CE, Vaughn JE, Saito K, Barber R, Roberts E: Glutamate decarboxylase localization in neurons of the olfactory bulb. *Brain Res* **126**:1, 1977.

121. Tougard C, Tixier-Vidal A, Avrameas S: Comparison between peroxidase-conjugated antigen or antibody and peroxidase-antiperoxidase complex in a postembedding procedure. *J Histochem Cytochem* **27**:1630, 1979.

122. Johansson O, Backmann J: Enhancement of immunoperoxidase staining using osmium tetroxide. *J Neurosci Meth* **7**:185, 1983.

123. Vacca LL, Abrahams SJ, Naftchi NE: A modified peroxidase-antiperoxidase procedure for improved localization of tissue antigens: Localization of substance P in rat spinal cord. *J Histochem Cytochem* **28**:297, 1980.

124. Ordonneau P, Petrusz P: Immunocytochemical demonstration of anterior pituitary hormones in the pars tuberalis of long-term hypophysectomized rats. *Am J Anat* **158**:491, 1980.

125. Ordonneau P, Lindstrom PB-M, Petrusz P: Four unlabeled antibody bridge techniques: A comparison. *J Histochem Cytochem* **29**:1397, 1981.

126. Marucci AA, Di Stefano HS, Dougherty RM: Preparation and use of soluble ferritin-antiferritin complexes as specific markers for immunoelectron microscopy. *J Histochem Cytochem* **22**:35, 1974.

127. Clark C, Downs E, Primus FJ: The unlabeled antibody method using glucose oxidase-antiglucose oxidase complexes. A sensitive alternative to immunoperoxidase for the detection of tissue antigens. *J Histochem Cytochem* **30**:27, 1982.

128. Nauta JJW, Pritz MB, Lasek R: Afferents of the rat caudoputamen studied with horseradish peroxidase. An evaluation of retrograde neuroanatomical research method. *Brain Res* **67**:219, 1974.

129. Priestley JV, Somogyi P, Cuello AC: Neurotransmitter-specific projection neurons revealed by combining PAP immunocytochemistry with retrograde transport of horseradish peroxidase. *Brain Res* **220**:231, 1981.

130. Bouker RM, Westland KN, Sullivan M, Coulter JD: A combined retrograde transport and immunocytochemical staining method for demonstrating the origin of serotonergic projections. *J Histochem Cytochem* **30:**805, 1982.

131. Beitz AJ: The nuclei of origin of brain stem enkephalin and substance P projection to the rodent nucleus raphé magnus. *Neuroscience* **7:**2753, 1982.

132. Lechan RM, Nestler JC, Jacobson S: Immunohistologic localization of retrogradally and anterogradally transported wheat germ agglutinin within the central nervous system of the rat. Application of immunostaining of a second antigen within the same neuron. *J Histochem Cytochem* **29:**1255, 1981.

133. Kawata M, Sano Y, Inenaga K, Yamashita H: Immunohistologic identification of lucifer yellow labeled neuron in the rat supraoptic nucleus. *Histochemistry* **78:**21, 1983.

134. Silverman A-J, Gadden CA, Zimmerman EA: Effects of adrenalectomy on the incorporation of ^{3}H-cytidine in neurophysin and vasopressin-containing neurons of the rat hypothalamus. *Neuroendocrinology* **30:**285, 1980.

135. Lauder JM, Petrusz P, Wallace JA, Dihome A, Wilkie MB, McCarthy K: Combined serotonin immunocytochemistry and ^{3}H-thymidine autoradiography. In vivo and in vitro methods. *J Histochem Cytochem* **30:**788, 1982.

136. Lehy T: Self-replication of somatostatin cells in the antral mucosa of rodents. *Cell Tiss Kinet* **15:**495, 1982.

137. Shivers RD, Harlan RE, Morrell JI, Pfaff DW: Absence of oestradiol concentration in cell nuclei of lutienizing hormone-releasing hormone-immunoreactive neurons. *Nature* **304:**345, 1983.

138. Rhodes CH, Morrell JI, Pfaff DW: Estrogen-concentrating neurophysin-containing hypothalamic magnocellular neuron in the vasopressin-deficient (Brattleboro) rat: A study combining steroid autoradiography and immunocytochemistry. *J Neurosci* **2:**1718, 1982.

139. Mohler M, Richards JG, Wu J-Y: Autoradiographic localization of benzediazepin receptors in immunocytochemically identified γ-aminobutyrergic synapses. *Proc Natl Acad Sci USA* **78:**1935, 1981.

140. Basbaum A, Glazer EJ, Lord BAP: Simultaneous ultrastructural localization of tritiated serotonin and immunoreactive peptides. *J Histochem Cytochem* **30:**780, 1982.

141. Brandtzaeg P: Prolonged incubation time in immunocytochemistry. Effect on fluorescent staining of immunoglobulin and epithelial components in ethanol and formaldehyde-fixed paraffin-embedded tissues. *J Histochem Cytochem* **29:**1302, 1981.

142. Nash DR, Crabbe PA, Heremans JF: Sequential immunofluorescent staining: a simple and useful technique. *Immunology* **16:**785, 1969, Blackwell Scientific Publications Limited.

143. Hökfelt T, Rehfeld JF, Skirboll L, Iremnck B, Goldstein M, Mackey K: Evidence for coexistence of dopamine and cholecystokinin in meso-limbic neurons. *Nature* **285:**476, 1980.

144. Tramu U, Pillez A, Leonardelli J: An efficient method of antibody elution for the successive or simultaneous localization of two antigens by immunocytochemistry. *J Histochem Cytochem* **26:**322, 1978.

145. Nakane PK: Simultaneous localization of multiple tissue antigens using peroxidase-labeled antibody method: a study on pituitary glands of the rat. *J Histochem Cytochem* **16:**557, 1968.

146. Vandesande F, Dierickx K: Identification of the vasopressin producing and of the oxytocin producing neurons in the hypothalamic magnocellular neurosecretory system. *Cell Tiss Res* **164:**153, 1955.

147. Ajika K: Simultaneous localization of luteinizing hormone-releasing hormone and catecholamine in rat hypothalamus. *J Ana* **128:**331, 1979.

148. Larsson L-I, Goltermann N, de Magistris L, Rehfeld J, Schwartz TW: Somatostatin cell processes as pathways for paracrine secretion. *Science* **205:**1393, 1975.

149. Sternberger LA, Joseph SA: The unlabeled antibody method. Contrasting color staining of paired pituitary hormones without antibody removal. *J Histochem Cytochem* **27:**1424, 1979.

150. Joseph SA, Sternberger LA: The unlabeled antibody method. Contrasting color staining of β-lipotropin and ACTH associated hypothalamic peptides without antibody removal. *J Histochem Cytochem* **27:**1430, 1979.

151. Valnes K, Brandtzaeg P: Unlabeled antibody peroxidase-antiperoxidase method combined with direct immunofluorescence. *J Histochem Cytochem* **29:**703, 1981.

152. Löfberg H, Strömblad L-G, Grabb AO, Olson S-O: Demonstration of γ-trace in normal and neoplastic endocrine A-cells of the pancreatic islets: An immunocytochemical study in monkey, rat and man. *Biomed Res* **2:**527, 1981.

153. Grubb A, Löfberg H: Human γ-trace. Structure, function and clinical use of concentration measurements. *Scand J Clin Lab Invest,* in press.

154. De Pasquale A, Peterlini D, Quaglino D: Immunocytochemical demonstration of different antigens in paraffin-embedded histologic sections. *Clin Lab Haematol* **4:**267, 1982.

155. Mason DY, Sammons R: Alkaline phosphatase and peroxidase for double immunoenzymatic labelling of cellular constituents. *J Clin Path* **31:**454, 1978.

Chapter Four

Tissue Preparation

The surface of free-floating cells can be stained in suspension. Precautions are necessary to prevent capping of surface antigens (page 44). Staining of free-floating cells is the most common application of immunocytochemistry to the study of the immune response, since cells of reticuloendothelial origin are naturally free floating. They are best studied by immunofluorescence which leaves their viability intact and permits enumeration and separation of cell types in a cell sorter.

The staining of free-floating cells by methods other than direct immunofluorescence is inconvenient because of the many centrifugations that are necessary in extensive washings. However, cells can be stained on slides. They can be smeared or cytocentrifuged onto the slides. Adhesion and penetration of immunocytochemical reagents is aided by fixation in solutions such as formolacetone mixtures, or if it is desirable to stain only cell surfaces, adhesion may be mediated by the use of poly-L-lysine treated slides. Normal serum pretreatment in the immunocytochemical staining is essential to obviate nonspecific adherence of antiserum to poly-L-lysine. Fc receptor reactivity must be excluded.

Free-floating cells can also be extruded from lymphoma biopsy specimens. However, Mason and Biberfeld (1) experienced diagnostic unpredictability, presumably due to the greater fragility of malignant cells and possibly because of the tendency of some cells to remain adherent to the reticular framework of the tissue.

Free-floating cells, of course, negate the main purpose of immunocytochemistry: that of detecting an antigen in situ in relation to surrounding tissue structure. Diagnostically, this can be a major drawback in lymphoma biopsies (page 289), in cases in which only a fraction of a specimen consists of malignant cells. If the specimen is examined in situ, the malignant area would be distinguished from surrounding tissue and examination of monoclonality of the immunoglobulin produced (an index of malignancy, page 291) would be restricted to the tumor area. If cells are extruded into suspension, the malignant cells will be mixed with normal cells and diagnosis of monoclonality may be missed.

Tissue culture cells, with the exception of blood cells and their precursors, grow in monolayers on surfaces. If stained immunocytochemically without fixation, only cell surface antigens are revealed. In order to observe the interior of the cells, similar fixatives as those used for solid tissues can be employed, or alternatively, the cells may be treated with lipid extractants, such as alcohol, acetone, or alcohol-ether mixtures.

Solid tissues must be sectioned to avoid scattering of image-forming light. For light microscopy at a resolution of 2 μm, interference of tissue overlaying the focal plane is minimal if the thickness of the section is less than that of an average tissue cell. Sections of 0.5 μm to 100μm thickness are suitable for immunocytochemical staining on the section.

Fresh tissues are not rigid enough for sectioning. Rigidity can be conferred upon tissue by freezing for sectioning in a cryostat. Alternatively, the tissue can be made rigid by a chemical process called *fixation*. After fixation, the tissue can be cut in a Vibratome (vibrating razor blade) or can be dehydrated, embedded in paraffin, sectioned, and deparaffinized prior to staining. Finally, plastic sections can be used instead of paraffin.

Fixation confers rigidity upon tissue by cross-linking proteins, and, in some cases, lipids or carbohydrates. The better the cross-linking, the better the morphological preservation. However, extensive cross-linking impairs antigens by direct chemical effects and by structural distortion. Fixatives are selective in the chemical groups they attack. Most fixatives bind covalently with amino groups, and leave carboxy groups and tyrosine and histidine unaffected. These unaffected groups may be important parts of epitopes that are, thus, retained for immunocytochemical reaction. Immunocytochemical detection of an antigen in fixed tissue depends only on those groups that are not destroyed by a fixative. However, direct covalent reaction of the fixative is not the only factor that impairs reactivity. Fixatives, by virtue of conferring rigidity to tissue, also impair accessibility of immunoreagents in certain situations, although promoting, in general, permeability of cell membranes. Fixation may also induce conformational changes in the antigens. Thus, total impairment of immunoreactivity may be extensive, even though the fixative may directly affect only selected chemical groups.

The loss of epitopes affects immunocytochemical staining. These effects are different, whether antisera or monoclonal antibodies are used. Antisera contain many heterogeneous antibodies, reacting, if specific, with different epitopes of a given antigen. Fixation may destroy most of these epitopes, leaving, however, some of them unaffected. It is via the unaffected epitopes that immunocytochemical examination of fixed tissue is possible. Most of the antibodies in antisera are unable to participate in the immunocytochemical reaction, and evaluation of staining is dependent on the few antibodies that may react with the few unaffected tissue epitopes.

In the early days of immunocytochemistry, methods were not sensitive enough to detect these few remaining epitopes. It had become axiomatic, that fixation, if used at all, must be of mild nature. However, fixation is necessary for good preservation of tissue morphology. Therefore, a compromise had to be made between the degree of fixation and the degree of desirable immunocytochemical reactivity. Preference for mild fixation or no fixation at all prompted the invention of the cryostat (2). Carefully prepared frozen sections leave immunoreactivity unaffected. However, lack of fixation often causes loss of antigens through leakage. Also, frozen sections, as well as poorly fixed tissues, often stain nonspecifically yielding background that is generally attributed to Fc receptors (page 51) or to "endogenous peroxidase" (page 113).

Once the PAP method has been introduced, it became apparent that one can sacrifice with impunity the loss of much antigenic reactivity. Not only has it become possible to use fixatives quite regularly, but it also became feasible to subject tissues to solvent extraction, heat, and conformational distortion encumbent to embedding in paraffin or plastic, at least in the case of light microscopy. This opened the avenue for re-examining a wealth of pathologic specimens stored in museums throughout the world. It permitted re-evaluation of tissues that had been fixed decades before the discovery of the specific antigens they contained. It also permitted surgical pathology on fixed, paraffin-embedded material, and increased thereby diagnostic acumen.

The caution of mild fixation was no longer necessary, and many optimal fixatives for tissue preservation found application in immunocytochemistry. However, the development was slow to come. Even while Baskin et al. (3) and Nancy Sternberger (4) found osmium tetroxide at times superior to other fixatives for light microscopic immunocytochemistry, it was possible to hear in scientific meetings that "Of course, everyone knows that osmium tetroxide abolished all immunoreactivity."

There is a big difference in the preservation of immunocytochemical reactivity after fixation, whether antisera or monoclonal antibodies are used. With monoclonal antibodies, immunoreactivity may be present or absent after fixation. Monoclonal antibodies react with only single epitopes (and cross-react with chemically related epitopes). If, in an antigen, most epitopes are destroyed by fixation, most monoclonal antibodies will no longer react. This phenomenon can be used to advantage. Abolition of reaction with monoclonal antibodies by fixation or other chemical treatment of the tissue may tell us something about the nature of the monoclonal antibody idiotype. Suppose paraformaldehyde treatment abolishes reactivity; we may suspect that the antibody reacts with amino groups, especially if treatment with fluorodinitrobenzine has the same effect. Suppose iodination abolishes reactivity; we may suspect an antibody specific for a tyrosine or histidine group. Suppose phenylmethylsulfonyl fluoride abolishes immunoreactivity with certain hydrolases; we may suspect an antibody specific to a serine or threonine group.

Since monoclonal antibodies, reactive with a native antigen, more often than not fail to react when tissue is fixed and embedded, the selection of suitable monoclonal antibodies for immunocytochemistry becomes an important aspect of hybridoma technology if intended for use on tissue sections (page 251).

FIXATIVES

Fixatives are solutions that harden the tissue and immobilize its constituents. Immobilization is needed to prevent leaching of constituents during immunocytochemical staining and to preserve the structural relationship of retained constituents. Poor fixation is readily observable in the microscope by poor structure.

More stringent preservation of structure is needed for electron microscopy than for light microscopy.

Fixation must be irreversible. Alcohols or acetone harden tissue and presumably prevent dislocation of constituents. However, their reaction with many proteins is reversible, so that when the tissue is hydrated during immunocytochemical reaction, structure will be lost. Still, these solvents are useful for fixation of free-floating cells immobilized on sections.

As expected, different antigens vary in their susceptibility to fixation. One could be tempted, therefore, to devise an optimal fixative for each antigen. However, antisera also differ in the composition of antibodies reactive with a given antigen. Therefore, a fixative optimal for a given antigen with one antiserum may not be optimal with another. With monoclonal antibodies, this effect is even more pronounced, in that the antibodies may react well when tissue is fixed with one fixative and not at all when fixed with another.

Since the choice of a fixative depends both on antigen and antiserum, we think it is unrealistic to examine a large battery of fixatives for every antigen and every single antiserum used for detection of this antigen. Fortunately experience has led to selection of a number of fixatives that are suitable for many systems.

We will discuss in the following those fixatives that are most commonly recommended and will try to arrive at a single strategy for the choice of a fixative, which although not necessarily selecting the best fixative for a given system, usually permits adequate immunocytochemical staining without necessity of a great deal of preliminary work.

Formaldehyde, or preferably its redissolved solid polymer, paraformaldehyde, reacts mainly with free amino groups. Cross-linkage among proteins may occur via polymerized forms of formaldehyde. Polymerized forms may be present in the fixative solution, or they may form after reaction with tissue. Polymerization is not very extensive, so that we can classify paraformaldehyde at concentrations of up to 4% as a reasonably mild fixative. Calcium formol is often used in routine pathology. It is generally a satisfactory fixative for immunocytochemistry. Sometimes tissue fixation in routine specimens is poor and immunocytochemical reaction may be absent or complicated by background. In general, these problems derive from inadequate penetration of fixatives, rather than the fixative itself. Postmortem changes may also contribute to nonspecific staining.

Sometimes the staining in formaldehyde-fixed specimens is poor or absent. Isaacson et al. (5) found that, especially in lymphoma diagnosis, these are the cases that most likely benefit from tryptic digestion of the sections prior to immunocytochemical processing (page 109).

Aldehydes do not react with neurosecretory peptides that possess N-terminal pyroglutamate and no lysine. Immunoreactivity attributed to these peptides in aldehyde-fixed material is due to other substances (page 386).

Bouin's fixative is a saturated solution of picric acid containing 4% paraformaldehyde and 1% acetic acid. It is the fixative that has found widest application in experimental work as a perfusion and postfixation solution. When convenient, it is also recommended as primary fixative in surgical pathology. Its use in autopsy material would help in retrospective immunocytochemistry. Tissues that require tryptic digestion after formaldehyde fixation alone, may not need it after Bouin's fixative.

Zamboni's fixative is a saturated solution of picric acid containing paraformaldehyde in neutral phosphate buffer. Poorly cross-linking aldehydes, such as formaldehyde, do not preserve structure well enough to be suited for electron microscopy. Zamboni's fixative appears to be milder than Bouin's fixative, and the presence of picric acid appears to help in maintaining at least some ultrastructure. It has been the principal fixative for postembedding staining electron microscopy.

Glutaraldehyde is a dialdehyde with much greater cross-linking potential than formaldehyde. It preserves structure better, as mainly evident by the preservation of membranes in electron microscopy. Glutaraldehyde reacts primarily with the ε-amino groups of protein lysine to form complexes of unknown composition, to a lesser extent with α-amino groups and thiol groups, and to still lesser extent with the phenolic ring of tyrosine and imidazol ring of histidine. Glutaraldehyde seems to destroy, in most instances, detectability of antigen by immunofluorescence. However, it has been a useful fixative in the unlabeled antibody method. Glutaraldehyde increases the autofluorescence of tissue and thus the background in immunofluorescence.

Glutaraldehyde, by virtue of its cross-linking qualities, hardens tissues so much that it prevents its own penetration, whether in perfusion or immersion fixations. Mixtures of formaldehyde with glutaraldehyde do not encounter these difficulties. For electron microscopic immunocytochemistry, a 4% solution of paraformaldehyde with 0.2% glutaraldehyde is usually satisfactory (page 127). It can be used in the pre- or postembedding mode. Glutaraldehyde concentration may be increased, more so for light than for electron microscopy. Paraformaldehyde concentration may be decreased to 2%.

Carnegie et al (6) found that a labile antigen, such as ovine chorionic gonadotropin, can nevertheless be visualized by immunofluorescence if fixed in 3% glutaraldehyde and embedded at low temperature in the water miscible resin, glycomethacrylate.

Using glutaraldehyde with or without formaldehyde admixture, Smart et al. (7) was able to visualize, by the peroxidase-conjugated antibody method, immunoglobulin in semithin sections of Spur low viscosity resin-embedded human tonsils. When glutaraldehyde alone was used, trypsinization of sections was essential for light microscopic, but not for postembedding staining electron-microscopic localization (Fig. 4-1). Trypsinization impaired structural detail for electron microscopy. If formaldehyde was admixed with glutaraldehyde, trypsinization was not necessary even for light microscopy. These data led credence to the thought that one function of trypsinization is accessibility of the tissue antigen to the immunocytochemical reagents. Such accessibility would be especially called for in glutaraldehyde-fixed material, when penetration has been impaired. It was no longer necessary when glutaraldehyde-fixed material has been thin sectioned for electron microscopy.

Using a variety of antigens and antibodies, we did not see improvement in visualization of Bouin-fixed material by tryptic digestion nor did Isaacson et al. (5) find a need for digestion in non-formaldehyde-fixed material. These findings suggest that the advisability of proteolytic digestion does not only depend on the antigen under study, but may also be a function of fixation.

Glutaraldehyde fixation may be followed by osmium tetroxide for further

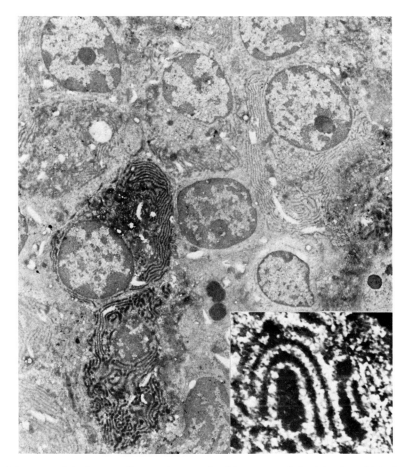

Figure 4-1. κ-reactivity in two adjacent plasma cells of human tonsil fixed in glutaraldehyde. Plasma cells in the right upper corner are unstained. Insert shows localization in the cisternae of the endoplasmic reticulum. Postembedding staining peroxidase-conjugated antibody method. This is one of the few instances in which postembedding staining electron microscopy revealed antigen in a location other than secretion granules. Immunoglobulin is a very abundant end product of plasma cells. ×5000. Inset: 25,200 (From Smart et al. (7).]

membrane stabilization. If used in postembedding staining electron microscopy, the osmium must be removed by oxidation with hydrogen peroxide, periodic acid, or permanganate with oxalic acid (3).

Perfix consists of isopropyl alcohol, paraformaldehyde, trichloracetic acid, and zinc chloride. Eng (8) found formaldehyde a satisfactory fixative in his work on glial fibrillary acidic protein (GFAP) immunocytochemistry in adult tissues. However, in developing animals (9), staining was poor with formaldehyde but excellent with Perfix (Fig. 4-2). These findings illustrate different susceptibilities to fixation by tissues of different origin. Here, use of another fixative was important in demonstration of the earliest time of appearance of GFAP in development. Without investigation of fixatives, an erroneously late date would have been assigned.

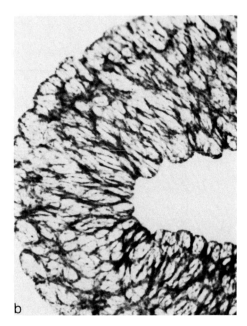

a   b

Figure 4-2.   A 19-day old rat exhibits no glial fibrillary acidic protein in the optic nerve when fixed in 2% paraformaldehyde (a). Fixation in Perfix reveals the protein (b). PAP method. ×300. [Reprinted by permission of Raven Press from Eng LF: The glial fibrillary acidic protein in Bradshaw RA, Schneider DM (eds) *Proteins of the Nervous System*. 2nd ed. New York 1980 (9).]

Periodide, an entirely different fixative that depends mainly on cross-linking of sialic acid-containing cellular membranes, has been introduced by McLean and Nakane (10). The fixative contains periodate, lysine, and paraformaldehyde. The periodate oxidizes the membrane carbohydrate to aldehydes which are then cross-linked via lysine. Paraformaldehyde was added to stabilize intracellular proteins on the assumption that it does not react appreciably with the added lysine.

Benzoquinone is a cross-linking fixative that reacts in two stages. According to Bu'Lock et al. (11), its primary reaction is with nucleophilic amino groups which involves the formation of monosubstituted hydroquinones. However, this material must be oxidized, either by oxygen or another molecule of hydroquinone, to restore the quinone capable of undergoing the second substitution, and thus the cross-linking. Therefore, fixation is best carried out at 37°C in well-oxygenated, slightly alkaline buffer.

Benzoquinone introduced as a fixative by Pearse and Polak (12) permitted preservation of neurosecretory peptides in situations in which other fixatives gave less intense staining (13). Perhaps the biphasic nature of the reaction of hydroquinone retards its cross-linking reactivity compared to that of glutaraldehyde and permits, thereby, more penetration of this reagent into tissue prior to effecting cross-linkage.

Acrolein is a γ-monaldehyde which because of its α-β unsaturation acts as a cross-linking agent. King et al. (14) found it to be a superior fixative for neurosecretory peptides, when used in perfusion fixation. If only restricted to immer-

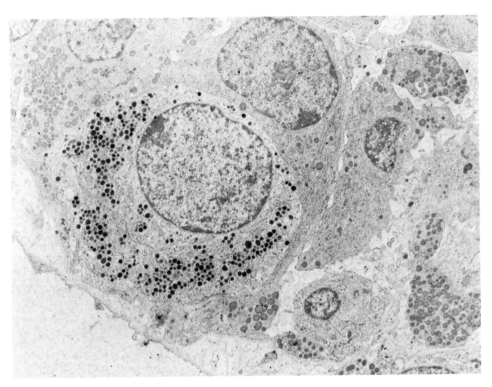

Figure 4-3. Luteinizing hormone (revealed by antiluteinizing hormone-β) is found in the secretion granules of a rat gonadotroph fixed by immersion in acrolein. PAP postembedding technique. Uranyl acetate counterstain. ×4,670. [From Smith and Keefer (15).]

sion fixation, glutaraldehyde is not suitable because of its poor penetration qualities. However, in the hands of Smith and Keefer (15), acrolein was an excellent immersion fixative for pituitaries (Fig. 4-3).

Osmium tetroxide made a late entry into immunocytochemistry as a fixative. Osmium tetroxide insolubilizes unsaturated fatty acids by cyclization of its double bonds. However, it also reacts with protein. Nielson and Griffith (16) blocked amino acids in a manner similar to their blocking in peptide bonds and found that osmium tetroxide forms stable complexes with histidine, lysine, cysteine, and methionine under conditions that simulate tissue fixation. Apparently osmium tetroxide forms intermolecular and intramolecular bonds via these amino acids. Osmium tetroxide seems to stabilize antigens, especially toward reactivity of the reagents used in polymerizing epoxy resins. It has, therefore, been found especially suitable for work with semithin sections produced for light microscopy (3,4).

FIXATION STRATEGIES

Using the fixatives described, we may now return to the question, "Which fixative to use in a given, new situation?" There is no generally applicable answer, but experience with the above fixatives by many investigators permits delineation of a simple strategy which should give good localization for most antigens:

For pathological specimens: Try whatever fixative is routinely used in the hospital. If staining is negative or poor, try proteolytic digestion of the sections. If this fails, try Bouin's fixative.

For most antigens in experimental situations: Use perfusion fixation whenever feasible (Nembutal anaesthesia). Bouin's fixative is first choice. If this fails, try formaldehyde with added glutaraldehyde, with and without proteolytic digestion. If this fails, try osmic acid, alone or after glutaraldehyde-formaldehyde. If this fails, try acrolein or benzoquinone, with and without postosmication.

For neurosecretory peptides: Try Bouin's fixative. If this fails, or if localization is sparse, try benzoquinone. If this fails to improve results, try acrolein.

For semithin sections: Use glutaraldehyde-formaldehyde mixtures with or without osmication. If this fails, use Bouin's fixative. If this fails, try acrolein with or without osmication.

For pre-embedding staining electron microscopy: Start with glutaraldehyde-formaldehyde mixtures. If this fails, use acrolein. If this fails, use benzoquinone.

For postembedding staining electron microscopy: Try acrolein for best structure. Benzoquinone may be tried, but experience is limited. If this fails, try formaldehyde-glutaraldehyde mixtures. If this fails, try Zamboni's fixative. Structure will not be very good with Zamboni's fixative.

SECTIONING

Thin sections for electron microscopy are usually 70 nm thick. For light microscopy, we have a choice of section thickness from 0.5 μm to 100 μm. Resolution is better, the thinner the section. Thick sections are useful to trace fiber structures over long distances.

Vibratome Sections

The Vibratome sections with a vibrating razor blade to usuable thicknesses of 20 to 100 μm. At these thicknesses, it is not necessary to embed the tissue. As a consequence, the deleterious effects of dehydration in the preparation of paraffin sections and dehydration and polymerization in that of Epoxy sections are obviated. Lipid-soluble material is retained, and cell membrane antigens are well visualized.

If a mild procedure is desired, Vibratome sections are the approach of choice. Fixation is desirable because tissue is sectioned easier and loss of important constituents from leaching during staining may be prevented. However, it is possible to section unfixed material with the Vibratome especially if tissue is kept cool. In contrast to tissue chopper sections, Vibratome sections do not distort the tissue severely and can be mounted on glass slides without loss of orientation toward adjacent sections. In contrast to frozen sections, structural details are better preserved with Vibratome sections. Vibratome sections are best stained in 24-well culture dishes. Sections are transferred to wells with an artist's brush. They wrap around the brush, but flatten upon reimmersion in liquid.

Immunocytochemistry in Vibratome sections requires a sensitive method, where sensitivity is measured by ratio of signal to noise. The structures to be stained in Vibratome sections range from 1 to 20 μm in diameter. The sections may be up to 100 μm in thickness. All the section's thickness contributes to background. The contribution to signal strength by the stained structure is limited by its size. With the PAP method and monoclonal antibodies, even Vibratome sections are free of background. With antisera, freedom of background depends on the nature of the first antibody and its dilution. Under conditions of high dilution of antisera, Piekut and Casey (17) have shown that Vibratome sections are essentially free of background (Fig. 4-4).

In the work of Nancy Sternberger et al. (18), the use of 100-μm-thick Vibratome sections permitted the tracing of oligodendrocyte processes for considerable distances by merely changing the focal depth in Normarski differential interference optics (Fig. 3-8). A reconstruction of images thus obtained from the same field (Fig. 3-9) showed that 4- to 38-μm-long processes from a single cell could attach to 10 different axons forming myelin sheaths that belong to longitudinally and transversely oriented fiber tracts. The finding explains how a single plaque in multiple sclerosis (page 485) may lead to widely divergent, disseminated symptoms.

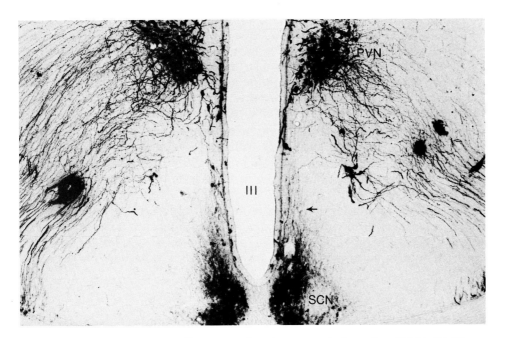

Figure 4-4. Vasopressin-containing fibers emerge from the paraventricular nucleus (PVN) in this 80-μm-thick Vibratome section contributing to the hypothalamo-hypophyseal tract. Some fibers approach the third ventricle (III). Some of the vasopressin fibers from the suprachiasmic nucleus (SN) extend dorsally. Antivasopressin 1 : 20,000. PAP method. Bar is 100 μm. [From Piekut and Casey (17).]

Paraffin Sections

Whenever possible, paraffin sections are to be preferred because they are easy to produce in quantity. It is the section of first choice when exploring new antigens in the PAP method. Immunofluorescence sensitivity is often not sufficient for routine paraffin sections, but both, sensitivity and background, may be improved by proteolytic digestion after paraffin removal and before immunocytochemical staining.

Paraffin sections of 2- to 7-μm thickness are suitable for immunocyto-chemistry. Structural detail is superior with 2-μm-thick sections, and immunocy-tochemical staining is strong. Thin paraffin sections are well suited for examina-tion of colocalization of a number of antigens in serial sections. These paraffin sections are cut from cool tissue blocks. The thinness of these sections assures that most cells are repesented in two to four adjacent sections.

Seven-μm-thick sections are to be preferred for routine work. Penetration of immunocytochemical reagents is complete (at least when fixation is in Bouin's solution) and uniforn staining is obtained if the antigen possesses uniform distri-bution.

Two-μm-thick sections stain slightly less intensely than 7-μm-thick sections, but the morphology is better. However, the appearance of longitudinal nerve fiber projection is somewhat punctate compared to distinct bundles that can be identified in 7-μm-thick paraffin sections.

Direct immunofluorescence has been quite successful in paraffin sections. Weisenburger et al. (19) were able to conduct a retrospective study on sporadic legionnaire's pneumonia and identified the causative bacillus, Legionella pneumophilia, on paraffin sections. Again using direct immunofluorescence, Qualman and Keren (20) and Mera et al. (21) were able to detect immunoglobu-lins in paraffin-embedded biopsy specimens of kidney or skin, respectively, pro-vided the sections were treated with trypsin before immunostaining.

Deparaffinized sections adhere well during the staining procedure, provided clean slides treated with chrome alum are used. Huang et al. (22) found im-proved adhesion when treating slides with poly-L-lysine. Polymers of molecular weight of 350,000 and a concentration of 0.05% to 0.1% were most effective. After poly-L-lysine treatment, it may be particularly important to incorporate the normal serum step as first step in the immunocytochemical staining procedure (page 105), in order to ensure that all positive lysine charges are neutralized before applying specific antibodies. For best adhesion, it is desirable to glue sections on the slides. The procedure (page 110) is especially important, if sec-tions are to be treated with proteolytic enzymes, such as in some studies on the nature of epitopes visualized by given antibodies (page 448).

Plastic Sections

Semithin plastic sections, 0.5 μm to 1 μm thick, give the best resolution for light microscopy. Spurr's low-viscosity epoxy resin, Epon, or Epon-Araldite mixtures are suitable for embedding. Resins must be removed prior to staining to permit penetration of immunoreagents. Rodning et al. (23) used 2% ethanolic sodium methoxide, while Nancy Sternberger (4) used 50% ethanolic sodium methoxide. Baskin et al. (3) introduced osmium tetroxide as a fixative for such sections, and Nancy Sternberger (4) found not only superior resolution in semithin sections but also superior immunocytochemical staining intensity after osmium tetroxide fixation (Fig. 4-5).

In the use of plastic sections for light microscopy, it is necessary to remove the plastic from the sections. Complete removal is contraindicated in electron microscopy, because the integrity of the plastic section is needed for support of the

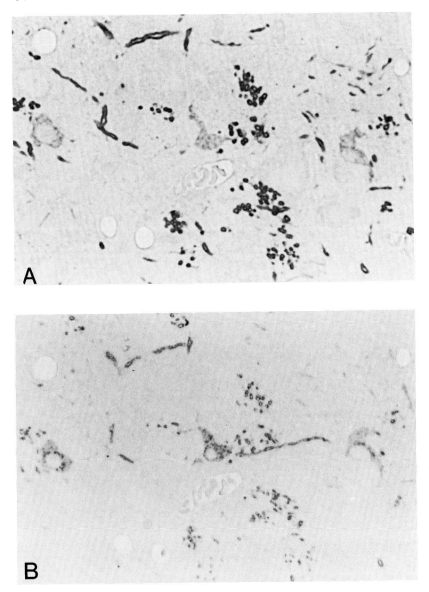

Figure 4-5. Brainstem of 7-day old rat. Glutaraldehyde-osmium tetroxide fixation. 1-μm-thick Epon section stained with antimyelin basic protein (a) and antimyelin-associated glycoprotein (b). PAP method. ×800. [From Nancy Sternberger (4).]

tissue during staining on uncoated grids. Therefore, for electron microscopy, it is necessary that the section only be etched, or that otherwise the permeability of its superficial layers be increased. Horobin and Proctor (24) have shown that aqueous hydrogen peroxide is an effective agent for this purpose, as it removes 8% of the weight of plastic sections.

Using 1-μm-thick plastic sections, Bloch et al. (25) were able to show that in most neurons of the rat arcuate nucleus, β-melanocyte-stimulating hormone, β-endorphin, α-melanocyte-stimulating hormones, and 17-39 ACTH were coloca-

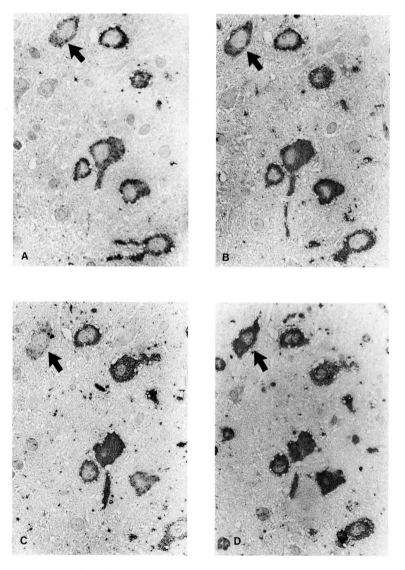

Figure 4-6.   Arcuate nucleus of rat after intravenous injection of colchicine. Zamboni's fixation. Araldite embedment. Serial sections, 3-μm thick. Stained with (A) anti-β-melanocyte-stimulating hormone; (B) anti-β-endorphin; (C) anti-α-melanocyte-stimulating hormone; (D) anti-17-39-ACTH. PAP method. One cell (arrows) in (A), (B), and (D) is unstained with anti-α-melanocyte-stimulating hormone shown in (C). ×415. [From Bloch et al. (25).]

lized, as expected, from the obligatory post-translational assembly of these peptides from a common precursor (page 359). However, one cell did not express α-melanocyte-stimulating hormone even though 1-39 ACTH in this cell was cleaved to 17-39 ACTH, as indicated by the staining for the latter peptide (Fig. 4-6). This raises the possibility that either α-melanocyte-stimulating hormone was cleaved further, or that in some cells the precursor is different from preproopiomelanocortin. It is conceivable that rare forms of preproopiomelanocortin still may await discovery. While preproopiomelanocortin may have been the only opioid peptide precursor in the pituitary tumor from which it had first been isolated, and even though considerable homology exists between this preproopiomelanocortin and that found in the arcuate nucleus, evidence does not permit the conclusion that every ACTH neuron in the arcuate area necessarily forms the same preproopiomelanocortin (page 360).

REFERENCES

1. Mason DY, Biberfeld P: Technical aspects of lymphoma immunohistology. *J Histochem Cytochem* **78:**731, 1980.

2. Coons AH, Kaplan MH: Localization of antigens in tissue cells. II. Improvement in a method for the detection of antigen by means of fluorescent antibody. *J Exp Med* **91:**1, 1950.

3. Baskin DG, Erlandsen SL, Parsons JA: Immunocytochemistry with osmium-fixed tissue. I. Light microscopic localization of growth hormone and prolactin with the unlabeled antibody enzyme method. *J Histochem Cytochem* **27:**867, 1979.

4. Sternberger NH: Patterns of oligodendrocyte function seen by immunocytochemistry, in Norton WT (ed): *Advances in Neurochemistry*, Vol 5, Chapt 4, New York, Plenum 1984, pp 125–173.

5. Isaacson P, Wright DH, Judd MA, Jones DB, Payne SV: The nature of immunoglobulin-containing cells in malignant lymphoma: An immunoperoxidase study. *J Histochem Cytochem* **28:**761, 1980.

6. Carnegie JA, McCully ME, Robertson AA: Embeddment in glycol methacrylate at low temperature allows immunofluorescence localization of a labile tissue protein. *J Histochem Cytochem* **28:**308, 1980.

7. Smart Y, Jerrome D, Millard PR: Ultrastructural demonstration of immunoglobulin in glutaraldehyde-fixed resin-embedded human tonsil by an indirect immunoperoxidase method. *J Immunol Meth* **45:**95, 1981.

8. Dixon RG, Eng LF: Glial fibriallary acidic protein in the optic nerve of the developing albino rat: An immunoperoxidase study of paraffin-embedded tissue. *J Comp Neurol* **201:**215, 1981.

9. Eng LF. The glial fibrillary acidic protein, in Bradshaw RA, Schneider DM (eds): *Proteins of the Nervous System*. 2nd ed. New York, Raven Press, 1980, pp 85–117.

10. McLean IW, Nakane PK: Periodate-lysine-paraformaldehyde fixative. A new fixative for immunoelectron microscopy. *J Histochem Cytochem* **22:**1077, 1974.

11. Bu'Lock AJ, Vaillart C, Dockray GJ, Bu'Lock JD: A rational approach to fixation of peptidergic nerve cell bodies in the gut using parabenzoquinone. *Histochemistry* **74:**49, 1982.

12. Pearse AGE, Polak JM: Bifunctional reagents, as vapor and liquid phase fixatives for immunocytochemistry. *Histochem J* **7:**179, 1975.

13. Roberts GW, Woodhams PL, Bryant MG, Crow TJ, Bloom SR, Polak JM: VIP in the rat brain: Evidence for a major pathway linking the amygdala and hypothalamus via the stria terminalis. *Histochemistry* **65:**103, 1980.

14. King JC, Lechan RM, Kugel G, Anthony ELP: Acrolein: A fixative for immunocytochemical localization of peptides in the central nervous system. *J Histochem Cytochem* **31:**62, 1983.

15. Smith PF, Keefer DA: Acrolein/glutaraldehyde as a fixative for combined light and electron

microscopic immunocytochemical determination of pituitary hormones in immersion-fixed material. *J Histochem Cytochem* **30**:1307, 1982.

16. Nielson AJ, Griffith WP: Tissue fixation by osmium tetroxide. A possible role for proteins. *J Histochem Cytochem* **27**:997, 1979.

17. Piekut DT, Casey SM: Penetration of immunoreagents in vibratome sectioned brain: A light and electron microscope study. *J Histochem Cytochem* **31**:669, 1983.

18. Sternberger NH, Itoyama Y, Kies MW, Webster H de F: Immunocytochemical method to identify brain protein in myelin-forming oligodendrocytes of newborn rat central nervous system. *J Neurocytol* **7**:251, 1978.

19. Weisenberger DD, Helms CM, Renner ED: Sporadic legionnaire's disease. A pathologic study of 23 fatal cases. *Arch Path Lab Med* **105**:130, 1981.

20. Qualman SJ, Keren DF: Immunofluorescence of deparaffinized, trypsin-treated renal tissues. Preservation of antigens as an adjunct to diagnosis of disease. *Lab Invest* **41**:483, 1979.

21. Mera SL, Young EW, Bradfield JWB: Direct immunofluorescence of skin using formalin-fixed paraffin-embedded sections. *J Clin Path* **33**:365, 1980.

22. Huang WM, Gibson SJ, Facer P, Gu J, Polak JM: Improved section adhesion for immunocyto-chemistry using high molecular weight polymers of L-lysine as a slide coating. *Histochemistry* **77**:275, 1983.

23. Rodning CB, Erlandsen SL, Coulter, HD, Wilson ID: Immunocytochemical localization if IgA antigens in sections embedded in epoxy resin. *J Histochem Cytochem* **28**:199, 1980.

24. Horobin RW, Proctor J: Estimating the effect of etching agents on plastic sections. *J Microsc* **126**:169, 1982.

25. Bloch B, Bugnon C, Fellman D, Lenys D, Gouget A: Neurons of the rat hypothalamus reactive with antisera against endorphins, ACTH, MSH- LPH. *Cell Tiss Res* **204**:1, 1979.

Chapter Five

Specificity of Antisera

Lack of background from the immunocytochemical reagents determines the quality of an immunocytochemical method (pages 83 and 142). In indirect and unlabeled antibody methods, the quality of immunoreagents or *method specificity* is established by substituting buffer for the first antiserum in the otherwise complete staining sequence that includes pretreatment of sections with normal serum or equivalent reagents. Once method specificity has been established, we are ready to examine the specificity of the first antibodies. Poor specificity of the first antibody may be expressed by diffuse staining of many structures besides those bearing the antigen used for immunization. In this case, the first antibody will produce background, irrespective of the immunocytochemical method used. In case the first antibody does not produce background, poor specificity could still be expressed by staining a number of defined structures besides those bearing the antigen used for immunization. A classic example is the staining of thyrotrophs by antiluteinizing hormone, which is due to antibodies to α-chains that are identical in luteinizing hormone and thyrotropic hormone.

Antisera, because of the presence of a large array of antibodies to unknown constituents, will give background if used at high concentrations. Most of these antibodies are present in small amounts and may have primary specificities for other epitopes than those found in the tissue. This contribution to background is produced because of *cross-reaction,* rather than the specific reaction with unknown antigens that may have evoked them. Cross-reactions are, by definition, reactions of low affinity. For this reason, many of the broad-spectrum cross-reactions resulting from antiserum can be eliminated by dilution. Thus, dilution reduces background. The specific reaction is retained, because of the high affinity of specific antibodies. Therefore, it is important, in immunocytochemistry, to use diluted first antibodies. High dilutions of antibody can only be accomplished when *sensitive* methods are used. In permitting high dilutions of first antisera, a more sensitive method also becomes a more *specific* method.

In contrast to antisera or antibodies, affinity-purified from antisera, monoclonal antibodies usually do not encounter background. They still may cross-react with structures other than those possessing the immunizing antigen. Monoclonal antibodies only give a staining which looks like background if they are specific to epitopes distributed throughout the tissue examined.

CAUSES OF IMPAIRED SPECIFICITY

In examining specificity with antisera, we must consider (Table 5-1):

1.   Antibodies to antigens which the immunized host has encountered prior to immunization.
2.   Antibodies to impurities in the immunizing antigen.
3.   Antibodies to regions in a given antigen determined by genes shared with other antigens.
4.   True cross-reacting antibodies.

If we were to substitute affinity-purified antibodies derived from antisera, we will eliminate antibodies not reactive with the purifying antigen. However, we will retain antibodies to impurities in this antigen and may increase cross-reactivity of the purified antibody, because purification yields preferentially the antibodies of lowest affinities (page 28), liable to the highest degrees of cross-reactivities.

With properly selected monoclonal antibodies, we eliminate antibodies to previous immunologic experience of the host lymphocytes and antibodies to impurities in the immunizing antigen. Selection of monoclonal antibodies gives us opportunity to eliminate or to detect antibodies to regions in the immunizing antigen, shared with different antigens, but determined by identical genes. Because of high-affinity selection of monoclonal antibodies, we are also likely to decrease immunocytochemical cross-reactivity.

The issues of immunocytochemical specificity between antisera and antiserum-derived antibodies on the one hand, and monoclonal antibodies on the other, are so different, that we have discussed them in separate chapters.

The question to be asked about specificity is whether an antiserum localizes immunologically only antigens presumed to be used for immunization, or does it

Table 5-1.   Causes of Poor Specificity

	Antisera	Antibodies Purified from Antisera	Monoclonal Antibodies
Antibodies from previous immunologic experience	Present	Absent	Absent
Antibodies to impurities in antigen	Present	Present	Absent
Antibodies reacting with shared determinants in different antigens	Present	Present	Present
True cross-reacting antibodies	Present	Enhanced	Diminished

localize in addition one of the following: unrelated substances or different forms of the immunizing antigen.

With monoclonal antibodies, we will ask the same questions, if we use defined antigens for immunization. We may refine our question by asking which epitope in our antibodies mediates the immunocytochemical reaction. However, if we deal with unknown antigens and use monoclonal antibodies to define new antigens, the question must be raised differently. Instead of asking whether the reaction is specific, we ask which is the epitope that mediates the reaction. This question requires a more specific answer than the question whether an antigen is specific and, indeed, has formed the basis for providing monoclonal antibody immunocytochemistry as a tool to monitor biochemical processes in situ (Chapters Six and Ten).

Antibodies from Previous Immunologic Experience

These antibodies are sometimes called natural antibodies. Since gnodobiotic animals form little immunoglobulin, it is likely that most natural antibodies are, in fact, the result of a previous unknown and undefined immunologic experience of the host. However, it is possible that even without any antigenic stimulation, a minimal amount of antibody secretion occurs continually, so that in addition to the idiotypic receptors on the cell surface, normal animals possess small amounts of antibody in circulation that are determined genetically and whose production has not been reinforced by any immunologic experience. These antibodies would be true natural antibodies. Common natural antibodies are small amounts of antibody to sheep erythrocytes found in most mammals except sheep. Antiblood group activities in normal human sera may, however, be the result of previous antigenic experience with carbohydrates similar to those of the blood group antigens, except that individuals of a given blood group, say blood group B, would be tolerant of blood group B antigens (page 475). Normal antibodies probably have lower affinities than immune antibodies, because immunization involves a drive toward higher affinities.

Antibodies to Impurities in the Immunizing Antigen

When a mixture of antigens is used for immunization, in general most of the antibodies react with the predominant fraction. However, the proportion of antibodies reacting with a minor component to those reacting with a major component is higher in the antiserum than the proportion of minor and major components in the antigen. Thus, the effect of impurities in an antigen preparation is magnified by immunization. Hence, it is common to observe more than one precipitin line when an antiserum against an isolated, presumably purified antigen, is reacted with nonpurified antigen in immunodiffusion. For example, rabbit antiserum to isolated human α-fetoprotein (page 469) gives two precipitin lines with α-fetoprotein-containing adult serum. Removal of one of these lines by absorption with normal adult human serum (devoid of α-fetoprotein) is one of the steps necessary to make the serum monospecific for the diagnostic immunocytochemical reaction for primary hepatoma (the other step is separation from antibodies reacting with normal human liver by absorption with and elution from an immunoabsorbent of insolubilized human α-fetoprotein).

Antibodies to Regions in the Immunizing Antigen Determined by Genes Shared with Other Antigens

Most protein antigens possess different regions that are antigenic. Each antigenic region usually bears different epitopes. Each epitope evokes its own types of antibodies. Some proteins possess specific epitopes, as well as epitopes shared with other proteins. These shared epitopes may lead to nonspecific staining. The detection of the class of immunoglobulin contained in an antiferritin-producing cell (Fig. 3-69) requires antisera monospecific for the class. The immunization of rabbits with IgM, for example, yields antibodies specific for IgM that form a single immunodiffusion line and suggests that the IgM used for immunization probably is free of major impurities (Fig. 5-1). However, the antibodies also react with IgG, forming a line of identity with IgM (there would be two lines, that cross at the point where they meet, if the antigens were nonidentical). The line of identity is due to antibodies to IgM L-chains that are identical to the IgG L-chains. In addition, however, there is a spur over the line between IgM and the antiserum. This spur is due to antibodies in the antiserum not reactive with IgG. These antibodies penetrate the domain of the diffused IgG without precipitating. They will precipitate only when reaching the fringe of the domain of diffusion of the IgM. These antibodies must be isolated, free of antibody cross-reacting with IgG in order to ensure unequivocal localization of the IgM-producing cell (Fig. 3-69, AM). Absorption of the antiserum with L chains makes it monospecific for IgM (Fig. 5-2). However, immunodiffusion will not be a sufficient criterion for immunocytochemistry.

Another example of impaired specificity because of common epitopes in different antigens is the immunocytochemical reaction of antisera to the pituitary glycoproteins, luteinizing hormone, follicle-stimulating hormone, and thyrotrophic hormone. These antigens share common α-chains and will "cross-react."

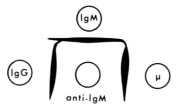

Figure 5-1. Immunodiffusion of an antiserum specific to an antigen that possesses common epitopes with another antigen (schematic). The antiserum (e.g., anti-IgM produced by immunization with IgM) forms a single line of identity with its specific antigen (IgM) and a nonspecific antigen (IgG). A second line spurs over this line of identity between the antiserum and the IgM well. This line is due to antibodies that do not precipitate with the IgG and, hence, penetrate its domain until they reach the IgM. Their line of precipitation is confluent with the line of identity because the epitopes responsible for it are in the same molecule as those responsible for the line of identity. The line of identity between IgM and μ chains is due to the antigenic determinants responsible for this spur (schematic).

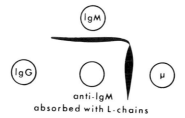

Figure 5-2. After absorption of the antiserum (Fig. 5-1) with the epitopes shared by the immunizing antigen (IgM) and the nonspecifically reacting material (IgG)—namely, after absorption with light chains—immunodiffusion has become specific. The line between IgG and the antiserum has disappeared, and only the spuring line of Fig. 5-1 remains (schematic).

Antiserum to luteinizing hormone-releasing hormone (LHRH) reveals pathways considered to be those of LHRH. However, LHRH is lost from the section during its preparation and staining. It has been shown that we deal here with an immunocytochemical reaction not due to LHRH, the synthetic immunizing antigen, but due to a precursor of the hormone (page 386).

True Cross-Reacting Antibodies

The cross-reactions discussed so far are not true cross-reactions. Indeed, they are specific reactions. Antibodies specific to α-chains of luteinizing hormone will be equally specific to α-chains of thyrotrophic hormone. Antibodies to an epitope in LHRH will be equally specific to the same epitope if it is accessible in an LHRH precursor. However, antibodies may have *true cross-reactivities*, which are due to *coincidental* similarity of genetically unrelated epitopes. For instance, the sequence His-Pro may occur in many unrelated proteins. If we immunize with this epitope, we may obtain widely cross-reacting antibodies. Because of the small sequence, the antisera are likely to be of low affinities, at least in their reaction with these two amino acids. Antibodies that recognize seven C-terminal amino acids of LHRH would have high affinity. It is unlikely that the same seven amino acid sequence occurs in many non-LHRH or non-LHRH precursor sites because of mere coincidence of sharing of this sequence by other proteins.

In general, the bigger the epitope involved in the reaction with antibody, the higher the affinity. Schechter (1) studied antibodies produced by immunization with poly-L-alanyl human serum albumin (HSA), purified by immunoabsorption with this antigen and elution with tetra-L-alanine. Binding of the antibody with tetra-L-alanine and tetraalanine in which one or more L-alanines was replaced by D-alanine showed that the antibodies were heterogeneous in their combining sites, the majority of molecules only recognizing the N-terminal and pentultimate amino acids. Some antibodies recognized the three terminal alanines, and very few were specific to the sequence of our alanines. If these data were interpolated to any antiprotein antibody, one would assume that the majority of such antibodies would recognize only a sequence of two amino acids, and since there are 21 amino acids, antiprotein antibodies could not in general recognize more than $21^2 = 441$ different antigenic determinants. Hence, cross-reactions would be extensive. In fact, such extensive cross-reactivity has not been observed in immunocytochemistry. Indeed, it is likely that hundreds of thousands of different antiprotein specificities are within the immunocompetence of a normal mammalian host. The explanation of the discrepancy probably lies in the selection of antibodies during purification. By using tetra-alanine for elution, only 37% of the poly-L-anine reactivity and much less of the total antipolyalanyl HSA activity was eluted. It is probable that here—and as we shall see in other applications of immunospecific purification as well—only the antibodies with the lowest binding affinities were eluted, while the highest quality antibodies remained on the immunoabsorbent. These low-binding antibodies exhibited strong cross-reactivity due to the fact that by the very purification procedure only antibodies specific to small sequences were selected. The purified antibodies may well react with many proteins in any tissue containing two adjacent alanine residues in a suitably accessible position. Nevertheless, such antibodies, despite their probable presence in most immune sera, prove no threat to immunocytochemical specificity. Their affinities, being weak compared to that of antibodies specific to longer sequences, makes them more easily dissociable from tissue during washing. This type of cross-reaction is eliminated when monoclonal antibodies are used.

In order to produce antibody to a small hapten, such as p-Gly-His-ProNH$_2$ (thyrotropin-releasing hormone, TRH), one conjugates the hapten with a carrier, such as hemocyanin, by cross-linking, for example, the TRH histidine-2 to a hemocyanin tyrosine or histidine via coupling with bisdiazotized benzidine. The high-affinity, specific antibodies formed will react with pyroglutamate, proline amide, modified histidine, plus at least the adjacent benzidine, if not even the hemocyanin histidine or tyrosine. The immunizing antigen possesses these epitopes and can, therefore, be used to elicit the high-affinity binding. The TRH to be detected immunocytochemically provides, however, only the pyroglutamate and proline amide in the form identical to that of the immunizing antigen, and only these groups are available for reaction with the antiserum. Therefore, the TRH is likely to react with lower affinity than the immunizing antigen. Because of its small size, its reactivity with the high-affinity antibodies reactive with the immunizing antigen will probably not exceed its reactivity with low-affinity antibodies. Thus, the immunocytochemical reaction for TRH depends entirely on low affinities. Low affinity means high cross-reactivity. Pyroglutamate is a frequent amino-terminal group of neuropeptides, and an amidated carboxyterminal group is also frequent. There probably exists a multiplicity of yet undiscovered neuropeptides. With the use of antisera to TRH, a wide distribution of material similar to TRH was found in multiple areas of the brain by immunofluorescence (2) and PAP methods (3). The specificity of the reaction at most, but not necessarily all, sites was made plausible, however, by identical electrophoretic mobility of TRH and immunocytochemically identified extracts from the stained regions.

TESTS FOR SPECIFICITY

In the following pages, we will discuss several tests for specificity of antisera and antibodies derived from antisera, some of them useful and others less useful.

Table 5-2. Interpretation of Test Results for Specificity of Antisera

	If Successful	If Unsuccessful
Normal serum substitution	Does not exclude contaminating and cross-reacting antibodies	Establishes poor specificity
Antibody dilution	Does not exclude contaminating antibodies	Little value
Liquid-phase absorption, synthetic haptens	Does not exclude cross-reacting antibodies	Little value
Liquid-phase absorption, natural macromolecular antigens	Does not exclude contaminating and cross-reacting antibodies	Establishes poor specificity
Solid-phase absorption, synthetic haptens	Does not exclude cross-reacting antibodies	Establishes poor specificity
Solid-phase absorption, natural macromolecular antigens	Does not exclude contaminating and cross-reacting antibodies	Establishes poor specificity
Immunodiffusion	No value	May establish poor specificity
Radioimmunoassay	No value	No value
One-dimensional immunoblot	Suggests specificity with limitations	Establishes poor specificity
Two-dimensional immunoblot	Suggests specificity with limitations	Establishes poor specificity

Some of these tests (Table 5-2), if successful, make specificity plausible. Others, if unsuccessful, prove nonspecificity. Tests to prove nonspecificity by their failure are often more convincing than tests to prove specificity by their success.

Substitution of Normal Serum

Animals of the same species are generally immune to pathogens of their normal environment. The immunoglobulins of normal sera consist largely of antibodies to antigens with which an animal had previous experience. Gnodobiotically reared animals are poor in immunoglobulins. If we assume that most animals of the same species have similar antigenic experience, substitution of normal serum for antiserum may detect whether an immunocytochemical reaction with antiserum is due to antibodies normally present in the host and not the result of the specific immunization.

It is sometimes preferred to use the preimmunization serum of the same animal which has donated the antiserum after immunization, thus assuring that both sera contain antibodies to the same preimmunization immunologic experience. However, results must be interpreted with some caution, since immunization may recall increased antibody production not only to the immunizing antigen, but also to antigens of previous experience.

If normal serum stains a given structure at the same dilution as the antiserum under investigation, we can be almost certain that the reaction of the antiserum is not specific. Of course, if the normal serum does not stain, it provides no evidence that the antiserum reaction is specific.

At high concentration, normal serum will stain almost certainly. The stain is due to low-affinity cross-reactions of one or the other antibodies found in normal serum. This is the prime reason for using diluted antisera for immunocytochemistry. Antisera diluted less than 1 : 1000 should be avoided. Normal sera do not contain many antibodies specific to normal tissue constituents. The antibodies that do react with normal tissue constituents are likely to be specific to other, unknown antigens that are capable of cross-reacting with tissue antigens. For instance, antibodies to many bacterial carbohydrates cross-react with blood group antigens and cell membrane glycoproteins. These cross-reactions are of low affinity and disappear when serum is diluted. For this reason, immunocytochemistry requires sensitive technique that permits staining with diluted antisera. Increased sensitivity provides, thereby, increased specificity.

Antibody Dilution

Although preimmune serum may not stain, we are not assured that the stain of the immune serum is due to the immunizing antigen rather than a recall reaction of antibodies from a previous immunologic experience. However, if preimmunization serum does not stain at a dilution of 1 : 1000, and antiserum does stain at a dilution of 1 : 10,000, we may be reasonably sure that the stain is due to antibodies to the immunizing antigen. We do not exclude, however, antibodies to contaminants in the immunizing antigen.

If high dilutions of antiserum stain, we also exclude cross-reacting antibodies. Therefore, if our antigen is synthetic, and the staining is intense at dilutions higher than 1 : 10,000, we may assume, even without additional tests, that the reaction is due to an antigen of conformation similar to that of the immunizing antigen. However, we still will not exclude the possibility that the tissue reaction is due to an epitope genetically shared with a different antigen. For instance, an antiserum, or for that matter even a monoclonal antibody (page 386), reacting at high affinity and high dilution with the C-terminal region of luteinizing hormone-releasing hormone, may also react at high affinity, and consequently high dilution, with a precursor molecule of luteinizing hormone-releasing hormone extended at its N-terminal end. This is a high-affinity reaction which cannot be eliminated by dilution.

Antibodies to vasopressin (page 379) cross-react with oxytocin. The cross-reaction can be abolished by absorption with oxytocin. However, Van Leuween (4), in considering that cross-reactions have lower affinities than specific reactions, has shown that he can eliminate the cross-reaction with oxytocin by simple dilution. In his postembedding electron-microscopic localization of oxytocin and vasopressin in rat neurohypophysis, he found that antivasopressin diluted 1 : 1600 no longer stained nerve endings of the Brattleboro rat, which is congenitally deficient in vasopressin but not oxytocin. At this dilution, the serum had become specific for vasopressin. In the normal rat, this dilution stained the same nerve endings that remained unstained with antioxytocin, diluted 1 : 400 (Fig. 5-3). Similarly, granules in other nerve endings that were stained positively after

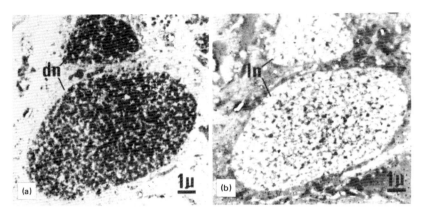

Figure 5-3. Adjacent Epon sections of rat neurohypophysis treated with (a) antivasopressin, 1 : 1600, and (b) antioxytocin, 1 : 400 as first antisera in the PAP method. dn: Electron-opaque neurosecretory granules; ln: electron-lucent neurosecretory granules. [From Van Leeuwen (4).]

antioxytocin, diluted 1 : 400, remained unstained after treatment of an adjacent section with antivasopressin, diluted 1 : 1600. Higher concentrations of antivasopressin or antioxytocin stained, however, both sets of granules. These findings provide an illustration for the advisability of high dilutions of antiserum in any immunocytochemical work. Therefore, a sensitive method is required. In the work of Van Leeuwen (4), the use of a peroxidase-conjugated antibody was attempted, in addition to PAP. However, specific reaction could not be attained with conjugate because staining had become indistinct at dilutions of antivasopressin beyond 1 : 320, thus preventing use of antiserum diluted to the range in which cross-reactivity had been abolished.

Significance can be attributed if higher dilutions of antiserum eliminate staining in one structure while retaining it in another. The loss of staining is either due to lower concentration of antigen in that area, or to a cross-reaction. Dilution of antiserum is more a precaution against low-affinity cross-reactions than an evidence for specificity.

Liquid-Phase Absorption with Macromolecular Antigens

Absorption denotes the removal of immunocytochemically staining first antibody by the antigen of interest. If the antigen of interest is the same antigen that is stained, successful absorption should abolish the staining. The purpose of the test is to identify the stained antigen with the antigen of interest.

There are two limitations to the test:

First, we have to know what the antigen of interest is. Sometimes immunocytochemistry is used to detect new, unknown antigens, not previously revealed by other methods. Even with this limitation, absorption can be carried out. Antisera to renal glomeruli will stain glomeruli as well as nonrenal tissue. Absorption with lung will remove some of nonrenal antibodies, but the procedure is erratic in obtainment of well-defined kidney-specific antibodies, because the amount of antibodies with organ cross-reactivity overwhelms the amount of any kidney-

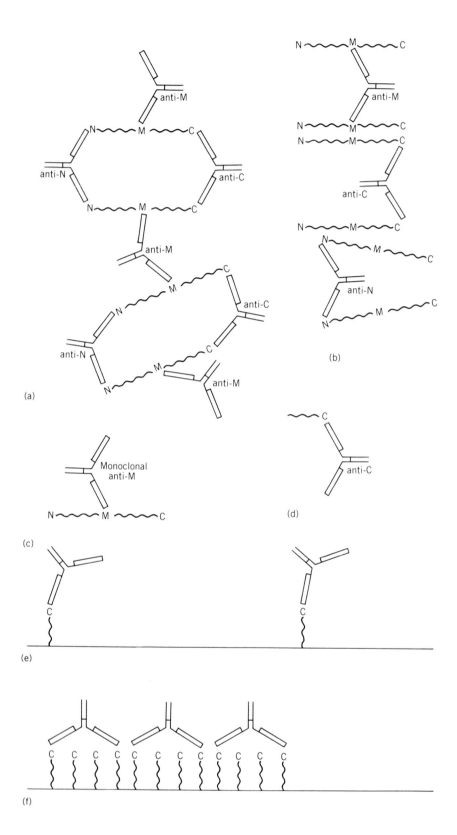

(a)

(b)

(c) Monoclonal anti-M

(d)

(e)

(f)

specific antibodies. Detection of new, unknown antigens is difficult with antisera. It is one of the domains of monoclonal antibodies (page 429).

Second, we must be sure that the antigen used for absorption is free of contaminants detectable within the sensitivity range of immunocytochemistry. Most nonsynthetic antigens are purified to "homogeneity," which implies single bands or peaks by electrophoresis, sedimentation, or high-performance liquid chromatography. These methods for detection of contaminants are usually not as sensitive as immunocytochemistry. With synthetic antigens, absorption is usually more reliable, especially when purity of the antigens was determined with an adequate quantity of sample. While here again some trace contaminants, in the form of byproducts of synthesis or degradation products, may have escaped detection, it is unlikely that the immunocytochemical reaction, if due to these contaminants, reveals a tissue constituent that is not at least metabolically related to the antigen of interest. Any possible error from this cause will probably not vitiate the overall true localization at the light microscopic level.

Absorption can be carried out in solid or liquid phase. In solid-phase absorption, the antigen is immobilized. Antibody will be removed from solution by the immobilized antigen. In liquid-phase absorption, antigen is admixed with antiserum in solution. The antigen in solution competes with the antigen on the tissue section and, thus, reduces staining. If the antigen concentration in solution is sufficiently high, staining will be abolished. The antibody is set to be *neutralized* or *blocked.*

Usually, the antigen concentration required for liquid-phase absorption is relatively high, requiring a large excess of antigen over antibody.

In examining the efficiency of liquid-phase absorption, we must consider the individual and functionl affinities of the interaction of antibody and epitopes. *Individual affinity* is the ratio of the rate of association and dissociation of antibody and antigen at a single idiotype-epitope binding site. It has been shown that each antibody binding site reacts independently. There is no cooperative effect between the two antibody binding sites in a single antibody molecule when measurements are made in solution, such as by equilibrium dialysis (page 18), using antisera and monovalent haptens. Under these conditions, no precipitate of antigen and antibody ensues (Fig. 5-4d). However, if we deal with a multivalent antigen possessing many epitopes and antiserum containing heterogeneous antibodies, large aggregates of antigen and antibody can form (Fig. 5-4a). Each single antibody-epitope interaction will still follow its individual, independent binding kinetics, but the total aggregate can only be dissociated if all bonds are

Figure 5-4. If a hypothetical antigen that possesses three epitopes (N, M, and C) react with antiserum in antibody excess or at equivalence, large aggregates can form (a) and the functional affinity of reaction is higher than the individual affinity of each bond. In antigen excess, however, soluble complexes consist of small aggregates only (b) and the functional affinities equal the individual affinities. With monoclonal antibodies, in general, large aggregates cannot form whether in antigen or antibody excess (c) and the functional affinity equals the individual affinity. When a small hapten is used with antiserum, again large complexes cannot form (d) and the functional affinity also equals the individual affinity. On the tissue section, if an epitope is widely spaced, only one antibody-combining site can react with each epitope, and the second antibody-combining site remains free (e). The functional affinity is likely to equal the individual affinity. If on the tissue section, an epitope is densely packed, antibody will react with both of its combining sites (f) and the functional affinity is higher than the individual affinity.

broken simultaneously. This occurs so rarely that the reaction may be considered practically irreversible. Thus, *functional affinity* is greatly magnified compared to individual affinity.

In immunocytochemical, liquid-phase absorption, we add antigen to the liquid phase to compete for the antibody with its reaction to the antigen bound on the surface of the tissue. If an epitope in solution is identical to that on the tissue, individual affinities of both reactions will be identical. However, the functional affinity will differ, depending on the condition of reaction in solution, as well as on the condition of reaction on the tissue surface.

If the tissue epitope is widely spaced, antibody will be able to react only via one of its combining sites (Fig. 5-4e). Barring any nonspecific effect of the tissue surface (solid-solution interface), the affinity of reaction will be the same as the individual affinity measured for a single bond in solution. On the other hand, if the tissue antigen is closely spaced, the antibody will react via both combining sites, leading to ring formation that results in a greatly heightened functional affinity (Fig. 5-4f).

Let us first consider the case of widely dispersed epitope sites in the tissue. If our antigen is a hapten, neutralization of the antibody in solution will follow individual binding kinetics, since only one hapten can react with one idiotype site, in antibody excess, or two haptens with both sites of bivalent antibody, in hapten excess (Fig. 5-4d) (There is no cooperativity among both idiotype sites). If the reaction in the tissue is specific, that is if the tissue hapten is the same as that used for absorption, the affinity of reaction with the hapten in solution will be the same as that with the hapten in the tissue. The reaction in the tissue is easily inhibited, and the higher the affinity of the antibody, the lower the concentration of hapten necessary for inhibition.

A similar situation will prevail with macromolecular antigens that possess many epitopes provided we use monoclonal antibody. Unless the epitopes on the antigen are repetitive, monoclonal antibody will not form large aggregates with the antigen, and again ensuing reaction sites can be considered independently and individual reaction kinetics prevail (Fig. 5-4c). Consequently, the higher the antibody affinity, the lower the concentration of antigens needed for inhibition.

The situation differs, however, if the antigen is macromolecular, possessing multiple epitopes, and the antibodies are heterogeneous, such as serum antibodies. Now multiple epitopes on the antigen can react with different antibodies that form large aggregates in antibody excess or in equivalence (Fig. 5-4a). If the concentrations of antigen and antibody are high, a visible precipitate will form. If the concentrations are below the solubility product of such precipitates, as they usually are with the solutions of antigen and antibody used in immunoabsorption for immunocytochemistry, the aggregates will remain in solution. Nevertheless, they are effectively removed from the situation in which each epitope-idiotype bond can be considered independently. Functionally, the interaction of antigen with antibody becomes irreversible. The reaction affords very effective competition to the single-antibody epitope bonds on the tissue section, in case the epitopes are widely dispersed on the section. Consequently, relatively low concentrations of antigen are sufficient for inhibition of the immunocytochemical reaction, even if the affinity of the antibody is not very high.

However, when the concentration of absorbing antigen is raised, we will obtain soluble antigen-antibody complexes (Fig. 5-4b). In conditions of extreme antigen excess, each binding site will again dissociate independently and the reaction of the antibody in solution will again be equal to that on the tissue. Any antigen in solution will no longer react preferentially to that in the tissue, but because the excess of antigen is high, inhibition will occur if the reaction is specific.

In general, liquid-phase absorption is a valuable approach, if the epitopic density on the tissue is not very high.

However, the situation is quite different if the tissue is rich in an antigen and the epitopic density on the section is high. Now the reaction on the tissue is practically irreversible. This reaction cannot be inhibited by hapten in solution at any reasonable concentration, even if the reaction is specific. A case in point are attempts to inhibit the reaction of antibodies to receptor-bound luteinizing hormone-releasing hormone (LHRH) in gonadotrophs by LHRH in solution (page 403). Even though we know the reaction is specific, because it was LHRH that had been added to the tissue to begin with, and because solid-phase absorption of antiserum abolished the immunocytochemical reaction, no concentration of LHRH was found that inhibited the reaction in liquid phase. At the same time, LHRH immunoreactivity in the hypothalamus was easily inhibited. In the gonadotrophs, we have a case in which a *specific* reaction could not be abolished by liquid-phase absorption.

If a macromolecular, polyepitopic antigen is densely distributed in tissue, again its reaction with antibody is functionally irreversible. However, the reaction of the antigen with antibody in solution is also functionally irreversible, at least in antibody excess or equivalence (Fig. 5-4a). Hence, relatively low concentrations of antigen are sufficient for successful absorption, if the reaction is specific. However, if the antigen concentration is raised, we obtain soluble complexes in solution (Fig. 5-4b), and the functional affinity becomes reduced to the individual affinity of each antigen-antibody bond. The antigen in solution now offers poor competition to the antigen in the tissue section. This may explain the observation that with some macromolecular antigens, such as luteinizing hormone or ACTH in the pituitary, at times inhibition is successful by absorption with moderate concentrations of antigen, but unsuccessful with high concentrations. Hence, we can no longer equate high affinity with low concentration of inhibiting antigen. While such relationships hold in radioimmunoassay, they may be confusing in immunocytochemistry. If an immunocytochemical reaction requires high concentrations of one antigen for inhibition, but only low concentrations of another, we cannot conclude that the low concentration reaction is the specific one and the high concentration reaction nonspecific. The reverse may be closer to the truth.

Syncytiotrophoblasts contain peptides of the preproopiomelanocortin system (page 359). Halmi and Krieger (5) found staining in these cells with antiserum to one of the opiomelanocortin peptides, β-lipotropin. The reaction was inhibited by β-lipotropin, but also at equal concentrations by human prolactin and by α-chains of pituitary glycoprotein hormones. The explanation offered for this paradoxical observation considered possible conformational homologies between the absorbing hormones. However, we do not know how important conformational changes are in determining antibody specificity. With monoclonal antibody specific to neuronal proteins, we observed little, if any, reactions with nonneuronal elements in peripheral tissues (page 432). Hence, conformational homology in the absence of shared primary structres must be very rare in immunocytochemical reactions. It may be equally possible that the absorption reaction by anti-β-lipotropin was due to impurities in the antigen used. Assuming the reaction was, indeed, specific to β-lipotropin, the concentration of 3 μg/ml, as used by Halmi and Krieger (5), may have provided antigen excess to the antibody used at a dilution of 1 : 3000. If the tissue was rich in β-lipotropin, that is, if the epitopes were closely spaced, this would not provide a very efficient absorption. Hence, high concentrations were needed. If the other absorbing hormones were contaminated with β-lipotropin, 3 μg/ml would not have provided equal antigen excess for the contaminant. In fact, the reaction of the contaminant in solution may have been in equivalence or antibody excess. In this situation, it could have provided effective competition to the tissue antigen, and absorption may have been successful, even if the absorbing antigen contained only a trace of β-lipotropin. So the reaction for β-lipotropin in the syncytiotrophoblasts may have been specific after all.

Of course, we do not know *a priori* whether an epitope is widely dispersed or closely spaced on tissue sections. The failure of this knowledge deters from the degree of interpretation we may give on a basis of successful liquid-phase absorption. Nevertheless, the test is useful in many instances. Successful absorption with synthetic haptens, reasonably well examined for purity, usually denotes some specificity. However, we cannot determine whether the reaction is due to the antigen under investigation or a close analogue. For instance, the reaction of anti-LHRH with hypothalamic cell bodies and fibers is easily inhibited by LHRH. However, the reaction has been shown not to be due to LHRH, but rather to a N-terminally extended precursor molecule (page 386). The reaction with an analogue may be of equal or lower affinity. If the reaction is of lower affinity, and if the synthetic antigen and its analogue are haptens, the inhibiting concentration of the analogues will be higher than that of the specific hapten.

If a synthetic antigen does not inhibit, it does not disprove specificity, because tissue antigen may be closely spaced.

Successful absorption with nonsynthetic antigens is of little value, because impurities in the absorbing antigen cannot be excluded. Unsuccessful absorption with a macromolecular, epitopic antigen, if carried out over a wide range of antigen concentrations, including low concentrations, is a useful test for demonstrating nonspecificity.

Solid-Phase Absorption

For solid-phase absorption, the antigen is usually bound covalently on a matrix. Cyanogen bromide-activated Sepharose reacts with amino groups of antigens. Some haptens, such as luteinizing hormone-releasing hormone, do not contain amino groups. This hapten can be immobilized by the use of a spacer, such as RNAse or any other protein. Luteinizing hormone-releasing hormone is first coupled with RNAse via its tyrosine groups by bisdiazotized benzidine, and the product is then reacted with activated Sepharose via the amino groups of RNAse (6).

Immunoabsorbents produced by covalent bonding of an antigen to a matrix can be used as *columns* and the absorbed antiserum is obtained in the effluent, or they can be admixed with the antigen in *suspension,* and the absorbed antiserum is obtained in supernate after centrifugation. It is important to use control absorbents to minimize the possibility of nonspecific elimination of antibodies by the specific immunoabsorbent.

There are two advantages of solid-phase absorption over liquid-phase absorption:

1.   By removing the antibody from solution, the possibility of preferential reaction of antibody with densely spaced tissue eptiopes over that with etiopes in solution is eliminated. Consequently, in a specific reaction, absorption cannot fail. Thus, failure of absorption becomes an index for low specificity.

2.   A specific reaction may not be masked by the use of too high concentrations of absorbing antigens.

If solid-phase absorption of antiserum is unsuccessful, the specificity of the immunocytochemical reaction should be questioned. However, one has to assume that production of the immunoabsorbent did not destroy the epitope under study. Production of immunoabsorbents requires relatively high concentrations of antigen. Therefore, one must also ensure that the immunoabsorbent concentration suffices to remove the antibodies under consideration.

Solid-phase immunoabsorption can also be carried out with cross-reacting antigens. For instance, if it is observed that an antiserum to vasopressin reacts at a dilution of 1 : 1000 in the pituitary not ony with vasopressin terminals of the posterior lobe, but also with α-melanocyte-stimulating hormone (α-MSH)-containing cells of the intermediate lobe, one may be tempted to conclude that vasopressin cross-reacts with α-MSH. If a long α-MSH column is used, or if an efficient immunoabsorbent is mixed with antivasopressin, this conclusion may be erroneous. By definition, any idiotype will react with high affinity with its specific epitope (which may be known or unknown). It will react with slightly lesser affinity with substances that resemble this epitope in structure. It will react with low affinity with nearly everything. Assume our antibodies have an average affinity for vasopressin of $10^9/M$. The serum may well react with α-MSH at the low affinity of 10^2 to $10^3/M$. Solid-phase immunoabsorbents rich in α-MSH and used in antigen excess may well deplete the antiserum of antivasopressin. If used in the form of columns, the immunoabsorbents may retard the antibodies appreciably. The very purpose of chromatography columns is utilization of low-affinity binding for separation. In immunocytochemistry, on the other hand, the staining with antivasopressin with an affinity of $10^9/M$ can probably be carried out at a dilution of 1 : 100,000. In order to visualize a cross-reaction of an antigen with an affinity for antivasopressin of, say, $10^4/M$, we would need a 100,000 times higher concentration, that is, undiluted antiserum. However, undiluted antisera almost certainly will stain nonspecifically, and, therefore, are to be avoided in immunocytochemistry. At a dilution of 1 : 1000, the low-affinity reaction of antivasopressin with α-MSH will be undetected, and, therefore, any cross-reaction of antivasopressin with α-MSH becomes irrelevant, even though insolubilized α-MSH may absorb vasopressin immunoreactivity in the batch or column procedure. Consequently, it is not possible to conclude that reaction of antivasopressin with α-MSH cells is due to a cross-reaction with α-MSH. It is more likely to be due either to antibodies other than antivasopressin in the serum, or to the presence of vasopressin-like material in the α-MSH cells. Monoclonal antibodies would distinguish between these two alternatives.

It is apparent, therefore, that solid-phase absorption with an unrelated antigen does not establish cross-reactivity of the immunocytochemical reaction. It also follows, that when the nature of an antigen is undefined, successful solid-phase absorption with any antigen does not establish the nature of the immunocytochemically localized antigen. If solid-phase absorption removes an antibody, it does not prove that the immunocytochemical reaction is identical with that of the antigen used for absorption, rather than being cross-reactive or due to an antibody to an impurity in the immunoabsorbent. Neither does solid-phase absorption with a suspected cross-reacting antigen establish cross-reactivity in the immunocytochemical reaction. Consequently, solid-phase absorption remains of limited value in establishing immunocytochemical specificity of antisera or affinity-purified antibodies.

Immunodiffusion

This test for cross-reactions among different antigens (Figs. 5-1 and 5-2) requires at least 1 μg antigen/ml. As shown by Petrusz (7), the calculated detection sensitivity of immunocytochemistry is one million times higher. Hence, failure of cross-reaction by immunodiffusion does not exclude low specificity by immunocytochemistry. However, if an antigen has been shown to be cross-reactive by immunodiffusion, it almost certainly will be of poor specificity in immunocytochemistry. Thus, immunodiffusion may suggest undesirable antibodies that can be removed by absorption. For instance, antisera to factor VIII were shown by McComb et al. (8) to cross-react with immunoglobulins by immunodiffusion. The sera stained endothelial cells as well as plasma cells. Following absorption, the plasma cell staining had disappeared, leaving intact the specific endothelial staining. Gröschel-Stewart (9) has emphasized that, in this kind of absorption, it is better to insolubilize the undesired antigen and use the effluent antiserum, rather than to insolubilize the desired antigen and affinity purify the antibody. The latter procedure reduces yield and affinities.

Radioimmunoassay

Both immunocytochemistry and radioimmunoassay are tests for antigen. Immunocytochemistry depends, for its evaluation, on the specificity of antibodies. Radioimmunoassay, however, is largely independent of the specificity of antiserum. Instead, unknown antigens are detected competitively with the labeled antigen. The test depends, therefore, on the specificity of the labeled antigen.

The specificity of the labeled antigen depends on its nature and purity. Radioimmunoassay only detects those unknown antigens that cross-react on given antibodies with the labeled antigen. The antibodies that participate in this cross-reaction are antibodies to epitopes that are not destroyed by radioiodination. Tyrosine and histidine are affected by iodination and, thus, radioimmunoassay can utilize only antibodies to epitopes devoid of these amino acids as principal contributors to specificity. Immunocytochemistry, in contrast, uses only antibodies to epitopes that are not destroyed by fixation. Most fixatives affect primary amines and leave tyrosine and histidine groups unaffected. The antibodies that participate in the immunocytochemical reaction are antibodies to epitopes that are devoid of amines as primary determinants. Antibodies that react by radioimmunoassay and by immunocytochemistry are, therefore, different in most cases. Consequently, there can be no correspondence in radioimmunoassay and immunocytochemical titers. Indeed, even in a number of consecutive bleedings from the same animal during the course of immunization, we found no correlation between both titers (6). Often, antisera have good titers both by radioimmunoassay and by immunocytochemistry. However, the individual antibodies in antisera that contribute toward these titers are different and any correspondence in titer is merely coincidental. With monoclonal antibodies, the difference in titers by both methods is exacerbated (page 251).

Antibodies to epitopes destroyed by iodination are not the only antibodies that are missed in radioimmunoassay. A competing antigen may contain epitopes shared with the radioiodinated antigen, as well as unshared epitopes. The antiserum may contain antibodies to both. By competitive radioimmunoassay, the unshared epitopes are not detected. They can be detected, however, by a direct radioimmunobinding assay. For instance, some widely distributed antisera to rat follicle-stimulating, thyrotrophic, and luteinizing hormones are known to exhibit only minimal cross-reactions with human chorionic gonadotrophin in radioimmunoassay, when human chorionic gonadotrophin is labeled and the competing follicle-stimulating, thryotrophic and luteinizing hormones are unlabeled. However, when labeled rat luteinizing hormone was used in the reaction with antihuman chorionic gonadotrophin, Wakabayashi (10) found cross-reactivity to the extent of 30%.

Angiotensin I is the decapeptide precursor to the bioactive octapeptide angiotension II. Although Hackenthal and Taugner (11) found that by radioimmunoassay antisera to both peptides possessed only 0.01% cross-reactivity, they gave similar immunocytochemical localization in the renal afferent arteriole. However, upon an examination by direct radioimmunobinding assay, in which both labeled angiotension I and labeled angiotensin II were reacted with the antisera in separate tubes, cross-reactivity was 20%.

Even for the use of second antisera, radioimmunoassay is no reliable criterion. It is known that some good antirabbit IgG crossreacted with guinea pig IgG sufficiently to make them useful as reagents for guinea pig first antibodies in immunocytochemistry (page 180). Baskin et al. (12) found that a goat antirabbit IgG which reacted poorly with guinea pig IgG on radioimmunoassay, provided nevertheless an excellent second antibody for the detection of insulin in pancreatic B cells with guinea pig antibody.

One-Dimensional Electro-Immunoblot Analysis (Western Blots)

Since we do not know the composition of the tissue constituent examined by immunocytochemistry in search of an antigen, we generally resort to methods other than immunocytochemistry for validation of the specificity of antiserum. Such methods would be reliable if we were able to identify by an independent method the immunocytochemically localized antigen in whole tissue extract. A requirement for this analysis is that the independent method is as sensitive as immunocytochemistry and utilizes the same antibodies. Such a method does not exist, but one method that at least approaches this requirement is electrophoresis-electroblot analysis. This method combines the separation efficiency of electrophoresis with the staining efficiency of immunocytochemistry. To obtain good staining, it is important to transfer gel-separated proteins to nitrocellulose paper.

In the electroblot transfer method of Towbin et al. (13), single-dimension electrophoresis is conveniently carried out in separating gels containing 375 mM Tris hydrochloride, pH 8.8/0.1% sodium dodecyl sulfate/8% acrylamide. Sample-containing starting gels consist of 125 mM Tris hydrochloride, pH 6.8/0.1% sodium dodecyl sulfate/4% acrylamide. Reservoir buffer consists of 25 mM Tris hydrochloride, pH 8.3/0.192 mM glycine/0.5% sodium dodecyl sulfate. Electrophoresis times vary depending on the size of the antigen. For antigens ranging from 30,000 to 200,000 daltons, 4.5 to 5 hours at 150 V with cooling are convenient.

After electrophoretic separation, transfer to nitrocellulose is carried out in 50-mM sodium phosphate buffer, pH 7.4, at 100 mA overnight. Strips corresponding to the gel lanes are cut out from the nitrocellulose paper and stained immunocytochemically. Molecular weight standards are electrophoresed and transferred with the antigens and stained with Coomassie blue.

Electroblot analysis was used by Nancy Sternberger et al. (14) to establish specificity of antibodies to myelin basic protein in their study on the heterogeneity of this protein. With rabbit antiserum to myelin basic protein and rabbit PAP, they found four electroblot bands with purified myelin basic protein (Fig. 5-5). When using whole brain homogenates, they found the same four bands plus some fractions that failed to enter the gel. The latter are presumably precursors

Figure 5-5. Electrophoresis-immunoblot of myelin basic protein with antiserum to myelin basic protein. PAP method. [From Nancy Sternberger et al (14).]

to myelin basic protein. With monoclonal antimyelin basic protein and Clono-PAP, they found two bands when using either purified myelin basic protein or whole brain homogenate. The failure to show additional bands that entered the gel when whole homogenate is compared with purified material suggests immunocytochemical specificity in tissue sections.

There remain, however, limitations to the technique. First of all, we must be sure that all the bands visualized with the purified antigen are due to the antigen under investigation and not to impurities. This can usually be established by independent biochemical techniques. Secondly, we must be sure that electroblot analysis is as sensitive as immunocytochemistry in tissues. The staining reactions are probably of equal sensitivities. However, the sensitivity by which antigens can be separated on the gel varies. The method increases in sensitivity when the gels are loaded with higher quantities of antigen (page 449). However, when the gels are overloaded, nonspecific staining occurs. Overloading is particularly prone to happen in the comparison with unpurified antigens (whole tissue homogenate) which is so essential for use of the method as a criterion for specificity.

A third limitation is the low degree of separation that can be obtained on the basis of molecular weight only, when compared to the high discrimination power of immunocytochemical distribution in the microscope. Thus, we have observed heterogeneity of neurofilaments on the basis of morphologic distribution, as well as by single-dimension electrophoresis (page 438). However, heterogeneity was more pronounced at the microscopic level.

Two-Dimensional Electrophoresis-Electroblot Analysis

The sensitivity of electrophoretic separation can be increased by first separating an antigen according to charge (by electrophoretic focusing) in one dimension, and then according to molecular weight in another (15). The gel sheet is then electroblotted onto nitrocellulose and stained immunocytochemically.

Using two-dimensional electrophoresis, we could detect neurofilament heterogeneity beyond that detectable by one-dimensional electrophoresis (page 442).

STRATEGIES FOR TESTING SPECIFICITY OF ANTISERA

Always use high dilutions of antisera. Always run a normal serum control to exclude major nonspecificities.

If the antigen is synthetic and well characterized, use liquid-phase immunoabsorption. If this fails, resort to solid-phase immunoabsorption. Successful absorption makes specificity plausible, but does not prove it.

If the antigen is a naturally occurring substance, compare the elecroblot lines obtained with the purified antigen and the crude homogenate of its tissue of origin and ensure that the homogenate does not reveal additional lines. One- and two-dimensional electroblots may be used. Although these tests do not have the same sensitivity and resolution as immunocytochemistry, they do provide at least a first approximation to reasonable specificity.

Neither the absorption tests for synthetic antigen, nor the electroblot tests with natural antigens will ensure freedom of nonspecificity to minor contaminations in the antigen. Exclusion of this important source of nonspecificity requires monoclonal antibodies.

None of the tests described so far will exclude cross-reactivities due to the analogues of the epitope under investigation, if an analogue possesses equal affinity as the presumptive antigen. However, in these cases, the analogue probably will have an immunocytochemical distribution similar to that of the investigated epitope, or at least exhibit a physiologic relationship with it, either as precursor or as metabolite.

REFERENCES

1. Schechter I: Mapping of the combining sites of antibodies specific for poly-L-alanine determinants. *Nature* **228**:639, 1970.

2. Hökfelt T, Fuxe O, Johansson O, Jeffcote S, White N: Thyrotroxin releasing hormone (TRH)-containing nerve terminals in certain brain stem nuclei and in the spinal cord. *Neurosci Lett* **1**:133, 1975.

3. Johansson O, Hökfelt T, Jeffcote SL, White N, Sternberger LA: Ultrastructural localization of TRH-like immunoreactivity. *Exp Brain Res* **38**:1, 1980.

4. Van Leeuwen FW: Immunoelectronmicroscopic visualization of neurophypophyseal hormones: Evaluation of some tissue preparations and staining procedures. *J Histochem Cytochem* **25**:1213, 1977.

5. Halmi NS, Krieger DT: Immunostaining of human syncytiotrophoblast with anti-β-LPH: An illustration of the limitations of immunocytochemistry. *J Histochem Cytochem* **30**:538, 1982.

6. Sternberger LA, Petrali JP, Joseph SA, Meyer HG, Mills KR: Specificity of the immunocytochemical LHRH receptor reaction. *Endocrinology* **102**:63, 1978.

7. Petrusz P: Essential requirements for the validity of immunocytochemical staining procedures. *J Histochem Cytochem* **31**:177, 1983.

8. McComb RD, Jones TR, Pizzo SV, Bigner DD: Specificity and sensitivity of immunohistochemical detection of factor VIII/van Willebrand factor antigen in formalin-fixed, paraffin-embedded tissue. *J Histochem Cytochem* **30**:371, 1982.

9. Gröschel-Stewart U: Herstellung und Reinigung von Antikörpern für die Immunozytochemie am Beispiel des Aktin-Myosin-Systems. *Acta Histochem Suppl* **XXV**:37, 1982.

10. Wakabayashi K: Some criticism on the methods used for localization of LHRH. *Endocrinol Japon* **57**:355, 1981.

11. Hackenthal E, Taugner R: The specificity of angiotensin antisera. A cautionary note. *Histochemistry* **77**:201, 1983.

12. Baskin DG, Gorray RC, Fujimoto WY: Immunocytochemical detection of B-cells in the guinea pig pancreas using quinea pig antiserum to porcine insulin. *J Histochem Cytochem* **29**:567, 1981.

13. Towbin H, Staeblin T, Gordon J: Electrophoretic transfer of proteins from polyacrylamide gels to nitrocellulose sheets: Procedure and some applications. *Proc. Natl Acad Sci USA* **76**:4380, 1979.

14. Sternberger NH, Murant FG, Parkinson JA, Kies MW: EAE in the Lewis rat: An immunocytochemical study. *Transact Amer Soc Neurochem* **15**:154, 1984.

15. O'Farrel PT: High resolution two dimensional electrophoresis of proteins *J Biol Chem* **250**:4007, 1975.

Chapter Six

Specificity of Monoclonal Antibodies

In earlier days, biochemistry, immunology, and anatomy were fairly separated disciplines. Biochemistry dealt mainly with tissue extracts and serum constituents. Anatomy was largely descriptive at the various levels of histologic magnification employed. Immunology dealt with physiological aspects of allergy, immunity, and serology.

The second quarter of our century solidified some of the fundamental discoveries that were destined to permeate all recent research. Particle physics had become verified, sensitive biochemical separation procedures had been designed, conditions for successful cell culture were established, nucleic acids were found to be basic to genetics, and neurosecretory principles to intercellular communication. Modern biochemistry has gradually become more and more cellular and celebrated this event by its name change to *molecular biology*. In immunology too, most modern research deals with *cellular immunology*. Modern anatomy is spurred by the desire to become functionally oriented in the form of *biochemical anatomy*. Yet, this desire has been beset with many difficulties. The first hope to accomplish a biochemical anatomy has been derived from the discovery of Scharrer and Sinden (1) that enzyme histochemistry was able to delineate the same arrangement of layers in the optic tectum as pure morphology. The correlation of structure with chemistry was called by these authors *chemoarchitectonics*.

Since many different enzymes react with the same available artificial substrates used in histochemistry, the specificity of enzyme histochemistry is fairly low. It had been hoped, therefore, that identification of histologic structure be better served by immunocytochemistry. As we have seen in the preceding chapter, this approach again had limitations: ambiguity was due to the specificity in the antisera used. Upon immunization, many immunocompetent cells are stimulated, and each one of them is likely to produce a different antibody, even if the immunizing antigen is purified. These antibodies react with different epitopes on the antigen. Even if an epitope is presented in a well-defined manner, such as for instance dinitrophenyllysine in dinitrophenyllysyl hemocyanin, and the antibodies are affinity-purified with dinitrophenyllysyl albumin, the antidinitrophenyllysyl antibodies produced by the progeny of each stimulated immunocompetent cell are likely to be of different idiotypes, reacting to different degrees with epitopes in dinitrophenol alone, dinitrophenyllysine and dinitrophenyllysine plus adjacent epitopes in the dinitrophenyllysyl hemocyanin. All these antibodies are secreted into the serum. Consequently, serum antibodies are of *heterogeneous idiotypes.* The antibodies are *polyclonal,* even if affinity-purified. If we use these antibodies in immunocytochemistry, some may react specifically, and others may cross-react with unknown tissue constituents. There is no easy way to separate these antibodies, and, therefore, as we have seen, many results of immunocytochemistry with serum-derived antibodies are ambiguous.

While mixtures of idiotypes are secreted into serum by the combined effort of the progeny of different immunocompetent cells stimulated by antigen, the antibody produced by each single cell originally stimulated, as well as by its progeny, consists of a single idiotype only. The antibody is considered to be *monoclonal,* that is, it is produced by the clone derived from a single, antigen-stimulated cell. The methodology for producing monoclonal antibodies depends on isolating progeny from such a single, antigen-stimulated cell. This is best done by cell culture in which clones are derived from single cells.

Monoclonal antibodies are *specific.* When they react with high affinity, they bind approximately seven amino acids in a polypeptide. By mere coincidence, similar sequences rarely occur in unrelated polypeptides. Therefore, if a high-affinity monoclonal antibody does not only react with high immunocytochemical affinity with the antigen with which we think it should react, but also with something else, we cannot say that the other reaction is nonspecific. It may be an unexpected reaction, but in all likelihood it is due to a region in a seemingly unrelated antigen determined by identical genes. For instance, Nancy Sternberger et al. (2) found that antisynapse-associated monoclonal antibody 02-24 reacts with a 22-kDa protein in adult rat brain (page 459). In the newborn, however, it reacts with two proteins of 114- and 94-kDa size, respectively. Either there are several genes that determine the adult polypeptide, which are expressed in the newborn in the form of two polypeptides, or the adult polypeptide is posttranslationally processed from a larger precursor, while in the newborn the processing is incomplete and terminates at two larger sizes. Another example is the localization of antiphosphorylated neurofilament monoclonal antibody 06-68 in neuronal nuclei in newly developing regions of the brain and in axons in developed regions (page 440). However, despite the abundance of epitopes in a vertebrate, monoclonal antibodies to given constituents exhibit rarely any immunocytochemical reactivity with more than one unrelated constituent throughout the organism (3).

The specificity of monoclonal antibodies is not absolute. Were they reactive with more than seven amino acids, they would be more specific than the presumably highest affinity polyclonal antibodies available. However, the specificity *is* high. More important than their ultimate degree of specificity is, however, the fact that monoclonal antibodies are pure antibodies that are not contaminated with other antibodies to different or even related epitopes. Therefore, within the limits of their measurable specificity (expressed as affinity), monoclonal antibodies are reliable reagents capable of conferring genuine specificity to immunocytochemistry. As a consequence, biochemical processes can be monitored in situ, thus providing chemoarchitectonics in the sense that immunocytochemistry does not only describe the *location* of chemical constituents but also their *assembly* and *processing* (page 448). Thus, observations that have required isolation and purification of tissue constituents can be obtained directly in tissue sections. Biochemistry became cellular a long time ago, but now anatomy has become biochemical too.

The use of monoclonal antibodies for detection of biochemical processing of given antigens in situ is the fortunate result of the fact that antibodies do not recognize a macromolecular antigen in toto, but only a small portion thereof, with an apparent maximal size of seven amino acids or corresponding size of sugars or lipids. Consequently, different monoclonal antibodies recognize different portions of the same molecule, and post-translational changes in these molecules can be monitored in situ by appropriate antibodies to changed and unchanged configurations (4). In addition, certain biochemical treatments of sections may change staining patterns and have permitted, thereby, certain inferences on the conformation of antigens in normal and pathologic tissues.

A second contribution of monoclonal antibodies to immunocytochemistry is the detection and discovery of new, yet undescribed antigens. Conventional biochemistry requires knowledge of a physiologic property to monitor the isolation of a new principle. Monoclonal antibodies produced with nonpurified antigens may detect antigens of characteristic immunocytochemical distribution. These are often new antigens whose function may remain unknown (page 460). However, the monoclonal antibodies themselves, being purified antibodies, provide efficient reagents for affinity-purification of such new antigens (page 262).

PREPARATION OF MONOCLONAL ANTIBODIES: PRINCIPLE

Essential to the production of monoclonal antibodies is the preparation of clones derived from single antibody-producing cells. Cultures containing single cells can be obtained by plating them on semisolid media at dilutions that makes it probable that each spot on the medium will hold only one cell. Progeny cells will stick to these sites and, therefore, represent clones derived from single cells. Alternatively, cell suspensions can be diluted extensively, so that a given volume contains, on the average, only 0.5 to 0.8 cells. Dispension of these *limiting dilution* volumes into individual culture wells makes it probable that each culture will be the progeny of a single cell.

Normal antibody-producing spleen cells do not replicate in culture. However, malignant cells, such as those obtained from mouse and with lesser success, from human myelomas, do replicate. The principle of monoclonal antibody production as developed by Köhler and Milstein (5) involves fusion of immune spleen cells with myeloma cells, so as to confer to the spleen cells the replicative capability of the myeloma cells and to the myeloma cells the antibody-producing capability of the immune spleen cells.

The products of fusion are: (1) spleen cells fused with myeloma cells, (2) spleen cells fused with spleen cells, (3) myeloma cells fused with myeloma cells, (4) unfused spleen cells, (5) unfused myeloma cells. The fusion efficiency is low, either because most fused cells do not survive, or because most cells do not become fused. Among 2×10^8 spleen and an equal number of myeloma cells, we expect to obtain, in favorable circumstances, 400 viable, fused cells, out of which about 80 will produce antibodies. Four hundred cells are only one cell in one million used for the fusion. The unfused spleen cells and the fusions of spleen cells with spleen cells will not survive. However, the unfused myeloma cells (up to 2×10^8) and fusions from myeloma with myeloma cells will survive. Hence, if the fused cell suspension were plated to limiting dilution, it would be difficult to chance upon an antibody-producing clone. Most clones would merely be myeloma cells. Therefore, it is necessary to eliminate the myeloma cells from the culture.

MOP/c myeloma is a mouse myeloma cell strain which produces low-affinity antibodies to phosphoryl choline (they probably have high affinity for an unknown epitope). Mutants of these cells are useful for cell fusion. Doubly mutant strains have been developed. The first mutation is selection of a clone from this cell line which has lost its capability to produce immunoglobulin. This is desirable, for otherwise the immunoglobulin secreted by the myeloma-immune spleen cell fusion would be only 25% bivalent antibodies to the epitope of interest, 25% bivalent antibodies to phosphoryl choline, and 50% *heteroligating antibodies* with dual specificities for phosphoryl choline and the epitope of interest. These latter antibodies would be contaminants that reduce the purity of desirable antibodies secreted by the clone.

The purpose of the second mutation is the elimination of unfused myeloma cells with selective growth media. As a safeguard for survival, cells possess two pathways for desoxynucleotide synthesis. In one pathway, the synthesis is carried out *de novo* from single building stones which include diphosphoribose, phosphate, glutamine, glycine, and others. In the other pathway, metabolites of spent DNA are *recovered* and reincorporated into new desoxynucleotides. Cells need only one of the pathways for survival. Littlefield (6) has shown that mutants lacking the recovery pathway, can be poisoned by inhibition of the *de novo* synthesis pathway. In the application to immune cell fusion (5), this phenomenon formed the basis for elimination of the myeloma cells and survival of the fused immune spleen cell-myeloma cell hybrids (*hybridomas*). For fusion, MOP/c cells that have lost their immunoglobulin-forming capacity are further selected from mutants that have lost their recovery pathway. In myeloma cells successfully fused with immune spleen cells, the recovery pathway has been restored by the genome of the spleen cell. When the fusion mixture is exposed to inhibitors of the neosynthesis pathway, the unfused myeloma cells will die. However, the fused cells will survive even in media containing the inhibitor of the neosynthesis pathway (*selective media*). As long as the cells are grown in these selective media, they will depend entirely on their recovery pathway.

Hypoxanthine-phosphoribosyl transferase is an X-chromosome-linked enzyme that converts hypoxanthine to inosin in the purine nucleoside recovery pathway (Fig. 6-1). The genome for the enzyme is defective in one out of one million X-chronosomes. Azaguanine or thioguanine can be incorporated into the recovery pathway instead of guanine. Guanylate kinase, the enzyme that

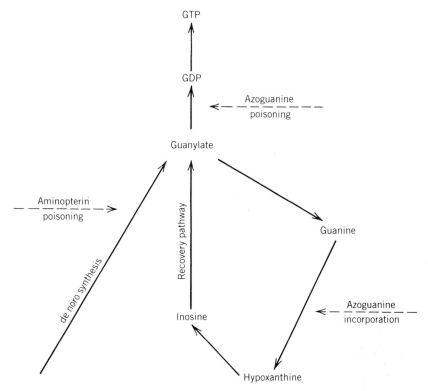

Figure 6-1. Simplified schematics of the guanylate neosynthesis and salvage pathways and their loci of selective poisoning. Azaguanine-resistant mutants of P3 myeloma cells lack hypoxanthine-guanine phosphoribosyl transferase. They will die in aminopterin. In surviving hybridomas from fused P3 cells and immune spleen cells, the salvage pathway is restored. The cells will live in aminopterin, especially if hypoxanthine and thymidine are added to the medium.

adds phosphate to guanylate (guanosine desoxyribose) is poisoned by azaguanylate or thioguanylate. The cell will die because both, the recovery and the neosynthesis pathways, utilize guanylate kinase in the final steps of triphosphate synthesis. However, the mutants that lack hypoxanthine phosphoribosil transferase will not have incorporated the azaguanine or thioguanine and will, therefore, survive. These mutants possess no recovery pathway and will depend entirely on their neosynthesis pathway.

Aminopterin poisons the neosynthesis pathway. When fusions of immune spleen cells with azaguanine-resistant myeloma cells are grown in media containing aminopterin, the unfused myeloma cells and the myeloma-myeloma cell fusions will die. The fused immune spleen cell-myeloma cell hybridomas will survive, because they possess an intact recovery pathway. Hypoxanthine and thymidine are added to the aminopterin-containing media (*HAT medium*) in order to supplement metabolites of the recovery pathway.

Following a fusion, the cell suspension in HAT medium is distributed into a sufficient number of culture wells, so that on the average, only one out of five wells contains a dividing cell. The appropriate number of wells is arrived at experimentally on the assumption that only one in a million cells used will be a replicating hybridoma between an immune spleen cell and a myeloma cell. At the chosen dilution, the probability is high that the cultures will be *clones* derived from single cells. The supernates from these cultures will have to be assayed for antibody activity for three reasons:

1.   Not all spleen cells are immune cells or antibody-producing cells. On the average, one out of five clones produces antibodies.
2.   A clone may have lost its antibody-producing genome.
3.   We usually like to select antibodies for a given purpose. Monoclonal antibody technique offers the opportunity to select antibodies to a given epitope and reject others.

Once antibody-secreting cultures have been identified, it is necessary to subclone them two more times to limiting dilutions. Finally, the cells are propagated as ascites tumors or cultured in hollow fiber systems.

The subcloning to limiting dilution is done for the following reasons:

1.   The original cultures may have been polyclonal.
2.   The clones or part of the clones may be unstable and may lose their antibody-producing capacity.
3.   The clones may be monoclonal with regard to antibody-producing cells, but may contain hybridomas of non-antibody-producing spleen cells with myeloma cells. At best, these cells will dilute the antibody-producing culture. At worst, they will overgrow it. Subcloning to limiting dilution will select the antibody-producing cells. We found that usually all limiting-dilution subcultures will produce antibodies, but occasionally we find that only one in as many as 24 limiting-dilution cultures is antibody-producing. On other occasions, we found that none in 400 limiting-dilution culture wells from a previously cloned culture produced antibodies on a first trial, and that occasionally a repeat trial will yield some antibody-producing cultures that continue growing vigorously from then on.

When the product of a fusion is first divided into multiple wells in HAT medium, the unfused myeloma cells are unable to divide and will die soon. The dying unfused spleen cells and the myeloma cells, as well as any nonviable fused cells, provide additional DNA metabolites to the surviving hybridoma cells in their dependence on the recovery pathway. By the time the unfused cells have died, the hybridoma cells have not yet reached sufficient abundance to provide essential metabolites, and, therefore, they benefit by the addition of feeder cells or their products, provided by mononuclear cells from spleen or peritoneum (they do not divide) or by supernates from old cultures of myeloma cells.

METHODS OF CLONE SELECTION

Assay of antibody production at frequent intervals throughout the cloning procedure and prior to and after ascites formation is essential. Any immunologic method can be used, provided it is sensitive enough. Since the number of assays required is large, in general the most convenient methods have been employed.

This may, however, have drawbacks. The epitopes in a given antigen that participate in the assay reaction may be different from those looked for in the final application of the antibody produced. Thus, antibodies of high affinity, originally selected, may be unreactive in the final use. Even if the antibody may react with the same epitope in both situations, the configuration of this epitope may be different in the final application than in the original test. Since in the original test, the best reacting antibodies have been selected, they may react in the final test at best with equal affinities, but more likely with lower affinities.

Several tests for selection of antibodies are used with some frequency.

Radioimmunoassay

Culture supernates are mixed with radioiodinated antigen and the radioactivity precipitated with a second antibody in the presence of carrier immunoglobulin is analyzed. The test is that of choice if we are interested in the production of monoclonal antibodies for radioimmunoassay. If we use these antibodies for immunocytochemistry, they are likely to be worse than in radioimmunoassay (i.e., have lower titers) or they may not react at all. Our monoclonal antibodies to luteinizing hormone-releasing hormone (LHRH) had originally been detected in hybridoma supernatants by radioimmunoassay and were found to react with unusually high association constants of $K = 10^{10}/M$ (7). The antibodies provided an extremely sensitive tool for the isolation of an LHRH precursor and its characterization by radioimmunoassay (page 386). However, the antibodies reacted poorly in immunocytochemistry, giving maximal reactivities at dilutions not less than 1 : 2000, an unusually high concentration for ascites-borne monoclonal antibodies. In contrast, serum antibodies to LHRH reacted in immunocytochemistry either better or worse than in radioimmunoassay. The reason is that some of the antibodies in the serum react only by radioimmunoassay, others only in immunocytochemistry, and some in both tests. Consequently, radioimmunoassay grade antisera can be used for immunocytochemistry as reported by Elias and Johnsen (8). However, monoclonal antibodies, being only one idiotype among the many found in antisera, are not necessarily expected to react in both tests. Antibodies detected in culture supernates by radioimmunoassay may react with amino-terminal groups in proteins. These groups are destroyed by fixation. Antibodies useful in immunocytochemistry may react with tyrosine-containing epitopes. These antibodies remain undetected in a selection procedure based on radioimmunoassay.

Immunofluorescence

Assay by immunofluorescence is often used to select antibodies reactive with surface antigen. It is the test of choice, if it is desired to produce antibodies for specific absorption of given classes of lymphocytes, cell purification by affinity columns, or if it is desirable to separate such cells with the fluorescent cell sorter (page 46).

Enzyme-Linked Immunosorbent Assay (ELISA)

The antigen is adsorbed on polystyrene plates and reaction with hybridoma supernates is assayed by immunocytochemical methods. Again, clones selected by ELISA will produce antibodies that react best in ELISA and equally well, less well, or not at all in immunocytochemistry on fixed tissues. They will not react better in immunocytochemistry than in ELISA. Again, the reason is the different treatment of the antigen. In immunocytochemistry, the antigen has been subject to fixation and embedding. In ELISA, native antigen is used. However, the adsorption itself may produce conformational changes sufficient to expose different epitopes in the ELISA test than those available in the tissue section (page 115). Thus, monoclonal antibodies against prostatic acid phosphatase selected by ELISA may not always be suitable for diagnosis of the prostatic origin of prostatic tumor metastases (page 472). This is an expected phenomenon that should not detract from the use of monoclonal antibodies in surgical diagnosis. The staining patterns of monoclonal antibodies are more specific than those obtained with antisera, and moreover, are free of background. Consequently, the diagnostic acumen is increased, provided properly selected monoclonal antibodies are used.

Immunocytochemistry

If we wish to use monoclonal antibodies in immunocytochemistry, it is best to carry out the hybridoma selection also by immunocytochemistry, using the same fixative and the same tissue preparation as that intended finally. All our immunocytochemically used monoclonal antibodies have been selected by this procedure (9) and we believe this is the reason for their high affinities in immunocytochemistry and the possibility of using them at high dilutions (10). While it is relatively easy to carry out 1000 tests a day by radioimmunoassay or ELISA, immunocytochemistry in our hands had to be restricted to a maximum of 120 sections. The hybridoma selection procedure had to be adjusted accordingly.

PREPARATION OF MONOCLONAL ANTIBODIES FOR IMMUNOCYTOCHEMISTRY: PROCEDURE

The basic culture medium is RPMI 1640. *Supplemented medium* consists of 500 ml RPMI 1640/10 ml pencillin-streptomycin mixture (each at 5000 units per ml)/5 ml L-glutamine, 200 mM/5 ml sodium pyruvate, 100mM. *Complete medium* consists of supplemented medium containing 15% fetal bovine serum. HAT stock solution is made as a solution in RPMI 1640 containing 10^{-4} M hypoxanthine/4 $\times$ 10^{-7} M aminopterin/1.6 $\times$ 10^{-5} M thymidine. *HAT medium* is made by adding 1 part of HAT stock solution to 100 parts of complete medium. About 1 to 2 hours prior use, flasks containing media are placed in the carbon dioxide incubator (7% carbon dioxide) with their tops loosened in order to permit equilibration of temperature and carbon dioxide.

For fusions, we use the procedure of Köhler and Milstein (5) as modified by de St. Groth et al. (11) with minor adaptation to its specific use for production of antibodies for immunocytochemistry. Prior to a fusion, it is necessary to grow myeloma cells in sufficient numbers, using either P3x63Ag8 cells or the more rapidly growing P2/0Ag cells. About 2×10^8 cells are needed. They will be provided by six 50 ml cultures grown in flasks to 50% to 75% confluence. The procedure requires not more than 6 days if P3 cells are used starting from 1 million frozen cells.

A small and separate aliquot of the P3 cells is occasionally grown in complete medium containing 0.1 mM azaguanine, to assure that all cells die and the culture is free of hypoxanthine-guanine phosphoribose transferase-containing revertants.

On the day before fusion, the cells from a normal female BALB/c spleen are extruded into HAT medium for use as feeder cells. Coarse particles are allowed to settle, and the supernate is diluted in HAT medium to 5×10^5 viable white cells per milliliter counted by hemocytometer for total cells and trypan blue exclusion for viable cells. The suspension is plated in six 96-well plates in amounts of 200 μl per well. The plates are incubated overnight to assure sterility.

Also on the day before fusion, a solution of 50% polyethylene glycol weight/volume in RPMI 1640 is prepared. Polyethylene glycol of molecular weight of 4000 seems to be suitable. Dimethylsulfoxide may be added to the fusion mixture. It is supposed to stabilize the cells from damage incumbent to the polyethylene glycol treatment. Polyethylene glycol solutions are made at 37°C. They can be sterilized by ultrafiltration after they have been prepared.

For the fusion, the P3 cells are centrifuged at $200 \times g$, 25°C, 10 minutes, resuspended in a small volume, such as 5 ml, of RPMI 1640, and counted. The adjuvant-immunized mouse, which has been boosted by an intraperitoneal injection without adjuvants 3 days before fusion, is sacrificed. Under surgical technique, the abdomen is cleaned with alcohol and the skin separated without injuring the peritoneum. The peritoneal endothelium is again cleaned with alcohol, and then, using fresh surgical instruments, the peritoneum is opened and the intact spleen removed into a Petri dish containing about 5 ml of RPMI 1640. The spleen cells are extruded, the suspension is transferred to a 15-ml centrifuge tube, and the coarse particles are allowed to settle. The supernatant cells are transferred to a 15-ml centrifuge tube and counted by hemocytometer and trypan blue exclusion. Their number will usually be $1-2 \times 10^8$. An equal or slightly lesser number of P3 cells are added, and the mixture is centrifuged at $200 \times g$, 25°C, 10 minutes. The supernatant is aspirated as completely as possible, and the cells are smeared onto the sides of the conical bottom of the centrifuge tube by means of a Pasteur pipette with a beaded, blunt tip produced by melting in a Bunsen burner. One ml of polyethylene glycol solution is then added over a period of 30 seconds while the tube is being rotated constantly. The tube is centrifuged at $200 \times g$, 25°C for 2 minutes. The exposure time to polyethylene glycol, including centrifugation, should be 8 minutes. The polyethylene glycol is then aspirated, the suspension is centrifuged in RPMI 1640 once, and resuspended in 36 ml of HAT medium in a 50-ml centrifuge tube. Twenty μl of the cell suspension is added to each well of the six 96-well plates prepared on the preceding day with 200 μl of feeder cells containing complete medium.

The cultures are incubated without disturbing for 7 days. The remaining cells from the fusion are centrifuged at $200 \times g$, $25°C$ for 10 minutes and resuspended in 2.0 ml of freezing medium. This medium consists of 7 parts complete medium, 3 parts fetal bovine serum, and 1 part dimethylsulfoxide. One ml of the suspension is then transferred into each of two 3-ml freezing tubes. These tubes are placed in a styrofoam box kept at room temperature. The box is tightly closed and placed on the bottom of a freezer at $-85°C$, taking care not to agitate the cells during the freezing process. They may be transferred to regular freezer storage boxes the next day.

On the seventh day of incubation and 3 times a week thereafter, the cells in the 96-well plates are fed by removing 100 μl of supernate and adding either 100 μl of feeder cells in HAT medium, or a mixture of equal parts of spent supernate from P3 cells and double strength HAT in complete medium. Feeder cell suspensions may be kept in the refrigerator for 7 days or more.

From the seventh day on and until about the 19th day, cultures are inspected daily for cell growth which is apparent by white, glistening spots seen from below the culture plate against the room lights, usually at the rim of the wells. Growth is confirmed in the inverted microscope under phase illumination. Healthy, dividing cells are identified by their round shape, smooth contours, and relatively clean cytoplasm, and growing cultures are identified by frequent paired cells that are still adherent to each other after the last cell division, by occasional dumb-bell shaped cells in anaplasia, and by frequent mitotic figures (if rat, rather than mouse spleen cells are fused with mouse myeloma cells, they may have bizarre yet smooth outlines). Inspection of cultures is done rapidly to avoid undue exposure to carbon dioxide-free environment.

When cells have reached 50 to 75% confluence, 75 to 100 μl of culture medium is placed for 1 hour onto paraffin sections that have been pretreated with 3% normal rabbit serum. Following application of rabbit antimouse IgG, mouse ClonoPAP, and diaminobenzidine with hydrogen peroxide, staining is evaluated (for supernates from rat/mouse fusions, rabbit antirat IgG and rat ClonoPAP are used). The relatively short incubation time in supernate is chosen, because a decision has to be made rapidly whether to accept or reject a culture. An accepted culture must be subcultured on the same day to avoid overgrowth.

Only a fraction of growing cultures will secrete immunocytochemically detectable antibody. Lack of detectable antibody may be due to fusion of nonantibody-producing spleen cells, to loss of the antibody-producing genome after fusion, or to secretion of an antibody not detectable in paraffin sections. For the last reason, it is important to use an assay procedure similar to that intended for the final use of the antibodies obtained. If it is desirable to visualize intracellular antigens, paraffin sections are a convenient choice. If it is desirable to observe cell surface antigen in tissue cultures, the living cultures should be used for assay.

Once a section is stained, the selection of antibodies is made. It is neither feasible, nor desirable to develop further all the antibodies appearing in supernates at this stage. If we are interested in antibodies to neuron-specific antigens, we will use paraffin sections of brain and select those supernates that stain neuronal cell bodies or their axons or dendrites without also staining glia or connective tissue surrounding the brain. Many antibodies will be found that also stain these latter structures and they will be discarded. Cultures secreting antibodies that appear to be specific for neurons will be kept. Their detailed staining pattern, reactivity with nonneuronal antigens in peripheral tissues, if any, and identification of the nature of the antigen with which they react will be deferred to a later stage, when larger amounts of antibodies have become available.

Selected cultures from the 96-well plates are transferred into 1 ml of HAT medium (24-well plates). When 50 to 75% confluence has been reached, they are subcultured into 3×1 ml complete medium supplemented with hypoxanthine and thymidine, but devoid of aminopterin (HT medium). Again these cells are subcultured into 3×6 ml HT medium (6-well plates) and then into 3×20 ml complete medium devoid of HT (80-ml flask). Upon reaching 50 to 75% confluence, they are shaken off the surface of the flask by gentle tapping and the cells in the suspension are counted.

For subculturing to limiting dilution, 320 cells are then transferred into a tube containing 8.0 ml of complete medium. Twenty μl of this suspension is added to each well of four 96-well plates into which have been placed, on the preceding day, 200 μl of feeder cells in complete medium.

The remainder of the culture is centrifuged at $200 \times g$, 25°C, 10 minutes, and resuspended in freezing medium in amounts of about 1 million cells/ml. Cells are frozen as described above and stored in two -85°C electrical freezers or in one electrical and one liquid nitrogen freezer.

The subcloned cultures will reach 50 to 75% confluence on the 9th to 19th day. Supernates will again be asayed and any positive cultures will be chosen at random for expansion, again into 3×20 ml of medium as described above. Subcloning to limiting dilution will be repeated once more. Following assay of the final culture (3×20 ml), 1 million cells will be injected intraperitoneally into BALB/c female mice that have been pretreated with 1 or 2 intraperitoneal injections of 1.0 ml of Pristane within 1 month. The remainder of the cells are centrifuged and placed into freezing medium in amounts of 1 million cells per ml in freezer vials. Mice will be weighed daily or observed for development of ascites fluid. Once ascites has developed, but before the mouse is moribund, the fluid is aspirated, centrifuged to remove cell debris, and assayed immunocytochemically with ClonoPAP at dilutions ranging from 1 : 1000 to 1 : 500,000.

Instead of growing cells as ascites tumors, antibodies can also be obtained on a large scale by growing cells in vitro only. The amount of antibody per milliliter is about 1/5,000 of that obtainable as ascites. Apparently antibody production in vitro depends on the total surface to which the cells can attach and not only on the amount of medium supplied. The surface area can be increased by growing cells in hollow fiber matrices through which medium is circulated by a pump. We found that antibodies in culture supernates are not always stable at -85°C. Since the concentration of antibody in culture supernates is relatively low, it is desirable to concentrate them. This can be done by affinity purification with insolubilized antigen, if available. The antigen does not have to be of highest purity in the case of monoclonal antibodies. Alternatively, it can be done by absorption on and elution from staphylococcal protein A covalently bound to an insoluble matrix or supplied in the form of staphylococci. However, not all mouse immunoglobulins react with staphylococcal protein A. Even in unconcentrated supernates, the fetal bovine serum in culture supernates does not interfere with immunocytochemical staining and does not confer background if ClonoPAP is used. Furthermore, it has been shown by Cleveland et al. (12) that hybridomas can be grown in entirely protein-free media provided essential trace elements are supplied and that the cells are grown attached to surfaces at high densities. Cells previously grown in media containing fetal bovine serum have been slowly adapted to the cell-free media by gradual reduction in serum concentration.

High titered antisera are obtained by repeat injections of antigen. The repeat or *recall* reaction of *educated* immunocytes is faster and more extensive than a primary reaction (page 280). However, shortly after injection of an antigen, no serum antibodies are available because circulating antibodies have been combined with the injected antigen. This problem is not encountered in hybridoma technology. Spleen cells exposed to excess antigen in vitro can be freed of the antigen by mere centrifugation. It is possible, therefore, to obtain monoclonal antibodies from cultures with spleen cells from normal BALB/c mice that have been exposed to antigen in vitro for a few days prior to centrifugation and fusion with myeloma cells. Spleen cells will survive short-time cultures. When this technique is used, only monoclonal IgM is obtained and these antibodies are generally of low affinities. An advantage of the technique is the need of only minute doses of antigen for immunization.

Fox et al. (13) found that the frequency of fusion can be enhanced if spleen cells from a hyperimmune BALB/c mouse are cultured in the presence of antigen for 3 to 4 days prior to fusion. Alternatively the cells can be transferred into x-irridiated BALB/c mice for 4 days prior to fusion. It was felt that the increased fusion efficiency was due to absence of a possible immunosuppressor cell effect (page 283) during initial culture or in the x-irradiated mice.

As discussed above, one of the reasons of low ratios of antibody-producing clones to total viable cultures that come to assay in a fusion, is the need of successful retention in the hybridoma cells of the genome for antibody production as well as that for hypoxanthine-phosphoribosyl transferase. Taggart and Samloff (14) introduced a technique, in which fused cells that have lost their antibody-producing capability (heavy chain immunoglobulin locus on chromosome 12) will be unable to survive. This is accomplished by employing, as immune spleen cell donor, mice of the Robertsonian 5 Bnr strain in which the immunoglobulin locus on chromosome 12 (of which only 1 allele is expressed, page 14) is genetically linked to the adenosine-phosphoribosyl transferase (APRT) marker on chromosome 8. If a hybridoma loses its immunoglobulin-producing capability, it will also lose the expression of APRT. Therefore, if grown in a selective medium that requires ARTP, the hybridoma will die and will not appear as a culture to be assayed for antibodies. A selective medium that contains azaserine will block the *de novo* synthesis of purine nucleotides, and, therefore, cells will have to possess APRT activity to survive by the recovery pathway. Myeloma cells that are APRT deficient are used, so that both the myeloma cells as well as the hybridomas that have lost the genetically linked immunoglobulin-APRT genome will fail to survive.

INTERPRETATION OF SPECIFICITY

We have seen that in immunocytochemistry with antiserum, absorption tests are often used in attempts to make specificity plausible. Successful solid-phase absorption was questioned because of the possibility of impurities in the absorbing antigen and because of affinity considerations. Impurities in the absorbing antigen may falsely attribute specificity to a nonspecific antiserum. On the other hand, solid-phase absorption with cross-reacting antigens not detectable by immunocytochemistry at high-antibody dilution, may remove specific antibodies. Consequently, a reaction which by absorption with a cross-reacting antigen may appear to be nonspecific may have been specific after all.

With monoclonal antibodies, these difficulties do not arise because absorptions are not only unnecessary, they are redundant. Monoclonal antibodies have been defined by the selection procedure to be specific to epitopes that mediated the immunologic selection reaction used. This is the reasons why it is so important to use proper selection procedure. The antibodies, once obtained in ascites, will react with the same epitope as that which mediated the selection reaction. Nothing new is learned by absorbing these antibodies with this particular epitope. The antibodies are specific to this epitope and since they are monoclonal, they will not be contaminated with antibodies that are not specific.

Specificity must be understood as a quantitative term which, in the case of monoclonal antibodies, is synonymous with affinity. Specificity tests of monoclonal antibodies are, therefore, nothing but determination of affinities with which the antibody reacts with various antigens. There will always be an epitope with which the antibody reacts with highest affinity. This epitope may not necessarily be that with which it reacted in the selection procedure. However, the chance is high that the selection procedure epitope is closer to one of high specificity than one of low specificity with the antibody. The antibodies in the supernates used for selection of the 96-well cultures are the product of about 1000 cells. These are not very large amounts of antibody. Any antibody that passes the immunocytochemical selection test is likely, therefore, to be of high affinity. High affinity is confirmed, if ascites fluid can be used at high dilution in the 10^{-4} to 10^{-5} range.

Although monoclonal antibodies are specific by definition, their reaction with specific epitopes must be distinguished from reaction with crossreacting epitopes, that is, epitopes with better fit into the idiotypic site must be distinguished from those with lesser fit. Dilution of antibodies can distinguish between high and low affinities, and thus, better or worse fit, provided the antigens are known and their concentrations are measured. In immunocytochemistry, we do not know the concentrations of antigens. If staining disappears upon dilution of antibody in one area of a section and not in another, two interpretaions are possible. Either the antigen in the first area is present in lower concentration or it is cross-reactive and presents an altered epitope. By immunocytochemistry alone, distinction of these alternatives is difficult.

Sometimes it is possible to separate the antigens by electrophoresis-electroblots and determine their protein concentrations. Once the protein concentration is known, the immunocytochemical reaction on the blots could be interpreted in terms of affinity only and a higher affinity reaction could theoretically be distinguished from a low-affinity reaction. For instance, phosphorylated neurofilament monoclonal antibody 06-17 (page 442) reacts well with the 200 and the 150-kDa neurofilament polypeptides, while antiphosphorylated neurofilament antibody 04-7 reacts well with equal concentrations of the 200 kDa but only faintly with the 150-kDa polypeptide. One may be tempted to conclude that 04-7 reacts with higher affinity with the 200-kDa than the 150-kDa polypeptide, and that, therefore, the specific epitope in the 200-kDa polypeptide is only partially represented in the 150-kDa polypeptide. However, this conclusion is not quite feasible, because of heterogeneity of neurofilaments within classes of equal molecular weight (page 438). Thus, antibody 04-7 may react poorly with the 150-kDa polypeptide merely because the antibody is specific to a form of this polypeptide which is not very abundant. The problem could be resolved by improved separation procedures, such as two-dimensional electrophoresis electroblots. However, protein determination of blots is less sensitive than immunocytochemistry and many spots appear that can be stained immunocytochemically but whose protein concentration is not easily determined.

In most cases, however, the question whether a monoclonal antibody reacts more specifically with a given structure or reflects merely a cross-reaction is not too important. Most monoclonal antibodies are extremely specific in visualizing only expected structures immunocytochemically. Thus, antibody to cilia (page 432), for instance, reacts immunocytochemically only with ciliated epithelia and not with any other tissue components, despite the large number of epitopes available throughout the organism and the possibility of epitope analogy by mere coincidence. Therefore, tests for specificity of monoclonal antibodies become largely unnecessary.

Even cross-reactivities in monoclonal antibodies are less likely to occur than in any single indiotype in serum antibodies, because the selection procedure for monoclonal antibodies favors high-affinity antibodies and thus permits their immunocytochemical use at high dilutions (Table 5-1).

STAINING

With antisera or affinity-purified antibodies, there are two contributions to background: low method specificity and low antibody specificity (page 47). The unlabeled antibody method eliminates problems of low method specificity. However, background from low-antibody specificity cannot be entirely abolished with every antiserum. With monoclonal antibodies, this cause of poor specificity is eliminated and immunocytochemically stained sections are regularly free of background. No longer is it necessary to avoid background by dilution of first antibodies. Monoclonal antibodies can be used at high dilutions or at high concentrations. However, at dilutions of 1 : 1000 or less sometimes a mild Eng-Bigbee effect (prozone phenomenon, pages 106 and 176) is observed.

The three peroxidases in PAP prepared from antiserum are inhibited in their enzymatic reactivity to varying extents (15). The inhibition varies in preparations from different antisera and seems to be the result of steric hindrance by antibodies reacting at or near the catalytic site of peroxidase. Use of monoclonal antiperoxidase gave us the opportunity to eliminate this hindrance effect. When clones were selected from fusions of spleen cells from mice or rats immunized with peroxidase, only those were accepted that secreted antibodies which reacted with peroxidase without inhibition of its enzymatic activity, that is, which combined with peroxidase at sites away from the catalytic site. As a consequence, it was found that ClonoPAP prepared from mouse or rat monoclonal antibodies was much more reactive than PAP prepared from mouse or rat antisera.

Becker et al. (16) selected monoclonal antibodies specific for monocytes and macrophages, for monocytes, macrophages and selected T cells, and for an antigen common to all leukocytes, respectively, by their ability to attach to un-fixed cells in suspension as assayed by a radiolabeled second antibody. Even though the four-layer unlabeled antibody technique may, at times, result in background because of poor specificity of the second antibody, Hancock et al. (17) found that it is more sensitive and specific in detecting tissue antigens than fluorochrome or peroxidase-conjugated antibody methods. Only with the PAP method was it possible to determine the tissue distribution of two of the three antileukocyte monoclonal antibodies. Also, in contrast to other methods, signal intensity was stronger while background was negligible.

A similar procedure was applied by Morich et al. (18) in a slide assay for identification in limiting-dilution cultures of hybridomas that produce antibodies to human leukocyte cell surface antigens. Suspensions of cells were placed on slides that had been prepared in such a way that single spots were surrounded by nonwettable areas, thus preventing confluence of reagents during immunocytochemical staining. This was accomplished by placing drops of gum arabic on a slide, then coating the slide with a suspension of nonwettable microparticles, removing the gum arabic, replacing the gum arabic spots with cell suspension, fixing in glutaraldehyde, and immunocytochemical staining with the four-layer PAP procedure.

As expected, the four-layer PAP procedure (hybridoma supernatant, rabbit antimouse immunoglobulin, swine antirabbit immunoglobulin, rabbit PAP) yielded some background due to the second antibody (page 142), which would not occur in the three-stage procedure (hybridoma supernate, antimouse immunoglobulin, mouse ClonoPAP). However, the background could be eliminated by absorption of the rabbit antimouse immunoglobulin with human tonsil homogenate. The PAP method was found to be more sensitive than radioimmunoassay, ELISA with peroxidase-conjugated antibodies, or immunofluorescence and was capable of detecting a larger number of antibody-producing clones. The avidin-biotin method gave problems because of background staining.

With antisera, an Eng-Bigbee effect is rarely seen in paraffin sections. With monoclonal antibodies, it is a common occurrence when ascites are diluted less than 1 : 1000, albeit it may require quantitative immunocytochemistry for detection. We believe that the effect is due to the nature of binding of the first antibody. The anti-immunoglobulin in the second antibody is antiserum-derived and contains polyclonal mixtures of antibodies, some reactive close to the idiotypic site of the first antibody and others at some distance from these sites. Under normal circumstances, both combining sites of the first antibody are attached to tissue antigen (Fig. 3-4). This binding sterically hinders epitopes in the first antibody near its idiotypic site. Consequently a selection takes place among the second antibodies for those reactive away from the idiotypic site of the first antibody. These antibodies will be able to react with PAP, where again the idiotypic sites of antiperoxidase may be sterically hindered by binding with peroxidase. If, however, a very large excess of first antibody is used, it will react, at least in part, via one idiotypic site only, and present an uncombined second idiotypic site to the second antibody. Consequently, antibodies in the second antiserum specific for epitopes close to these sites will be permitted to react. However, these antibodies cannot interact with PAP, because in PAP the anti-peroxidase idiotypic sites may be sterically hindered. As a result, the immunocytochemical reaction is inhibited. The inhibition appears to be small, because apparently the combination of first antibody via both idiotypic sites is preferred (page 6) and can be diminished only if its concentration is extremely high.

Antisera to mouse immunoglobulin generally do not cross-react with rabbit immunoglobulin and antisera to rabbit immunoglobulin generally do not cross-react with mouse immunoglobulin. Consequently, it is possible to demonstrate colocalization of two antigens with a rabbit antiserum and a mouse monoclonal antibody provided both antigens are presented in a degree of proximity that is within the sterically hindered confines of antibody. In the case of such colocalization, pretreatment with rabbit antiserum will block reaction of the monoclonal antibody, antimouse immunoglobulin, and mouse ClonoPAP. The antimouse immunoglobulin will not react with the rabbit antibody. The reverse sequence, that of blocking the reacting of rabbit antiserum with monoclonal antibody, followed by goat antirabbit immunoglobulin and rabbit PAP may be less informative, because of the presence of multiple antibodies in rabbit antiserum, some of which may have a broader reaction distribution than the monoclonal antibody. However, the sequence may be useful if only for the purpose of establishing this fact.

Since monoclonal antibodies can be obtained in large amounts in pure form, they are good candidates for direct immunofluorescence.

Monoclonal antibodies produced in culture may be labeled isotopically with a degree of specific radioactivity sufficient for immunocytochemistry. Cuello et al. (19) incubated hybridomas producing antisubstance P in media containing ^{3}H-lysine and used these antibodies for the pre-embedding electron microscopic localization of substance P terminals in the substantia gelatinosa of the nucleus spinalis of the trigeminal nerve as visualized by autoradiography. The technique was used to provide a contrasting label, with PAP staining, for the simultaneous localization of substance P and enkephalin at the electron microscopic level. Substance P mediates nociceptive stimuli from the trigeminal ganglion and (leu)enkephalin inhibits them, thus possibly providing a gating effect. Dual localization of both peptides would provide information on the circuitry of this interaction. Cryostat sections were first stained with rabbit antiserum to (leu)enkephalin, rabbit PAP and diaminobenzidine and hydrogen peroxide, and then with tritiated monoclonal antisubstance P and developed by autoradiography. Substance P and (leu)enkephalin terminals were seen to synapse, sometimes, onto common dendritic profiles.

Antibodies bearing two different idiotypes, one for tissue epitopes and one for a marker, such as ferritin or an immunocytochemically detectable enzyme, could be useful in immunocytochemistry. Antibody-forming cells do not produce such antibodies of dual specificities. Light and heavy chains are coded by different messengers. Light and heavy chains possess considerable homology, combining rapidly, sometimes even before their separate assembly on ribosomes has been completed. In vitro, light and heavy chains combine specifically. Chains of identical idiotypes will home to each other in a mixture of divergent idiotypes.

In vivo, pairs of light and heavy chain recombinants will bind to form the four-chain immunoglobulin basic unit that possesses two idiotypic sites. Since only one allele for heavy chain formation is expressed in a cell (page 11), only one idiotype can be formed, and, therefore, both combining sites of a naturally produced antibody are identical. We have seen (Fig. 1-3) that when both heavy chains are separated in vitro by pepsin digestion and reduction to form F(ab)' fragments, they will recombine on oxidation via the hinge region portion of their heavy chains to reconstitute F(ab)'₂ fragments. However, heavy chains or heavy chain fragments of identical idiotypes will not home to each other. Recombination among F(ab)' fragments of different idiotypes is random and, thus, *heteroligating antibodies* of dual specificity can be formed, albeit in low yield (20). A hybridoma cell differs from an unfused cell in that it possesses chromosomes derived from both parent lines. A hybridoma derived from an antibody-producing spleen cell and an immunoglobulin-producing myeloma cell may retain two pairs of immunoglobulin-producing chromosomes within which each allele may produce one immunoglobulin-coding messenger. Milstein and Cuello (21) have utilized this phenomenon to produce heteroligating monoclonal antibodies in which one idiotypic site is antisomatostatin and the other antiperoxidase. These heteroligating antibodies reacted with somatostatin-secreting granules in somatostatinergic hypothalamic fibers by pre-embedding staining electron microscopy and could be revealed by reaction with peroxidase. The heteroligating antibodies were produced by fusion of spleen cells from rats immunized to somatostatin with mutant hybridomas that secreted rat antiperoxidase. Azaguanine-resistant mutants (page 248) have been selected from the hybridoma, so that unfused hybridoma cells became sensitive to HAT medium.

Fused cells expressed light and heavy chains of antisomatostatin as well as antiperoxidase idiotypes. It could be expected that the light and heavy chains of antiperoxidase idiotypy combined rapidly and specifically after their formation, and that the light and heavy chains of antisomatostatin idiotypes also homed to each other. Half-antibody molecules, consisting of one light and one heavy chain, are processed in the endoplasmic reticulum and Golgi system (page 285). Only after the light and heavy chain combination, is the four-chain antibody unit assembled. There is no homing for idiotypes in this latter combination and, therefore, half of all four-chain antibody molecules are expected to be of dual specificities for somatostatin and peroxidase, with one idiotypic site for each, while one-quarter of all antibodies would be antiperoxidase with two identical idiotypic sites and one-quarter antisomatostatin with two identical idiotypic sites (compare with Fig. 1-3). The theoretical proportion is somewhat effected by the less than absolute homing of light and heavy chains. In the work of Milstein and Cuello (21), antisomatostatin light and heavy chain recombination was nearly quantitative, but the homing of antiperoxidase light and heavy chains was not pronounced.

The homoligating antisomatostatin (which possesses two idiotypes for somatostatin) competes with the heteroligating antibodies and reduces sensitivity. If the functional affinity of the homoligating antibody is higher than that of the heteroligating antibody (page 236), the competition could be pronounced. It would be desirable, therefore, to purify such antibodies by affinity chromatography on peroxidase.

AFFINITY PURIFICATION OF ANTIGENS

Attempts have been made occasionally to use antisera or their products for affinity purification of antigens. The approach suffered from a number of difficulties:

1. Specific antibodies are only a fraction of total protein in antisera or immunoglobulin fractions prepared from antisera. Nonspecific protein is covalently bound to the affinity column along with any specific antibody, and reduces column efficiency.

2. The antibodies are polyclonal, and, therefore, elution from the column, usually carried out by acidification, will not occur in a sharp zone but over a wide range of pH depending on the affinity of each antibody involved and its relative specificity for ionizable and nonionizable portions of the epitope. Some antibodies do not dissociate at any pH (page 95) and may retain, thereby, the antigen on the column.

Monoclonal antibodies avoid these difficulties. In immunoglobulin fractions, derived from ascites fluid, at least 50%, but more commonly as much as 90% of all protein is monoclonal antibody. Thus, efficient columns can be produced. Since we are dealing with only one antibody, dissociation of antigen from the column will occur at a narrow and reproducible zone when lowering the pH in a gradient. In some cases, this zone may vary, at least in theory, with the presentation of the specific epitope. However, in our experience with purification of a precursor for LHRH this did not occur (7). Thus, it was possible to standardize the zone at which LHRH is released with an acid gradient from an affinity column made with monoclonal anti-LHRH. It was found that if an LHRH precursor is applied to the column, it is released at exactly the same gradient zone as LHRH itself.

STRATEGIES FOR USE OF MONOCLONAL ANTIBODIES

In immunocytochemistry, monoclonal antibodies not only satisfy the requirement of antibody specificity, but permit new approaches not possible previously: use of monoclonal antibodies to discover new antigens by virtue of their unique immunocytochemical distribution is discussed on page 429. Monoclonal antibodies properly selected have provided tools for the specific immunocytochemical visualization of antigens that have been purified only partially, and in turn, the antibodies provided reagents for their final purification. Use of monoclonal antibodies to identify different epitopes in single antigens has supplied data on heterogeneity as well as on conformational changes in given molecules.

Sun et al. (22,23), by the use of three monoclonal antibodies to keratin, have been able to classify keratins into two major families and subclassify these in turn into seven classes that have different histologic distribution and functional significance. On electroblots (Fig. 6-2) with keratin preparations, nine bands appeared when staining with Coomassie blue for protein. Each of the monoclonal antibodies stained more than one polypeptide, indicating shared epitopes. Antibody AE1 stained a 50- and 56-kDa band, and revealed on tissue sections the

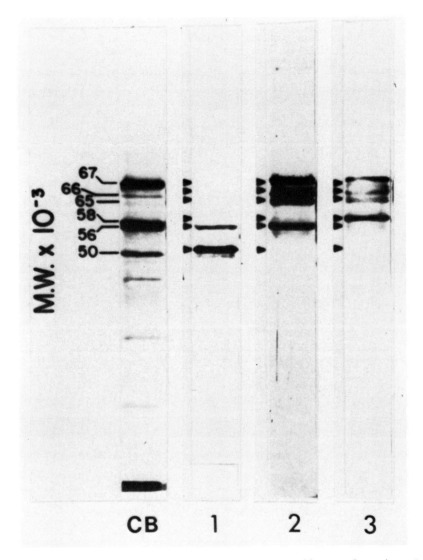

Figure 6-2. Electrophoresis-electroblot of human keratin. Coomassie blue stain for total protein (lane CB). Monoclonal antikeratin AE1 (lane 1), AE2 (lane 2), and AE3 (lane 3). PAP staining. [From Sun et al. (22).]

basal epidermal layer selectively (Fig. 6-3). Antibody AE2 stained the 56.5-kDa and the 65- to 67-kDa bands, and was selective on immunocytochemistry for the suprabasal layers. Antibody AE3 stained the 58-kDa and the 65 to 67-kDa bands, and revealed immunocytochemically, all layers of the epidermis. That some of the epidermal antigens may be masked in situ was detected by preparing serial sections of human heel epidermis and analyzing them by immunoblots. Using, for example, AE1 antibody, it was found that the 50- and 58-kDa keratin poly-peptides were present in all living epidermal layers, including the basal layer,

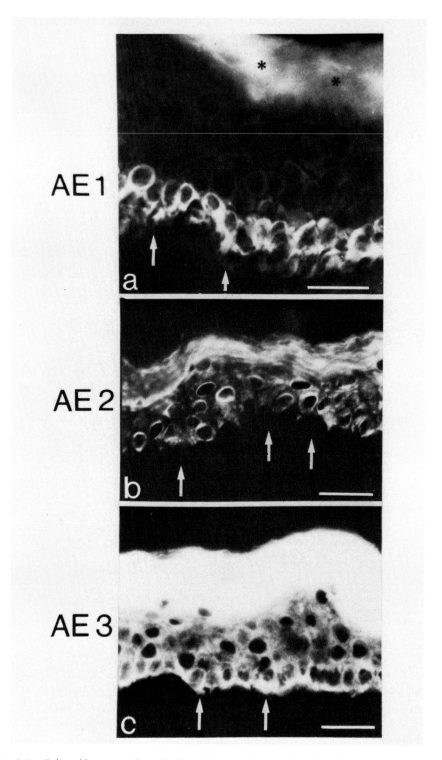

Figure 6-3. Cultured human epidermal cells. With monoclonal antikeratin AE1 (hybridoma supernate), the basal layer (a), with AE2 the suprabasal layer (b), and with AE3 all epidermal layers are stained (c). Supernate of P3 cells served as control (not shown). Immunofluorescence. Arrows indicate cell junctions, presumably desmosomes. Bar is 25 μm. [From Sun et al. (23).]

and that the 56.5- and the 65- to 67-kDa polypeptides were specific for the suprabasally located, terminally differentiated cell layers.

AE1 reacts exclusively with more acidic and AE3 with more basic keratins. Thus, these antibodies classify keratins into two mutually exclusive *families*. However, members of each family share at least one epitope as defined by the three monoclonal antibodies. These molecules can be further subdivided into a total of seven *classes* according to size. The 50-kDa keratin class of the AE1 family, for example, contains a 50 K component present in all stratified epithelia. Similarly the 58-kDa keratin class of the AE3 family contains a 58 K component present in all stratified epithelia. In tissue distribution, it seems that the small molecular classes are widely distributed, but the larger ones are limited to more complex epithelia.

Keratin is an example of intermediate filaments (10-nm-diameter filaments). Other intermediate filaments are desmin, vimentin, fodrin, glial fibrillary acidic protein, and neurofilaments. There are similarities between keratin and neurofilaments. They include the association of more than one component to form a twisted filamentous structure. Also common is the wider distribution and lesser specificity of the smaller as compared to the larger components. Detection of neurofilaments with monoclonal antibodies has also revealed heterogeneity.

The neurofilament triplet consists of three polypeptides of 68, 150, and 200 kDA. Schlaepfer and his associates (24) immunized with the electrophoretically separated polypeptides and prepared monoclonal antibodies specific for each polypeptide, as well as antibodies recognizing epitopes shared by the 150-kDa peptide with either the 200- or the 68-kDa peptide, and finally, antibodies reacting with all the three peptides (Fig. 6-4). The antibodies to the 150- and 200-kDa polypeptides were highly neuron specific. Antibodies to the smaller, 68-kDa polypeptide, were more widely distributed (Fig. 6-5), suggesting again, as in the case of keratin, that the small component is less specific and possesses shared epitopes with other intermediate filaments.

The specificity of antibodies to the 150- and 200-kDa proteins was illustrated in the work of Trojanowski et al. (25,26) in the differential diagnosis of brain tumors. Tumor cells within glial tumors were uniformly negative. Tumor cells within tumors of neuronal origin were positive in more benign cases (such as ganglioneuromas or pheochromocytomas) but negative in some of the more malignant ones (such as medulloblastomas). It seems, therefore, that monoclonal antibodies to the larger neurofilament polypeptides are useful tools in grading tumors of neuronal origin (Figs. 6-6).

Monoclonal antibodies were useful in detecting heterogeneity and post-translational changes in neurofilaments (page 455).

Choline acetyltransferase is the rate-limiting enzyme for the synthesis of acetylcholine and its localization is, therefore, the method of choice for identification of cholinergic neurons. With antisera, previous work on choline acetyltransferase localization has been ambiguous, because it was doubtful whether choline acetyltransferase purified to homogeneity was indeed pure enough to provide a specific antigen of antiserum production. With monoclonal antibodies, a partially purified bovine or rat antigen could be used and antibody-producing clones assayed by precipitation of choline acetyltransferase enzymatic activity with a second antibody, as in the work of Levey et al. (27), thus proving that the

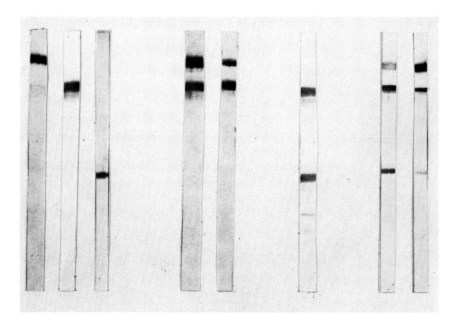

Figure 6-4. Immunoelectroblot analysis of a neurofilament preparation with monoclonal antibodies from fusion of mouse myeloma cells with spleen cells from rats immunized with neurofilaments. Lanes reveal, from left to right, antibodies with specificities to the following neurofilament subunits: (1) 200 kDa only, (2) 150 kDa only, (3) 68 kDa only, (4) 200 and 150 kDa, (5) 150 kDa stronger than 200 kDa, (6) 150 and 60 kDa, (7) 150 and 68 kDa with some reactivity with the 200-kDa subunit, (8) 200 and 150 kDa with some reactivity with the 68-kDa subunit. These data show that each neurofilament subunit possesses cross-reactive epitopes as well as subunit-specific epitopes. [From the work of Virginia M.-Y. Lee.]

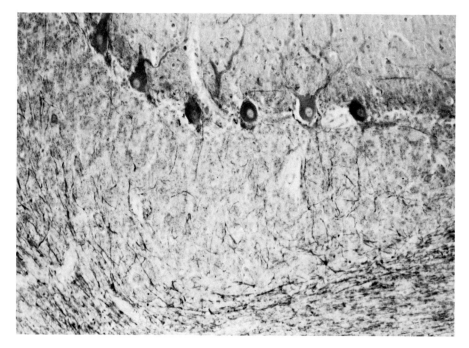

Figure 6-5. Bovine cerebellum. Bouin fixation. Paraffin section. Monoclonal rat antibody to the 68-kDa neurofilament subunit. PAP method. Hematoxylin counterstain. Axons, dendrites, and Purkinje cell bodies as well as a Golgi perikaryon (at left) are revealed. [From the work of Virginia M.-Y. Lee.]

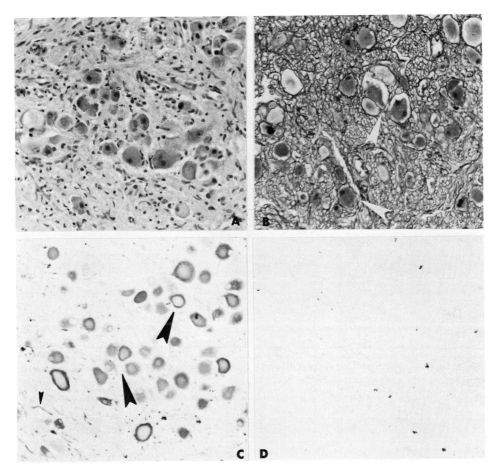

Figure 6-6. (A) Ganglioneuroma stained with hematoxylin and eosin. (B) Stained by Bodian silver impregnation. Axons in the tumor and other tissue elements are revealed. (C) Stained with culture supernate from a clone recognizing both the 150- and 200-kDa subunits of neurofilaments. PAP method. Intracytoplasmic neurofilament protein in tumor neurons (arrows) and neurites are stained, but background from other tissue elements seen in B is absent. (D) Stained with culture supernate from unfused myeloma culture. PAP method. ×600. [From Trojanowski and Lee (26).]

antibodies were specific for the enzyme. The monoclonal antibodies reacted with different epitopes in the enzyme, as some antibodies reacted only with the bovine immunogen, while others exhibited narrow or broad cross-reactivity with the enzyme from other mammalian species. The species cross-reacting antibodies localized in rat brain, known cholinergic structures including motor neurons, basal forebrain neurons, and neostriatal neurons. Nagai et al. (28) again started with a partially purified enzyme preparation for the production, in this case, of antibodies to human choline acetyltransferase. Only large cells were stained in the putamen and the substantia nigra. In the substantia innominata (Fig. 6-7), the distribution of cell bodies closely corresponded to the basal nucleus of Meynert. This nucleus is apparently the main focus of origin of choline acetyltransferase in the primate central nervous system. Degeneration of cholinergic neurons in this nucleus seems to be a predominant lesion in Alzheimer's disease (page 461).

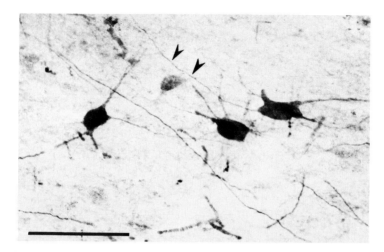

Figure 6-7. Human substantia inominata stained with a monoclonal antibody to choline acetyltransferase. PAP method. Long neuronal processes can be followed (arrowheads). [From Nagai et al. (28).]

REFERENCES

1. Scharrer E, Sinden, J-A: A contribution to the "chemoarchitectonics" of the optic tectum of the brain of the pigeon. *J Comp Neurol* **91**:331, 1949.

2. Sternberger NH, Osterhout DJ, Sternberger LA: A study of synaptogenesis using monoclonal antibodies. *Transact Am Soc Neurochem* **15**:118, 1984.

3. Östermann E, Sternberger NH, Sternberger LA: Immunocytochemistry of brain-reactive monoclonal antibodies in peripheral tissues. *Cell Tiss Res* **228**:459, 1983.

4. Sternberger LA, Sternberger, NH: Monoclonal antibodies distinguish phosphorylated and nonphosphorylated forms of neurofilaments *in situ*. *Proc Natl Acad Sci USA* **80**:6126, 1983.

5. Köhler G, Milstein L: Derivation of specific antibody-producing tissue culture and tumor lines by cell fusion. *Europ J Immunol* **6**:511, 1976.

6. Littlefield JW: Selection of hybrids from matings of fibroblasts in vitro and their presumed recombinants. *Science* **145**:709, 1964.

7. Knapp R, Sternberger LA: Heterogeneity of luteinizing hormone-releasing hormone studied with a monoclonal antibody. *Soc Neurosci Abstr* **13**:138, 1983.

8. Elias JM, Johnsen TA: The utilization of RIA antibodies for the immunohistochemical staining of polypeptide hormone on paraffin-embedded tissue. *Am J Clin Path* **71**:489, 1979.

9. Sternberger LA, Harwell LW, Sternberger NH: Neurotypy: Regional individuality in rat brain detected by immunocytochemistry with monoclonal antibodies. *Proc Natl Acad Sci USA* **79**:1326, 1982.

10. Sternberger NH, Sternberger LA: Neurotypy: The heterogeneity of brain proteins. *Ann NY Acad Sci* **420**:90, 1983.

11. De St Groth SF, Scheidegger D: Production of monoclonal antibodies: Strategies and tactics. *J Immunol Meth* **35**:1, 1980.

12. Cleveland L, Wood I, Erlanger BF: Routine large-scale production of monoclonal antibodies in a protein-free complete medium. *J Immunol Meth* **56**:22, 1983.

13. Fox PC, Berenstein EH, Siraganian RP: Enhancing the frequency of antigen-specific hybridomas. *Europ J Immunol* **11**:431, 1981.

14. Taggart RT, Samloff IM: Stable antibody-producing murine hybridomas. *Science* **219**:1228, 1983.

15. Sternberger LA, Hardy PH JR, Cuculis JJ, Meyer HG: The unlabeled antibody enzyme method of immunohistochemistry. Preparation and properties of soluble antigen-antibody complex (horseradish peroxidase-antihorseradish peroxidase) and its use in identification of spirochetes. *J Histochem Cytochem* **18:**315, 1970.

16. Becker GJ, Hancock WW, Kraft N, Lanyon HC, Atkins RC: Monoclonal antibodies to human macrophage and leukocyte common antigen. *Pathology* **13:**669, 1981.

17. Hancock WW, Becker GJ, Atkins RC: A comparison of fixatives and immunohistochemical techniques for use with monoclonal antibodies to cell surface antigens. *Am J Clin Path* **78:**825, 1980.

18. Morich EJ, Momburg F, Moldenhauer G, Hartman K-U, Bross KJ: Immunoperoxidase slide assay (IPSA): A new screening method for hybridoma supernates directed against a cell surface antigen compared to other binding assays. *Immunobiology* **164:**192, 1983.

19. Cuello AC, Priestley JV, Milstein C. Immunocytochemistry with internally labeled antibodies. *Proc Natl Acad Sci USA* **79:**665, 1962.

20. Hämmerling U, Aoki T, Wood HA, Boyse EA, de Harven E: New visual markers of antibody for electron microscopy. *Nature* **233:**1158, 1969.

21. Milstein C, Cuello AC: Hybrid hybridomas and their use in immunocytochemistry. *Nature* **305:**537, 1983.

22. Sun T-T, Eichner R, Nelson WG, Tseng SCG, Weiss RA, Jarvinen M, Woodcock-Mitchell J: Keratin classes: Molecular markers for different types of epithelial differentiation. *J Invest Dermatol* **81:**109s, 1983, William & Wilkins Co., Baltimore.

23. Woodcock-Mitchell J, Eichner R, Nelson WG, Sun T-T: Immunolocalization of keratin polypeptides in human epidermis using monoclonal antibodies. *J Cell Biol* **95:**579, 1982.

24. Lee V, Wu HL, Schlaepfer WW: Monoclonal antibodies recognize individual neurofilament triplet proteins. *Proc Natl Acad Sci USA* **79:**6084, 1982.

25. Trojanowski JQ, Lee VM-Y, Schlaepfer WW: An immunohistochemical study of human central and peripheral nervous system tumors, using monoclonal antibodies against neurofilaments and glial filaments. *Hum Path* **15:**248, 1984.

26. Trojanowski JQ, Lee VM-Y: Antineurofilament monoclonal antibodies: Reagents for the evaluation of human neoplasms. *Acta Neuropath* **59:**155, 1983.

27. Levey AI, Armstrong DM, Atweh SF, Terry RD, Wainer BH: Monoclonal antibodies to choline acetyl transferase: Production, specificity and immunohistochemistry. *J Neurosci* **3:**1, 1983.

28. Nagai T, Pearson T, Peng F, McGeer EG, McGeer PC: Immunohistochemical staining of human forebrain with monoclonal antibody to human choline acetyl transferase. *Brain Res* **265:**300, 1983.

Chapter Seven

The Immune Response—
Lymphomas

The specificity of the immune response lies in the large number of genes that encode for the variable region of heavy, and to a lesser extent, that of light chains. These genes are expressed in lymphocyte surface receptors. The expressed phenotypes may undergo further variation by somatic mutation after antigenic stimulation (page 13). Functional diversity of the product of the immune response is not only obtained by coexpression of variable region genes in peptides of various antibody isotypes, but also by coexpression, at times, with molecules that are not immunoglobulins. In stimulated cells, idiotype-specific receptors act in conjunction with major histocompatibility complex antigens to augment or suppress an antibody response, or to effect a specific cell-mediated cytotoxic response, that includes viral immunity, delayed sensitivity of the tuberculin type, allograft rejection, and graft versus host reaction.

The *mononuclear cells* that mediate an immune response are isolated from circulation on Ficoll-Hypaque gradients. These cells include macrophages and lymphocytes. Macrophages possess many functions, most of which have to do with host defense. They include secretion of enzymes that break down bacteria, such as lysozyme, cathepsin, or phosphatases. In addition, macrophages provide help in the immune reaction. Macrophages are capable of dividing in circulation and assuming increasing specialization during the process (1).

The various functions of the immune response rest in diversity of different lymphocytes. Several major classes of lymphocytes can be distinguished on the basis of these functions. Since the various immunologic functions are encoded by similar genetic regions, it is perhaps not surprising that they are mediated via similar cells. Except for variations in size and presence of villi, most lymphocytes look alike. However, lymphocytes of different functions have different chemical characteristics, which can sometimes be identified by immunocytochemical means. For methodologic reasons, those chemical differences that are expressed on the cell surface have so far received most attention. Because of the similarity

270

of morphology of all lymphocytes, immunocytochemical markers for different classes of lymphocytes are important.

The markers include antibodies that differentiate immature and mature lymphocytes, or distinguish sets of lymphocytes (2,3). The functional classification of lymphocytes should, however, take precedence over classification by markers. The functional differentiation of lymphocytes has become possible from studies of deficiency states. *Nude mice*, which are congenitally deficient in thymic function, or neonatally thymectomized mice, are unable to reject skin grafts or carry out other functions of cell-mediated cytotoxicity, yet they do respond with circulating antibodies upon injection of certain antigens that possess repetitive determinants, such as found in polymerized flagellin. Congenital thymic aplasia (diGeorge's syndrome) is the human equivalent of this disorder. In contrast, birds from which the bursa of Fabricius has been removed are unable to form circulating antibodies, yet they reject skin grafts normally. The human equivalent of this disorder is congenital hypogammaglobulinemia. On the basis of these disorders, two major classes of lymphocytes can be discerned: lymphocytes that potentially produce circulating immunoglobulins (*B cells*), and lymphocytes that mediate cellular immunity (*T cells*).

Several hormones in the thymus affect the immune response. *Thymosin,* for example, has been attributed to the epithelial cells of the organ. Aita et al. (4) produced antiserum to thymostimulin, a thymic factor corresponding to a family of polypeptides which restore T cell-dependent immunocompetence in thymic-deprived animals. Immunocytochemical localization with this antibody was restricted to the reticuloepithelial cells. In normal, mammalian development, undifferentiated lymphocytes become committed as T cells by hormonal influence following passage through the thymus. Undifferentiated lymphocytes become committed as B cells by bone marrow factors.

The various subsets of B cells and the functionally more heterogeneous subsets of T cells, as well as that portion of macrophages committed to the immune response, make up the immunologic compartment of mononuclear cells. The two cell types that can be separated from a mononuclear cell suspension with confidence are the macrophages and the B cells. The macrophages are adherent cells (*A cells*), which is an intrinsic property of their physiology. They will adhere to a plastic Petri dish, while lymphocytes will remain floating in suspension. The B cells possess IgM and occasionally IgD on their surfaces as an essential prerequisite for their eventual antibody formation. Therefore, they can be removed by an affinity column made by insolubilization of $F(ab')_2$ from anti-μ and anti-δ. $F(ab')_2$ rather than IgG is needed to prevent nonspecific removal of cells possessing Fc receptor.

Once macrophages are removed, the remaining mononuclear cell population consists of lymphocytes. Separation of lymphocytes into sets and subsets depends upon specific *markers*. It is desirable that these markers are cell surface antigens, so that separation can be carried out without irreversible damage to the cell. Some of the existing markers react with surface antigens whose essential function appears to be known. These markers will classify lymphocytes into functional sets. Other markers react with still unknown antigens. It is not surprising that these markers may label more than one functional set of lymphocytes (page 295). It is unlikely, however, that unknown antigens have no function. It is expected that once these functions become known, the corresponding markers may detect new functional subsets of lymphocytes. Since some markers detect more than one subset of lymphocytes, but only a portion of all the cells within a given subset, it is likely that some lymphocytes possess more than one function assigned to them on the basis of our present day definitions.

Cell surface markers useful for immunocytochemical detection and preparative separation of classes of lymphocytes which all look alike morphologically are:

1.   Idiotypic receptors identified by antiidiotypic antibodies. Only a small portion of the total repertoire of B and T cells possess a given idiotype. The function of these receptors is in the selection of B and T cells that participate specifically in the response to a given antigen.

2. μ and δ chains that express the immunoglobulin which a B cell may produce upon antigenic stimulation without help from T cells. The function of these markers is the recognition of epitopes for which a given host is capable of mounting an antibody response.

3.   Receptors for Fcγ or Fcμ which are found on macrophages and some T and B cells and may invoke a *bystander pattern* of lymphocytes in cytotoxic lesions by cells which themselves have not been stimulated by the specific antigen.

4.   Receptors of unknown function for sheep red blood cells on T cells, which form easily recognizable *rosettes* around the cells and may be used for preparative separation of T cells from B cells.

5.   The selection of monoclonal antibodies to mononuclear cells has led to a large array of markers, of which a few classify lymphocytes into known subsets, even though the nature of the antigens and their specific function still requires elucidation in most cases. The best monoclonal antibody markers include T4, OKT4, Leu 3_a, and Leu3_b, which identify helper T cells (page 283), and T8, OKT8, Leu 2_a, and Leu2_b which identify suppressor T cells (page 283) and natural killer T cells (page 284), but do not distinguish between both of the latter subsets. Additional monoclonal antibodies seem to differentiate mature and immature lymphocytes, while still others react with subsets of T cells, B cells, or macrophages.

Two precautions must be followed when evaluating living mononuclear cells by immunocytochemistry, both derived from the fact that many of the cells possess Fc receptors. Because of these receptors, cells absorb serum immunoglobulins nonspecifically. Reaction of this nonspecific immunoglobulin with anti-immunoglobulin in vitro might be confused with specific *surface immunoglobulin* (μ and δ chains) produced by B cells. Fortunately, the affinity of Fc receptor for nonaggregated immunoglobulin is low. Immunoglobulins absorbed from serum by cells prior to isolation can be removed by incubation of cell suspensions at 37° C for 30 minutes or by brief exposure to acetate buffer, pH 4 (5).

A second source of nonspecificity comes from reaction of immunologic reagents during staining via Fc receptors rather than via antigen-antibody bonds. This source of error is especially serious in immunofluorescence because of its relatively low sensitivity and requirement of high concentrations of antibodies. Therefore, nonspecific binding will occur despite the low affinity of Fc receptors. These problems are avoided if fluorescein isothyocyanate-conjugated F(ab')$_2$ or

Fab are used instead of IgG in the direct technique. In the indirect technique, the second antibody would also have to be a F(ab')$_2$ or a Fab. However, Alexander and Sanders (6) have shown that goat immunoglobulin does not react with human Fc receptor.

Immunofluorescence is the method of choice for identification of cells whose viability must be preserved, and the direct method is preferable for the use with unfixed material.

Mason and co-workers (7,8) have shown that mononuclear cell markers can be identified on smears of cells fixed in formol acetone if the PAP technique is used (Fig. 7-1). Background was reduced compared to that of immunofluorescence and sensitivity was increased. Surface staining could be well delineated, and cytoplasmic staining, absent in immunofluorescence, could also be discerned. Immunostaining did not interfere with conventional counterstaining of cells. However, when a cell was heavily stained for surface immunoglobulin, nuclear counterstaining was somewhat impaired. Cytoplasmic immunostaining did not interfere with nuclear counterstaining.

Interestingly, nonspecificity because of Fc receptor was no problem despite the Fc in link antibody (page 104) and PAP. Even high concentrations of link antibody did not produce nonspecific staining. Nor did a 1 : 5 dilution of PAP lead to nonspecific staining, even though PAP because of its contents of *two* Fc's is an excellent reagent for Fc receptor (9), apparently overcoming the low affinity of the receptor by dual binding of Fc on the surface (page 145). It is likely that

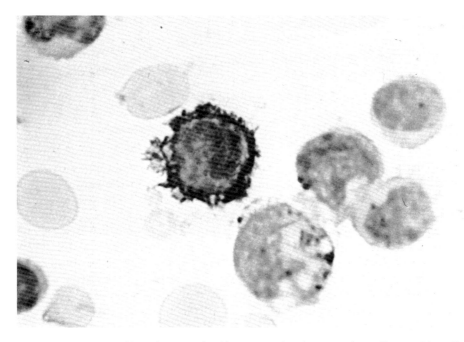

Figure 7-1. In a smear of formol acetone-fixed human peripheral mononuclear cells, 5% of the cells are identified as B cells by reaction with anti-μ. IgM is distributed throughout the surface of the highly villous, "hairy" cell. PAP immunostaining. Hematoxylin counterstaining. ×1850. [From Mason et al. (8).]

in the work of Mason et al. (7,8), Fc receptor reactivity has been successfully impaired by the formol-acetone fixation.

Staphylococcal protein A can also be used to exclude Fc receptor binding of antibodies specific to cell surface markers (10). For instance, antithymocyte serum is a specific reagent for a large fraction of T cells. However, it is necessary to exclude adhesion of the antibody to some Fc receptor-bearing cells also commonly found among T cells. Staphylococcal protein A is a specific reagent for Fc. It blocks the Fc region of antibodies. Thus, antithymocyte antibodies reacted with protein A will no longer bind with Fc receptors, but still react with T cells. When FITC-conjugated staphylococcal protein A is used, the protein-antithymocyte complex becomes a fluorescent label for the intended T cells.

Only immune responses that involve circulating antibodies utilize B cells. Cell-mediated cytotoxicity, which does not require antibodies, involves only T cells. Although B cells differentiate during immunization to antibody-secreting cells, they do require the help of T cells and A cells in the response to the majority of antigens. This help magnifies the total response and promotes the selection of high-affinity antibodies. Such a response is initiated upon binding of unprocessed or processed epitopes by specific receptors on a few selected B and T cells, respectively. These cells are transformed as measured by tritiated thymidine incorporation. However, only the progeny of clonally dividing B cells produce immunoglobulin. T cells, when invoked in an immunoglobulin-producing response, provide either *help* or *suppression*.

A *secondary response* to an antigen differs from a *primary response* by accelerated and magnified antibody production and is mediated by the presence of a stable population of *educated* (antigen-stimulated) cells, also called *memory cells*. Such memory cells exist in the T- and B-cell series.

Not each immune response leads to antibody secretion or cellular immunity. Instead, *tolerance*, a state of active refractoriness to antigen, may be induced by a variety of control mechanisms at the B- and T-cell level and by special *T suppressor cells*.

COMMON B- AND T-CELL FUNCTIONS

If a population of lymphocytes, such as obtained from normal mouse spleen or lymph nodes, is exposed to a specific antigen, such as bovine serum albumin, about 1 in 1000 cells are found to bind antigen specifically. The cells so selected possess specific receptors for bovine serum albumin. Both B and T cells possess specific receptors. Binding is detected by immunocytochemical methods, such as immunofluorescence, or immunoferritin, or by autoradiography with ^{125}I-labeled antigen. Cells with receptors to flagellin can be detected by binding and immobilization of specific flagellate bacteria and counted by formation of bacterial colonies upon plating on semisolid media. The proportion of cells revealing specific receptor varies with the sensitivity of the method of detection. Thus, Miller et al. (11) show that when β-galactosidase or horseradish peroxidase is used as antigen and binding assayed cytochemically by specific chromogenic substrate, enzyme action provides a cytochemical amplifier, and the number of specifically marked normal lymphocytes increases to as many as 40 per 1000 from the usual 1 per 1000.

The specific binding of antigen upon contact with a few selected lymphocytes is necessary for initiation of the immune response. Elimination of specific receptor cells from a population of lymphocytes abolishes the immune response. The antibody-forming capacity of the cell population to a specific antigen can be deleted by passing the cells through a column of glass beads coated with the specific antigen. Also, radioactive antigen of high specific activity results in destruction of the specific receptor-bearing cells, while leaving the remaining cells unaffected: upon transfer of the cells to iradiated recipient animals, injection of unlabeled specific antigen fails to result in antibody formation, while unrelated antigen results in a normal response (the recipient animals are irradiated in this commonly used assay of antibody-producing cells in vivo in order to eliminate the host's own mononuclear cells, to permit a rapid replication of transferred cells, and to prevent graft rejection of the injected cells).

The binding of a *hapten,* such as dinitrophenol (DNP), by receptor is less strong than the binding of moderately or heavily DNP-conjugated proteins (*hapten-carrier*), because the latter combines with a larger site on the cell (binding affinity increases exponentially with the size of the binding site). Thus, pretreatment with *low concentrations* of DNP inhibits neither the binding of DNP-protein nor the immune response to the hapten. However, when the DNP is converted to a compound that reacts covalently with protein [such as α-N-bromacetyl-εN-(2,4-dinitrophenyl)lysine], the hapten becomes an *affinity label* that reacts irreversibly with the receptor with a high degree of specificity. Subsequent exposure to DNP-protein fails to result in an anti-DNP response.

The specificity of the receptor is the only known mechanism of selection of the specificity of the antibody produced. However, if as many as 4% of lymphocytes specifically recognize a single antigen such as β-galactosidase, and if these cells recognize only this antigen to the exclusion of other antigens, there could not be formed more than 25 different noncross-reacting antibodies to protein. In fact, however, thousands of different noncross-reacting antibody specificities and millions of different, although cross-reacting hypervariable region sequences, can be formed by an individual. It follows that subsequent to the first encounter with antigen there must be some selection of the most specific receptor.

Binding of β-galactosidase can be observed cytochemically by using 5-bromo-4-chloro-3-indol-β,D-galactoside as a substrate to yield on oxidation an insoluble indigo blue reaction product deposited in the vicinity of the receptor-bearing cell. Binding of peroxidase can be evaluated on cell populations treated with hydrazine to destroy intrinsic peroxidase activity. Hydrogen peroxide substrate with 3-amino-9-ethyl carbazol as hydrogen donor yields a red indamine reaction product with peroxidase. The frequency of cells revealing both blue and red deposits and, therefore, accepting both enzymes approximates the product of frequencies of cells staining only blue for β-galactosidase and only red for peroxidase. The finding would appear to suggest, that receptor distribution is random, and that a cell can possess more than one idiotype of receptor. If this is the case, other findings (page 277) would require that both receptors are coexpressed on the same molecular complex. Alternatively, there exists only one receptor per cell, and the binding of both enzymes is the expression of a cross-reaction, in line with the low affinity of μ and ϑ receptors.

If fluorescein-di-β-galactoside is used as substrate for β-galactosidase, sensitive fluorescence assay of the free fluorescein reaction product provides measurement of the product of a single enzyme molecule. When enzyme-treated, washed lymphocytes are placed into microdroplets along with the substrate, release of reaction product from a single cell and the number of specific enzyme receptors per cell can be measured. This number exhibits great variation from cell to cell, ranging from 30,000 to 1,000,000 which is probably due to different affinities of the receptor idiotypes in different cells. Thus, cells that bind 1 million galactosidase molecules are high-affinity binders for this antigen, while cells that bind 30,000 galactosidase molecules are probably of high affinity for another antigen and react with galactosidase with the low-affinity characteristic of a crossreaction.

The antigen receptors on B and T cells differ. T-cell receptors seem to have a broader specificity. Although T-cell receptors seem to have a characteristic hypervariable region, they do not possess chains resembling the constant regions of immunoglobulins. B-cell receptors, on the other hand, possess μ and δ chains. Lymphocytes respond to reaction of receptors with ligands or antigens by a series of reactions that can be measured by incorporation of tritiated thymidine (*blast transformation*) and lead eventually to *clonal expansion*. Apparently, any factor capable of aggregating receptors in the fluid mosaic of the cell membrane will institute blast transformation. Antigens will do so only with cells that possess specific receptors for a certain epitope. Blast transformation can also be accomplished nonspecifically by antibodies to cell surface markers characteristic of the class of cells. The first step in the process is aggregation of the marker, visualized in light microscopy as *cap formation* (Fig. 7-2) and accompanied on scanning

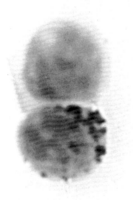

Figure 7-2. When peripheral mononuclear cells are incubated in suspension with F(ab')$_2$ anti-μ, then placed on smears and fixed in formol acetone, cap formation is evident after completion of the PAP staining sequence. Capping is accompanied by loss of villi. Hematoxylin counterstained. ×1850. [From Mason et al. (7).]

electron microscopy by loss of surface villi. B cells, as a group, irrespective of specificity of their surface markers to a given epitope, can be capped by antibodies to μ and δ chains and by the nonspecific ligand, bacterial lipopolysaccharide. T cells can be capped by specific antigens or by the nonspecific ligands, concanavalin A or phytohemoagglutinin. Caps are usually formed at the uropod of the cell. Cap formation is prevented by inhibiting the contractile cytoskeletal system with agents such as cytocatalasin B, sodium azide, or dinitrophenol. Cap formation is followed by rapid endocytosis and eventual thymidine incorporation.

SPECIFIC B-CELL FUNCTIONS

B cells possess IgM or IgD markers on their surfaces. Preparations of pure B cells can be stimulated with certain antigens not only to undergo blast transformation but to proceed toward specific antibody production. However, only a few antigens that possess highly repetitive presentation of identical epitopes are capable of stimulating antibody responses with B cells alone. Such typical *B-cell antigens* are bacterial lipopolysaccharide, polymerized bacterial flagellin, or haptens, such as dinitrophenol (DNP) conjugated with a homologous carrier, such as mouse red blood cells in the immunization of mice. The response of isolated B cells does not differ from the response of unfractionated mononuclear cells from nude or thymectomized mice. It is a pure IgM response. The antibody formed is apparently identical in specificity and class to that of the antigen receptor (the cell surface markers). Affinity of the antibody does not change during immunization, no memory cells form, and there is no secondary or booster response upon repeat administration of antigen.

If B cells are treated with anti-idiotypes, the antigen receptor is inhibited and antibody formation to the specific antigen will cease (12). This suggests that the idiotype of the secreted antibody resembles the idiotype of the specific receptors on the preimmunization B cells (see also page 275). In a single B cell, specific antigen will cap 95% of the total surface immunoglobulin as revealed by immunofluorescence with anti-μ, suggesting that all the surface immunoglobulin of a single cell possesses identical receptors—that is, the receptors in each cell are monospecific as is the antibody that eventually will be secreted by the progeny of such cells.

We have already seen that some antibodies can react with two unrelated epitopes (such as menadione and dinitropheonl, page 17). When B cells primed to produce such antibody are given a secondary stimulus with one of the substances coupled to carrier, say dinitrophenyl bovine-γ-globulin, early secondary response will be to both haptens (13). Apparently, the early antibody produced is a pure replica of the receptor. The antigen used in these experiments is not a pure B-cell antigen. It stimulates T cells also, and eventually mediates responses typical of B- and T-cell cooperation, which include change in affinity. This change in affinity is reflected, in this case, by later antibodies that show preferential bindings for dinitrophenol and lesser binding for menadione. However, it is the early response, that which forms a replica of the receptor, which we deal with in a pure B-cell response. This response must be of the same class as that of the receptor—it is an IgM response. Quite generally, even with antigens that do not induce a pure B-cell response, but rather a cooperative B- and T-cell response, the earliest antibody secreted is IgM, is of low affinity, and probably represents a pure B-cell reaction.

The coexistence of receptors for galactosidase and peroxidase on a single cell (page 275) may represent a similar linkage as that of menadione and dinitrophenol.

Individual antibody-secreting cells are usually revealed by *hemolytic plaque assay*. Cells forming antibodies to sheep red blood cells (sRBC) are plated on semisolid media containing sRBC and *complement*. Complement is a cascade of enzymes which leads to cell lysis in antibody (IgG or IgM) or cell-mediated cytotoxicity. The antibodies secreted into the environment of each individual B cell will form a translucent plaque as a result of hemolysis. Enumeration of plaques will give an index of the number of antibody-forming cells. When the antibody produced is specific to a hapten, such as dinitrophenol, dinitrophenyl-conjugated sRBC are used in the plaque assay system.

Complement fixation requires aggregated Fc. Complement-dependent hemolysis with the limited amounts of antibody secreted by a single cell in the hemolytic plaque assay system, is a sensitive index only for IgM, which provides aggregates by virtue of its being pentameric. Therefore, the plaque assay is an index only for IgM formation such as obtained in a pure B-cell response. The assay can be expanded to detection of IgG by using it in an *indirect* form, in which a second antibody is added (such as sheep antimouse if the antibody-producing cell is murine). The secreted antibody forms aggregates with the second antibody and mediates complement-dependent hemolysis. IgG responses cannot be invoked with pure B cells alone. Therefore, comparison of direct and indirect assay may be used to differentiate whether an antigen is a *B-cell antigen*, requiring only B cells, or whether it is a *T-cell antigen*, requiring the help of non-B cells. Dinitrophenyl-conjugated sheep red blood cells (DNP-sRBC) are a T-cell antigen in mice, while DNP-conjugated mouse red blood cells are a B-cell antigen. If the amount of DNP groups conjugated to each sRBC becomes increased, the T antigen becomes progressively converted to a B antigen (14,15). At a point where substitution is so intensive that all sRBC antigenicity is lost, the conjugate has become a pure B antigen.

In addition to surface IgM and IgD, which act as specific receptors for antigen, B cells contain receptors for Fc and for the third component of the complement cascade (C3) and they also possess allotypic surface determinants specified by the *Ir* genes (page 14). Fc receptors are assayed by binding of aggregated immunoglobulin (16). Binding of aggregated immunoglobulin may be visualized immunocytochemically. Alternatively, sRBC reacted with anti-sRBC in the absence of complement may be added to the lymphocytes. A lymphocyte that possesses Fc receptors is delineated by the rosette of sRBC that surrounds the cell.

The immunocytochemical detection of Fc receptor depends on the use of reagents that possess more than one Fc group to ensure against loss of low-affinity-bound reagent during washing. Both PAP and FAF complexes (page 186) have been used by Itoh et al. (9,17).

C3 receptor can also be assayed by rosette formation, using sRBC treated with anti-sRBC in the presence of a nonhemolytic dose of complement in the cold.

Capping of surface immunoglobulin does not cocap Fc and C3 receptors. Fc, in contrast to C3 receptors, are lost at 37°C and cannot be detected in the presence of sodium azide. Blocking of Fc receptor rosette formation with antigen-antibody complex does not affect C3 receptors. Therefore, surface immunoglobulin and Fc and C3 receptors are distinct entities (18). However, reaction of Fc receptor is inhibited by alloantisera specific for antigens determined by the *Ir* region of the histocompatibility (H2) complex (Ia antigens). The reaction is not inhibited by antisera to antigens specific for other regions of the H2 complex (19). The findings suggest a close association of Fc receptor and Ia antigens. Interestingly, it is these two surface determinants that are not specific for B cells, but can be expressed, perhaps in different forms, also on some T cells and macrophages.

Ir genes determine whether animal strains are high responders or low responders to a given antigen. Synthetic copolymers of tyrosine, glutamic acid, alanine, and lysine are T-cell antigens. Even though T and B cells do possess Ia antigens, it is on the B cell and not on the T cell that responsiveness to these particular copolymers is determined (20).

Heterozygous animals can express two allelic markers on each of their immunoglobulin chains. However, a single antibody-producing cell secretes homogeneous immunoglobulin and thus expresses only one marker. Nevertheless, both markers may be present in the surface immunoglobulin of nonsecreting lymphocytes. Lithicum and Sell (21) have demonstrated both markers on the same cell by an unlabeled antibody technique in which antiallotype to one Gm marker of a heterozygous rabbit (page 14), say b4, was used as link antibody (page 104) for attachment to ferritin-labeled IgG of b4 allotype while alloantibody to the other marker, say b6, was used as link antibody for attachment to hemocyanin-labeled IgG of b6 allotype (Fig. 7-3). The hemocyanin marker was visible in electron microscopy because it protruded from the cell surface. Both markers were found to cap independently. Since capping is thought to be an initial step in blast transformation that may eventually lead to antibody formation, the separate capping of both markers may help to explain how allelic exclusion (page 11) takes place during cell differentiation, so that eventually only immunoglobulin possessing one of the allelic markers is secreted by an individual cell.

Small antigens (haptens) do not in themselves induce antibody formation. However, Prage et al. (22) have shown that they do effect clonal expansion of B lymphocytes. Stimulation with L-tyrosine-*p*-azophenyltrimethylammonium chloride [Tyr(TMA)] increased the affinity of B-surface receptors for this hapten even though it failed to lead to antibody production, whether IgM or IgG. The complete antigen, Tyr(TMA)-human ζ-globulin, led to the expected T-cell-dependent antibody-secreting response. The findings show that the proliferative phase of the immune response—namely, antigen recognition, clonal expansion, and receptor maturation—are independent of T cells.

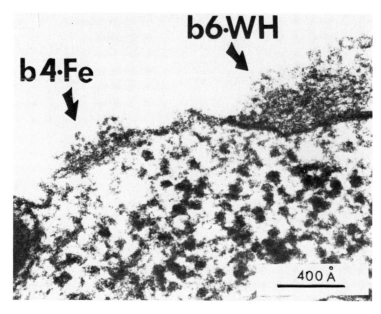

Figure 7-3.   Ferritin-conjugated IgG of c4b4 allotype was used as final layer antigen, and anti-b4 as link antibody to detect b4 allotype on the surface of rabbit lymphocytes by the unlabeled antibody method. Hemocyanin-conjugated IgG of b6 allotype was used with anti-b6 for similar detection of b6 allotype. Some, but not all, lymphocytes in heterozygous rabbits carry both allelic surface markers. [From Lithicum and Sell (21).]

B-CELL MEMORY

Clonal expansion can be measured by incorporation of tritiated thymidine. Most antibody-forming cells are short-lived as indicated by rapid disappearance of the label.

A secondary antibody response differs from a primary response by faster appearance of secreted antibody and by its production in large amounts. Apparently, some host cells possess a *memory* of the primary immunization that can be recalled and magnified in the secondary immunization. The memory resides in special subgroups of B and T cells. Animals rich in B cells can be obtained by thoracic duct drainage, which causes depletion of T cells. By this technique, memory B cells were found to consist of a distinct cell population of B cells that are nondividing and possess unusual stability, as indicated by retention of tritiated thymidine incorporated in the primary immunization. By passage of these tritiated cells over a specific antigen-bearing affinity column, they were shown to be the very same cells that possessed receptors for the antigen (23), supporting the notion of existence of a stable proportion of memory cells that do not divide until they encounter a secondary antigenic stimulus.

B-CELL TOLERANCE

An immune response may not necessarily lead to expression of antibody secretion or cellular immunity. Instead, it may lead to an active inhibition of these phenomena, so that a secondary injection of antigen again will fail to elicit a response. Between the extremes of complete *tolerance* and maximal response are various intermediate stages, in which suppressor and feedback mechanisms control the degree of responsiveness.

Immune tolerance is the usual response in embryonic life where the immune response is thought to be immature. An antigen that is mainly an *immunogen* in adulthood may at the same dose level be primarily a *tolerogen* in immature animals. Tolerogenicity is favored over immunogenicity with increase of the dose of antigen and with the state of desaggregation of antigen. When a preparation of human immunoglobulin is centrifuged at high speed, the sediment consisting of aggregated immunoglobulin is an immunogen, while the supernatant is primarily a tolerogen, even to adult animals. Similarly, heat-aggregated human immunoglobulin becomes a good immunogen.

For responses to antigens that require both B and T cells, tolerance in either B or T cells prevents antibody formation. Irradiated mice reconstituted with thymus cells tolerant of human immunoglobulin and normal spleen cells do not form antibodies after injection of aggregated normal human immunoglobulin. Irradiated mice reconstituted with bone marrow cells tolerant of human immunoglobulin and with normal thymus cells again fail to form antibodies after injection of aggregated human immunoglobulin.

Large doses of soluble antigens induce tolerance. With a typical B-cell antigen, such as polymerized flagellin, the tolerance will be a B-cell tolerance. When a moderate dose of the antigen is given, capping of the receptor-bearing B cell occurs immediately and is followed within 4 to 5 hours by reappearance of receptors on the cell surface at higher density than those originally present. Exposure of such cells to tolerogenic (large) doses of the antigen failed to induce capping and, thus abrogated the formation of further antigen receptors, effectively eliminating the antigen-receptor-bearing cells from continued immune response (24). When mice primed with a tolerogen (desaggregated human immunoglobulin) were given radioiodinated antigen, a decrease in specific receptor-bearing cells became evident as compared to animals primed with an immunogen [aggregated human immunoglobulin (25)].

Responses to T-cell-dependent antigens that require help of T cells for antibody formation, can also be abrogated at the B-cell level. Thus, treatment of mice with hapten-conjugated syngeneic RBC (a B-cell antigen) suppressed the response to hapten-conjugated heterologous RBC (a T-cell antigen). Thymus cells failed to restore responsiveness, but T-cell-depleted spleen cells did (26).

B-cell tolerance may not be restricted to the level of antigen recognition. When cells in the secretory phase, after stimulation with a T-cell-dependent antigen, such as DNP-foul immunoglobulin, are temporarily incubated with DNP-polymerized flagellin, a B-cell antigen, antibody secretion becomes abrogated. Thus, tolerance can apparently also be induced at the effector level (27).

It has been postulated that formation of anti-idiotypes could follow antibody production and, thus, establish *idiotype-anti-idiotype networks* that control and limit the immune response, either by interaction of the anti-idiotypes with idiotypes or with cellular receptors for antigen. It remains doubtful, however, whether this mechanism is of physiologic significance. Anti-idiotypes may suppress or stimulate an immune response. Antibodies to the idiotype of antihepatitis B virus can substitute for the viral antigen in immunization (28). In this case, the stimulating effect was clearly due to presentation of antigen-like structure (anti-idiotype) to idiotype cellular receptors. As to the suppressor effects mediated by anti-idiotypes in experimental conditions, it remains possible that it is due to antiallotypes produced by the host as a result of injection of the antiidiotype which, of necessity, was raised in another strain or species of animals. Therefore, it is unclear whether anti-idiotypic networks control or limit the immune response under normal conditions (see also page 15).

SPECIFIC A-CELL FUNCTIONS

When a suspension containing B and T cells is depleted of adherent cells (*A cells*), no antibody plaque-forming response to T-cell antigen takes place. The response can be elicited if the A cells are resupplied. Most antigens are T-cell dependent. These antigens include serum proteins, hormones, enzymes, whole cells, as well as these substances used as carriers for haptens when the hapten-carrier ratio is moderate and when the carrier is species heterologous to the immunized host. The B cell will not form antibodies unless more or less simultaneously T cells have recognized the antigen as well.

T cells will only respond if the antigen is properly presented. The processing of antigens for presentation is a function of the A cells, which requires about 30 minutes after the antigen is taken up by these phagocytes (29,30). The processed antigen is presented to the T cell in conjunction with gene products of the A cell elaborated in the Ia region of the major histocompatibility complex (MHC). The interaction between stimulated A cells and T cells is *heterocytotrophic* in that the processed epitope must recognize a specific idiotype receptor on the T cells. Reaction is also *homocytotrophic* in that the Ia region of the A cell and that of the T cell must be identical. Reaction will, therefore, only take place if both A and T cells are derived from histocompatible donors that possess identical MHC and if, in addition, the MHC complex includes expressed Ia genes that code for the specific idiotype on T cells for recognition of the epitope.

The MHC is represented by eight genetic loci, out of which five (the *Ir* regions) participate in the immune response (31,32). Within the *Ir* region, the A region controls cell-mediated toxicity and T-cell help in antibody production. The J region seems to control T suppressor functions. The expressed dimer of the MHC glycoprotein consists of a variable chain and a constant, β-microglobulin chain. It is of evolutionary interest that β-microglobulin, as shown by Gottlieb et al. (33), cross-reacts with constant region domains of immunoglobulin. The homocytotrophic reaction is effected by the variable chain. The discriminatory capacity of the homocytotrophic reaction is high. Substitution of as few as one or two amino acids prevents interaction (34).

In addition to specifically interacting principles that attach to the cell membrane of the A cell in association with glycoproteins, the stimulated A cell also secretes soluble *interleukin 1* into its environment (35). Interleukin 1 promotes T-cell, granulocyte, and fibroblast proliferation as well as fibrinogen synthesis in the liver.

SPECIFIC T HELPER CELL FUNCTIONS

B cells will not produce antibodies to T-cell-dependent antigens (page 277) without the cooperation of T helper (T_h) cells. There are two mechanisms for interaction of T_h cells and B cells, one, specific and highly effective, requiring relatively few T_h cells, and the other nonspecific, requiring relatively large amounts of T_h cells (36). Both types of T cells are distinct. The nonspecific mechanisms are mediated by *interleukin 2*. The specific mechanism is doubly restricted for similar idiotypy of the T_h and B cells and by shared Ia antigens. While even substitution of as few as one to two amino acids are not allowed in the MHC contribution of the interaction, the specificity of the idiotypic reaction is not that narrow. Apparently, the T-cell idiotypic receptor exhibits broader cross-reactivity (less specificity) among different epitopes than the B-cell receptor.

SPECIFIC T SUPPRESSOR CELL FUNCTIONS

Nude mice (page 271) produce a higher response to a B-cell antigen (trini-trophenyl-mouse red blood cells, TNP-mRBC) than a T-cell antigen (trini-trophenyl-sheep red blood cells, TNP-sRBC). These findings suggest that some T cells possess a regulating factor, including a suppressor factor against response to self-antigens, such as mRBC. Similarly, old mice show a decline in anti-TNP-sRBC response, but not in anti-TNB-mRBC response (37). Old mice immunized with sRBC also dislay a high cross-reactivity with TNB-mRBC. Since old mice are known to be deficient in T-cell function, these findings again suggest a regulatory role of T cells in young mice.

Tolerance can be induced by low or high doses of desaggregated antigens. When mouse spleen cells, made tolerant with high doses of desaggregated human immunoglobulin (hIg), are transferred to irradiated, syngeneic recipients along with nondesaggregated hIg, they will not lead to an immune response: cells transferred from the tolerant donor induce tolerance in the recipients. These cells are thymus-derived: they are *T suppressor (T_s cells)*. Interestingly, these cells repress the response not only to hIg but also to bovine immunoglobulin, reflecting the lower specificity of T-cell receptor idiotypes than those on B cells (38).

When tolerance was induced with low doses of desaggregated hIg, it could not be transferred onto normal cells upon injection into irradiated, syngeneic recipients. Low-dose tolerance in T cells is apparently a direct effect on receptor idiotypes that abort an available clone of cells. In high-dose tolerance, suppressor T cells may provide an additional safeguard against antibody production by suppressing any new receptor-bearing cells, once the aborted clone has become replenished. Immunosuppression is also effected by direct feedback of antibody. Spleen cells preincubated with specific antibody have a reduced in vitro response to antigens (39). This reduced response could not be reverted by addition of fresh A cells. $F(ab')_2$ was unable to mediate suppression of the in vitro response. Thus, it seems that feedback inhibition is mediated upon A cells via their strong Fc receptors. Apparently, the presence of specific antibody on the A cell surface interferes with processing of the antigen by the A cell.

T cells seem to play an active role in the control of the immune reaction in normal and immunized individuals. The failure to produce antibodies against one's own constituents is the result of an active surveillance by T suppressor (T_s) cells. It is the breakdown of the surveillance, which apparently is a critical factor in the induction of autoimmune disease (page 476).

T_s cells contain idiotypic receptors. Cerny et al. (40) found that five anti-idiotypes which specifically block the response of a pneumococcal antigen in B cells, did not affect T_h cells. Neither did they affect the activation of T_s cells which depends on A cell-T cell interaction. However, the antibodies did inhibit the suppressor effect of activated T cells. The data suggests that the idiotype repertoire of the activated T_s cell bears similarity to that of the activated B cell. Somatic mutation in idiotypes can occur during maturation of B cells (page 13). The suppression of T_s effector function by anti-idiotypes produced with se-creted antibodies, suggests that there is overlap with the idiotypic repertoire induced during maturation of T_s cells.

MEMORY T CELLS

Memory T cells are long-lived. These long-lived, antigen-primed T_2 cells deliver help to B cells within 24 hours, in contrast to nonprimed T cells which deliver help in only 3 days (41).

SPECIFIC FUNCTION OF NATURAL KILLER CELLS

In a lesion produced by injection of antigen, a fair number of antibody-forming cells are seen. These are differentiated B cells that possess a rich endoplasmic reticulum and are even by light microscopy distinguishable as *plasma cells* from unstimulated lymphocytes. In general, the plasma cells form a minority of cells in the lesion. They are surrounded by other cells including a large number of small lymphocytes. Some of these lymphocytes may be B cells that have not yet become plasma cells. Others may be T_h and T_s cells. However, the majority of them look as if they are in the lesion just for the ride. There is another group of T lymphocytes, *natural killer (NK) cells,* which possess Fc receptors. If the im-munoglobulin they absorb is an antibody to antigen in a nearby cell, they medi-ate destruction of the cell. NK cells form rosettes with sheep red blood cells, but these rosettes are more labile than those formed by other T cells. NK cells are not adherent and, therefore, are not A cells. NK cells bear no surface im-munoglobulin, and therefore, are not B cells (42).

Some thymocytes may be activated by nonspecific factors, such as mycobac-teria or allogeneic cells, to generate soluble factors that react with immuno-globulin in the presence of antigen in vitro to form cytophilic complexes. These complexes are taken up by a group of Fc receptor-bearing lympho-cytes, which in turn can act as helper cells in the production of antibody by B cells (43).

B-CELL DIFFERENTIATION

Even without interaction of T cells and even after stimulation with a T-cell-dependent antigen, a B cell will cap, incorporate tritiated thymidine, and release an increasing amount of antigen receptor to its surface, thus being capable of binding additional antigen.

During the process of antigen-driven replication, B cells also become more differentiated. They first become *blast* cells with a moderate, and later plasma cells with a profuse, endoplasmic reticulum. Immunoglobulin specific to the immunizing antigen is found in blast and plasma cells (Figs. 7-4, 7-5). Conceivably, some of the IgG detected by Mason et al. (8) in the interior of normal human peripheral leukocytes is, indeed, immunoglobulin in occasional stimulated blast cells.

Isotype shift (page 12) and drive to somatically mutated idiotypes (page 13) occurs as a result of interaction of T_h cells. Each antibody-producing cell, in general, secretes homogeneous antibodies of equal isotype. However, the isotype-shift mechanism may permit a cell to be heterogeneous with regard to isotype, although it is still restricted with regard to its idiotype. In lymphomas, cases presenting two isotypes of immunoglobulins are rare. Even more uncommon are those producing two light chains (kappa and lambda), but identical heavy chains.

DISTRIBUTION OF LYMPHOCYTES IN LYMPHOID TISSUE

Neoplasms are commonly classified by the cell and tissue from which they arise, and once so identified, they are graded as to degree of malignancy. Since different lymphocytes look alike, an immunocytochemical classification of tumors of lymphocytic origin, which include non-Hodgkin's lymphomas and lymphocytic leukemia, appears to be indicated. Diagnosis not only requires appropriate

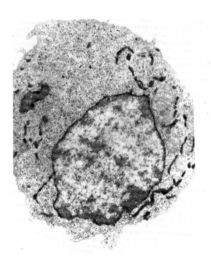

Figure 7-4. A blast cell from the efferent lymph of a sheep after a secondary response to horseradish peroxidase. Cells have been fixed in 1.25% glutaraldehyde and exposed to horseradish peroxidase for 30 minutes at room temperature, refixed in glutaraldehyde, stained with diaminobenzidine and hydrogen peroxide, fixed in osmium tetroxide, and embedded in Epon. Antiperoxidase is found in the perinuclear space, on cytoplasmic polyribosomes, and in the endoplasmic reticulum. In these cells, the Golgi region is usually not stained, even if the endoplasmic reticulum contains much antibody. There is no evidence of sequential appearance of antibody in any particular order. Thus, at times the perinuclear staining is absent. At other times, the ribosomal staining is absent. ×10,000. [From Hay et al. (44).]

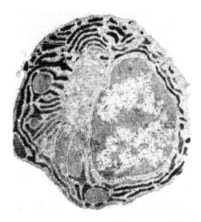

Figure 7-5. A lymph node plasma cell 120 hours after a secondary challenge with horseradish peroxidase. Concentric channels of endoplasmic reticulum contain antibody. Such cells are never found in the
efferent lymph. ×10,000. [From Hay et al. (44).]

markers, but also knowledge of the normal distribution of the various sets of
lymphocytes.

Lymphoid tissues, whenever in lymph nodes, spleen, tonsil, or Payer's
patches, consist of primary and secondary follicles, marginal zones and T-cell-
dependent paracortical regions.

Primary follicles are spherical collections of lymphocytes, which in the lymph
node are located in the cortex. During an active immune response, *secondary
follicles* develop by acquisition of a lighter staining *germinal center* within the
follicle. A layer of *mantle lymphocytes* surrounds the germinal center. In an established secondary follicle, the germinal center is divided into a darker and lighter
zone (Fig. 7-6). The darker zone contains mainly centroblasts, which are large
cells of a deeply basophilic cytoplasm, while the light zone consists of weakly
basophilic cells with scant cytoplasm. As established by Stein et al. (45), primary
follicle lymphocytes and follicle mantle lymphocytes (that surround germinal
centers) are rich in surface IgM and IgD, but are practically devoid of surface
IgG or IgA (Fig. 7-7). Therefore, these cells are resting B cells that have not
undergone isotype shift, and the primary follicle and follicle mantles are areas
through which B lymphocytes recirculate.

More information is obtained by staining for intracellular immunoglobulin in
paraffin-embedded tissues. Under these conditions, primary follicle lymphocytes and follicle mantle lymphocytes are negative, while in the secondary follicles, both centroblasts and centrocytes, contain intracellular immunoglobulin of
any isotype as well as J chains (page 26). Positively increases with duration and
intensity of immunization. This confirms the secondary follicles as a zone of
active antibody production as well as of the post-translational change of immunoglobulins effected by J chains.

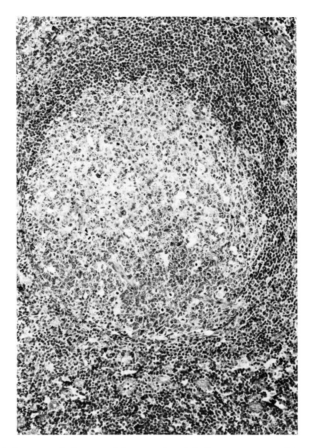

Figure 7-6.   The dark zone at the bottom of the secondary follicle contains centroblasts. The light zone in the upper half contains chiefly centrocytes and dendritic reticulum cells. Giemsa stains. ×50. [Reprinted by permission of Elsevier Science Publishing Co., Inc. from Immunohistologic analysis of the organization of normal lymphoid tissue and non-Hodgkin lymphomas by H. Stein, A. Bank, G. Tolksdorf, K. Lennet, H. Rodt, J. Geredés, *Journal of Histochemistry and Cytochemistry* **28:**746. Copyright 1980 by The Histochemical Society, Inc. (45).]

Follicle mantle lymphocytes, germinal centers, and primary follicle lymphocytes display in frozen sections equally intense staining for C3 receptors and Ia antigen (45).

Using antihuman T lymphocyte antigen (HTLA) as a marker, many T cells were found in the light zone of the germinal center, but few or none in the dark zone (Fig. 7-8). It appears likely that these cells interspaced in the secondary follicle and mantle zones consist of T_s and T_h cells.

Plasma cell reaction induced by T cell-independent antigens start in the marginal zone. In frozen sections, cells in these areas in tonsil or spleen stain stronger for surface IgM and weaker for surface IgD than those in primary follicles and mantle zones (45). The thymus-dependent *T zone* consists of a dense accumulation of cells with surface staining for HTLA.

Immunocytochemistry of these lymphocyte markers is important in the understanding of early events in autoimmune disease. One of the problems in

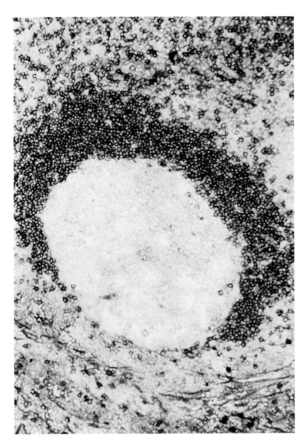

Figure 7-7. Human tonsil, frozen section. IgD is in follicular mantle lymphocytes. Germinal centers and intracellular immunoglobulin networks are unstained. PAP method. ×100. [Reprinted by permission of Elsevier Science Publishing Co., Inc. from Immunohistologic analysis of the organization of normal lymphoid tissue and non-Hodgkin lymphomas by H. Stein, A. Bank, G. Tolksdorf, K. Lennet, H. Rodt, J. Geredés, *Journal of Histochemistry and Cytochemistry* **28:**746. Copyright 1980 by The Histochemical Society, Inc. (45).]

inflammatory lesions of the brain is distinction of lymphocytes from oligodendrocytes. Traugott et al. (46) stained multiple sclerosis lesions with monoclonal anti-T4 for helper T cells, with monoclonal anti-T8 for suppressor and natural killer cells, and with antiserum to galactocerebroside (page 351) for oligodendrocytes. In active, chronic multiple sclerosis plaques (page 487), T helper cells are found in the lesion edge and expanded far into adjacent, normal-appearing white matter. In contrast, T suppressor or natural killer cells were at the lesion edge and in a *narrow* zone of adjacent white matter and often in perivascular areas (Fig. 7-9). Oligodendrocytes were distinct from lymphocytes.

LYMPHOMAS

While the classification of tumors by tissue or cells of origin is easy if the tumor is well differentiated and is growing locally, it becomes increasingly difficult with

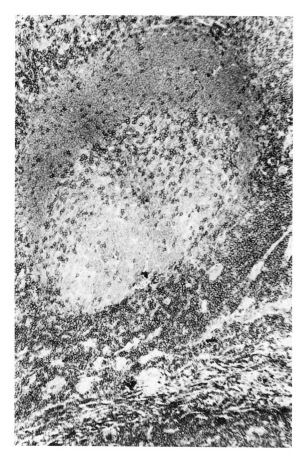

Figure 7-8. Human tonsil, frozen section. Human T-lymphocyte surface antigen-containing cells are abundant in the light and rare in the dark zones of the germinal center. However, the dark germinal center zone is bordered by a follicle mantle with rich exhibition of T cells. PAP method. ×40. [Reprinted by permission of Elsevier Science Publishing Co., Inc. from Immunohistologic analysis of the organization of normal lymphoid tissue and non-Hodgkin lymphomas by H. Stein, A. Bank, G. Tolksdorf, K. Lennet, H. Rodt, J. Geredés, *Journal of Histochemistry and Cytochemistry* **28**:746. Copyright 1980 by The Histochemical Society, Inc. (45).]

dedifferentiation of tumors, especially if the tumor is first discovered at metastatic sites. Since there is a continuous spectrum in most tumors between poorly and well-differentiated forms, the experienced pathologist still can classify most tumors by comparison of a few characteristic features of a less differentiated form with the known features of a slightly more differentiated form. Immunocytochemistry of retrospective material (page 212) has been of great help in confirming older diagnoses and in adding new parameters to classification. There are two features in neoplasia that favor the use of immunocytochemistry as an adjunct in studying both the tissue of origin as well as the degree of dedifferentiation of a tumor:

1.   Differentiation antigens are characteristic of the embryonic or malignant cell and are absent from the normal adult cell.

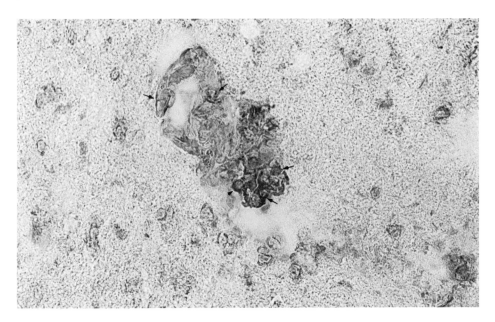

Figure 7-9. Active, chronic multiple sclerosis lesion double stained with anti-T8 and antigalactocerebroside by PAP technique without antibody elution (page 196). Heavily labeled T8 cells (arrows) are in perivascular areas, while the less intense oligodendrocytes are in the parenchyma. In the original preparation, T8 cells were brown and oligodendrocytes were blue. ×480. [From Traugott et al. (46).]

2.   It has become apparent that production of a specific substance, such as immunoglobulin in B cells or tyrosine hydroxylase in neurons is not necessarily only a property of mature, differentiated cells. Less differentiated cells may produce these substances too, although not necessarily in the same pattern. In the lymphatic system, even the normal cell is an undifferentiated cell in a continuous process of turnover and regeneration. The differentiated cell is, in fact, only the product of an antigenic stimulus. Since clonal expansion and differentiation is a normal process, it is not surprising that a tumor of a cell originating in a given stage of differentiation is composed of rapidly dividing cells. Hence, even a tumor of differentiated cells, in the lymphoid system, is malignant. Consequently, the majority of lymphomas, even though malignant, represent cells in fairly advanced stages of differentiation that can be characterized by the antigens which the differentiated cells secrete.

The other side of the spectrum is occupied by nerve cells. Adult neurons are incapable of division. Neurofilaments are one of the characteristic neuron proteins that are expressed late in development (47). Hence, as shown by Trojanowski and Lee (48), neurofilaments are found with regularity in benign tumors of neuronal origin, but are absent from most malignant tumors (page 265). However, differentiation of cells is not necessarily revealed by expression of new antigens. On the contrary, differentiation may be viewed as a process of specialization in which the expression of multiple proteins becomes restricted to few (47). Thus, cultured sympathetic ganglion cells have been shown to express neurotransmitters not found in the normal ganglion cells (page 317), and neuroblastoma cells established in vitro are rich in multiple neurotransmitter synthetic enzymes.

From these considerations, it is apparent that visualization of antigens can be an aid in the classification of differentiation of tumors. Appropriate classification is becoming increasingly important, as establishment of degree of dedifferentiation dictates the proper choice of chemotherapy.

The classification of lymphomas and allied conditions on the basis of functional properties requires availability of a large series of tumors of different morphologic classification. Therefore, methodology had to be adaptable to routinely fixed, paraffin-embedded tissues. Taylor (49,50) was the first to undertake such study, using initially peroxidase-conjugated antibodies. With this method, it had indeed been possible to identify the proteins produced by actively secreting tumors, such as multiple myeloma. Difficulties were encountered with less profuse protein formers, such as the lymphoid cells in Hodgkin's lesions. These required PAP technique for identification of their immunoglobulin contents. Another difficulty with the peroxidase-conjugated antibody method was the rather frequent appearance of polyclonal tumors, which reacted either with antisera to two different heavy chains or with anti-κ as well as anti-λ. These could usually be resolved by the use of PAP technique: some polyclonal staining was eliminated as nonspecific while other polyclonal staining was confirmed as specific. The main difficulty with the labeled antibody method is probably the nonspecificity of the second antiserum (page 143) and the need for higher concentrations of first antisera, whereby cross-reactions are invited (page 232). For these reasons, the PAP method has been employed in a majority of later studies.

About 60% of lymphomas secrete immunoglobulin. The remaining 40% of tumors are either T-cell tumors that could be classified by other antigens, or if of B-cell origin, are too undifferentiated to secrete immunoglobulins. Evaluation of serum immunoglobulin by radioimmunoassay of serum constituents depends upon finding one component, for example, IgG1, in unusually high proportion compared to those of other immunoglobulins. However, the diagnostic significance of radioimmunoassay is limited, because of the high noise provided by the normal serum immunoglobulin components, and because of the fact that in many disorders other than non-Hodgkin's lymphomas, elevation of one immunoglobulin component compared to another may be significant. These are some of the reasons why diagnosis of immunoglobulin-secreting lymphomas depends upon immunocytochemistry of tissues. Monoclonality of the immunoglobulins, as established by immunocytochemical staining of paraffin sections, with antibodies to heavy and light chains of immunoglobulin is the most important, but not only, immunocytochemical criterion. Most tumors, as they originate from single cells are monoclonal, and secrete only one isotype of heavy or light chains. This is the most important criterion that differentiates non-Hodgkin's lymphomas from benign, reactive hyperplasia, in which stimulation of a number of B cells leads to polyclonality. It is important to obtain sufficiently large pieces of tissue to be able to distinguish islands of monoclonal tumor foci from surrounding or infiltrating, polyclonally reactive tissue. This is the main reason why diagnosis should depend on immunocytochemistry rather than evaluation of secretory product in serum. Accurate diagnosis requires multiple markers, both for the surface and the interior of the cell. Although surface markers can be visualized in paraffin-embedded material, fresh cells or fresh frozen tissues are sometimes used in addition, as the cell membranes are better preserved. However, fresh frozen tissues may not always be available. If sensitive immunocytochemical technique is used, surface antigens can well be localized in fixed tissues, as illustrated in the nervous system by localization of synapse-associated antigens in paraffin sections (page 433). In lymphomas, the required antibodies are for as large a number of heavy chain isotypes as possible (α_1, α_2, γ_1, γ_2, γ_3, γ_4, ε, α_1, α_2, and μ), for κ and λ chains, for J chains, for T-cell surface markers, and for lysozyme and serum albumin.

For the localization of immunoglobulin in paraffin sections, it is often expedient and sometimes necessary to predigest tissue sections with proteinases. Digestion is more important if labeled, rather than unlabeled, antibody techniques are employed, presumably because of the lesser sensitivity of the former. Brandtzaeg and Rognum (51) emphasized the risk in proteolytic predigestion, since different immunoglobulin components possess different susceptibility to digestion, and since background from serum immunoglobulin, absent before digestion, and stained after digestion, may make recognition of monoclonal lesions difficult. Unmasking of cross-linked antigen in fixed tissue is probably not the mechanism of the effects of protease treatment. Immunoglobulin epitopes appear to be more sensitive than most other proteins to alteration by aldehyde fixation. However, the coiled structure of the molecule makes many sites inaccessible to the fixative. Digestion may reveal these sites. Since the sites differ in different immunoglobulin subunits, the effect of proteinase is not expected to be uniform in all immunoglobulins.

Apparently, protease digestion is not necessary or expedient for the detection of immunoglobulin in sections fixed in Lillie's "B-5" fixative (mercuric chloride/sodium acetate/formaldehyde) or in Bouin's fixative (picric acid/acetic acid/formaldehyde). The reaction of formaldehyde with tissue amine is slow in these acidic fixatives as compared to neutral or alkaline solutions, and much of the hardening of tissue seems to be due to the mercuric salt or picric acid, respectively. Consequently, formaldehyde-sensitive groups in immunoglobulin may be protected and immunoreactivity preserved in exposed regions that are destroyed by alkaline aldehydes.

Cells entering the interior of lymphoreticular organs are held there for varying periods of time to undergo maturation and differentiation, or degradation, as the case may be (52). These cells apparently possess intrinsic properties that hold them in place, since tumors of these cells, although widely distributed, are solid lymphomas. In contrast, tumors of recirculating cells do not form nodules and appear as *leukemias*. Recirculating B cells are found in primary follicles and in the follicle mantle. These cells have not undergone differentiation and, therefore, produce no immunoglobulin. They are, therefore, negative for intracellular immunoglobulin. They will possess surface IgM and IgD (page 277). Studying lymph nodes of patients with B-type chronic lymphocytic leukemia, Stein et al. (45) found, indeed, surface IgD and IgM on all small cells in lymph follicles, along with monoclonal light chains, indicating the clonal origin of these cells. However, in *pseudofollicles* which contain larger cells, surface IgD was decreased relative to IgM, suggesting a limited degree of differentiation into germinal center cells or marginal zone cells, which normally lose their IgD.

Terminal desoxynucleotidyl transferase is a DNA polymerase which was revealed immunocytochemically by Stass et al. (53) as nuclear antigen in a large percentage of lymphoblastic leukemias. The immunocytochemical detection may be important in identifying patients who may respond to vincristine and prednisone. Similar treatment is indicated in blastic transformations that often occur as a preterminal event in chronic granulocytic leukemia. Neiman (54) found that the majority of megaloblasts in such cases contain hemoglobin (Fig. 7-10). This supports the notion that the disorder involves the hemopoietic stem cell.

In the diagnosis of *lymphomas*, an interlaboratory comparison carried out by Vernon and Morgan (55) found good correspondence in diagnosing mono-clonality for κ and λ chains. Light-chain monoclonality is probably the best criterion for malignancy. There are isolated reports of tumors secreting both κ and λ chains, but the significance of these data has been questioned. Conceivably, slow fixation may have led to infiltration of serum immunoglobulin and, thus, gained false impression of polyclonality. However, one should consider that a malignant cell may not necessarily express only one chromosome in antibody production. If in rare tumors allelic exclusion (page 11) has been suppressed, indeed two different light chains may be expressed in a clone from a heterozygous cell. Polyclonality with regard to heavy chains, although still rare, has been reported more frequently than polyclonality of light chains. The interpretation, if in truly malignant lesions, may the same as that for light-chain polyclonality. However, one may also imagine that cells while in the process of isotype shift (page 12) may secrete two heavy chains, one of them being IgM, even though a mechanism for such dual secretion conceivably characteristic for certain malignancies, will still have to be found. In any event, simultaneous

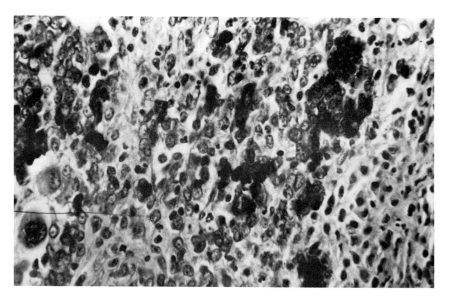

Figure 7-10.   Spleen of blastic transformation in chronic granulocytic leukemia, paraffin section. Hemoglobin in the cytoplasm of almost all the blast cells. PAP method. Tinctorial counterstain. ×400. [From the work of Richard S. Neiman.]

polyclonality with regard to both light chains (either cell surface or intracellular immunoglobulin) and intracellular heavy chains is almost certain evidence against malignancy, provided, however, that not two tumors are simultaneously present in the same lesion and that enough tissue is available to include any malignant nodules that may have been interspaced within reactive tissue.

Despite the occasional appearance of polyclonality, the diagnosis of monoclonality remains important in the distinction of lymphoma from benign, reactive lymphoid hyperplasias, such as seen in some cases of infectious mononucleosis, toxoplasmosis, tuberculosis, and sacroidosis. Staining in benign conditions is polyclonal, since a number of antibody clones participate in the lesion. Therefore, one can conclude that if a lesion is monoclonal it is almost certainly malignant. The contrary conclusion that a polyclonal lesion is benign cannot be made, since several malignant lesions were polyclonal.

However, in addition to light- and heavy-chain monoclonality or polyclonality, there are other immunocytochemical tests that help to differentiate malignant from reactive lesions.

J chains form the bridges in dimerization and pentamerization of IgA and IgM, respectively (page 26). J chains are synthesized independently of immunoglobulin. Brandtzaeg (56) found by immunofluorescence that J chains are absent from plasma cells containing IgG or monomeric IgA, present in IgM-secreting plasma cells and poorly represented in plasma cells secreting dimeric IgA. However, J chains are present in follicle centers of human tonsils as well as IgG plasmacyotomas. Accordingly, the presence of J chains in cells containing immunoglobulins suggests that the cells are active in the process of becoming immunoglobulin-secreting cells. Therefore, J chains should help differentiating a lymphoma cell from cells that have passively taken up immunoglobulin from the environment, as well as from mature normal plasma cells that secrete immunoglobulins other than IgM or IgA. Isaacson (57) has shown that the presence of J chains is characteristic of monoclonal lymphomas. In Reed-Sternberg cells of Hodgkin's disease, in which immunoglobulin is polyclonal, J chains were absent, suggesting that the immunoglobulin in these cells is not synthesized by them and that, therefore, they are not derived from B cells. However, Brandtzaeg (60) cautions that even normal B cells, according to their stage of maturity, may contain J chains. Therefore, the presence of J chains is not necessarily an absolute criterion for malignancy and J-chain positivity can be used better to differentiate lymphoma cells from cells that have passively taken up immunoglobulin, such as Reed-Sternberg cells, rather than from active antibody-producing cells of nonmalignant nature. Nevertheless, the uniform distribution of J chains would suggest malignancy, while a distribution that varies from cell to cell may be the most one can expect from a reactive lesion, in which lymphocytes and plasma cells are found in various stages of differentiation.

Ree and Hsu (61,62) found that application of the lectin (page 61), peanut agglutinin, followed by immunocytochemistry for the lectin, yields in the normal lymph node cytoplasmic staining of macrophages, histiocytes, and possible dendritic reticulum cells in the form of large, medium, and small cells. Surface staining in the normal lymph nodes corresponded to lymphocytes, and their distribution varied from one germinal center to another. In contrast, in neoplastic follicles, the absence of cytoplasmic staining and the uniform distribution of surface-staining cells provided an additional marker for the lymphomatous nature of the lesion.

Immunocytochemistry is especially important in unusual tumors at unusual locations. Diagnosis of malignant lymphoma from pulmonary cytologic material is infrequent. "Signet cell" lymphoma is a rare form of malignant lymphoma of mediastinal origin. It presents cells with "empty" cytoplasmic vacuoles and nuclear compression that resembles adenocarcinoma. Vernon (63) diagnosed such a case with infiltration in the bronchi by immunocytochemical establishment of monoclonal immunoglobulin in cytologic material. The distinction from adenocarcinoma is important, since the prognosis of lymphoma is improving steadily, while that of adenocarcinoma has remained essentially unchanged for years.

Nonmalignant or reactive lymphoid lesions are not uncommon in the intestinal tract and must be differentiated from extranodal lymphomas that constitute 1% to 4% of intestinal malignancies. In the series of Saraga et al. (64), malignant lymphomas either displayed a monoclonal immunoglobulin chain-staining pattern (Fig. 7-11) or failed to stain entirely within a homogeneous field. When stained, 50 to 100% of cells within the field were positive. Homogeneously staining fields were distinguished from reactive plasma cells with polyclonal patterns that were sometimes interspaced among tumor cells. Importantly, the prognosis of lymphomas that were positive for immunoglobulin proved better than those that were negative.

An unusual case of plasma cell tumor that involved the mandible and secreted only λ chains was reported by Aufdemorte and Humphrey (65). Immunocytochemical diagnosis of λ chains, in the absence of heavy chains, was important, because of the poor prognosis of these tumors.

Several monoclonal antibodies have been developed that differentiate B cells, T helper cells (OKT4 and Leu3a), and T suppressor cells along with natural killer cells (OKT8 and Leu2a). They are useful as markers for normal lymphocytes, but have been disappointing in the hands of Barcos et al. (66) in the differentiation of T cells from B cells in lymphomas. The distinction of normal B and T cells is correlated by functional differences. Markers that correspond to specific cellular functions, like B-cell intracellular immunoglobulins destined for secretion, are useful and meaningful. The monoclonal T-cell typing antibodies react with antigens whose function is still not understood. It is, therefore, not surprising that they do not provide a clear distinction between helper and suppressor functions unless it happened that the antigens localized by these antibodies are indeed involved in these functions. T cells (if defined as non-B lymphocytes) may have many surface markers with many functional properties. Individual markers are not necessarily exclusive. For instance, in the simplest case, a T cell may possess markers a and b, another cell markers b and c, and the third cell markers c and a. Thus, each new set of monoclonal antibodies could provide, in theory, a new classification of T cells. For this reason, it appears to be desirable that the functional significance of new markers be investigated prior to their extensive clinical use (see also page 272).

Muramidase (lysozyme) is widely distributed in tissues. It is present in granulocytes and macrophages (67,68), but is absent from lymphocytes. Muramidase is, therefore, a marker for reactive inflammatory lesions, for granulomas, and Hodgkin's disease, in distinction to lymphomas and lymphocytic leukemia. Blen-

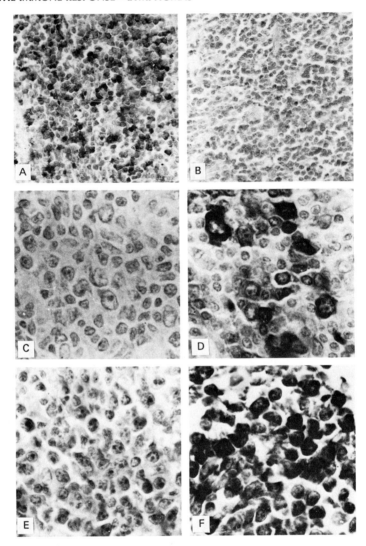

Figure 7-11.   Diffuse lymphocytic, poorly differentiated malignant lymphoma of the small bowel, positive for λ chains (A), negative for κ chains (B). Diffuse, lymphocytic, poorly differentiated malignant lymphoma of the rectum, negative for lysozyme (C), positive for λ chains (D). Diffuse, lymphocytic, poorly differentiated lymphoma of the appendix, negative for κ chains, positive for λ chains. Paraffin sections. PAP method. Hemotoxylin and eosin counterstain. A, B ×260. C, D, E, F ×600. [From Saraga et al. (64).]

nerhassett and Papamitriou (69) have shown uniform presence of muramidase in monocyte-derived, epithelioid, and giant cells of immunological granulomas in which frequent anamnestic reactions lead to differentiation of macrophages to epithelioid cells. These are the granulomas of tuberculosis, tuberculoid leprosy, sarcoidosis, and granulomatous hepatitis. However, granulomas of foreign body reactions in the absence of strong immune response, such as foreign body granulomas or lipomatous leprosy, possess macrophages that vary in their contents of muramidase.

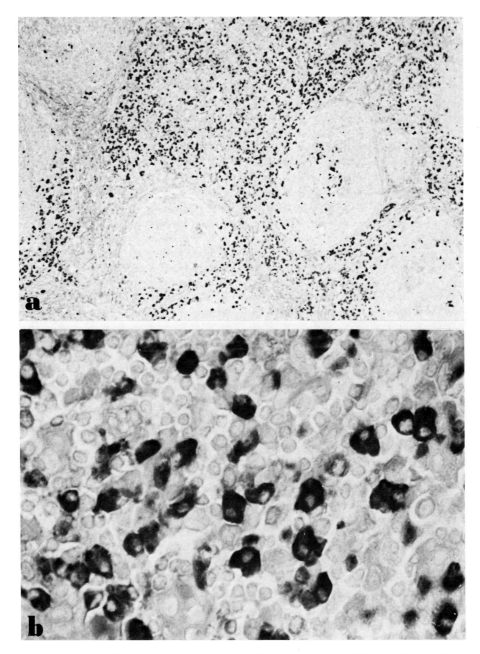

Figure 7-12. Giant cell lymph node hyperplasia. Paraffin section. The interfollicular plasma cells contain λ chains (a) and κ chains (b). PAP method. A, ×120. B, ×550. [From Dura et al. (70).]

Giant lymph node hyperplasia presents itself either as asymptomatic solitary or multiple lymph node swellings, or it may be associated with fever, anemia, hypergammaglobulinemia or hypogammaglobulinemia, leukocytosis, or nephrotic syndrome. Surgery is curative and, therefore, differential diagnosis from lymphoma is important. Dura et al. (70) have established a clear-cut polyclonal pattern, both with regard to light and heavy chains, in these lesions (Fig. 7-12).

Palutke et al. (71) divided their lymphoma biopsies into groups in which more than 25% of lymphocytes bore a single type surface or cytoplasmic immunoglobulin and into the rest of lesions in which less than 25% of cells were monoclonal. By using this differentiation, the first group contained a number of cases that would have been defined as polyclonal by most criteria, and in which indeed monoclonality was only exhibited by some of the cells. While most of these cases, indeed, were polyclonal and benign, some developed subsequent lymphomas and many were associated with collagen disorders known to be associated with lymphoid proliferation. It is worthwhile, therefore, to follow up cases in which an otherwise polyclonal lesion contains a disproportionate number of cells secreting a common type of immunoglobulin.

Another polyclonal lesion is lymphocytic interstitial pneumonia which is a primary, diffuse lymphoreticular disorder, and may be the pulmonary analog of Sjögren's syndrome. The disease may be a disturbance in immunoregulatory mechanisms and is often associated with defects in T cells. In a case of lymphocytic interstitial pneumonia of six years' duration, Banerjee and Ahmad (72) demonstrated a polyclonal immunoglobulin staining pattern of pulmonary lymphocytes. However, lymph node biopsy revealed a monoclonal pattern. Apparently, this was a case of reactive B-cell disturbance, in which a lymphoma has developed secondarily, again suggesting careful follow-up of some lesions that appear polyclonal on first examination.

CLINICAL PATHOLOGY OF PERIPHERAL LEUKOCYTES

The classical identification of lymphocyte types depends on cell surface markers as detected largely by immunofluorescence. Cells are labeled in suspension and identified after washing. Artifacts resulting from secondary effects of antibodies on cells in suspension must be avoided. The more convenient procedure of staining cells after fixation in smears on glass slides has found little application by immunofluorescence. The technique has not been sensitive enough to detect cell surface markers after these manipulations. In addition, smearing and fixation seems to promote nonspecific fluorescence. For instance, Fc receptors have not been detectable by immunofluorescence in fixed, routinely prepared smears of normal lymphocytes. However, in Burkitt lymphoma cells, which are known to be especially rich in Fc receptor, immunofluorescence was able to detect IgG binding even on smears.

Mason et al. (8) used fixed, smeared peripheral blood cells for identification of surface and intracellular antigens and have shown that PAP-stained and tinctorially counterstained preparations are morphologically as informative as Romanowsky-stained cells, that smears can be stained prior to immunocytochemical processing, that a large number of fixatives, with formolacetone used preferentially, are satisfactory for preservation of antigenic reactivities, including those of immunoglobulins, and that, presumably because of higher sensitivity and specificity, information beyond that obtained from immunofluorescent staining in suspension may be obtained.

Antibodies to erythrocytes are difficult to detect by immunofluorescence on fixed smears. Mason and Taylor (73) have described successful localization of A antigen by PAP techniques on human blood smears.

In a study of Triosil-Ficoll-separated human mononuclear cells on fixed smears, Mason et al. (8) found surface IgM in approximately 5% of normal lymphocytes (Fig. 7-1). These cells revealed typical villous cell margins. Cells so stained accepted less intense nuclear tinctorial stain than immunocytochemically negative cells. Occasional cells, however, had diffuse cytoplasmic staining and their nuclei counterstained normally. The latter cells have no counterpart in cells stained by immunofluorescence in suspension.

When a low concentration of first antiserum is increased, the number of stained cells progressively increases until a plateau is reached. Therefore, with excess first antiserum the total number of reacting cells can be defined. Interestingly, there was a close correspondence in number of IgM-positive cells with two different anti-μ sera, using PAP technique on smears. On comparison with imunofluorescence, carried out by staining in suspension, only half as many cells were stained by PAP technique. Apparently, the PAP technique detects a subset of lymphocytes reactive with anti-μ. It does detect true surface IgM rather than IgM absorbed from serum. This was corroborated by the absence of loose-surface IgM staining that would have disappeared on incubation at 37°C or treatment of pH 4.0 prior to smearing. However, incubation in anti-μ at 0°C prior to smearing caused patchiness of staining and warming to 37°C led to capping and endocytosis. The rare lymphocytes showing cytoplasmic staining were not affected by this procedure. Depletion experiments showed that the IgM cells were B cells.

Intracellular IgM in normal circulating lymphocytes has rarely been observed by immunofluorescence. Its more frequent detection by PAP technique may be a reflection of sensitivity.

Surface IgD was seen in very few cells by Mason et al. (8). However, IgG was seen in 25% of cells. Staining was relatively weak compared to IgM and was diffuse when cells were prepared at 0°C prior to smearing. In cells prepared at 37°C, staining was discontinuous, often over the cell uropod and in small cytoplasmic vesicles. The percentage of cells containing IgG is consistent with the sum of Fc receptor-bearing B cells and natural killer T cells determined by other techniques.

IgG-containing, polymorphonuclear cells have been detected by immunofluorescence in various disease states. By PAP technique, IgG is also seen in normal polymorphs as well as in monocytes, reflecting greater sensitivity of the technique. Apparently the immunoglobulin has become ingested into these cells from surrounding serum.

Bross et al. (74) used immunocytochemistry to identify cell surface antigens in human histocompatibility testing. Ficoll-Hypaque-isolated human mononuclear cells were depleted of monocytes and attached on glass slides covered with poly-

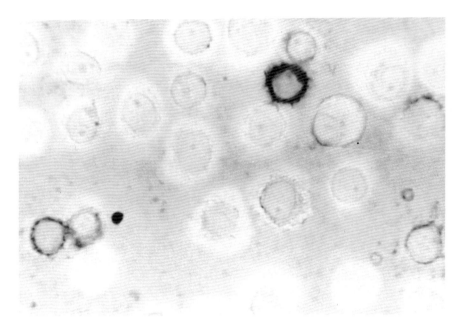

Figure 7-13. Surface immunoglobulin in human peripheral lymphocytes is revealed by incubation in autologous serum followed by anti-immunoglobulin as first antiserum in the PAP technique. ×1000. [From Bross et al. (74).]

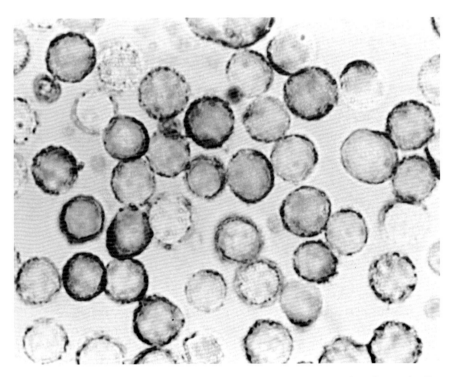

Figure 7-14. Histocompatability antigens are revealed by the increase in number of stained cells compared to Fig. 7-13, when the mononuclear cells are exposed to histocompatibility-positive serum prior to rabbit antihuman IgG, goat antirabbit IgG, and rabbit PAP. ×1000. [From Bross et al. (74).]

L-lysine. The staining sequence consisted of pretreatment with gelatin buffer to block free poly-L-lysine sites, followed by 10 μl of human serum as first antiserum (normal serum, serum from women who had one or two pregnancies, or from patients who had blood transfusions), rabbit antihuman IgG, goat antirabbit IgG, and rabbit PAP. With buffer instead of first antiserum 17%, and with autologous first serum, 40% of cells revealed surface immunoglobulin (Fig. 7-13). Therefore, a serum reaction was described as positive only if more than 40% of cells reacted. In comparison to complement-dependent lymphocytotoxicity assay, a number of additional positive reactions were obtained by PAP technique with sera from individuals known to be immunized by pregnancy or blood transfusion (Fig. 7-14), indicating a higher sensitivity in the detection of histocompatibility antibodies by PAP.

REFERENCES

1. Sugimoto M, Dannenberg AM Jr, Wahl LM, Ettinger WH Jr, Hastie AT, Daniels DC, Thomas CR, Demoulin-Brahy L: Extracellular hydrolytic enzymes of rabbit dermal tuberculous lesions and tuberculous reactions, collected in skin chambers. *Am J Pathol* **90**:583, 1978.

2. Hsu S-M, Cossman J, Jaffe ES: Lymphocyte subsets in normal human lymphoid tissues. *Am J Clin Path* **80**:21, 1983.

3. Chain MM, Tada N, Kimura S, Hoffman MK, Miller RA, Sutman O, Hammerling U: Characterization of T lymphocyte subsets with monoclonal antibodies. Discovery of a distinct marker, Ly-m22, of T-suppressor cells. *J Immunol* **130**:2075, 1983.

4. Aitu M, Cocchia D, Minella AB, Amanten A: Identification of thymostimulin-reacting cells in calf thymus by immunoperoxidase method. *Histochemistry* **80**:207, 1984.

5. Kumagi K, Abo T, Sekizawa T, Sasaki M: Studies on surface immunoglobulins on human B lymphocytes. I. Dissociation of cell bound immunoglobulin with acid pH or at 37 C. *J Immunol* **115**:982, 1975.

6. Alexander E, Sanders S: F(ab') reagents are not required if goat, rather than rabbit, antibodies are used to detect human surface immunoglobulin. *J Immunol* **119**:1084, 1977.

7. Mason DY, Farrel C, Taylor CR: The detection of intracellular antigens in human leucocytes by immunoperoxidase staining. *Brit J Haematol* **31**:361, 1975.

8. Mason DY, Labaume S, Preud'homme J-L: The detection of intracellular antigens in human leucocytes by immunoperoxidase staining. *J Clin Pathol* **29**:413, 1977.

9. Itoh G, Suzuki I: Immunohistochemical detection of Fc receptor. I. Light microscopic demonstration of Fc receptor using soluble immune complexes of peroxidase-antiperoxidase immunoglobulin G. *J Histochem Cytochem* **25**:252, 1977.

10. Alles EW, Phillips DJ, Shore SL, Gordon DS, La Via MF, Black CM, Reimer CB: Analysis of mononuclear cell surfaces with fluorescinated staphylococcal protein A complexed with IgG antibody or heat aggregated γ-globulin. *J Immunol* **117**:2119, 1976.

11. Miller A, DeLuka D, Decke J, Ezzell R, Secarz EE: Specific binding of antigen to lymphocytes. *Am J Pathol* **65**:451, 1971.

12. Raff MC, Feldmann M, De Petris S: Monospecificity of bone-marrow-derived lymphocytes. *J Exp Med* **137**:1024, 1973.

13. Vargo JM, Konigsberg WH, Richards FF: Antibodies with multiple binding functions. Induction of a single immunoglobulin species by structurally dissimilar haptens. *Proc Natl Acad Sci USA* **70**:3269, 1973.

14. Naor D, Morecki S, Mitchell GF: Differential induction of antitrinitrophenyl plaque forming cell responses to lightly and heavily conjugated trinitrophenylated heterologous and autologous erythrocytes in mice. *Eur J Immunol* **4**:311, 1974.

15. Klaus GGB, Cross AM: The influence of epitope density on the immunologic properties of hapten-protein conjugates. I. Characteristics of the immune response to hapten-coupled albumin with varying epitope density. *Cell Immunol* **14**:226, 1974.

16. Basten A, Warner NL, Mandel T: A receptor for antibody on lymphocytes. II. Immunochemical and electron microscopic characteristics. *J Exp Med* **135**:627, 1972.

17. Itoh G, Suzuki I: Immunohistochemical detection of Fc receptor. II. Electron microscopic demonstration of Fc receptor using soluble immune complexes of ferritin-antiferritin immunoglobulin G. *J Histochem Cytochem* **25**:259, 1977.

18. Parish CR, Hayward JA: The lymphocyte surface. I. Relation between Fc receptors, C'3 receptors and surface immunoglobulin. *Proc R Soc Lond B* **187**:47, 1974.

19. Dickler HB, Sachs DH: Evidence for identity or close association of the Fc receptor of B lymphocytes and alloantigens determined by the Ir region of the H-2 complex. *J Exp Med* **140**:779, 1974.

20. Taussig MJ, Mozes E, Isac R: Antigen-specific thymus cell factors in the genetic control of the immune response to poly-(tyrosyl, glutamyl)-poly-D,L-alanyl-poly-lysyl. *J Exp Med* **140**:301, 1974.

21. Lithicum DS, Sell S: Surface immunoglobulin on rabbit lymphoid cells. III. Double expression and separate endocytosis of surface immunoglobulin allotypes on heterozygous lymphocytes demonstrated by immunoelectron microscopic labeling. *Cell Immunol* **27**:240, 1976.

22. Prage CA, Green C, Nitecki DE, Bellone CJ: Antigen binding lymphocytes in guinea pigs. I. B cell expansion to the monovalent antigen L-tyrosine-*p*-azophenyl trimethylammonium (tyr(TMA)) in the absence of antibody production. *J Immunol* **118**:1311, 1977.

23. Iverson J-G: Long-lived B memory cells separated on antigen coated bean columns. *Nature {New Biol}* **243**:23, 1973.

24. Diener E, Paetkau VH: Antigen recognition: Early surface receptor phenomena induced by binding of a tritium-labeled antigen. *Proc Natl Acad Sci USA* **69**:2364, 1972.

25. Louis J, Chiller JM, Weigle WU: Fate of antigen-binding cells in unresponsive and immune mice. *J Exp Med* **137**:461, 1973.

26. Hamilton Ja, Miller JFAP: Hapten-specific tolerance: unresponsiveness in the T cell depleted population. *Eur J Immunol* **3**:457, 1973.

27. Schrader JW, Nossal GJV: Effector cell blockade. A new mechanism of immune hyporeactivity induced by multivalent antigens. *J Exp Med* **137**:1582, 1974.

28. Kennedy RC, Melnick JC, Dreesman GR: Antibody to hepatitis B virus induced by injecting antibodies to the idiotype. *Science* **223**:930, 1984.

29. Sprent J: Major histocompatibility complex regulation of lymphocyte development and interaction. *Fed Proc* **40**:214, 1981.

30. Scala G, Oppenheim J: Antigen presentation by human monocytes: Evidence for stimulant processing and requirement for interleukin 1. *J Immunol* **131**:1160, 1983.

31. Doherty PC, Bennik JR: Monitoring the integrity of self: biology of major histocompatibility complex restriction of virus-immune T cells. *Fed Proc* **40**:218, 1981.

32. Klein J, Juretic A, Baxeranis CN, Nagy ZA: The traditional and new version of the mouse H-2 complex. *Nature* **291**:455, 1981.

33. Gottlieb AB, Engelhard M, Kunkel HG, Tanigaki N, Pressman D: A cross reaction between B_2-microglobulin and -light chains. *J Immunol* **119**:2001, 1977.

34. Nathanson SG, Ewinstein BW, Martinko JM, Nairn R, Nisizawa T, Uekava H, Yamaga K: Structural studies on H-2 products from mouse major histocompatibility mutant strains: Implications for cell-cell recognition. *J Supramol Struct Suppl* **4**:121, 1980.

35. Gillis S: Interleukin biochemistry and biology. *Fed Proc* **42**:2635, 1983.

36. Imperiale MJ, Faherty DA, Sproviero JF, Zanderer M: Functionally distinct helper cells enriched under different culture conditions cooperate with different B cells. *J Immunol* **129**:1843, 1982.

37. Naor D, Bonavida B, Walford RL: Autoimmunity and aging: the age-related responsiveness of mice of a long-lived strain to trinitrophenylated syngeneic mouse red blood cells. *J Immunol* **117**:2204, 1976.

38. Benjamin DC: Suppressor cells in tolerance to HGG: Kinetics and cross-suppression in high dose tolerance. Absence in low dose tolerance. *J Immunol* **118**:2125, 1977.

39. Abrahams S, Phillips RA, Miller RG: Inhibition of the immune response by 7S antibody. *J Exp Med* **137**:870, 1973.

40. Cerny J, Heusser C, Wallich R, Himmerling U, Eardley D: Immunoglobulin idiotypes expressed by distinct idiotypes detected by monoclonal antibodies on antigen-specific suppressor T cells. *J Exp Med* **156**:719, 1982.

41. Araneo BA, Marrack PC, Kappler JW: Functional heterogeneity among the T-derived lymphocytes of the mouse. VI. Memory T cells stored in the T_2 subpopulation. *J Immunol* **117**:2131, 1976.

42. Spiegelberg HL, Perlman H, Perlman P: Interaction of K lymphocytes with myeloma proteins of different IgG subclasses. *J Immunol* **116**:1464, 1976.

43. Paraskevas F, Lee ST, Orr KB: The function of T cells carrying receptors for complexes of Ig and antigen. *Immunol Commun* **5**:501, 1976.

44. Hay JB, Murphy MJ, Morris B, Bessis MC: Quantitative studies on the proliferation and differentiation of antibody-forming cells in lymph. *Am J Pathol* **66**:1, 1972.

45. Stein H, Bonk A, Tolksdorf G, Lennet K, Rodt H, Gerdes J: Immunohistologic analysis of the organization of normal lymphoid tissue and non-Hodgkin lymphomas. *J Histochem Cytochem* **28**:746, 1980.

46. Traugott U, Reichert EL, Raine CS: Monoclonal anti-T cell antibodies are applicable in the study of inflammatory infiltrates in the central nervous system. *J Neuroimmunol* **3**:365, 1982.

47. Goldstein ME, Sternberger NH, Sternberger LA: Developmental expression of neurotypy revealed by immunocytochemistry with monoclonal antibodies. *J Neuroimmunol* **3**:203, 1982.

48. Trojanowski JA, Lee VM-6: Antineurofilament monoclonal antibodies: Reagents for evaluation of human neoplasms. *Acta Neuropath* **59**:155, 198.

49. Taylor CR: The nature of Reed-Sternberg cells and other malignant "reticulum" cells. *Lancet*, Oct. 5, 1974, p. 802.

50. Taylor CR: An immunological study of follicular lymphoma, reticulum cell sarcoma and Hodgkin's disease. *Eur J Cancer* **12**:61, 1976.

51. Brandtzaeg P, Rognum TO: Evaluation of tissue preparation methods and paired immunofluorescence staining for immunocytochemistry of lymphomas. *Histochem J* **15**:655, 1983.

52. Weiss L: *The cells and tissue of the immune system. Structure, Function, Interactions.* Englewood Cliffs, NJ, Prentice-Hall, 1972.

53. Stass SA, Dean L, Peiper SC, Bollum FJ: Determination of terminal deoxynucleotidyl transferase on bone marrow smears by immunoperoxidase. *Am J Clin Path* **77**:174, 1982.

54. Neiman RS: Erythroblastic transformation in myeloproliferative disorders. Confirmation by an immunohistologic technique. *Cancer* **46**:1636, 1980.

55. Vernon SE, Morgan TW: Immunoglobulin light chain staining of lymph node biopsies: An interlaboratory comparison. *Ann Clin Lab Sci* **11**:545, 1981.

56. Brandtzaeg P: Studies on J chains and binding sites for secretory components of circulating human B cells. II. The cytoplasm. *Clin Exp Immunol* **25**:59, 1976.

57. Isaacson P: Immunocytochemical demonstration of J chains: a marker of B cell malignancy. *J Clin Path* **32**:802, 1979.

58. Brandtzaeg P: Prolonged incubation time in immunohistology: Effects of fluorescence staining of immunoglobulins and epithelial components in ethanol and formaldehyde-fixed paraffin-embedded tissue. *J Histochem Cytochem* **11**:1302, 1981.

59. Brandtzaeg P, Gjeruldsen ST, Korsrud F, Baklien K, Ek J: The human secretory immune system shows striking heterogeneity with regard to involvement of J chain positive IgD immunocytes. *J Immunol* **122**:503, 1979.

60. Brandtzaeg P: Presence of J chain in human immunocytes containing various immunoglobulin classes. *Nature* **252**:418, 1972.

61. Ree NJ, Hsu S-M: Lectin histochemistry of malignant tumors. I. Peanut agglutinin receptors in follicular lymphoma and follicular hyperplasia. An immunohistochemical study. *Cancer* **51**:1631, 1983.

62. Ree NJ: Lectin histochemistry of malignant tumors. II. Concanavalin A: A new histochemical marker for macrophage-histiocytes in follicular lymphoma. *Cancer* **51:**1639, 1983.

63. Vernon SE: Cytodiagnosis of "signet ring"-cell lymphoma. *Acta Cytol* **25:**291, 1981.

64. Saraga P, Hurlimann J, Ozello L: Lymphomas and pseudolymphomas of the alimentary tract. An immunohistologic study with clinicopathologic correlations. *Hum Path* **12:**713, 1981.

65. Aufdemorte TB, Humphrey DM: Immunperoxidase characterization of a malignant plasma cell tumor involving the mandible. *J Oral Macillofacial Surg* **40:**197 1982 (Am Assn Oral Maxillofacial Surgeons).

66. Barcos M, Minowada J, Minato K, Pollard L, Cancino M, Han T, Henderson E, Ozer H: Non-Hodgkin's lymphoma phenotypes: Problems in the use of heterologous and monoclonal antibodies. *Leukemia Res* **7:**523, 1983.

67. Mason Dy, Taylor CR: The distribution of muramidase in human tissues. *J Clin Pathol* **28:**124, 1975.

68. Sternberger LA, Osserman EF, Seligman AM: Lysozyme and fibrinogen in normal and leukemic blood cells: A quantitative electron-immunocytochemical study. *Johns Hopkins Med J* **126:**188, 1970.

69. Blennerhassett JB, Papamitriou JM: Muramidase content of cells in human granulomatous reaction. *Pathology* **13:**101, 1981.

70. Dura WT, Mioduszewska O, Porwit-Ksiatek A: Cytoplasmic immunoglobulin in giant lymph node hypoerplasia (Castleman's tumor). *Virchows Arch Cell Path* **38:**239, 1981.

71. Palutke M, Schnitzer B, Mirchandani I, Tabuczka PM, Franklin R, Eisenberg L, So K, Carillo C: Increased number of lymphocytes with single class surface immunoglobulins in reactive hyperplasia of lymphoid tissue. *Am J Clin Path* **78:**316, 1982.

72. Banerjee D, Ahmad D: Malignant lymphoma complicating lymphocytic interstitial pneumonia. A monoclonal B cell neoplasm arising in a polyclonal lymphoproliferative disorders. *Hum Path* **13:**780, 1982.

73. Mason DY, Taylor CR: Staining of the A antigen on human erythrocytes. *J Clin Pathol* **28:**594, 1975.

74. Bross KJ, Pangalis GA, Staatz CG, Blume KG: Demonstration of cell surface antigens and their antibodies by the peroxidase-antiperoxidase method. *Transplantation* **25:**6, 1978.

Chapter Eight

Neurocytochemistry—
Neuropathology

The complexity of facilitating and inhibiting signal transfer among multitudes of intercellular contacts is characteristic of the central nervous system. The fundamental principles of the physiology of neurons are similar to those of other cells. In all organs, cells communicate with each other, but in the brain the communication has reached a diversity and fine tuning that has eluded, thus far, an understanding in biochemical terms. The brain must possess more than a large amount of information that determines whether a neuron does or does not stimulate an adjacent neuron. Each neuron, through its wide arborization, engages in a multitude of synaptic and synaptoid contacts with a large number of other neurons. It is unlikely that all these contacts are stimulated simultaneously. Hence, there must exist factors that gate stimulating or stimulus-suppressing substances onto selected contacts to the exclusion of other contacts.

Substances that are released at the synapse and mediate depolarization at the postsynaptic membrane by interaction with specific receptors are *neurotransmitters*. In general, neurotransmitters are carried in small, clear vesicles and released upon stimulation from nerve terminals. There exist only a limited number of substances which fall within the criteria of this definition of neurotransmitters. They include noradrenalin, dopamine, serotonin (5-hydroxytryptamine), taurine, carnosine, acetylcholine, glutamate, and γ-aminobutyrate. These substances are widely distributed and shared by many neurons of different functions. They are specific to the nervous system and to paraneurons. They can, therefore, be considered specific mediators for nervous tissue.

To explain the fundamental differences among individual neurons, we must look for other substances that may monitor the release of neurotransmitters. Most nerves possess, besides small clear vesicles, large dense core vesicles. These vesicles are densely packed with proteinaceous substances and are found more extensively in some neurons than in others. In hypothalamic neurons, they are present in such abundance that by mere tinctorial staining they have permitted the Scharrers (1) to make analogies between neurons and endocrine cells, thus creating the basis of the science of neurosecretion. Neurosecretory principles are peptides that are shared by the brain and peripheral cells. They are a fundamental biologic principle for intercellular communication that is not restricted to synaptic transmission onto excitable membranes. Despite their broad distribution in the nervous system and in other organs, the existence of a fairly large number of peptides, and the coexistence of several peptides in the same neuron, increases the functional variability of one neuron from another beyond that which would have been possible were there only neurotransmitters.

The coexistence of such *regulatory peptides* (neuropeptides, bioactive peptides) with neurotransmitters (page 397) raises the question whether both kinds of substances act as neurotransmitters or whether regulatory peptides modulate the action of neurotransmitters. This is not merely an academic question about definitions, for if regulatory peptides were indeed modulators of transmission, rather than transmitters themselves, they may, at least in part, answer the question, which chemical mediation tells one neuron to act while at the same time another neuron rests.

There exist a large number of neurons in which, so far, only regulatory peptides but no specific neurotransmitter has been identified. These neurons may not be limited to those of the hypothalamo-pituitary tract, which end on capillaries and secrete their products into the general circulation (posterior pituitary) or into a "semiprivate" circulation (2) (anterior pituitary). By their ending on capillaries, rather than postsynaptic specializations, the need of neurotransmitters within the hypothalamo-pituitary tract has been dispensed with.

Intrinsic neurons in the gut (myenteric plexus) may act as interneurons that "transduce" signals from extrinsic autonomic nerves and may also play an autonomic role of their own. While most of these neurons are cholinergic or noradrenergic, some contain substance P, vasoactive intestinal peptides, leuenkephalin, or somatostatin. Laender et al. (3) have shown that vasoactive intestinal peptide reduces and substance P raises the resting tension of taeniae coli, compatable with the role of the former as inhibitor and of the latter as excitatory *neurotransmitter,* and that the role of vasoactive intestinal peptide and substance P neurons is that of motoneurons. However, the response *to* electrical stimulation was also affected by these peptides, compatible with a *neuromodulatory* role. Somatostatin had no direct effect, thus suggesting that somatostatin neurons act as interneurons. Enkephalin exerted a weak contractile effect on taeniae, suggesting that it modulates the release of transmitters from other fibers.

The effects of vasoactive intestinal peptide and substance P on resting taeniae were not affected by neurotransmitter inhibition such as atropine + guanethidine, atropine + propranolol + phenoxybenzamine, or by tetrodoxin, which suggests that these peptides act directly on the muscle in a manner analogous to a neurotransmitter rather than a neuromodulator.

Despite the direct action of neuropeptides on effector organs, when released from the nervous system into circulation or onto smooth muscle by nerve fibers which are, apparently, devoid of other neurotransmitters, neuropeptides that end in synaptic junctions upon other neurons have not been demonstrated to act under conditions in which neurotransmitter function is pharmacologically suppressed. It is likely, therefore, that in most circumstances, regulatory peptides act as modulators of neurotransmitter function, either within the same neuron, or trans-synaptically on adjacent neurons.

We will see (page 397) that given regulatory peptides are coexpressed with other peptides in the same neuron, and that a given regulatory peptide may not always be coexpressed with the same other peptide. Consequently, there exists considerable permutational variability in the expression of regulatory peptides, which gives neurons a high degree of individuality. The mechanisms of assembly and expression of this variability are discussed in Chapter Nine.

Despite the variability that neurons receive from their complement of bioactive peptides, these substances are not characteristic of the nervous system alone, but are shared with the peripheral endocrine system (2). There must exist substances which are characteristic of the nervous system, just as such substances as immunoglobulins or interleukin are characteristic of the immune system. Neuron-specific substances include neuronal enolase, olfactory protein, neuron-spe-

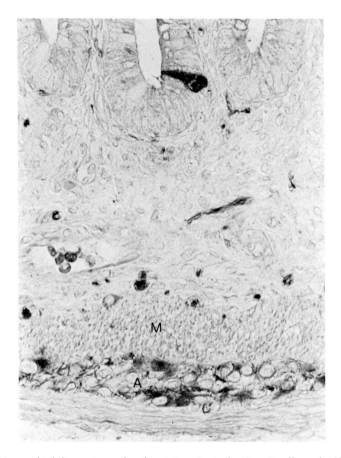

Figure 8-1. Human fetal ileum, 5 months of gestation. Bouin fixation. Paraffin embeddment. Staining with antiserum to brain tubulin. PAP method. Nerve cells in Auerbach's (A) and Meissner's (M) plexus, nerve fibers, and an enteroendocrine cell (upper part) are revealed. Adjacent sections have shown that the brain tubulin-stained enteroendocrine cells are distinct from those containing secretin, cholocystokinin, glycentin, neurotensin, or somatostatin. [From Iwanaga et al. (4).]

cific tubulin, and neurofilaments. Glia-specific substances include glial fibrillary acidic protein, myelin basic protein, myelin-associated glycoprotein, P2 protein, and galactocerebroside. Brain-specific tubulin has been shown by Iwanaga et al. (4) to possess certain parallelism to the neurosecretory principles (regulatory peptides) first discovered by the Scharrers (1): antibodies to brain-specific tubulin not only react with the submucosal plexus of Meissner and the myenteric plexus of Auerbach, but also with enteroendocrine cells of the human ileum, thus strengthening the concept that these endocrine cells are paraneurons despite their non-neuroectodermal origin (Fig. 8-1). A similar situation prevails for neuronal enolase (page 333).

Neurofilaments, at least many epitopes of the 200- and 150-kDa subunits, are, however, strictly specific to the nervous system. Both neuronal tubulin and neurofilaments are heterogeneous substances, the latter subject to immunocytochemically detectable post-translational processing. It is possible that these substances subserve a characteristic function of nerve cells, and that their post-translational changes may determine different functional states within individual segments of a neuronal projection, thus gating the activity of a given neuromodulator to program regions within a single neuron as a result of a given command. Approaches to studying this form of biochemical variability by immunocytochemical means are discussed in Chapter Ten.

In the present chapter, we will deal with classical neurotransmitters, with neuron-specific substances that have not, so far, revealed heterogeneity, and with glia-specific substances in normal and pathologic tissue.

ANTIBODIES TO NEUROTRANSMITTERS AND THEIR BIOSYNTHETIC ENZYMES

From an immunocytochemical point of view, there are two classes of neurotransmitters: those that can be insolubilized by common fixatives and those that cannot. Because of their solubility, neurotransmitters cannot be retained in unfixed, frozen sections. In formaldehyde-fixed sections, indole-derived neurotransmitters, such as 5-hydroxytryptamine (5-HT, serotonin) or catecholamine-derived transmitters (such as noradrenaline and dopamine) are cross-linked to tissue protein because an aromatic hydroxyl group of the neurotransmitter may be in close proximity to a protein amino group, thus fulfilling steric requirements for cross-linking by a small group, such as formaldehyde. The aldehyde apparently forms a Schiff base (R_1—N^+=CHR_2) with the protein, which in turn can react with the aromatic hydroxyl group of the neurotransmitter. The reaction modifies the neurotransmitter, but if an antibody is formed against the neurotransmitter hapten conjugated to protein amine by formaldehyde, the antibody may cross-react with the neurotransmitter altered in similar fashion by conjugation to surrounding protein in tissue fixed in formaldehyde. Using these principles, antibodies to serotonin and to noradrenalin were developed by Steinbusch et al. (5,6).

Antibodies to insolubilized glutamate and γ-aminobutyrate were produced by Storm-Mathison et al. (7) following conjugation of the neurotransmitters to bovine serum albumin with glutaraldehyde. These antibodies have been used immunocytochemically in tissue fixed with glutaraldehyde.

Certain transmitters, like acetylcholine, cannot be readily immobilized by fixation. Their immunocytochemical detection is indirect via antibodies to their biosynthetic enzymes, preferably rate-limiting biosynthetic enzymes. Antibodies to choline acetyl transferase localize sites of acetylcholine, antityrosine hydroxylase, those of dopamine, and, to a lesser extent, noradrenalin, and antidopamine β-hydroxylase those of noradrenalin.

The choice of carrier to confer antigenicity to a neurotransmitter hapten (page 16) by aldehyde conjugation is of some importance and will differ whether antisera or monoclonal antibodies are desired. Neurotransmitters are small molecules and the specificity of antibodies used immunocytochemically will reside only in the small portion of the idiotypic region that reacts with the transmitter itself, rather than with an epitope of the size of about seven amino acids (page 229). The antibodies are likely to react with high affinity with sites in antigen consisting of the hapten plus adjacent regions of the carrier. From this viewpoint, it would be most desirable to immunize with the same carrier-hapten complex as that which is formed by fixation of tissues. However, we do not know with which protein or group of proteins a given neurotransmitter reacts upon aldehyde fixation. Furthermore, in the production of antisera, carriers that are immunologically related to tissue proteins should be avoided, because carrier-specific antibodies unreactive with the hapten, will give false localization. Solid-phase absorption of antisera with carrier may be necessary, but liquid-phase absorption yields soluble antigen-antibody complexes that may give nonspecific localization, especially in electron microscopic immunocytochemistry. For this reason, carriers that are foreign to proteins of the tissues to be stained, such as hemocyanin or potato acid phosphatase, are preferred over serum albumin, which will cross-react with albumins of different species (8). When a foreign carrier is used, the immunocytochemical reaction will depend only on the specificity of the neurotransmitter and the adjacent formaldehyde carbon or glutaraldehyde chain, as the case may be. Since these are small groups, affinity may be low and specificity may be impaired. Fortunately, catechols and imidazoles are highly antigenic groups that contribute more to affinity than other groups of similar size. Nevertheless, a larger reactive group would probably be preferable. In the case of γ-aminobutyrate in which conjugation has been carried out via glutaraldehyde, affinity may have been aided by the four carbon glutaraldehyde spacer between the hapten and the carrier.

Monoclonal antibodies could provide an opportunity for producing high-affinity, and thus, high-specificity antitransmitter antibodies. Here it is possible to use, as immunizing antigen, conjugates of the neurotransmitter with the tissue to be studied. Antibody-producing clones will have to be selected in an ELISA system by reaction with a non-cross-reactive carrier, such as hemocyanin, conjugated to the neurotransmitter. To prevent distortion of the antigen on ELISA plates, we prefer, in our laboratory, to prepare plates by coating with hemocyanin, followed by antiserum to hemocyanin and hemocyanin conjugates.

SEROTONIN

Serotonin (5-hydroxytryptamine) is an excitatory neurotransmitter, particularly in the neostriatum. Its release from the caudate nucleus depends on impulses from the raphé-striatal pathway and is increased by depolarizing dorsal raphé neurons with glutamic acid (9).

A monoclonal antibody to serotonin prepared by Milstein et al. (10) seems to react by immunofluorescence specifically with serotonin neurons. It is nonreactive with dopamine neurons in vivo. In vitro, however, the antibody did cross-react with dopamine. For the in vitro test, sheep-red cells were coated with the formaldehyde conjugate of serotonin with bovine serum ablumin. Reactions were evaluated by hemoagglutination with the monoclonal antibody or by radioactivity incorporation into the red cells upon use of monoclonal antibody labeled by incorporation of ^{3}H-lysine in hybridoma cultures (page 260). Cross-reactive haptens were evaluated by inhibition of agglutination or radioactivity incorporation. As expected, the serotonin-albmin conjugate was the best inhibitor. Formaldehyde-treated serotonin required about 10 times higher concentrations for inhibition. Interestingly, however, formaldehyde-treated dopamine inhibited equally well as formaldehyde-treated serotonin, and compounds related biosynthetically to serotonin, such as tryptamine and 5-methoxytryptamine, were also good inhibitors.

Serotonin itself (not treated with formaldehyde) also inhibited, but relatively poorly. However, untreated dopamine and tryptamine, and even 5-methoxytryptamine, inhibited better than untreated serotonin.

The results illustrate (10) the dramatic change in antigenic conformation of these compounds upon aldehyde fixation. The product of interaction of formaldehyde with serotonin amine is a Schiff base which can further react by internal ring closure (Figs. 8-2, 8-3). (This aldehyde reaction is additional to that described on page 308.) The aldehyde derivatives are quite different from the untreated neurotransmitters, thus explaining their better reactivity with the antibodies. The cross-reactivity of the antibodies to neurotransmitter-protein conjugates with untreated dopamine, tryptamine, or methoxytryptamine, can be explained by the common side chain, and the cross-reactivity with the treated compounds by formation of rings identical to those in the immunizing antigen.

Once ring closure has been achieved, the compounds are no longer capable of conjugating onto protein via aldehyde by reaction of their side chains. This reaction must be achieved via other groups of the molecule (page 308). It was felt by Milstein et al. (10) that the tryptophan ring of serotonin is more reactive to aldehyde than the catecholamine ring of dopamine, and that, indeed, only tryptophan derivatives have been fixed in tissue while catecholamine derivatives have not.

The formaldehyde condensation products of these neurotransmitters fulfill all the requirements for fluorescence (page 36). This fluorescence forms the basis of the direct histofluorescence detection of the transmitters without immunocytochemistry (11). Brusco et al. (12) have shown that immunocytochemistry with antiserotonin reveals the same general distribution as histofluorescence, suggesting that the same fluorescent condensation product is detected by both methods. In histofluorescence, catecholamine and indole neurotransmitters are distinguished by their different absorption and emission spectra. However, distinction was sometimes difficult because of the lesser intensity of the catecholamine fluorescence and the rapid photodecomposition of the fluorophore (13).

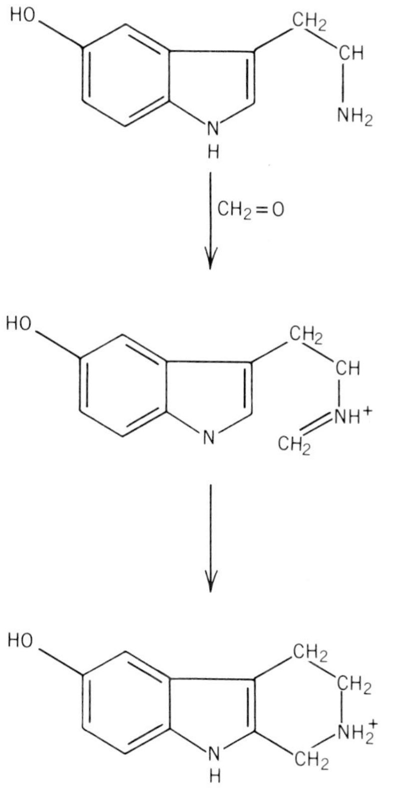

Figure 8-2. Possible initial reaction of serotonin with formaldehyde.

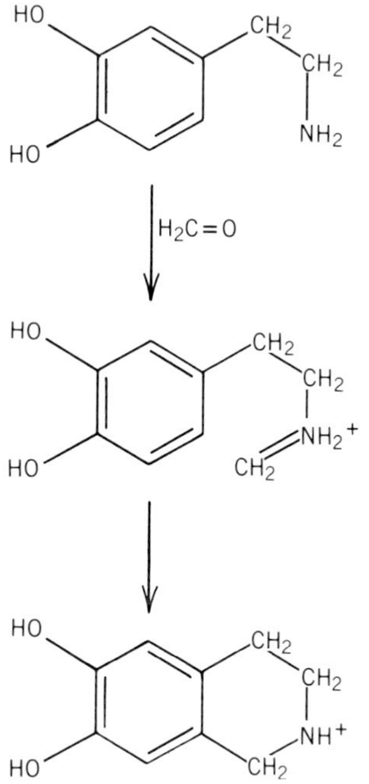

Figure 8-3. Possible initial reaction of dopamine with formaldehyde.

Steinbusch et al. (5,6) and Wallace et al. (14) found the main source of serotonin in cells in the raphé nuclei in the mesencephalon, pons, and medulla oblongata (Fig. 8-4, 8-5). Additional cell bodies were described by Takeuchi et al. (15) in a number of other locations including the periaqueductal gray and the reticular formation of the pons. Projections had a wide distribution. The most important projections were to the striatum, but other fibers reached the spinal cord, locus ceruleus, substantia nigra, hypothalamus, hippocampus, and cerebral cortex.

Pasik and Pasik (16) have shown by electron microscopic immunocytochemistry that relatively rare serotonergic axons in the striatum form visualizable synapses, in agreement with previous uptake studies of radioactive serotonin. However, occasional serial electron microscopic sections did reveal strongly asymmetric synapses on small dendritic spines (Fig. 8-6). This type of junction has been associated with excitatory synapses. The rarity of identifiable synapses suggests that serotonin may be released by a second, nonsynaptic mechanism. Such release may be more prolonged and may be responsible for the prolonged inhibition observed in striatal neurons after initial excitation. This action of serotonin may be more that of a neuromodulator than a neurotransmitter, and may be responsible for smoothing out impulses that pass through the

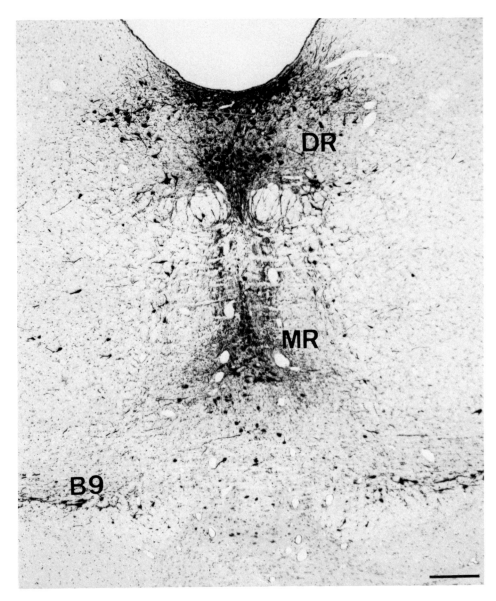

Figure 8-4. Serotonin in the dorsal (DR) and medial (MR) raphé nucleus and the B9 cell group. PAP method. Bar is 300 μm. [From Wallace et al. (14).]

striatum. Indeed, two receptors, possibly corresponding to the excitatory and neuromodulatory action of serotonin, have been described in the striatum (17).

Serotonin can also be localized immunocytochemically with antibodies to tryptophan hydroxylase. Wallace et al. (14) prefer the direct localization with antiserotonin, since antibodies to the biosynthetic enzyme do not permit evaluation of changes in regional distribution of serotonin following physiologic and pharmacologic manipulations.

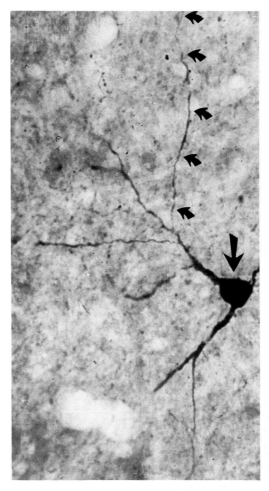

Figure 8-5. A serotonergic neuron from the lateral neuronal group of the dorsal raphé. Vibratome section. Soma (large arrow) with 3 emerging dendrites. A thin axon (small arrow) could be followed over a long distance. PAP method. ×600. [From Brusco et al. (12).]

TAURINE

Taurine is thought to be an inhibitory neurotransmitter in the cerebellum. L-cysteine sulfinic acid decarboxylase participates in taurine synthesis and antibodies to the enzyme are, therefore, suitable for immunocytochemical detection of taurine. Chan-Palay et al. (18) found taurinergic neurons organized in sagittal microsomes (Fig. 8-7), similar to the arrangement of motilin and γ-aminobutyric acid. The finding corroborates the orthogonal, anatomic, and physiologic arrangement of the cerebellar cortex in the sagittal plane. The four to five Purkinje cells that lie in the true midline of the vermal cerebellar cortex were found to contain coexisting (page 397) taurine, motilin, and γ-aminobutyric acid.

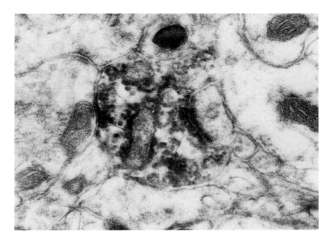

Figure 8-6. A serotonergic bouton from the monkey neostriatum forming an asymmetric synapse with a small spine. PAP pre-embedding technique. Bar is 500 nm. [Reproduced with permission from Pasik T, Pasik P: Serotonergic afferents in the monkey neostriatum *Acta Biol Acad Sci Hung* **33**:277, 1982. (16)]

In this work (18), the second antibody was peroxidase-conjugated, and any unlabeled second antibody contaminating the labeled second antibody preparation (page 59) was detected by subsequent application of PAP.

GAMMA-AMINOBUTYRIC AND GLUTAMIC ACIDS

Antisera to these neurotransmitters were produced by Storm-Mathison et al. (7) by conjugation with bovine serum albumin via glutaraldehyde. It was necessary to absorb the antisera with insolubilized bovine serum albumin and amino acids

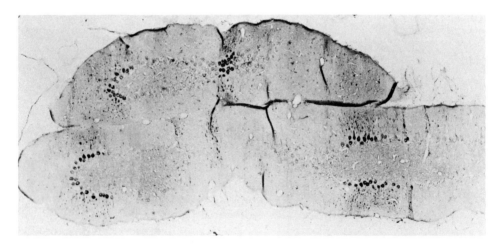

Figure 8-7. Coronal section through lobule IV of the rabbit cerebellar vermis. A midsaggital band of taurinergic neurons is flanked on either side by an unstained interband and then by a second set of wider bands. Peroxidase-conjugated antibody method. ×55. [From Chan-Palay et al. (18).]

before they became specific. Reactivity was tested by sepharose beads bearing amino acids conjugated to rat cerebral extract via glutaraldehyde and attached to pre-gelatinized microtitre plates (Fig. 8-8). The antibodies were able to differentiate immunocytochemically glutamic and γ-aminobutyric acid-bearing sites in the hippocampus.

γ-Aminobutyric acid is an inhibitory neurotransmitter. Glutamic acid decarboxylase is the biosynthetic enzyme for its formation and immunocytochemistry for the enzyme can be used for localization of γ-aminobutyric acid. Even though monoclonal antibodies have been used for the localization of γ-aminobutyric acid, there is a possibility that the enzyme itself is not specific for glutamic acid but may also react as a cysteine sulfonate decarboxylase and thus detect immunocytochemically taurine as well as γ-aminobutyric acid. These conclusions were arrived by Oertel et al. (19) who produced antisera with glutamic acid decarboxylase that co-precipitated with cysteine sulfonate decarboxylase. A radiolabeled irreversibly reacting substrate for detection of γ-amino decarboxylase was synthesized and γ-aminobutyric acid-specific antibodies identified in electrophoresis precipitin lines. The identified precipitates were used for production of a second set of antibodies, presumably specific for the enzyme. However, the antisera still precipitated γ-aminobutyric acid decarboxylase as well as cysteine sulfonate immunoreactivity.

γ-Aminobutyric acid is considered a major visual transmitter, and indeed, has been localized by Brandon et al. (20) to amacrine cell bodies and their laminated processes in the plexiform layer. Cultures from the anterior and retrochiasmic hypothalamus, as well from the midbrain, were shown by Reisert et al. (21) to rapidly take up tritiated γ-aminobutyric acid in low concentrations in a sodium-dependent manner. The assumption that the uptake identified functionally γ-aminobutyrerigic neurons was verified by the finding that apart from few excep-

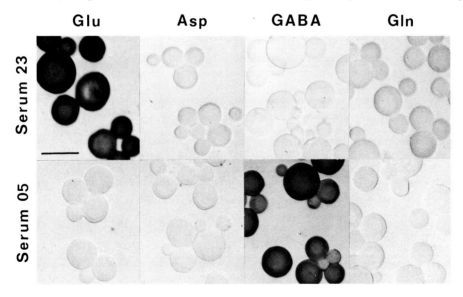

Figure 8-8. Reaction of antiglutamate (serum 23) and anti-γ-aminobutyrate (serum 05) with sepharose beads bearing amino acids conjugated to cortical extract. PAP method. [Reprinted by permission from *Nature* **301**:517, Copyright 1983 Macmillan Journals Limited (7).]

tions, autoradiographic labeling coincided with immunocytochemistry for γ-aminoglutamic acids decarboxylase.

The fate of released neurotransmitters is three-fold. Transmitters interact with receptors, part of the excess of transmitter is degraded, and part is taken up again by the axon terminals. Uptake distinguishes neurotransmitters from regulatory peptides. Monoamine oxidase is the degrading enzyme for catecholamines, acetyl cholinesterase for acetyl choline, and γ-aminobutyric acid transaminase for γ-aminobutyric acid. These enzymes are not absolutely specific for their transmitters. Thus, acetyl cholinesterase has proven not to be an accurate indication for cholinergic synapses. Chan-Palay et al. (22) have found that in the cerebellum glutamic acid transaminase activity did localize known γ-aminobutyrerigic neurons such as Golgi, basket, stellate, and Purkinje cells. In addition, the enzyme was found on postsynaptic membranes belonging to non-γ-aminobutyrerigic neurons, as well as in glial cells and their processes. γ-Aminobutyric acid transaminase activity was greater by the PAP method than by immunofluorescence and in formaldehyde-fixed than in unfixed frozen tissues.

CATECHOLAMINES

Tyrosine hydroxylase is a biosynthetic enzyme for dopamine, noradrenalin, and adrenalin, and tyrosine hydroxylase immunocytochemistry can, therefore, be used to reveal catecholaminergic transmitters. Pearson et al. have provided atlases for the development of catecholamine pathways in human fetuses (23) and neurologically normal adults (24). In the human, localization differs from that in the rat by striking increases in tyrosine hydroxylase-containing perikarya in upper pontine and mesencephalic regions. Catecholamine neurons are prominent in the midline of the ventral tegmentum and the upper parts of the central tegmental tracts. More catecholaminergic neurons are within and close to the superior cerebellar peduncles than in other species. As in other species, the locus ceruleus and related structures are a major condensation of catecholaminergic neurons. The entire cytoplasm of catecholaminergic neurons, with the exception of dendritic spines, is stained.

In the substantia nigra, different patterns of localization of tyrosine hydroxylase and substance P (Figs. 8-9, 8-10) suggest a functional and anatomic subdivision of this area.

The provision of an atlas for a neurotransmitter, as accomplished by Pearson et al. (24), is important because immunocytochemistry has provided information that biochemistry cannot. Whereas 50% of enzymatic activity of tyrosine hydroxylase is lost within 5 hours after death, immunoreactive tyrosine hydroxylase may persist for a prolonged postmortem interval in refrigerated specimens (25). Furthermore, low levels of biochemical activity in punched brain samples do not necessarily exclude the presence of high levels in immunocytochemically defined clusters of neurons.

Dopamine-β-hydroxylase is a biosynthetic enzyme specific for noradrenalin. Grzanna et al. (26) employed thick Vibratome sections to study the noradrenergic innervation of the rat neocortex with antidopamine hydroxylase. The thick sections facilitated tracing of nerve fibers over considerable distances by changing focal depth and superimposing images. Noradrenergic fibers had a wide distribution in the cingulate, somatosensory, motor, and visual cortex. In each of the six cortical layers, the fibers had a distinct distribution. The finding of long, tangential fibers in layers I and VI provided an anatomic correlate to the influence of noradrenergic axons on adjacent cortical columns over long distances in the coronal plane. In layers IV and VI, many noradrenergic axons made contact with cell bodies and proximal dendrites (Fig. 8-11).

Glazer and Joh (27) used antidopamine β-hydroxylase to trace noradrenergic fibers in the spinal cord from the lateral funiculus to the intermediolateral nucleus. Staining in the lower thoracic region was abolished by midthoracic cord transection. Reactive axonal varicosities were visualized predominantly in association with dendrites, and dopamine hydroxylase was localized in synaptic vesicles within axodendritic varicosities.

ACETYLCHOLINE

Choline acetyltransferase (CAT) is the biosynthetic enzyme for acetylcholine. We have seen (page 365) that not until the advent of monoclonal antibodies was it possible to be sure of the specificity of CAT immunocytochemistry and, hence, of the reliability of detection of cholinergic pathways. The work of Houser et al. (28) delineated many forms of cholinergic neurons and widespread distribution of their projections. CAT was present in spinal and cranial motor neurons (Figs. 8-12, 13), their dendrites and axons, and on motor end plates. In the thoracic cord, preganglionic sympathetic neurons were cholinergic. Cholinergic terminals were widely distributed in the ventral horn, synapsing on CAT-positive or negative neurons. CAT neurons were found in large amounts in the medial septal nuclei and in the nucleus of the diagonal band. CAT-containing axonal varicosities were seen in the hippocampus and the dentate gyrus. Cholinergic somata were found in the medial habenula and terminals in the interpedunculate nucleus (a pathway shared with many regulatory peptides, page 381). A major accumulation of cholinergic somata was in the nucleus basalis of Meynert with terminals in the neostriatum and cortex (see also page 461).

NEUROTRANSMITTER COLOCALIZATION

Sympathetic neurons are catecholaminergic as evidenced by staining with antityrosine hydroxylase. However, in vitro, sympathetic neurons can acquire cholinergic properties. Higgins et al. (29) have shown that at least 90% of neurons that can be identified electrophysiologically as cholinergic by inhibition of synaptic interaction with hexamethonium, are stained immunocytochemically with antityrosine hydroxylase. Therefore, the same neuron has reverted, in culture, to a dual cholinergic and adrenergic nature.

Immunocytochemistry has shown that single nuclei can be divided into subregions by virtue of the neurotransmitters they express. However, it is not possible, in general, to define certain areas within nuclei by a given neurotransmitter, because of considerable overlap of the maps for each individual transmitter. The

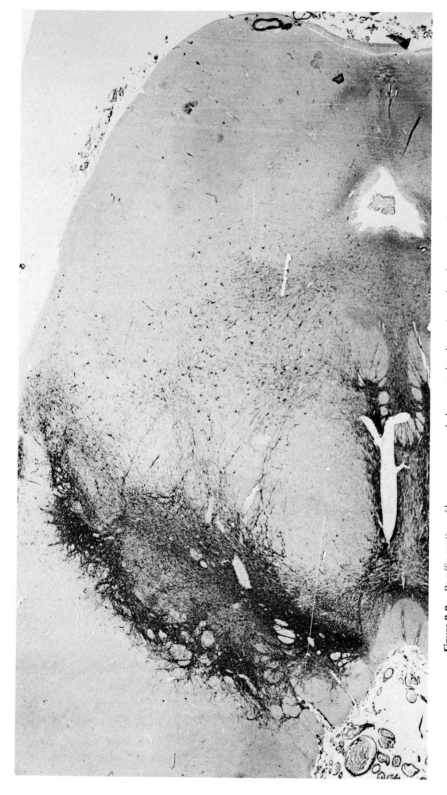

Figure 8-9. Paraffin section of human mesencephalon ventral to the periaqueductal gray reveals tyrosine hydroxylase in the substantia nigra. PAP method. [Reprinted with permission from *Neuroscience* **8:**3, J. Pearson, M. Goldstein, K. Markey, L. Brandeis, Human Brain Stem Catecholamine neuronal anatomy as indicated by immunocytochemistry with antibodies to tyrosine hydroxylase, Copyright 1983, Pergamon Press, Ltd. (24).]

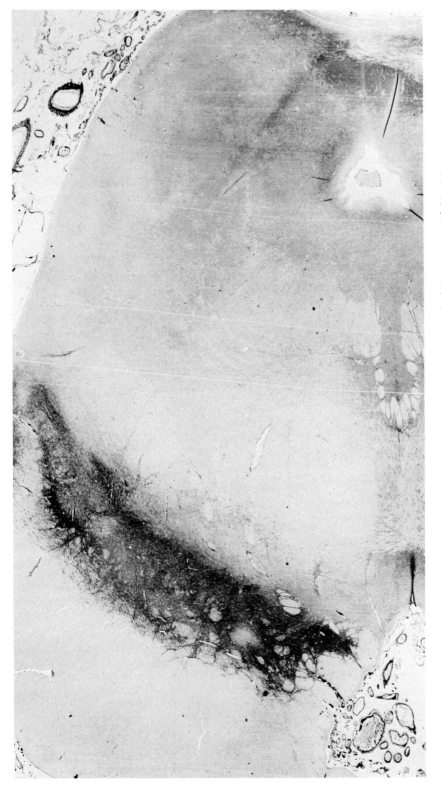

Figure 8-10. Substance P in a section adjacent to that of Fig. 8-9. PAP method. Comparison with Fig. 8-9 is assisted by identifying unstained axons of the oculomotor nerve which form a characteristic cluster. Tyrosine hydroxylase-reactive neurons extend ventrally and dorsally to the cluster. Substance P is confined to the substantia nigra ventral to it. [Reprinted with permission from *Neuroscience* **8**:3, J. Pearson, M. Goldstein, K. Markey, L. Brandeis, Human Brain Stem Catecholamine neuronal anatomy as indicated by immunocytochemistry with antibodies to tyrosine hydroxylase, Copyright 1983, Pergamon Press, Ltd. (24).]

complexity is compounded by the coexistence of one or more regulatory peptides either with a neurotransmitter in the same neuron, or in the same nucleus
but in adjacent neurons. Because of the complexity of maps obtainable, we will
restrict our discussion here to only one area, the corpus striatum, in which
Graybiel (30) has found exceptionally interesting compartmental organization.
We will limit, at this time, our discussion to neurotransmitters, but will return to

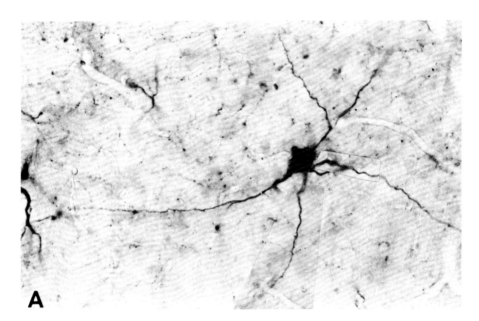

Figure 8-11. The Golgi method is a nonspecific silver impregnation which stains randomly selected
neurons in their entirety by coating the surfaces of somata and all their projections. Since only 1% to 2%
of cells are stained, their three-dimensional structure is magnificantly demarcated against a clear background. However, the method is entirely nonspecific. It is not known which factors determine whether a
neuron will accept the stain or not. Grzanna et al. (26) have developed a method for obtaining Golgi-like
pictures on immunospecific staining with the PAP technique. In their procedure, animals are perfused
with 2% paraformaldehyde and 0.1% glutaraldehyde. Vibratome sections 100 μm thick are treated with
first antiserum (antidopamine-β-hydroxylase, 1 : 1000, illustrated) for 24 hours in the presence of 0.4%
Triton X-100. Homologously or heterologously reacting second antiserum (page 180) and PAP, diluted
1 : 50, are applied in solutions containing 0.025% Triton X-100. Staining occurs throughout the 100-μm-
thick section. Changing the focal depth in the same field of observation provides a three-dimensional
Golgi-like picture, which is, however, immunospecific in that it includes neurons possessing specific
transmitter, while excluding neurons carrying other transmitters. In the photomontage (A) ($\times$140), a
dopamine-β-hydroxylase-containing neuron ventromedial to the nucleus locus ceruleus reveals long,
rectilinear dendrites that radiate in all directions. Although dendrites have been followed for 300 μm from
the soma, no dendritic spines have been seen, in contrast to Golgi silver impregnation of the same
neurons, which does reveal such spines. Those regions on the surface of neurons most highly specialized
for receiving afferents contain no transmitter-synthesizing enzymes. (B) A dopamine-β-hydroxylase-con-
taining fiber has been followed through the entire width of the collage constructed from coronal sections
of the motor cortex. While many long fibers have been seen traveling in all directions, the cortical
noradrenergic innervation seems to be characterized by predominantly tangential, antero-posterior fibers
originating in the locus ceruleus. Although widespread, dopamine-β-hydroxylase-containing neurons in
the cerebral, and for that matter, in the cerebellar cortex too, are not diffuse, but obey a highly ordered
geometric pattern. They do not innervate cerebral blood vessels. These figures illustrate how with a single
method the dendritic arborization of noradrenergic neurons and their teledendria can be studied. [From
Grzanna et al. (26).]

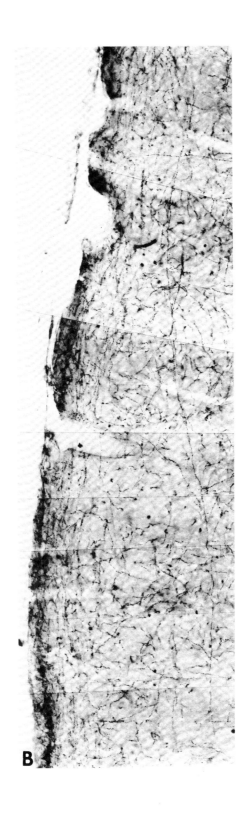

B

321

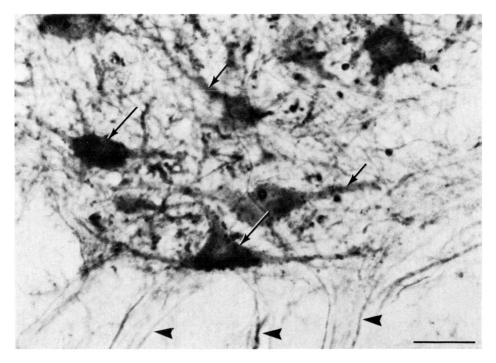

Figure 8-12. Rat spinal cord. 40-μm-thick Vibratome section. Choline acetyl transferase is in the cell bodies and dendrites (arrows) of motoneurons. Choline acetyl transferase axons (arrowheads) course toward the ventral root. Monoclonal anticholine acetyl transferase. PAP method. Bar is 40 μm. [From Hauser et al. (28).]

the organization of the striatum in the chapter on regulatory peptides (page 397).

In the developing cat striatum, Graybiel et al. (31) found an exact correspondence between acetyl cholinesterase-containing and dopamine-containing fiber islands, suggesting a coexistence of dopamine and acetylcholine, even though both entities were not necessarily localized in the same fiber (Figs. 8-14, 8-15). There was also some weaker acetyl cholinesterase staining in background areas that surrounded the islands, appearing in an anteroposterior gradient. Furthermore, there were acetyl cholinesterase-producing neurons in regions of the striatum in which neither acetyl cholinesterase background nor dopamine were present. Hence, there are three different acetyl cholinesterase-containing elements in the striatum with potentially different functions.

IDENTIFICATION OF PATHWAYS

By immunocytochemistry, we can identify transmitter-containing neuronal perikarya as well as synaptic terminals. However, immunocytochemistry alone does not tell us which terminal corresponds to which soma. To identify pathways, it is necessary to inject a tracer into a cell body for anterograde transport or into the

IDENTIFICATION OF PATHWAYS

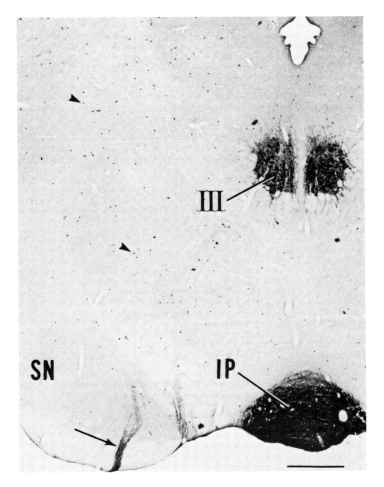

Figure 8-13. Rat midbrain, 40-μm-thick Vibratome section. Choline acetyl transferase is in the paired oculomotor nucleu (III) and in axons of the oculomotor nerve (arrows). Choline acetyl transferase is also in the interpeduncular nucleus (IP). Substantia nigra (SN) is unstained. Red blood cells (arrowheads) are stained nonspecifically because of so-called endogenous peroxidatic activity. Monoclonal anticholine acetyl transferase. PAP method. Bar is 40 μm. [From Hauser et al. (28).]

region of the terminal for retrograde transport. One of the most informative pathway studies by retrograde transport are those of Nauta et al. on the caudo-putamen (32). These investigations were carried out with horseradish perox-idase as a tracer which was injected hydraulically into brain or peripherally inner-vated tissue. The enzyme was taken up by nerve endings and transported to the cell bodies in retrograde movement. Histochemical reaction for peroxidase re-vealed the cell bodies corresponding to the terminals at the injection site. Retro-grade transport from injection sites resembles retrograde pathogenesis by teta-nus toxin or rabies virus from local lesions.

We have seen (page 186) that retrograde transport studies can be combined with immunocytochemistry to determine which neuron in a given anatomically defined pathway possesses a certain neurotransmitter or regulatory peptide.

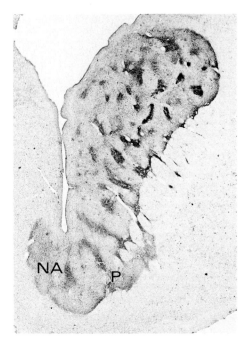

Figure 8-14. Fetal cat (embryonic day 57) striatum, 30-μm-thick frozen section. Striated patchworks of tyrosine hydroxylase localization. PAP method. P, putamen. NA, nucleus accumbens septi. [From Graybiel et al. (31).]

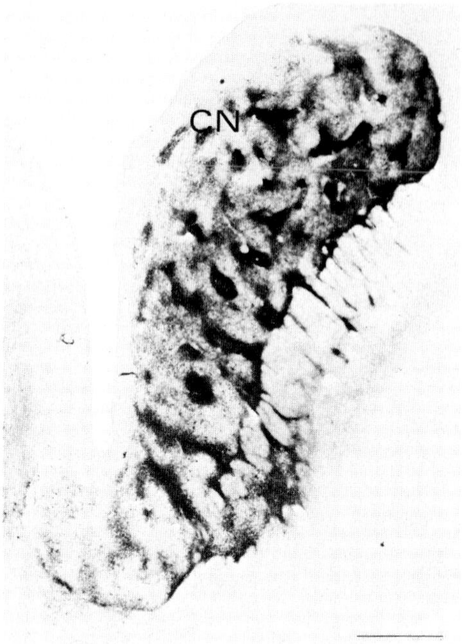

Figure 8-15. Section adjacent to that of Fig. 8-14 stained for acetyl cholinesterase by the thiocholine histochemical substrate method. The match between the microscopic patterns in Figs. 8-14 and 8-15 extended from the caudate nucleus (CN) to the putamen. [From Graybiel et al. (31).]

Since horseradish peroxidase injected for retrograde-tracing studies depends on enzymatic assay, it is necessary to use unfixed, frozen, or Vibratome sections for evaluation. Use of immunocytochemistry, rather than enzyme histochemistry, for detection of a retrogradally injected tracer, permits evaluation of fixed tissue, and thus, improves precision of localization (page 189) and makes simultaneous localization of retrograde tracer and specific neurotransmitter or neuropeptide easier.

Retrograde transport is an active process which is similar to the uptake of ligand-receptor complexes (page 411). This suggests a number of substances suitable for retrograde transport. One class of these substances are plant lectins which have the property of reacting with the carbohydrate of the cell membrane and initiating endocytosis. Representative substances are wheat germ agglutinin or tetanus toxin. Other tracers are antibodies to substances that are released at nerve endings. Apparently membrane-bound neurotransmitter-synthetic enzymes are exocytosed in this location and fused with the plasma membrane. If a specific antibody is injected onto the release site, it will react with the membrane-bound enzyme and taken up retrogradally only in nerves releasing the specific enzyme (page 327). The carbohydrate moiety of immunoglobulin G seems to be important in permitting membrane incorporation for retrograde transport. If injected into cell bodies, antibodies to neurotransmitter-synthetic enzymes will also be transported anterogradally along with the enzyme.

Steinbusch et al. (6) have delineated retrogradally projections from the nucleus raphé dorsalis to the caudoputamen by injection of the fluorescent dye, propidium iodide. Serotonin was identified by immunofluorescence with antiserotonin and noradrenalin by immunofluorescence with antinoradrenalin, both produced by conjugation of the neurotransmitters with bovine serum albumin via formaldehyde. The red propridium iodide fluorescence was distinct from the green immunofluorescence. The data showed that projections to the caudoputamen originate from serotonergic as well as nonserotonergic cells in the nucleus raphé dorsalis. Using horseradish peroxidase for retrograde transport and simultaneous localization of serotonin (page 188), Bowker et al. (33,34) have shown that raphé serotonergic neurons also project caudally. In fact, nearly three-quarters of all serotonin neurons in the nucleus raphé obscuros, raphé pallidus, and the ventral part of the reticular formation were found to project to the spinal cord. At least 90% of spinally projecting neurons of the medullary raphé neurons, identified by retrograde tracing, contained serotonin. In addition, some spinally projecting neurons also contained substance P and enkephalin. The neurons were morphologically similar to the serotonin neurons, and as it has been shown that serotonin can coexist with substance P or enkephalin (page 399), it is likely that the peptidergic neurons were identical to the serotonergic neurons.

Ruda and Coulter (35) injected wheat germ agglutinin into the facial vibrissal skin of the rat and found anterograde labeling in the superficial layer of the ipsilateral dorsal horn of the trigeminal nucleus caudalis. Injection of wheat germ agglutinin into mystatial vibrissal areas led to retrograde labeling of neurons in the ipsilateral facial motor nucleus.

The retrograde labeling was most commonly found in lysosomes in the neuronal cell body (Fig. 8-16). Wheat germ agglutinin was also seen on coated vesicle membranes of multivesicular bodies, as well as without clear membrane binding close to cisternae of agranular endoplasmic reticulum and Golgi. This localization is consistent with an active transport on membrane constituents, leading to degradation in lysosomes or re-utilization via Golgi and multivesicular bodies, similar to receptor reprocessing (page 425). Following anterograde labeling, wheat germ agglutinin was mainly localized in dendrites and neuronal cell bodies to multivesicular bodies, agranular reticulum, and vesicular strucutres (Fig. 8-17), suggesting processing in a manner characteristic of material designed for export, such as regulatory peptides or neurotransmitters.

The retrograde labeling with lectins or horseradish peroxidase is nonspecific, delineating pathways that terminate at the injection site irrespective of their transmitters. Specificity is identified, as we have seen, by combining retrograde labeling with immunocytochemistry. However, both sets of information can be obtained simultaneously by injection of antibodies to epitopes released at the injection site. Bowker et al. (36) were able to localize by injection of antidopamine-β-hydroxylase, noradrenergic neurons projecting to the spinal cord, and distinguish them from noradrenergic neurons projecting to the hypothalamus. One may assume that dopamine-β-hydroxylase is released at nerve terminals simultaneously with noradrenalin. The neurotransmitter interacts with the

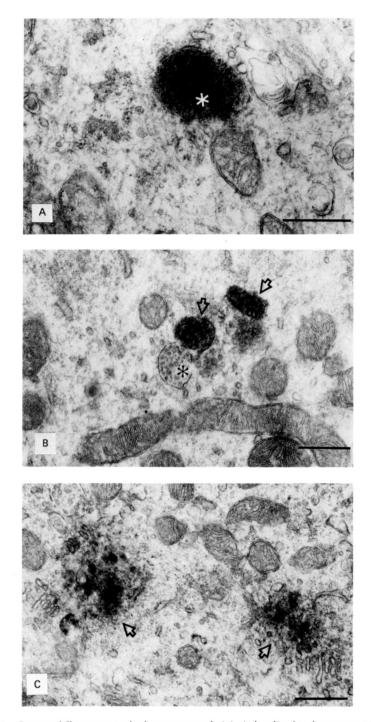

Figure 8-16. Retrogradally transported wheat germ agglutinin is localized to lysozomes (A, asterisk), multivesicular bodies (B), and to discrete, nonmembrane bound areas (C, arrows). Antiserum to wheat germ agglutinin. PAP method. Bar is 500 nm. [From Ruda and Coulter (35).]

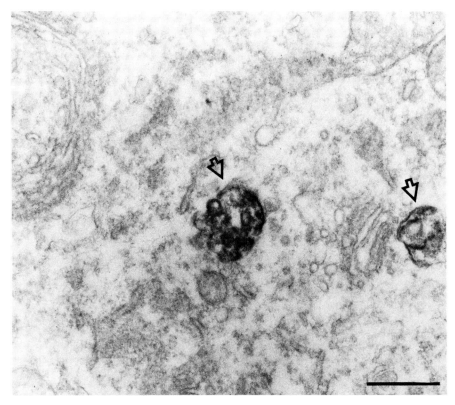

Figure 8-17. Anterograde-transported wheat germ agglutinin can be found in multivesicular bodies (arrows), as illustrated here in a perikaryon in the superficial dorsal horn. Antiserum to wheat germ agglutinin. PAP method. Bar is 500 nm. [From Ruda and Coulter (35).]

postsynaptic receptor, with the rest taken up again by the axon terminal or degraded by monoamine oxidase. However, the synthetic enzyme, dopamine-β-hydroxylase, which seems to be membrane-bound within an axon, is likely to fuse with the plasma membrane upon transmitter release and to follow the retrograde pathway of membrane endocytosis (page 411). This re-uptake is likely to be exacerbated by conglutination of the membrane-bound enzyme following reaction with specific antibodies (page 44). Thus, the antidopamine-β-hydroxylase will be transported retrogradally from the injection site in noradrenergic neurons, but not in other neuron terminals near the antibody-injection site. The retrogradally labeled neurons can then be identified by anti-immunoglobulin and PAP.

Following injection of antidopamine-β-hydroxylase in the spinal cord, cells ventral and caudal in the locus ceruleus and nearby areas, known to be noradrenergic, were labeled specifically (Fig. 8-18). Noradrenergic neurons in the medulla remained unlabeled. However, when antidopamine-β-hydroxylase was injected into the hypothalamus, the known medullary noradrenergic areas became labeled. Thus, noradrenergic neurons with ascending and descending projections were distinguished.

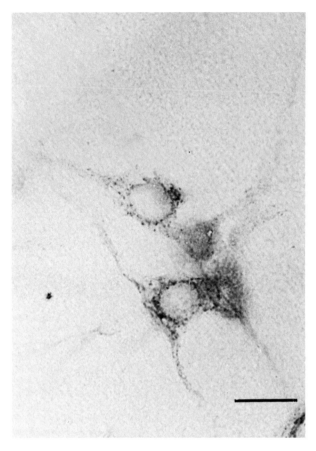

Figure 8-18.   A neuron in the Kölliker-Fuxe nucleus retrogradally labeled with antidopamine-β-hydroxy-lase. Stained with anti-immunoglobulin and PAP. The retrogradally transported antibody is localized in granular form, reflecting its transport in vesicular bodies and its disposition in lysozomes. This granular staining differs from the smooth pattern (not shown) which is obtained if the cell is stained for nascent dopamine-β-hydroxylase by antidopamine-β-hydroxylase, anti-immunoglobulin, and PAP. Bar is 25 μm. [From Bowker et al. (36).]

Chan-Palay et al. (37) injected antiserum to glutamic acid decarboxylase into the cerebellar cortex. Anterograde transport in Purkinje axons labeled deep cerebellar and several vestibular nuclei intensely. Retrograde labeling was seen in a number of pleomorphic deep cerebellar nuclei. Injection into the dentate nucleus produced retrograde labeling in Purkinje cell bodies and anterograde labeling in some mossy fiber rosettes. These studies confirm the γ-aminobuty-reargic nature of known reciprocal connections between cerebellar cortex and nuclei.

NEUROTRANSMITTER PATHOLOGY

Immunocytochemistry has permitted retrospective examination of cell and tissue components in archival pathology specimens (page 212). One condition for this re-examination is adequate fixation. In specimens from peripheral tissues and in small specimens of brain, this condition is often fulfilled.

In the brain, immunocytochemical pathology is especially important because it facilitates, for the first time, studies with a precision previously possibly only in experimental animals and experimental diseases. Even punch biopsies cannot provide analysis of single neurons or their projections, such as immunocyto-chemistry does. Pearson (38), in his extensive studies on human autopsy neuroimmunocyotchemistry, emphasizes that the immersion fixation of intact brain is a slow process often leaving deep tissues improperly fixed. Hence, many of the retrospectively obtained archival specimens were unsatisfactory for im-munocytochemistry unless they represented small structures, such as sympa-thetic ganglia. For study of deep structures in human brain, one is restricted, therefore, to material that has been fixed with special care which involves immer-sion of slices rather than blocks of brain in fixative. This necessity eliminates much of the en bloc-fixed material of yesteryears. Perfusion fixation, when feasible, should be even more effective than immersion fixation, and has the added advantage that it eliminates erythrocytes which react nonspecifically with diaminobenzidine. Methanolic hydrogen peroxide (page 113) suppresses this nonspecific staining in brains of adults and late fetuses, but not in brains of early fetuses.

A brown pigment, neuromelanin, is often encountered in human brain au-topsy material. Pearson (38) has blocked this material prior to staining by treat-ment with potassium permanganate and oxalic acid.

Pearson (38) found that in properly fixed autopsy material regulatory pep-tides are well preserved for immunocytochemical studies. Dopaminergic neu-rons can be studied with antityrosine hydroxylase (page 316). Antibodies to formalin conjugates of dopamine with protein were not satisfactory. Apparently, human tissue dopamine is not adequately conjugated to protein during fixation, and thus, escapes recognition by the antibodies.

Antiserum to serotonin gave incorrect localization in astrocytes, contrary to experimental studies in perfused rodents and monkeys, in which the localization was specific to the raphé system (page 309). This nonspecific localization in human brain was apparently due to slow and incomplete fixation by immersion. Apparently, serotonin was released from the dying neurons in association with its natural binding protein. This protein-serotonin complex is then taken up by astrocytes and converted to immunocytochemically stainable material once the fixative arrives at the location.

These findings illustrate the importance of adequate fixation to avoid not only loss of immunoreactivity of tissue constituents, but also their dislocation to non-specific sites (page 212).

Studies on human fetuses by Pearson et al. (23) have shown that by 9½ to 10 weeks of age, paraganglia contain noradrenalin as visualized by antityrosine hydroxylase, but not adrenalin as visualized by antiphenylmethyl-N-transferase. Cells migrating from the paraganglia to the adrenal medulla reveal adrenalin only once they have been exposed to the microenvironment of their final loca-tion.

Sympathetic neuroblasts share derivation from the dorsal crest with the dorsal root ganglia prior to their ultimate prevertebral location (23). The dorsal root

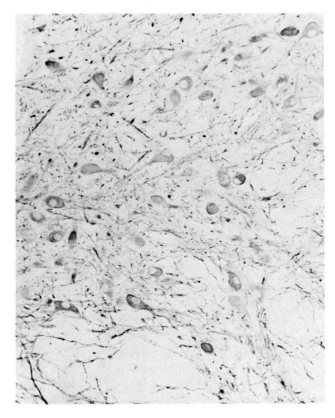

Figure 8-19. Normal human substantia nigra. Paraffin section. Dense network of dopamine axons and dendrites. Antityrosine hydroxylase that had been absorbed with liver powder to remove nonspecifically reacting antibodies. PAP method. Bar is 100 μm. [Reprinted with permission from *Progr Neuropath* **5**:41, by J. Pearson, 1983, Raven Press, New York (38).]

ganglia do not contain tyrosine hydroxylase. Again, it seems that the microenvironment of the sympathetic chain is necessary for the initiation of the noradrenalin synthesis. A similar need for establishment of appropriate microenvironment is necessary for other brain-specific substances, such as olfactory protein (page 333).

As expected, in Parkinson's disease tyrosine hydroxylase immunoreactive cells are diminished in number in the substantia nigra (38). The new findings, which required immunocytochemistry, were an accompanying loss of tyrosine hydroxylase-containing dendrites and of axons projecting to the basal ganglia (Figs. 8-19, 8-20). Prior to immunocytochemistry, such processes could not be recognized in the neuropil. Substance P fibers that descend from the basal ganglia were not diminished.

FAMILIAL DYSAUTONOMIA

Familial dysautonomia is a disorder of children and young adults that exhibits a wide spectrum of sensory, respiratory, cardiovascular, and motor dysfunctions,

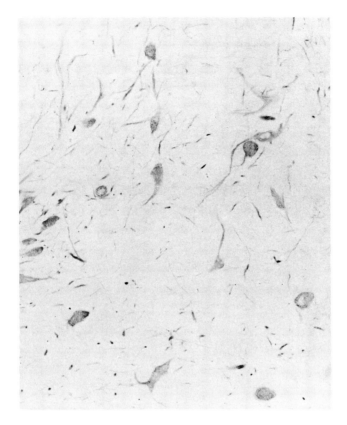

Figure 8-20. Parkinson's disease. Substantia nigra. Reduced number of dopamine axons and dendrites as compared to Fig. 8-19. Antityrosine hydroxylase. PAP method. [Reprinted with permission from *Progr Neuropath* **5:**41, by J. Pearson, 1983, Raven Press, New York (38).]

resulting from impaired baroreceptors, depletion of taste bud receptors, impairment of pain and temperature perception, insensitivity to hypoxia or hypercapnia with incumbent breath-holding spells and sleep apnea, absence of peripheral sympahetic noradrenergic terminals on blood vessels, abnormalities of upper esophageal mobility, and adrenal dysfunctions that may lead to crises of sudden release of excessive amounts of catecholamines. Sudden respiratory arrest is a frequent mode of death. Pearson et al. (39) found that neuronal and axonal depletion in the sensory and motor nervous system is the underlying pathology of the disease. The depletion extended through complex dysfunctions of the automonic nervous system. Axonal and neuronal loss was found in sensory components of reflex arcs and depletion of neurons in motor-sympathetic ganglia and the appropriate preganglionic structures in the central nervous system. By quantitative immunocytochemistry of recent autopsies as well as archival material, Pearson et al. (40) found that sympathetic ganglion volumes, neuronal population densities as well as total numbers of neurons per ganglion, were diminished. The major pathology of the disease appeared to be, however, in the central nervous system. Pearson emphasizes that the peripheral pathology that has been observed fails to explain the occurrence of emotional problems, altered EEG, abnormal response to blood gases, and anomalities in parasympathetic reflexes. A central substance P deficiency (page 367) appears to explain the reduced sensitivity to pain in familial dysautonomia. The pattern of defects prompted Pearson to postulate a nerve growth factor dysfunction in familial dysautonomia and has led to a search for abnormalities in nerve growth factor receptors.

Although the total number of neurons in the superior cervical ganglion in familial dysautonomia is typically reduced to less than 20% of normal, the proportion of tyrosine hydroxylase-rich cells, as examined by immunocyto-

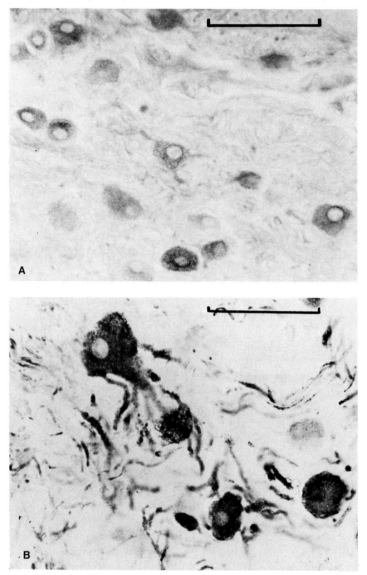

Figure 8-21. Superior cervical sympathetic ganglion from a control subject, age 14 years (A) and a patient with familial dysautonomia, age 15 years (B). Tyrosine hydroxylase per individual neuron is more abundant in the patient than in the control specimen. PAP method. Bars are 100 μm. [From Pearson et al. (40).]

chemistry, is higher than in normals, not only in the superior cervical ganglion (Fig. 8-21), but also in the substantia nigra. Furthermore, these selectively spared tyrosine hydroxylase-rich cells stained more intensely than those of normal ganglia. These observations are intriguing because nerve growth factor is needed for the noradrenergic component of the superior cervical ganglion which is tyrosine hydroxylase-poor, but is not so crucial for the dopaminergic SIF cells, which are tyrosine hydroxylase-rich.

Rubinstein et al. (41) saw tyrosine hydroxylase axons in neurofibromas in von Recklinghausen's disease. The findings suggest the possibility of reducing the incidence of disfiguring skin tumors in this disease by sympathectomy in cases in which the tumors are predominantly related to sympathetic axons.

Immunocytochemical neuropathology often helps in the identification of problem tumors (page 339). However, the potential of immunocytochemistry goes beyond classification of disease. For instance, as pointed out by Pearson et al. (40), it would be useful to know the neurotransmitter profile in biopsies of brain obtained in neurosurgical treatment of intractable epilepsy with possible view toward replacement therapy.

OLFACTORY PROTEIN

Olfactory epithelium shares, with other epithelia, their continous turnover. Primary olfactory neurons, as part of this epithelium, are unique among neurons in their capability of division even in adulthood. Olfactory protein isolated from these neurons has been shown by Graziadei et al. (42) to be specific to the primary sensory neurons of the olfactory pathway. No other neurons revealed staining. The protein has been used as a marker for cells isolated from the olfactory bulb. Such markers are important in isolation studies because brain cells loose their characteristic morphology once they are suspended in vitro. Olfactory bulb protein is closely associated with carnosine, a potent specific neurotransmitter in the olfactory system, and its synthetic enzyme, carnosine synthetase.

The work of Graziadei et al. (43) suggests that the primary olfactory neuron is a command neuron. It normally synapses with mitral cells in the olfactory bulb. When the olfactory bulb is removed, the regenerating neurons will establish direct synapses with the forebrain. In developing mice (44), the protein appears only 3 to 4 days after morphologic development of the olfactory neuron (Fig. 8-22). The protein does not enter the process of differentiation and early maturation of the sensory neuron. Apparently, the appearance of olfactory protein is dependent on the contact of the sensory neuron with elements of the central nervous system and may be the result of a feedback mechanism.

NEURON-SPECIFIC ENOLASE

Marangos et al. (45) discovered that a brain-specific acidic protein, called protein 14-3-2, had enolase activity. Enolases are dimeric 100-kDa proteins. Three subunits, α, β, and γ have been identified.

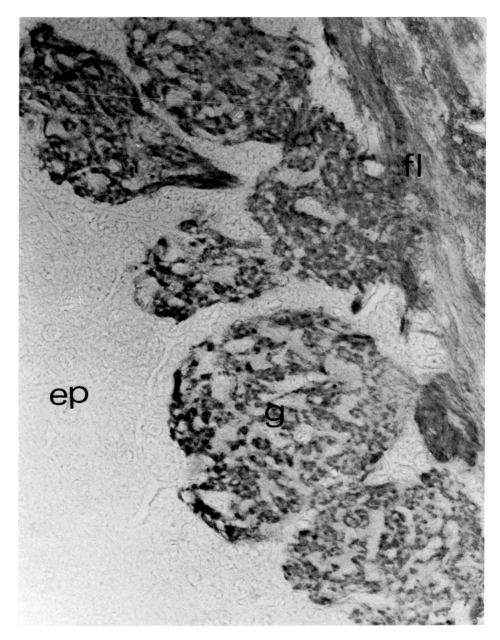

Figure 8-22. Olfactory bulb of the mouse, 30th postnatal day. Bouin fixation. Paraffin section. Olfactory protein is in sensory fibers from the superficial fiber layer (fl) of the olfactory bulb which forms the characteristic glomeruli (g). In the glomeruli, olfactory protein-containing areas are intermingled with dendrites of mitral, tufted, and periglomerular cells devoid of protein. ep, external plexiform layer. PAP method. ×450. [Reprinted with permission from *Neuroscience* **5:**1239, G. A. M. Graziadei, R. S. Starky, P. P. C. Graziadei, The olfactory marker protein in the olfactory system of the mouse during development, Copyright 1980, Pergamon Press, Ltd. (44).]

Schmechel et al. (46,47) found that the γ-γ form is immunocytochemically localized to neurons in the central and peripheral nervous system as well as to neuroendocrine cells. The α-α form is found in glia and is widely distributed in other nonneuronal tissues. The β-β form is characteristic for heart and skeletal muscle. Neurons switch from nonneuronal enolase to neuron-specific enolase during differentiation (48). It is, therefore, not surprising that considerable homology exists between α and γ chains and that, indeed, α-γ hybrids can form spontaneously during isolation. In platelets, a high level of α-γ enolase was found by Marangos et al. (49). In magakaryocytes, however, Kato et al. (50) found mainly α-α and γ-γ enolase. It appears, therefore, that the α-γ enolase of blood platelets is a product of the α-α and γ-γ enzymes of megakaryocytes.

PROTEIN S-100

A water soluble, highly acidic 20-kDa protein, protein S-100, has a wide immunocytochemical distribution. The protein consists of two components that possess wide sequence homology with calcium-binding sites of para-albumin, troponin C, and calmodulin. Hideka et al. (51) employed, therefore, a sepharose-bound antagonist for affinity purification of protein S-100 from adipose tissue and brain and found that both proteins co-migrated, thus confirming the immunocytochemical localization of the protein in both brain and adipose tissue. In brain, Cocchia et al. (52) found by pre-embedding staining electron microscopy, S-100 protein only in astrocytes and epenpymal cells. In the pituitary, it was localized to stellate cells of the pars distalis and to pituicytes of the neural lobe (53). These cells resemble glial cells in their performance as satellite cells. In the skin, the protein is found in melanocytes and Langerhans cells (54).

Despite the wide distribution of protein S-100 in many tissues, it is, within these tissues, still restricted to certain cells types. The protein is absent, for instance, from neurons, oligodendrocytes, muscle cells, fibroblasts, or histiocytes. Hence, antibodies still can be used as markers in special circumstances. For instance, Armin et al. (55) have shown that granular cell myoblastomas originate from Schwann cells, which do contain protein S-100, rather than from suspected fibroblasts, histiocytes, or undifferentiated mesenchymal cells which do not contain the protein.

GLIAL FIBRILLARY ACIDIC PROTEIN

In contrast to protein S-100, glial fibrillary acidic protein (GFA) is strictly specific to astrocytes and cells that can be considered astrocytic specializations. Accordingly, immunocytochemistry for GFA has received wide diagnostic applications. GFA has been discovered and characterized by Eng (56). GFA is one of the cytoskeletal proteins (page 265). The original isolation procedure of Eng (56) depended upon obtainment of a cytoskeletal preparation by centrifugation in the presence of Triton X-100, removal of myelin by flotation on 30% sucrose, delipidation of the sediment, and its resuspension in urea and Clelend's reagent. Following removal of the solvents, GFA was isolated by sucrose density sedimentation. Eng and De Armond (57) subsequently adapted the procedure to higher yields by obtaining tubulin-free GFA from the cytoskeletal preparation upon chromatography on a hydroxyapatite column.

The establishment of GFA specificity to astrocytes depended upon the purity of the antigen used for production of antisera. While immunocytochemistry has revealed strict specificity for astrocytes and related cells, the demonstration that the reaction within these cells was due to GFA depended upon immunocyto-chemical staining of electroblots (page 20). Eng and De Armond (57) found that on staining cytoskeletal preparations separated electrophoretically accord-ing to size, only the 49-kDa GFA protein was revealed, as well as small amounts of degradation forms ranging between 49 to 40 kDa (Fig. 8-23).

The reactivity of the antiserum with a single molecular weight species of nondegraded GFA was confirmed by cell-free synthesis in the studies of Bigbee and Eng (58). Utilizing immunoprecipitated mRNA as template in a radioactive methionine-containing reticulocyte lysate system, the in vitro synthesized protein was a single 50-kDa species. Two-dimensional electrophoresis of the in vitro synthesized protein revealed only two adjacent 50-kDa spots, while upon reac-tion with radioiodinated anti-GFA immunoglobulin, seven spots were revealed. The data suggested that heterogeneity of GFA is due to post-translational pro-cessing.

One of the post-translational changes is degradation by a calcium-dependent protease described by Schlaepfer and Zimmerman (59) and by De Armond et al. (60). The physiologic role of this protein, closely associated with the cytoskele-ton, appears to be selective depolymerization of glial filaments. GFA protein appears to turn over in 1 to 2 days.

The earliest class of glial cells that appear in development are the radial glial fibers. Levitt and Rakic (61) have shown that these fibers contain GFA protein early in the rhesus monkey gestation, and are present concomitantly with neu-rons. They fan out from the ventricular and subventricular zones and reach the pial surface by the end of the first trimester (Fig. 8-24). These findings contradict earlier suppositions that the ventricular matrix zone consists of only one class of cells from which neurons and glia differentiate. Immunocytochemistry facili-tated the distinction between glial and neuronal phenotypes.

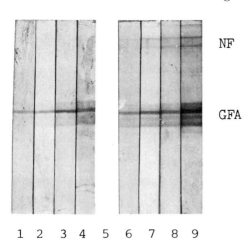

NF

GFA

1 2   3 4   5   6 7   8 9

Figure 8-23. PAP staining of immunoblots containing bovine spinal cord intermediate filament proteins. Antihu-man glial fibrillary acidic protein: 1, 1 : 5000 dilution; 2, 1 : 2000 dilution; 3, 1 : 1000 dilution; 4, 1 : 250 dilution. Lane 5, stained with amido black. Antibovine intermedi-ate filament protein: Lane 6, 1 : 5000 dilution; 7, 1 : 2000 dilution; 8, 1 : 1000 dilution; 9, 1 : 250 dilution. Addi-tional bands stained with the anti-intermediate filament proteins include neurofilament proteins (page 435) on the upper parts of the strips. NF, neurofilaments. GFA, glial fibrillary acidic protein. [Reprinted with permission, from L. F. Eng, S. J. De Armond, *Progr Neuropath* **5:**19, 1983, Raven Press, New York. (57).]

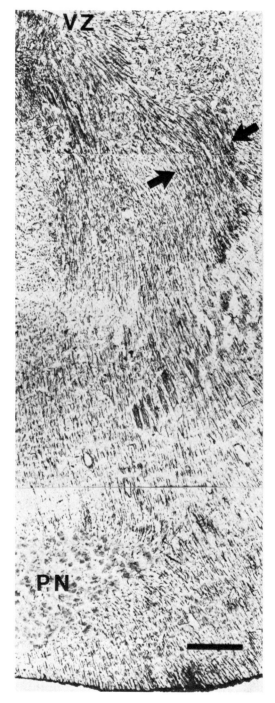

Figure 8-24. Glial fibrillary acidic protein in a midsagittal section through the brainstem at the level of the ponto-medullary junction of the rhesus monkey at embryonic day 54. PAP method. Cresyl violet counterstain. Glial fibrillary acidic protein-containing radial glial fibers sweep ventrally to the caudal portion of the developing pontine nuclei (PN). Other bundles of radial processes (between arrows) run from the same part of the ventricular zone (VZ) to more caudal brainstem levels (to the right) lying outside the area encompassed on the micrograph. Bar is 150 μm [From Levitt and Rakic (61).]

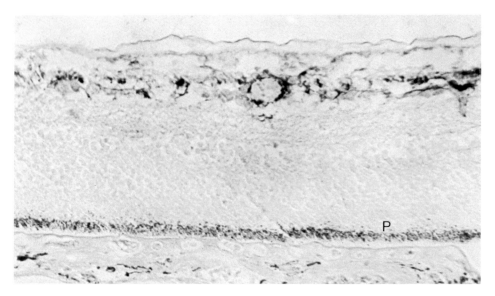

Figure 8-25.   In the normal adult human retina, glial fibrillary acidic protein positivity is delineated and confined to astrocytes of the nerve fiber layer. Müller cells are negative. The pigmented epithelium (P) and pigmented cells in the choroid are not glial fibrillary acidic protein positive. PAP method. ×400. [Reprinted with permission, from L. F. Eng, S. J. De Armond, *Progr Neuropath* **5**:19, 1983, Raven Press, New York. (57).]

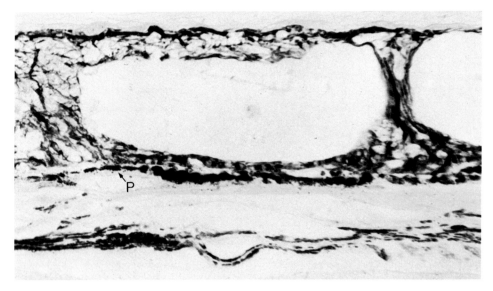

Figure 8-26.   Adult human retina. Microcystic degeneration. Intense glial fibrillary acidic protein positivity is located in astrocytes as well as reactive Müller cells. P, pigmented epithelium. PAP method. ×400. [Reprinted with permission, from L. F. Eng, S. J. De Armond, *Progr Neuropath* **5**:19, 1983, Raven Press, New York. (57).]

In contrast to the Golgi method, immunocytochemistry for GFA protein permitted a quantitative evaluation of glial fibers. In the Golgi method, quantification is impossible because of the unpredictable impregnation of individual fibers. Indeed, on the basis of the Golgi method, the very existence of radial fibers had been questioned. By immunocytochemistry, the radial fiber density was about 17,000 fibers per millimeter square. The number of migrating neurons in a millimeter square cortical section at embryonic day 70 was calculated to be 20,000. Thus, it appears that at the time of peak neuronal migration, each neuron can be in contact with at least one glial fiber, supporting the notion of glial guidance of developing neurons.

Upon completion of neuronal migration, the radial glial cells in most regions of the brain undergo morphologic transformation into protoplasmic and fibrous astrocytes and tanycytes.

Human embryonic ependyma contain GFA only transiently during the 15th to 20th week of gestation. Normal adult ependyma is devoid of immunocytochemically demonstrable GFA protein, but becomes strongly positive, as shown by Eng and Rubinstein (62) in response to inflammation, tumor invasion, or obstructive hydrocephalus.

As shown by O'Dowd and Eng (63), the mature human Müller cell is devoid of GFA protein, but becomes strongly positive following retinal injury and retinal degeneration (Figs. 8-25, 8-26).

Anderson et al. (64) report a strong GFA positivity in the glial reaction to spinal cord injury in fish. Regeneration of neurites and production of new neuronal cell bodies occur readily in these reaction areas. The findings dispel previous notions that scar tissue formed in response to injury inhibits axonal regeneration. To the contrary, they suggest that glial guidance may promote it.

BRAIN TUMORS

Using GFA protein immunocytochemistry on paraffin sections with the PAP method, Tascos et al. (65) obtained equally good results whether surgical, or recent, or 17-year-old autopsy material was used, either after Bouin or phosphate buffer-formalin fixation. The studies concluded that:

1. GFA protein is a reliable marker for both anaplastic and reactive astrocytes. The staining of most ependymomas may be due to a reversion of mature ependymal cells to more primitive stages. Rubinstein and Brucker (66) described a focal positivity of columnar cells around a GFA-negative core in chroroid plexus papillomas, suggesting different degrees of reversion for individual cells (Fig. 8-27).

2. A negative correlation between the degree of anaplasia and GFA positivity may be of prognostic value (65).

3. In a number of morphologically diagnosed ependymomas or oligodendromas, GFA positivity revealed the presence of malignant astrocytes. It remains to be evaluated whether the resultant diagnosis of mixed neoplasm has prognostic value.

4. In subependymomas, the astrocytic contribution was extensive.

5. In Rosenthal fibers, GFA protein was present only at the periphery.

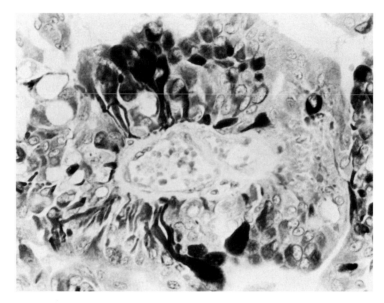

Figure 8-27. Glial fibrillary acidic protein in a choroid plexus papilloma of the fourth ventricle. PAP method. ×300. [From Rubinstein and Brucker (66).]

Goebel et al. (67) find GFA protein in well-differentiated, fiber-forming astrocytomas. In gliomas with few fibers, GFA, when present, was found in perinuclear locations and suggested astrocytic origin. Even in highly anaplastic glioblastomas, an astrocytic origin could be established by perikaryonal GFA protein in giant cells with bizarre nuclei. Of special importance was GFA protein immunocytochemistry to establish astrocytic origin of tumors that presented themselves at ectopic locations. Immunocytochemistry appeared to be especially indicated in the diagnosis of undifferentiated or ectopic astrocytomas, in mixed tumors, in the demonstration of strongly anaplastic regions within an otherwise well-differentiated astrocytoma, in undifferentiated ependymomas, and in nonastrocytic brain tumors that morphologically resembled astrocytomas.

From a study of childhood brain tumors, Marsden et al. (68) found that GFA immunocytochemistry was of prognositc value only in adult astrocytomas, where its presence was associated with more favorable outcome.

Roessman et al. (69) examined neuroepithelial neoplasms by GFA immunocytochemistry for astrocytic elements and by anti-68-kDa neurofilament immunocytochemistry (page 265) for neuronal elements. Primitive neuroectodermal tumors, central neuroblastomas, medulloblastomas, and gangliomas stained for either protein, and about 25% of the tumors stained for both. It has been suggested that medulloblastoma is a neuroepithelial neoplasm with or without capability of differentiation. If it does differentiate, it does so into neurons only, glia only, or both. From the immunocytochemical studies, it has been possible to propose a new, more detailed classification of medulloblastomas. Correlation of clinical behavior and therapeutic response of increasingly large series of tumors may provide support for the usefulness of such classification.

We have already discussed the relationship of neurofilament proteins to degrees of differentiation of tumors of neuronal origin (page 265).

Schindler and Gallotta (70) emphasized the need of large tissue samples in immunocytochemical pathology, in order to distinguish neoplastic cells from reactive cells infiltrating into the lesion.

Eng and Rubinstein (62) conclude that immunocytochemistry "will not, evidently, resolve all of our diagnostic problems concerning the interpretation of human brain tumors especially those of more primitive and anaplastic ones. Yet it is apparent that its selectivity and sensitivity may give a most powerful tool, which, if used with discrimination, is likely to prove almost essential for the more precise identification of difficult tumors of the central neuraxis."

MYELIN

The speed of impulses conducted in certain nerves is enhanced by the wrapping of several layers of a myelin membrane. Myelin is laid around central and peripheral nerves in segments by cytoplasmic processes of *oligodendrocytes* and *Schwann cells*, respectively. Each segment along peripheral nerve is separated by a narrow, myelin-free *node of Ranvier* (Fig. 8-28). During the wrapping of a cytoplasmic process around the nerve, its cytoplasm becomes flattened to a thick membrane, the *major dense line*. As multiple layers are wrapped around the nerve, each major dense line becomes separated by two layers of cell membrane, which because of their lipid contents are electron-lucent on routine electron microscopy. A fine dense line (*intraperiod line*) separates the two plasma membranes. This dense material presumably represents protein and carbohydrate of the outer surface of the cell membrane. The distance between two major dense lines is 18 nm (72).

Myelin is 70% lipid and 30% protein. The lipids are chiefly carbohydrates and sulfatides. In the central nervous system, the proteins are basic protein, glycoprotein, proteolipid, and Wolfgram protein. In the peripheral nervous system, there are a glycoprotein and two basic proteins, one of which is identical with that of the central nervous system.

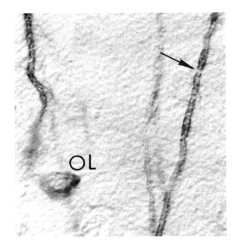

Figure 8-28. Myelin basic protein is found in oligodendrocytes (OL) and in myelin of this 7-day-old rat cervical spinal cord Vibratome section. Arrow indicates node of Ranvier. Formalin-mercury bichloride fixation. PAP method. Nomarski optics. ×900. [From Nancy Sternberger et al. (71).]

With density gradient-isolated myelin, Nancy Sternberger et al. (73) found basic protein to be confined to the intraperiod line. In oligodendrocytes themselves, basic protein was seen in the cytoplasm of cell body and cell processes (Fig. 3-8). This suggests that during the process of myelin development the basic protein is extruded from the cytoplasm to the outer surface of the cell membrane.

In peripheral nerves, cell bodies of Schwann cells display a close relationship to the myelin sheaths of associated axons, and each cell forms only one internode. In contrast, in the central nervous system direct connections between oligodendrocyte perikarya and myelin sheaths are not easily seen, except by immunocytochemistry.

Demyelination is the presenting lesion in many neuropathologic conditions (page 485). *Myelin basic protein*, discovered, isolated, and first characterized by Kies (74) embodies in its sequence a number of defined epitopes that are capable of evoking experimental autoimmune demyelination (page 487).

Basic protein was seen by Nancy Sternberger et al. (71) in myelin and oligodendrocytes of newborn rats in a region extending from the cervical spinal cord to the midbrain (Fig. 8-29), progressively decreasing in intensity at more rostral levels. Staining was absent in the diencephalon and cerebellar hemispheres at this stage of development. Stained oligodendrocyte processes could be traced from perikarya to terminal extrusions located around or along axons and their myelin sheaths. We have already seen from examination of 100-μm-thick Vibratome sections that oligodendrocyte processes from a single cell could be traced to multiple axons that may even belong to different nerve tracts (page 109). The wealth of ramifications of myelinating oligodendrocytic processes becomes apparent by visualization of their abundance even in 1-μm-thick sections (Fig. 8-30).

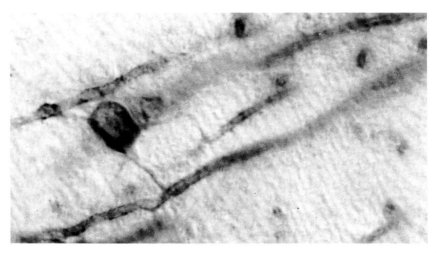

Figure 8-29. Rat medulla stained with antimyelin basic protein, 1 : 500, as first antiserum. A densely stained oligodendrocyte has processes extending to three heavily stained, longitudinally oriented myelin sheets. Axons, oligodendrocyte nucleus, and the remaining neuropil are unstained. PAP method. Nomarski optics. ×1250. [From Nancy Sternberger et al. (71).]

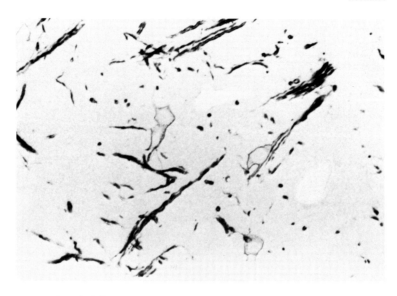

Figure 8-30.   Spinal cord of the rat, 7th postnatal day. Glutaraldehyde and osmium tetroxide fixation. Epon section, 1 μm thick. Myelin basic protein is seen in oligodendrocytes, their abundant processes, and in myelin. PAP method. [From Nancy Sternberger et al. (75).]

Myelin basic protein was restricted to myelin sheaths and oligodendrocyte cytoplasm during all stages of development. Neurons, astrocytes, endothelial cells, perineuronal oligodendrocytes (Fig. 8-31), and ependymal cells (Fig. 8-32) were consistently unstained.

Estimation of concentration of myelin basic protein could be made by the maximal dilution of antibasic protein that gave effective staining. In the medulla, pons, and midbrain of 3-day-old rats, oligodendrocytes were readily stained with a 1 : 8000 dilution of antiserum, the highest dilution tested. By the 25th day, more concentrated solutions were required, indicating a decrease in concentration of basic protein in oligodendrocytes. However, myelin itself was stained by all antiserum dilutions, both at 3 and 25 days of age. This suggests a high degree of myelin formation by oligodendrocytes on day 3 and a decline of activity by day 25.

The pattern of myelin formation differs with stage of development in different areas of the brain. Thus, in the tectospinal tract in the region of the pons, myelin is already found at birth, as indicated by basic protein staining of the nerve tracts throughout a 25-day postnatal period. However, oligodendrocyte staining varied through this period. Nancy Sternberger et al. (75) quantified these data by use of a digitalized image analyzer (page 153). They found maximal oligodendrocyte staining on the 3rd postnatal day. Staining intensity decreased progressively toward the 25th day (Fig. 8-33). Myelinization itself, however, became rapid only on the 9th day and proceeded until the 25th day, at which time oligodendrocyte staining has apparently declined (see also below). In the anterior commissure, on the other hand, no myelin was seen before the 12th day. On the 3rd day, neither myelin nor oligodendrocytes contained basic protein (Fig. 8-34). By the 7th day, oligodendrocytes were rich in basic protein, but

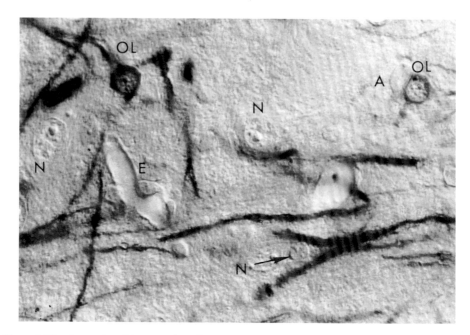

Figure 8-31. Seven-day-old rat spinal cord immunostained with 1 : 500 antimyelin basic protein. Neurons (N), astrocytes (A), endothelial cells (E), and a perineural oligodendrocyte (OL) are unstained. In contrast, myelin-forming oligodendrocytes (OL) are stained. PAP method. ×760. [From Nancy Sternberger et al. (75).]

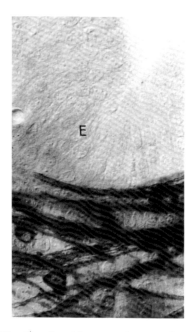

Figure 8-32. Five-day-old rat pontine ependyma immunostained with 1:500 antimyelin basic protein. Unstained ependymal cells (E) next to stained myelin sheets and oligodendrocytes. PAP method. ×450. [From Nancy Sternberger et al. (75).]

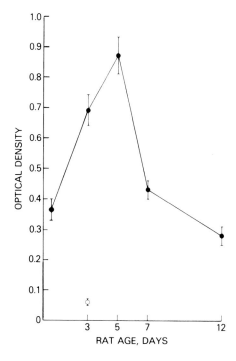

Figure 8-33. Absorbencies of tectospinal oligodendrocytes stained with antimyelin basic protein, 1 : 500, as a function of age. PAP method. [From Nancy Sternberger et al. (75).]

myelin had not yet appeared (Fig. 8-35). By the 12th day, oligodendrocytes as well as myelin contained basic protein (Fig. 8-36). The data show that myelin basic protein is synthesized before active myelinization begins.

For these studies, formalin-mercury bichloride-fixed Vibratome sections were used. This procedure failed, however, to stain basic protein in myelin on the 25th postnatal day, even though myelin had been well developed and abundant (Fig. 8-37). Apparently, the dense lipid covering prevented accessibility of antibodies. When 25-day sections were treated with 95% ethanol for 3 minutes prior

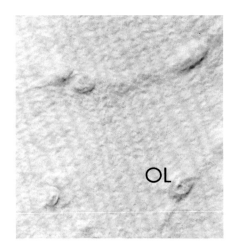

Figure 8-34. Three-day-old rat anterior commissure immunostained with 1 : 500 antimyelin protein. Oligodendrocytes (OL) are unstained, myelin is absent. PAP method. ×900. [From Nancy Sternberger et al. (75).]

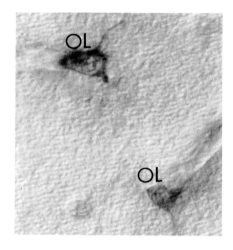

Figure 8-35. Seven-day-old rat anterior commissure immunostained with 1 : 500 antimyelin basic protein. Oligodendrocytes (OL) are stained, myelin is absent. PAP method. ×900. [From Nancy Sternberger et al. (75).]

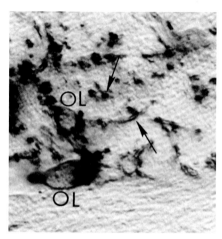

Figure 8-36. Twelve-day-old rat anterior commissure immunostained with 1 : 500 antimyelin basic protein. Oligodendrocytes (OL) are stained, myelin is absent. PAP method. ×900. [From Nancy Sternberger et al. (75).]

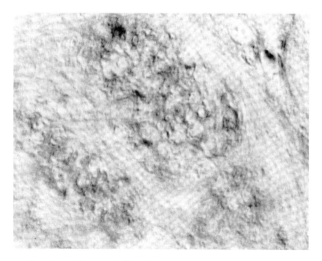

Figure 8-37. Twenty-five-day-old rat medulla oblongata. Coronal section through the medial longitudinal fasciculus. Formalin-mercury bichloride-fixed Vibratome section immunostained with 1 : 500 antimyelin basic protein. Although myelin is well developed, myelin basic protein is not visualized. PAP method. ×800. [From Nancy Sternberger et al. (75).]

346

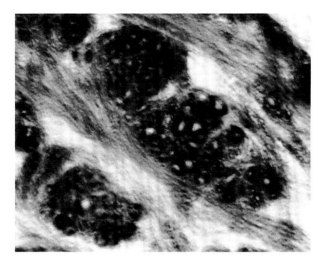

Figure 8-38.   Section adjacent to that of Fig. 8-37, but treated with 95% ethanol for 3 minutes prior to immunostaining. Myelin basic protein has become visualized. PAP method. ×900. [From Nancy Sternberger et al. (75).]

to immunostaining, localization of basic protein had become abundant (Fig. 8-38). Treatment with ethanol had no effect on myelin staining at earlier ages or on oligodendrocyte staining at any age.

These developmental studies had been carried on 100-μm-thick Vibratome sections that were pretreated with Triton X-100 to ensure penetration throughout the thickness of the section (page 127). Nancy Sternberger et al. (76) found, that at least in the case of 50-μm-thick sections, a 0.3 M solution of sodium

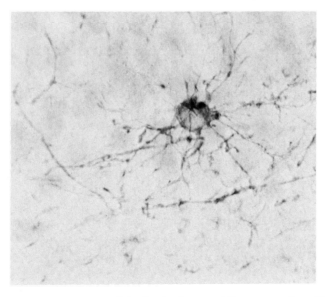

Figure 8-39.   Myelin basic protein in adult oligodendrocytes. Vibratome section, 50 μm thick. PAP method. [From Nancy Sternberger et al. (76).]

chloride could be substituted for the Triton in a procedure that appeared to be less damaging to tissue structure and to antigens. When in adult tissues Triton X was used, myelin basic protein was only found in assembled myelin, but was absent from oligodendrocytes. Upon omission of Triton X, however, Nancy Sternberger et al. (76) found myelin basic protein staining also in the oligodendrocytes, thus showing that myelination is a continuous process extending throughout life, although at reduced rates (Fig. 8-39).

Fifty percent of total myelin proteins are *proteolipids*. Agarwal et al. (77) found its immunofluorescence localization in oligodendrocyte cytoplasm and in myelin sheaths of the rat corpus callosum on the 10th postnatal day.

Wolfgram proteins (78) are mixtures of three compounds of 42, 50, and 55 kDa, respectively (79). The two lighter bands comigrate with tubulin (80) as well as with 2′,3′-cyclic nucleotide-3′-phosphodiesterase (81,82). With antibodies reactive with the 42 to 50-kDa proteins, Roussel et al. (83) described oligodendrocyte staining prior to the onset of myelination.

Myelin-associated glycoprotein (MAG), first isolated by Quarles (84), is the most prominent glycoprotein in purified myelin, even though it constitutes only of about 1% of total myelin protein. On the basis of the failure to identify MAG among the glycoproteins of peripheral nerve, it had previously been thought to be specific for the central nervous system. However, the immunocytochemical studies of Nancy Sternberger et al. (85) revealed, surprisingly, peripheral and central localization of comparable intensities. Therefore, a repetition of the isolation procedure was carried out by Figliewicz et al. (86) in which high amounts of ^{3}H-fucose were injected into the sciatic nerve. Labeled glycoprotein was isolated from the nerve that possessed identical electrophoretic mobility as ^{14}C-labeled central nervous system MAG. The findings were confirmed by identical peptide maps of digested peripheral and central MAG.

As in the case of myelin basic protein, Nancy Sternberger et al. (85) found MAG in oligodendrocyte cell bodies and processes early in development (Figs. 8-40, 8-41), although the peak time of staining was somewhat later than that apparent with antiserum to myelin basic protein. If MAG plays a role in establishing initial glial-axonal contact, as has been suggested, it would be expected that MAG should appear before other myelin proteins. The delayed appearance of MAG cannot be attributed to the fact that it constituted only 1% of total myelin, in contrast to myelin basic protein which makes up 30%, since the MAG antiserum is more efficient in detecting oligodendrocytes than several of the myelin basic protein antisera used.

The pattern of localization of MAG differs dramatically from that of myelin basic protein. While myelin basic protein is localized throughout the myelin sheath, Nancy Sternberger et al. (85,88) found that only the initial stages of myelination exhibit similarities in localization in oligodendrocyte processes (Fig. 8-42). With further development, MAG staining is seen in periaxonal locations and in the outer mesaxon. In the adult, the stain is predominantly in periaxonal and paranodal regions of central nervous system myelin sheaths (Figs. 8-43, 8-44, 8-45). In the peripheral nervous system, an additional locus of staining is in Schmidt-Lanterman incisures.

The periaxonal localization of MAG as contrasted with the compact myelin localization of myelin basic protein (89) has been confirmed in normal nerve by

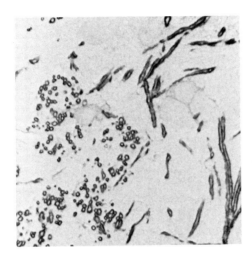

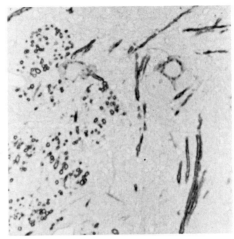

Figure 8-40. Myelin basic protein in oligodendrocytes in the rat spinal cord, 6th postnatal day. Glutaraldehyde osmium tetroxide fixation. Epon section, 1 μm thick. PAP method. [From Nancy Sternberger (87).]

Figure 8-41. Myelin-associated glycoprotein in a section adjacent to that of Fig. 8-40 is found in the same oligodendrocyte. PAP method. [From Nancy Sternberger (87).]

Trapp and Quarles (90), in chronic relapsing allergic encephalomyelitis by Nancy Sternberger et al. (91), and in multiple sclerosis by Prineas et al. (92).

Perineuronal *satellite oligodendrocytes* have previously been assumed not to participate in myelination. However, Ludwin (93) demonstrated electron microscopically remyelination by satellite oligodendrocytes during recovery from Cuprizone intoxication. Similarly, Nancy Sternberger (87) has seen satellite

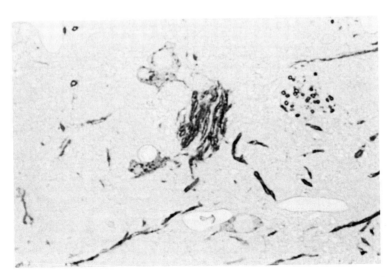

Figure 8-42. Myelin-associated glycoprotein is in oligodendrocytes and in myelin in the 7th postnatal day spinal cord. Glutaraldehyde osmium tetroxide fixation. Epon section, 1 μm thick. PAP method. [From Nancy Sternberger (87).]

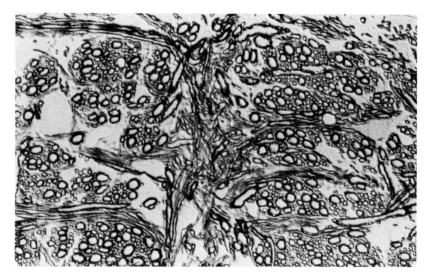

Figure 8-43. Myelin basic protein is found in all sheets of the myelin envelope. PAP method. [From Nancy Sternberger (87).]

oligodendrocytes intensely stain for MAG in shiverer mice, and staining could also be seen with antimyelin basic protein as well as anti-MAG in normal, satellite oligodendrocytes of developing rats.

Using 1-μm-thick plastic sections of glutaraldehyde-osmium tetroxide fixed material, Ulrich et al. (94) found that the immunocytochemical localization of myelin proteins in remyelinating cultures resembled closely that observed in developing animals, thus making organotypic cultures suitable for studying some of the factors that affect myelination.

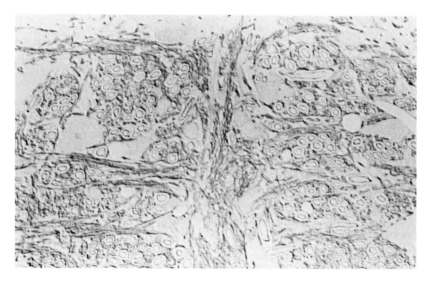

Figure 8-44. In a section adjacent to that of Fig. 8-43, myelin-associated glycoprotein is found only in periaxonal locations. [From Nancy Sternberger (87).]

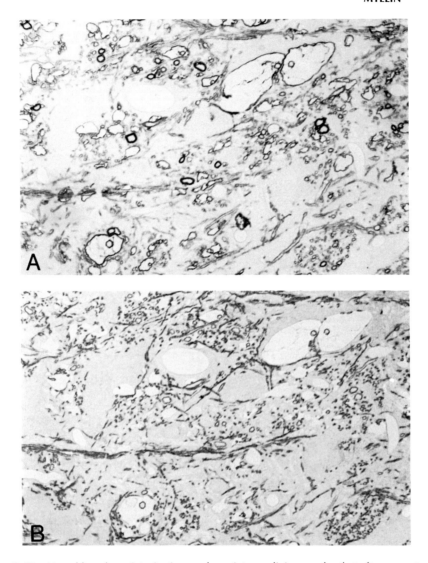

Figure 8-45. Hexachlorophene intoxication produces intramyelinic vacuoles that often separate compact lamellae from oligodendrocyte processes which surround axons. After such separation, myelin-associated glycoprotein staining remains periaxonal. (A) myelin basic protein. (B) myelin-associated glycoprotein. PAP method [From the work of Nancy Sternberger.]

The myelin membrane contains 70 to 85% lipid. Two galactosphingolipids, *galactocerebroside* and *sulfatide,* are found in the brain. Nancy Sternberger et al. (71) demonstrated galactocerebroside in tissue sections of developing rats (Fig. 8-46). The ready localization of galactocerebroside in oligodendrocytes of adult mice, even when the rate of myelination has declined, make galactocerebroside immunocytochemistry, as demonstrated by Zale et al. (95), a specific marker for oligodendrocytes, in addition to myelin basic protein and MAG.

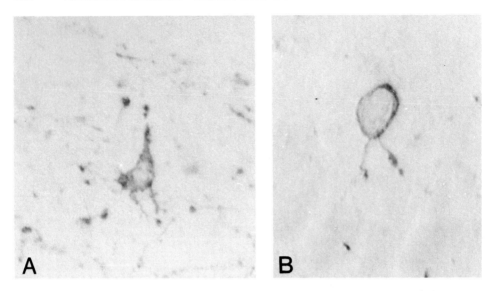

Figure 8-46. Galactocerebroside in myelin, and in cytoplasm (A) and cell surface (B) of oligodendrocytes. PAP method. [From the work of Nancy Sternberger.]

REFERENCES

1. Scharrer E, Scharrer B: *Neuroendocrinology.* Columbia University Press, New York, 1963.

2. Scharrer B: Neuroendocrinology and Histochemistry, in Stoward PJ, Polak JM (eds): *Histochemistry: The Widening Horizons.* New York, 1981.

3. Laender S., Håkenson R, Sundler F: Neurons containing substance P, vasoactive intestinal peptide, enkephalin or somatostatin in the guinea pig taenia coli. Distribution, ultrastructure and possible function. *Cell Tiss Res* **215:**21, 1981.

4. Iwanaga T, Fujita T, Ito S: Immunohistochemical staining of enteroendocrine paraneurons with antibrain tubulin antiserum. *Biomed Res* **3:**99, 1982.

5. Steinbusch HWM, Verhofstad AAJ, Joosten H: Localization of serotonin in the CNS by immunohistochemistry: description of a specific sensitive technique and some applications. *Neuroscience* **3:**811, 1978.

6. Steinbusch HWM, Niewonhuys R, Verhofstad AAJ, Van der Kooy D: The nucleus raphe dorsalis of the rat and its projection upon the caudoputamen. A combined cytoarchitectonic, immunohistochemical and retrograde transport study. *J Physiol Paris* **77:**157, 1981.

7. Storm-Mathison J, Leknes AK, Bore AT, Vaaland JL, Edmison P, Flang F-MS, Ottersen OP: First visualization of glutamate and GABA in neurons by immunohistochemistry. *Nature* **301:**517, 1983.

8. Sternberger LA, Petrali JP, Joseph SA, Meyer HG, Mills KR: Specificity of the immunocytochemical LHRH receptor reaction. *Endocrinology* **102:**63, 1978.

9. Glowinski J: In vivo release of transmitters in the cat basal ganlion. *Fed Proc* **40:**135, 1981.

10. Milstein C, Wright B, Cuello AC: The discrepancy between the cross-reactivity of a monoclonal antibody to serotonin and its immunohistological specificity. *Mol Immunol* **20:**113, 1983.

11. Falck B, Hillarp N-A, Thieme G, Thorp A: Fluorescence of catecholamine and related compounds with formaldehyde. *J Histochem Cytochem* **10:**348, 1962.

12. Brusco A, Peressini S, Pecci Saavedra J: Serotonin-like immunoreactivity of anti-5-hydroxytryptamine antibodies: Ultrastructural localization in the CNS. *J Histochem Cytochem* **31:**524, 1983.

13. Bjorklund A, Falck B, Lindwall J: Microspectrophotometric analysis of cellular monoamines after formaldehyde or glyoxylic acid condensation, in Bradley PB (ed): *Methods in Brain Research*. London, Wiley, 1975.

14. Wallace JA, Petrusz P, Lauder JM: Serotonin immunocytochemistry in the adult and developing rat brain: Methodological and pharmacological considerations. *Brain Res Bull* **9:**117, 1982.

15. Takeuchi Y, Kimura H, Sano Y: Immunohistochemical demonstration of the distribution of serotonin in the brainstem of the rat and cat. *Cell Tiss Res* **224:**247, 1982.

16. Pasik T, Pasik P: Serotonergic afferents in the monkey neostriatum. *Acta Biol Acad Sci Hung* **33:**277, 1982.

17. Perutka SJ, Lebovitz RM, Snyder SH: Two distinct central serotonin receptors with different physiologic functions. *Science* **212:**827, 1981.

18. Chan-Palay V, Palay SL, Wu J-Y: Sagittal cerebellar microbands of taurine neurons. Immunocytochemical demonstration by using antiserum against the taurine-synthesizing enzyme cysteine sulfuric acid decarboxylase. *Proc Natl Acad Sci USA* **79:**4221, 1982.

19. Oertel WH, Tappan ML, Kopin IJ, Ranson DH, Schmechel DE: Production of an antiserum to rat brain glutamate/cysteine sulfuric decarboxylase. *Brain Res Bull* **5:**713, 1981.

20. Brandon L, Lam DMK, Su YYT, Wu J-Y: Immunocytochemical localization of GABA neurons in the rabbit and frog retina. *Brain Res Bull* **5,** Suppl **12:**21, 1981.

21. Reisert I, Jirikowski G, Pilgrim L, Tappaz ML: GABAergic neurons-dissociated cultures of rat hypothalamus, septum and midbrain. *Cell Tiss Res* **229:**685, 1983.

22. Chan-Palay V, Wu J-Y, Palay SC: Immunocytochemical localization of γ-aminobutryic acid transaminase at the cellular and ultrastructural levels. *Proc Natl Acad Sci USA* **76:**2067, 1979.

23. Pearson J, Brandeis L, Goldstein M: Appearance of tyrosine hydroxylase immunoreactivity in the human embryo. *Devl Neurosci* **3:**140, 1981.

24. Pearson J, Goldstein M, Markey K, Brandeis L: Human brain stem catecholamine neuronal anatomy as indicated by immunocytochemistry with antibodies to tyrosine hydroxylase. *Neuroscience* **8:**3, 1983.

25. Pearson J, Goldstein M, Brandeis L: Tyrosine hydroxylase immunohistochemistry in human brain. *Brain Res* **165:**333, 1979.

26. Grzanna R, Molliver ME, Coyle JT: Golgi-like demonstration of central noradrenergic neurons in thick sections by the unlabeled antibody method. *Proc Natl Acad Sci USA* **75:**2502, 1978.

27. Glazer EJ, Joh TH: Immunocytochemical localization of dopamine-β-hydroxylase within noradrenergic terminals of the rat spinal cord. Ninth Annual Session, American Association of Anatomists, Detroit, 1977, p 588.

28. Houser CR, Crawford GD, Barber RP, Salvaterra PM, Vaughn JE: Organization and morphologic characteristics of cholinergic neurons. An immunocytochemical study with a monoclonal antibody to choline acetyl transferase. *Brain Res* **266:**97, 1983.

29. Higgins D, Iacovitti L, Joh TH, Burton H: The immunocytochemical localization of tyrosine hydroxylase within rat sympathetic neurons that release acetyl choline in culture. *J Neurosci* **1:**126, 1981.

30. Graybiel AM: The compartmental organization of the mammalian striatum. *Progr Brain Res* **58:**247, 1981.

31. Graybiel AM, Pickel VM, Joh TH, Reis DJ, Raysdale CW JR: Direct demonstration of a correspondence between the dopamine islands and acetyl cholinesterase patches in the developing straitum. *Proc Natl Acad Sci USA* **78:**5871, 1981.

32. Nauta JJW, Pritz MB, Lasek R: Afferents of the rat caudoputamen studied with horseradish peroxidase. An evaluation of retrograde neuroanatomical research method. *Brain Res* **67:**219, 1974.

33. Bowker RM, Steinbusch HWM, Coulter JD: Serotonergic and peptidergic projection to the spinal cord demonstrated by a combined retrograde horseradish peroxidase histochemical and immunocytochemical staining method. *Brain Res* **211:**412, 1981.

34. Bowker RM, Westlund KN, Coulter JD: Origin of serotonergic projections to the spinal cord in rat: An immunocytochemical and retrograde transport study. *Brain Res* **226:**187, 1981.

35. Ruda M, Coulter JD: Axonal and transaxonal transport of wheat germ agglutinin demonstrated by immunocytochemistry. *Brain Res* **249**:237, 1982.

36. Bowker RM, Westlund KN, Sullivan MC, Coulter JD: Mapping monoaminergic and peptidergic pathways. In *Proteins in the Nervous System: Structure and Function.* Alan Liss, 1982.

37. Chan Palay V, Palay SL, Wu J-Y: Gamma-amino butyric acid pathways in the cerebellum studied by retrograde and anterograde transport of glutamic and decarboxylase antibody after in vivo injection. *Anat Embryol* **157**:1, 1979.

38. Pearson J: Neurotransmitter immunocytochemistry in the study of human development, anatomy and pathology. *Progr Neuropath* **5**:41, 1983.

39. Pearson J, Axelrod F, Dancis J: Current concepts of dysautonomia: neuropathological defects. *Ann NY Acad Sci* **228**:288, 1977.

40. Pearson J, Brandeis L, Goldstein M: Tyrosine hydroxylase immunoreactivity in familial dysautonomia. *Science* **206**:71, 1979.

41. Rubinstein AE, Mytilienon C, Yahr MD, Pearson J, Goldstein M: Neurotransmitter anatomy of dermal neurofibromas. Implications for the pathogenicity and treatment of neurofibromatosis. *Neurology* **31**:1184, 1981.

42. Graziadei GAM, Margolis FL, Hardin JW, Graziadei PPC: Immunocytochemistry of the olfactory marker protein. *J Histochem Cytochem* **25**:1311, 1977.

43. Graziadei GAM, Levine RR, Monti-Graziadei GA: Plasticity of connection of the olfactory sensory neuron: Regeneration into the forebrain following bulbectomy in the neonatal mouse. *Neuroscience* **4**:713, 1979.

44. Graziedei GAM, Stanley RS, Graziadei PPC: The olfactory marker protein in the olfactory system of the mouse during development. *Neuroscience* **5**:1239, 1980.

45. Marangos PJ, Zomzely-Neurath C, Luk DCM, York C: Isolation and characterization of the nervous system-specific proteins 14-3-2 from rat brain. Purification, subunit composition and comparison to the beef brain protein. *J Biol Chem* **250**:1884, 1975.

46. Schmechel D, Marangos PJ, Zis AP, Brightman MJ, Goodwin FK: The brain enolases as specific markers of neuronal and glial cells. *Science* **199**:513, 1978.

47. Schmechel D, Marangos PJ, Brightman M: Neuron-specific enolase as molecular marker for peripheral and central neuroendocrine cells. *Nature* **276**:834, 1978.

48. Schmechel D, Marangos PJ, Brightman M: Neurons switch from non-neuronal to neuron-specific enolase during differentiation. *Brain Res* **190**:195, 1980.

49. Marangos PJ, Campbell IC, Schmechel DE, Murphy DC, Goodwin FK: Blood platelets contain a neuron-specific enolase subunit. *J Neurochem* **34**:1254, 1980.

50. Kato K, Ishiguro Y, Suzuki F, Ho A, Semba R: Distribution of neuron-specific forms of enolase in peripheral tissues. *Brain Res* **237**:441, 1982.

51. Hideka H, Endo T, Kawamoto S, Yamada E, Umekana H, Tanabe K, Hara K: Purification and characterization of adipose tissue S-100 b protein. *J Biol Chem* **258**:2705, 1983.

52. Cocchia D: Immunocytochemical localization of S100 protein in brain of adult rat. An ultrastructural study. *Cell Tiss Res* **214**:529, 1981.

53. Cocchia D, Miani N: Immunocytochemical localization of brain-specific S-100 protein in the pituitary gland of adult rat. *J Neuropath* **9**:771, 1980.

54. Cocchia D, Michetti F, Donato R: Immunochemical and immunocytochemical localization of S-100 antigen in human skin. *Nature* **294**:85, 1981.

55. Armin A, Connelly EM, Rowden G: An immunoperoxidase investigation of S-100 protein in granular cell myolastomas. Evidence for Schwann cell derivation. *Am J Clin Path* **79**:37, 1983.

56. Eng LF, Vandehagen JJ, Bignami A, Gerstl B: An acid protein isolated from fibrous astrocytes. *Brain Res* **28**:351, 1971.

57. Eng LF, De Armond SJ: Immunocytochemistry of glial fibrillary acidic protein. *Progr Neuropath* **5**:19, 1983.

58. Bigbee JW, Eng LF: Analysis and comparison of an in vitro synthesized glial fibrillary acidic protein with rat central nervous system intermediate filament protein. *J Neurochem* **38**:130, 1982.

59. Schlaepfer WW, Zimmerman V-JP: Calcium-mediated breakdown of glial filaments and neuro-filaments in rat optic nerve and spinal cord. *Neurochem Res* **6:**243, 1981.

60. De Armond SJ, Fajardo M, Naughton S, Eng L: Degradation of glial fibrillary acidic protein by a calcium-dependent protinease: an electroblot study. *Brain Res* **262:**275, 1983.

61. Levitt P, Rakic P: Immunoperoxidase localization of glial fibrillary acidic protein in radial glial cells and astrocytes of developing rhesus monkey brain. *J Comp Neurol* **193:**815, 1980.

62. Eng CF, Rubinstein LJ: Contribution of immunohistochemistry to diagnostic problems of human cerebral tumors. *J Histochem Cytochem* **26:**513, 1978.

63. O'Dowd DK, Eng LF: Immunocytochemical localization of glial fibrillary acidic protein in the Mueller cell of the human retina. *Transact Soc Neurosc* **5:**431, 1979.

64. Anderson MJ, Swanson KA, Waxman SG, Eng LF: Glial fibrillary acidic protein in regenerating teleost spinal cord. *J Histochem Cytochem,* in press.

65. Tascos NA, Parr J, Gonatas NK: Immunocytochemical study of the glial fibrillary acidic protein in human neoplasms of the central nervous system. *Hum Path* **13:**454, 1982.

66. Rubinstein LJ, Brucker J-M: Focal ependymal differentiation in choroid plexus papillomas. An immunoperoxidase study. *Acta Neuropath* **53:**29, 1981.

67. Goebel HH, Schlie M, Bode G, Spoerri O, Eng LF: Die immunohistologische Darstellung des Gliafaserproteins in der neuropathlogischen Tumordiagnostik. *Pathologe* **3:**164, 1982.

68. Marsden HB, Kumar S, Kahn J, Anderton BJ: A study of glial fibrillary acidic protein in childhood brain tumors. *Int J Cancer* **31:**439, 1983.

69. Roessman U, Velasco ME, Gambetti P, Autilio-Gambetti L: Neuronal and astrocytic differentia-tion in human neuroepithelial neoplasms. An immunohistologic study. *J Neuropath Exp Neurol* **42:**113, 1983.

70. Schindler E, Gallotta F: Glial fibrillary acidic protein in medulloblastomas and other embryonic central nervous system tumors of children. *Virchows Arch Path Anat* **398:**263, 1983.

71. Sternberger NH, Itoyama Y, Kies MW, Webster H de F: Immunocytochemical method to identify basic protein in myelin-forming oligodendrocytes of newborn rat CNS. *J Neurocytol* **7:**251, 1978.

72. Peters A, Palay SL, Webster H deF: *The Fine Structure of the Nervous System: The Neuron and Supporting Cells.* Philadelphia, Sanders, 1976.

73. Sternberger NH, Tabira T, Kies MW, Webster H deF: Immunocytochemical staining of basic protein in CNS myèlin. *Trans Am Soc Neurochem* **8:**157, 1977.

74. Kies MW: Myelin basic protein. *Scand J Immunol* **15:**125, 1982.

75. Sternberger NH, Itoyama Y, Kies MW, Webster H deF: Myelin basic protein demonstrated immunocytochemically in oligodendroglia prior to myelin sheath formation. *Proc Natl Acad Sci USA* **75:**254, 1978.

76. Sternberger NH, del Cerro C, Herndon RM: Myelin basic protein demonstrated immunocyto-chemically in adult oligodendrocytes. *J Neuroimmunol* **7:**355, 1985.

77. Agarwal HC, Hartman BK, Shaerer FC: Purification and immunohistochemical localization of rat brain proteolipid. *J Neurochem* **24:**495, 1977.

78. Wolfgram F: A new proteolipid of the nervous system. I. Isolation and amino acid analysis. *J Neurochem* **35:**461, 1966.

79. Norton WT: Biochemistry of myelin, in Waxman SG, Ritchie JM, (eds): *Demyelinating Diseases: Basic and Clinical Electrophysiology.* New York, Raven Press, 1981.

80. Nussbaum JL, Delaunoy JP, Mandel P: Some immunochemical characteristics of W1 and W2 Wolfgram proteins isolated from rat brain myelin. *J Neurochem* **28:**183, 1977.

81. Drammond RJ, Dean G: Comparison of 2′,3′-cyclic nucleotide 3′-phosphodiesterase and the major component of Wolfgram protein W1. *J Neurochem* **35:**1155, 1980.

82. Sprinkle TJ, Wells MR, Garver FA, Smith DB: Studies of the Wolfgram high molecular weight CNS proteins: Relationship to 2′,3′-cyclic nucleotide 3′-phosphodiesterase. *J Neurochem* **35:**1200, 1980.

83. Roussel G, Delaunoy JP, Nussbaum JC, Mandel P: Immunohistochemical localization of Wolf-gram proteins in nervous tissue of rat brain. *Neuroscience* **2:**307, 1977.

84. Quarles RH: Glycoprotein in myelin and myelin-related membranes, in Margalos RU, Margolis RK (eds): *Complex Carbohydrates of the Nervous System*. New York, Plenum, 1979.

85. Sternberger NH, Quarles RH, Itoyama Y, Webster H de F: Myelin associated glycoprotein demonstrated immunocytochemically in myelin and myelin-forming cells of developing rat. *Proc Natl Sci USA* **76:**1510, 1979.

86. Figliewicz DA, Quarles RH, Johnson D, Barbarash GR, Sternberger NH: Biochemical demonstration of myelin associated glycoprotein in the peripheral nervous system. *J Neurochem* **37:**749, 1981.

87. Sternberger NH: Patterns in oligodendrocyte function seen by immunocytochemistry. *Adv Neurochem* **5:**125, 1984.

88. Winchell KH, Sternberger NH, Webster H deF: Myelin-associated glycoprotein localized immunocytochemically in periaxonal regions of oligodendrocytes during hexachlorophane intoxication. *Brain Res* **239:**679, 1982.

89. Raine CS: Editorial to papers of Sternberger et al., Trapp and Quarles and Prineas et al. on the localization of myelin components in CNS and PNS tissue. *J Neuroimmunol* **6:**215, 1984.

90. Trapp BD, Quarles RH: Immunocytochemical localization of the myelin-associated glycoprotein—Fact or artifact? *J Neuroimmunol* **6:**231, 1984.

91. Sternberger NH, McFarlin DE, Traugott U, Raine CS: Myelin basic protein and myelin-associated glycoprotein in chronic, relapsing experimental allergic encephalomyelitis. *J Neuroimmunol* **6:**217, 1984.

92. Prineas JW, Kwon EE, Sternberger NH, Lennon VA: The distribution of myelin-associated glycoprotein in actively demyelinating multiple sclerosis lesions. *J Neuroimmunol* **6:**251, 1984.

93. Ludwin SK: The perineuronal satellite oligodendrocyte: A role in remyelination. *Acta Neuropath* **47:**49, 1979.

94. Ulrich J, Kasper M, Jancer H, Basler V, Heitz Ph U: Glial cells in myelinating tissue cultures visualized by postembedding immunocytochemistry. *Brain Res* **240:**199, 1982.

95. Zale B, Monge M, Dupouey P, Hauw JJ, Baumann NA: Immunohistochemical localization of galactoxyl and sulfogalactoxyl ceramide in the brain of the 30-day old mouse. *Brain Res* **211:**341, 1981.

Chapter Nine

Regulatory Peptides—Endocrine Pathology

In the preceding chapter, we have discussed some of the substances characteristic of the nervous system, including neurotransmitters, glial elements, and some specific proteins that have been found to exist only or predominantly in the nervous system. We have mentioned the communality between neurons and endocrine cells (page 306). We have not, however, discussed any factors capable of conferring degrees of individuality that distinguish one neuron from another. Unlike peripheral cells, neurons do not act in random consort. Each neuron communicates with an abundance of other neurons, as illustrated by the rich endowment of synpatic contacts in widely branching axonal terminals. Each neuron can function individually without necessary participation of anatomically adjacent neurons, and it may be speculated that each neuron is capable to determine which of its synpatic contacts should transmit at a given instance and which should be deactivated. We do not know the basis of this discriminatory capability and its relation to the complex control of motor, sensory, and cognitive coordination. We may assume, however, that it requires heterogeneity of the biochemical principles that confer such discriminatory power. We may perhaps make an analogy with immunoglobulins and certain nonimmunoglobulins that confer individuality to secretory products of lymphocytes and to lymphocytes themselves. These proteins have certain common characteristics, yet exhibit heterogeneity in detailed structure. The basic structures of heterogeneous proteins are, of course, different in the immune system and in the nervous system, as they belong to different families of proteins. Thus, immunoglobulin is a complex multichain protein that possesses invariant, common regions, and variant individual regions (page 4). Conceivably, some of the proteins that confer individuality to neurons also could possess constant and variable regions, but others express their individuality not in the form of complex component structure, but in the forms of fragments released from a single chain structure post-translationally.

There are at least two modes in which neurons can express their biochemical individuality. One mode is in the form of communication of messages to other neurons. This will be discussed in the present chapter. The other mode may be via discriminatory transport of bioactive molecules within axonal remifications. This may be mediated by functional heterogeneity of certain structural components of the neuronal skeleton involved in axonal transport, as will be discussed in the following chapter. Interestingly, substances that mediate communication between one neuron and another are not specific to nervous tissue, although it is possible that nervous tissue makes more discriminatory use of them than peripheral tissue. In contrast, the heterogeneous substances that may have to do with discrimination in axonal transport are highly specific to the nervous system.

THE SCHARRER CONCEPT OF NEUROSECRETION

The beginnings of the study of regulatory peptides are in the postulates of Ernst and Berta Scharrer (1,2), first formulated in 1939, that certain hypothalamic neurons possess properties of endocrine cells. Lacking the advantage of present-day technology, these investigators were led solely by an acute sense of observation and the chance that favors the ingenious mind. The original observations were based entirely on tinctorial histologic staining. The Scharrers found that certain cells in the hypothalamus did not only look like neurons, but also possessed staining characteristics of certain endocrine cells. They postulated that neurons can secrete hormones, and that there is considerable analogy between neuronal and peripheral endocrine secretion. The importance of this concept and its far-leading implications to modern biology lies in the fact that it forms the biochemical basis of the manner in which cells communicate with each other in multicellular organisms, be this through a widespread distribution via body fluids, or through a highly organized distribution emanating from a subregion of one cell onto a subregion of another via synaptic contacts. More recently, two further ways of communication were added to this classification by Berta Scharrer (3), a "private" one that includes short-loop communication among individual groups of cells (pages 196 and 417), and a "semiprivate" one that involves secretion into specialized portal vessels that connect adjacent, but functionally different tissues (page 306) or cells (page 370).

In the discussion in this and the following chapters, we will use the term regulatory peptides synonymously with neuropeptides, bioactive peptides neurosecretory substances (neurosecretion), peptide hormones, and peptidergic transmitters.

One of the most important confirmations of the universality of the Scharrer concept came from the discovery by Berta Scharrer of neurosecretory cells in invertebrates (2) similar to those described in vertebrates. This similarity was one of the earliest suggestions that neurosecretion is an important principle in biology that underlies a fundamental mechanism. Paralleling the significance of nucleic acids in determining protein assembly, or lipids in determining the structure of membranes, or post-translationally added carbohydrates in determining membrane insertion, regulatory peptides may be the basis that determines the manner of intercellular communication. Further confirmation of the importance of neuropeptides came from the discovery, by immunocytochemistry and by synthesis, of their conservative mode of inheritance. Identical or nearly identical neuropeptides are found in human and other mammals, in birds, amphibians, and fishes, as well as in invertebrates and even in coelenterates (page 394). Some of these peptides have first been discovered in molluscs, only later to be found to exist also in mammals (page 394). The very invariance of these peptides attests to their importance. Little genetic modification is tolerated.

If regulatory peptides are so important in cellular communication, the question arises, how can the complex mode of communication in the human brain be mediated by the same substances as those that are sufficient for communication in annelids or coelenterates? About 40 different peptides have been isolated from mammalian tissues and their number is not expected to be much lower in less complicated organisms. The answer to this question may lie in the mode of post-translational assembly of these peptides, as well in the mode of expression of their genes.

The biologically active forms of neuropeptides, at least those described so far, are relatively short sequences of amino acids. It is conceivable that longer bioactive principles also exist, especially since we known that certain peptide hormones, such as insulin or growth hormone, are macromolecular proteins. This is reinforced by the suspected presence in the brain itself of large protein hormones, such as renin and certain pituitary hormones. The usual isolation procedure for regulatory peptides which involves acid alcohol extraction as an initial step, will yield only small molecular peptides in solution and will reject large molecules in the precipitate, thus favoring our acquaintance with small regulatory peptides.

Sephadex chromatography, which separates molecules according to size, has often revealed immunoreactivity (as defined by radioimmunoassay) for a given peptide, not only in the zone corresponding to the known retention of a peptide, but also in fractions eluting earlier, and thus possessing higher molecular weights. In this manner, the existence of big luteinizing hormone-releasing hormone and big adrenocorticotropic hormone (ACTH) and larger analogs of other peptides has been suspected. The existence of these analogs led to the thought that neuropeptides are not assembled on ribosomes in the form in which they are released from the cell, but rather in the form of larger precursors. The processing to smaller regulatory peptides thus becomes a *post-translational* event. Additional support to post-translational processing comes from the structure of the regulatory peptides themselves. Many of these peptides have masked amino-terminal amino acids, such as pyroglutamate or acetylated amino acids, and masked carboxyterminal amino acids, such as glycine amide, or amides of other amino acids. However, there is no genetic coding for pyroglutamate, acetate, or amides. Reactions with these groups occur post-translationally, after or during assembly of the peptide on ribosomes.

OPIOID AND OTHER STRESS-RELATED PEPTIDES

An adrenocorticotropic hormone (ACTH)-secreting mouse pituitary tumor has been known to secrete, in addition to the 39 amino acid peptide, ACTH, several larger proteins that cross-react with ACTH on radioimmunoassay. Mains et al. (4) produced, by double antibody technique (page 21), precipitates from ³H-phenylanaline-labeled culture media of cell lines of this tumor and resolved the precipitates by dodecyl sulfate gel electrophoresis, which separates noncovalently bonded material into individual components. With anti-ACTH antiserum, four components of 31, 23, 13, and less than 4.5 kDa were resolved. Antiserum to endorphin also precipitated the 31-kDa unit, indicating that ACTH and endorphin are parts of the sequence of a common precursor. The tryptic peptides of the labeled material in the 31-kDa component were identical, whether anti-ACTH or antienkephalin were used for their precipitation. In both cases, the methionine-enkephalin sequences were contained in a tryptic digest peptide identical to β-lipotropin (β-LPH) 61-69. From the 31-kDa material, another peptide could be cleaved, which was precipitated by antienkephalin. This peptide was found to be similar to β-LPH. Antienkephalin precipitated from culture media the 31-kDa ACTH and an 11.7- and 3.5-Da component. The 3.5-Da component resembled β-endorphin. From these data, it can be concluded that a 31-kDa peptide exists, which is a precursor of ACTH and β-LPH. β-LPH in turn is a precursor of endorphins, which incorporate the structure of enkephalin. The 31-kDa peptide also incorporates the sequence of β-melanocyte-stimulating hormone (β-MSH).

Under physiologic conditions, the 31-kDa peptide, called preproopiomelanocortin, which is expressed in the anterior and intermediate lobe of the pituitary and in the arcuate nucleus of the hypothalamus, is broken enzymatically, first into three major components, 17-kDa peptide, ACTH, and β-lipotropin, the latter two having biologic activity. β-lipotropin is further processed into several endorphins, which act as opioid peptides pharmacologically, and into α-MSH. Although endorphin incorporates the sequence of the pentapeptide, met-enkephalin, another opioid peptide, it is not, under physiologic conditions, cleaved off β-endorphin peptides.

The 39 amino acid peptide, ACTH, is secreted as such in the anterior lobe of the pituitary. In the intermediate lobe, it is further processed to α-MSH and ACTH 17-39, both being bioactive peptides.

The 17-kDa peptide also incorporates one MSH sequence in the form of α-MSH. Thus, MSH peptides are expressed three times in the preproopiomelanocortin sequence, which presumably is the result of gene duplications.

The cleaved peptides of the proopiomelancortin system have been colocalized immunocytochemically. However, antienkephalin reactivity has not been detected. Instead, antibodies to enkephalin reacted in many other regions, such as for instance, in the adrenal medulla, or in the paraventricular nucleus. In the paraventricular nucleus, enkephalin colocalized with either oxytocin or vasopessin. This finding was not unexpected. Several investigators have suspected, for a long time, that neurons can acquire functional variety by possessing a number of neurotransmitters and neuropeptides. If a single peptide, such as enkephalin, would only be part of the sequence of preproopiomelanocortin, but not of other prehormones, it could be at best be coexpressed only with β-endorphin, β-lipoprotein, ACTH, and MSH. However, if it were, in addition, part of the sequence of another prehormone, it could also be expressed in other locations along with other peptides. The incorporation of given sequences as pieces of a variety of larger sequences, thus, permits a greater variety of combinations by which peptides may be coexpressed. A finite number of peptides may yield an enormous number of different expressions if they are permutated among a large number of different preprohormones. Conceivably, the ability of a given peptide to be coassembled with different peptides in different cells gives a complex structure, such as the human brain, more complexity than a simple structure such as a molluscan ganglion.

The existence for preprohormones of immunocytochemically detectable enkephalin in brain and adrenal has been determined by techniques different from those used for establishment of the existence of preproopiomelanocortin. The latter could be identified directly, because it was secreted in large amounts in a tumor that had originated from the mouse pituitary. No such tumor was available, at least for brain enkephalin. The amino acid sequence of the adrenal precursor, preproenkephalin, and the brain precursor, preprodynorphin, was arrived from the nucleotide sequence of its cloned cDNA (5). The main principle of isolation of the relevant DNA depends on identification of a specific mRNA complementary to at least part of its sequence. There are three strategies for this:

1.   In case of certain cells that produce large amounts of a given protein, one may assume that one of the major mRNA separated chromatographically or electrophoretically is the desired mRNA. The proper mRNA can then be selected by cell-free protein synthesis *in vitro.*

2.   If a monoclonal antibody is available to the terminal sequence of the peptide of interest, and if the sequence is also terminal during assembly on ribosomes, one can use this antibody in double immunoprecipitation to isolate the mRNA of interest.

3.   If a partial sequence of the peptide of interest is known, and if a sequence with little redundancy in the code can be chosen, one can synthesize the mRNA sequences coding for the amino acid sequence. Redundance of the code requires synthesis of a number of mRNA.

In either of these cases, ^{32}P-labeled cDNA is synthesized by reverse transcriptase, and hybridized with the restriction enzyme-produced library of genomic DNA. An appropriate DNA is identified and cloned.

The homologous genomic DNA is larger than the cDNA. The cDNA only incorporates the coding sequence of a small peptide. The genomic DNA represents nucleotides that determine both, expressed and nonexpressed portions of the peptide precursor. The nonexpressed portions are *introns.* The expressed portions are *exons.* They are excised from the genomic DNA and realigned. Excision at different sites and different modes of alignment may yield different preprohormones, which possess a number of identical sequences. Excision occurs during the expression of the genomic DNA. However, the genomic DNA separated for establishment of a cloning library itself is a product of restriction enzymes. Thus, excision and alignment that may occur at a level of still larger DNA sequences will not be revealed.

There are two opioid enkephalin pentapeptides, met-enkephalin with methionine as C-terminal amino acid, and leu-enkephalin, with leucine as C-terminal amino acid. When the coding sequence of leu-enkephalin was used for synthesis of a cDNA probe for genomic adrenal DNA, sequencing of the cloned DNA established a corresponding 260 amino acid sequence for the precursor, preproenkephalin. When the leu-enkephalin cDNA was used as probe for genomic brain DNA, the sequence of the cloned DNA also established a corresponding amino acid sequence for another precursor, preprodynorphin which again possessed 260 amino acids. Preproopiomelanocortin also possesses 260 amino acids.

The met-enkephalin sequence appeared once in preproopiomelanocortin, and the leu-enkephalin sequence appeared seven times in preproenkephalin and three times in preprodynorphin. MSH sequences in preproopiomelanocortin and leu-enkephalin sequences in preproenkephalin and preprodynorphin are flanked by arginine-arginine and arginine-lysine sequences. These paired amino acids, are extraordinarily susceptible to proteolytic degradation and are responsible for the cleavage of the smaller peptides at these positions.

Dynorphins are C-terminally extended sequences of leu-enkephalin (Table 9-1). There are six dynorphin sequences that can be expressed as cleavage products of preprodynorphin. Their opioid activity exceeds that of leu-enkephalin.

There is considerable homology in the three preprohormones for opioid peptides: the N-terminal leader sequences are of approximately equal sizes. This is followed by sequences of about equal length which contain paired cysteines (two pairs in preproopiomelanocortin, three pairs in preproenkephalin and preprodynorphin). Large N-terminal sequences incorporate the bioactive peptides in all the three preprohormones. Since cysteine pairs bring different portions of the amino acid chain into proximity, they may have something to do with the conformational properties of the preprohormones.

There are only two introns that flank the nucleotides for the total bioactive peptide region of these three preprohormones. The sequences coding for the peptides are not interrupted by introns. This restricts the genetic variability that can occur in the expression of a given assembled peptide, that is, the total bioactive peptide sequence of these three preprohormones are coded by a single gene. Apparently all these assembled peptides are so important that little genetic variation can be tolerated, not even excision of one of them. There are some common physiologic properties of the assembled peptides. They all have to do with defense against stress. ACTH mediates metabolic changes on meeting

Table 9-1. Bioactive Cleavage Products of Preprodynorphin[a]

α-Neoendorphin	Tyr-Gly-Gly-Phe-Leu-Arg-Lys-Tyr-Pro-Lys
β-Neoendorphin	Tyr-Gly-Gly-Phe-Leu-Arg-Lys-Tyr-Pro
Dynorphin A	Tyr-Gly-Gly-Phe-Leu-Arg-Arg-Ile-Arg-Pro-Lys-Leu-Lys-Asp-Asn-Gln
Dynorphin A-8	Tyr-Gly-Gly-Phe-Leu-Arg-Arg-Ile
Dynorphin B	Tyr-Gly-Gly-Phe-Leu-Arg-Arg-Gln-Phe-Lys-Val-Val-Thr
Leu-enkephalin	Tyr-Gly-Gly-Phe-Leu

[a] In the intact precursor, these opioid peptides are flanked by Lys-Arg or neutral aliphatic amino acid-Arg sequences. The smaller peptides listed are also derived from the larger ones by cleavage at similar sites that act as post-translational *processing signals*.

stressful situations. Dynorphin, β-endorphin, and enkephalin may help in stressful situations by reducing pain. Preproenkephalin is part of the adrenal medulla, apparently cosecreted with adrenalin.

The homozygous diabetes insipidus rat of the Brattleboro strain is unable to produce vasopression, but does produce oxytocin. Dynorphin radioimmunoassay values are also decreased, although not abolished. The depressed level of dynorphin may reflect its production in oxytocin neurons, but absence of production in vasopressin neurons. This suggests that vasopressin production and preprodynrophin are genetically linked. Separation of the genes for preprodynorphin and those for the hypothetical preprovasopressin-neurophysin (page 383) by way of one or more introns may facilitate unequal expression of both preprohormones in different cells of normal animals, permitting expression of either one or both of the preprohormones, or conceivably their expression along with other preprohormones. In general, it appears that a cell has the potential for expression of many more peptides than those that are normally secreted. They may, however, become expressed in malignant cells, leading to ectopic production of known hormones in unexpected locations, such as ACTH in lung tumors (page 417). When a tumor expresses ACTH, it usually also expresses other components of preproopiomelanocortin, as expected from the absence of intron regions that separate their nucleotide sequences in the genomic DNA.

The genomic DNA for prepromelanocortin, preproenkephalin, and preprodynorphin possess only three intron regions, albeit one of them is very large. The enkephalin cDNA hydridization probe is small compared to the thousands of bases represented in the genomic DNA it detects. If there were additional genomic DNAs in which determinants for individual peptides of the preproenkephalin or preprodynorphin sequences were separated by extensive intron regions, the size of the genomic DNA would be increased. A preprodynorphin genomic DNA, in which constituent peptides are separated by extensive intron regions, may express only small genes. These genes may be excised and ligated with genes for other peptides raising the possibility that peptides, such as enkephalin, may be colocalized in certain cells not only with peptides of the dynorphin and vasopressin-neurophysin sequences, but perhaps with entirely unrelated sequences.

Operationally, opioid peptides are defined by *nalaxone* inhibition of their interaction with receptors. Four classes of receptors have been distinguished so far: μ receptors mediate analgesia. They react best with endorphin or morphine and are mainly found in the hypothalamus. μ receptors are the only receptors in this group which are inhibited by nalaxone specifically and with high affinity. δ receptors mediate euphoria. They react primarily with enkephalin and are found mainly in the cerebral cortex and striatum. κ receptors mediate ataxia and sedation. They react primarily with dynorphin and are mainly found in the deep cerebral cortex. Finally, σ receptors mediate excitation. Nalaxone is a weak but not selective inhibitor of the last three receptors.

Other forms of receptors may undoubtedly exist as does the coexistence of opioid peptides with apparently unrelated peptides, such as vasopressin and oxytocin (page 399).

The three preprohormones for opioid peptides are processed differently by proteolytic cleavage enzymes specific for Lys-Arg, Arg-Arg, or neutral aliphatic amino acid-Arg bonds (Table 9-1). Specificity of processing enzymes is largely responsible for the expression of given small peptides from different precursors. Thus, enkephalin appears to be the main, if not only, physiologically active product of preproenkephalin, while ACTH is the main, yet not only, physiologically active product of preproopiomelanocortin. As already mentioned, in the intermediate lobe of the pituitary, ACTH is further processed to the bioactive, smaller peptides, α-melanotropin (α-MSH) and 17-39 ACTH while in the anterior lobe, 1-39 ACTH is secreted. If the enkephalin sequence were utilized in additional prepropeptides, besides the three known opioid prepropeptides, and if enkephalin were thus coexpressed with still other substances (page 399), the heterogeneity of coexistence of enkephalin with other peptides would be increased along with diversity of combinations of expressed peptides in individual neurons.

Krieger et al. (6) have shown that in the hypothalamus ACTH and α-MSH are produced independently of their synthesis in the pituitary. Hypothalamic ACTH and β-endorphin are the product of the same preprohormone as the pituitary peptides (7). Watson et al. (8), Sofroniew (9), and Cuello (10) corroborated the existence of the precursor in all central ACTH-containing sites by colocalization of β-endorphin in the same neurons. These neurons are concentrated in the arcuate nucleus and tuberal region of the hypothalamus (11). Their axons relay mainly to the anteior and midline regions of the hypothalamus, stria terminalis, and its bed nucleus, with lesser density of fibers to the periventricular thalamus, periaqueductal gray, locus cereleus, and the amygdala. This distribution of fibers is not too dissimilar from the major intracerebral projections of many other neuropeptides with cell bodies in the hypothalamus, except that most hypothalamic neurons contribute primarily to the hypothalamo-pituitary tract, while the preproopiomelanocortin neurons seem to project exclusively to intracerebral sites.

Preproenkephalin-derived enkephalin is easily distinguished from preproopiomelanocortin-derived β-endorphin, since antibodies to β-endorphin do not cross-react with antibodies to enkephalin, even though the enkephalin constitutes a fragment in the β-endorphin sequence. Preproenkephalin neurons have wider distribution than preproopiomelanocortin neurons, although their projections roughly include all the sites also served by preproopiomelanocortin neurons.

The wide distribution of enkephalin projections is reflected by a wide distribution of proenkephalin cell bodies, in contrast to the more restricted distribution of preproopiomelanocortin neurons. It follows that most enkephalin projections encompass local circuitry, although a few long projection fiber pathways have also been observed.

The many areas rich in enkephalin neurons revealed by the immunofluorescence studies of Hökfelt et al. (12) include, among others, the caudate-putamen, the interstitial nucleus of the stria terminalis, thalamic nuclei and midline structures, the arcuate, supraoptic and paraventricular nuclei of the hypothalamus, the interpeduncular nucleus, the central gray and the raphé complex. Fibers follow a similar distribution. Glazer and Basbaum (13) find spinal enkephalin neurons mainly in the marginal layer and in the substantia gelatinosa of the dorsal horn. Most substantia gelatinosa neurons are local circuit neurons, but a significant number of marginal neurons are at the origin of the ascending spino-thalamic tract. The majority of marginal neurons are nocireceptors. Short-loop enkephalinergic neurons in this area may provide inhibiting feedback to nociception. We have already seen that stimulation of the nucleus raphé magnus provides inhibition of nociceptive stimuli at the level of the spinal cord through descending serotonergic relays (page 189). Ruda (14) labeled medullary and spinal dorsal horn neurons retrogradally by injection of horseradish peroxidase into the thalamus and identified enkephalin containing axonal endings of these cells (Fig. 9-1). Thus, second-order projection neurons of nociceptive stimuli to thalamic relays are recipients of enkephalin-mediated input. It, therefore, appears that enkephalin may play a role not only in local circuitry, but also in suppressing the relays of nociceptive information from the periphery to higher centers. The presence of enkephalin-mediated synapses on projection neurons suggests that opiates act, at least in part, on postsynaptic receptors located on dorsal horn thalamic projections.

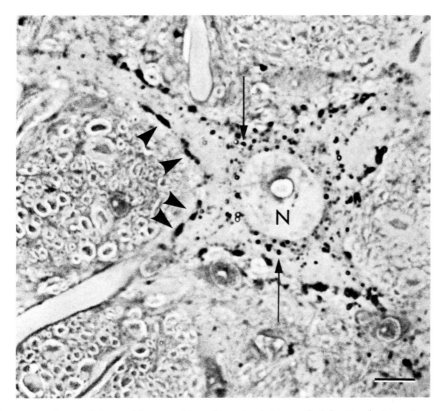

Figure 9-1. Horseradish peroxidase was injected into the thalamus of adult cats, plastic sections were stained for peroxidase, and the diaminobenzidine oxidative polymer blackened with cobalt chloride (page 188). The retrograde label is seen as granules in the cytoplasm (long arrows) of this medullary dorsal horn neuron with an unstained nucleus (N) and prominent, unstained nucleoles. The cell is surrounded by enkephalinergic varicosities (arrowheads) stained by PAP method and revealed with diaminobenzidine in brown color. Bar is 10 μm. [Reprinted with permission from *Science* **215**:1523, Ruda M: Opioid and pain pathways: Demonstration of enkephalin synapses on dorsal horn projection neurons. Copyright 1982, American Association of Science (14).]

Substance P is found in terminals of primary sensory neurons in the substantia gelatinosa. It promotes nociceptive stimuli and may act as neurotransmiter or neuromodulator. Cuello (15) found much overlap in substance P and enkephalin terminals in these areas. Electron microscopic visualization of substance P by autoradiography of monoclonal antisubstance P tritiated in culture (page 260), along with enkephalin by PAP method, failed to reveal any synaptic contact between both kinds of projections. The synaptic geometry of substance P and enkephalin terminals suggested that opiates act nonsynaptically on primary sensory terminals.

Enkephalin is also found in prevertrebral sympathetic ganglia. Dalsgaard et al. (16) injected Fast Blue as a fluorescent retrograde tracer into the inferior mesencephalic ganglion. The label was found in cells of the intermediolateral column of spinal cord identified as enkephalinergic by immunofluorescence. These findings reveal that at least some of the enkephalin-containing fibers in the inferior mesentery ganglion originate in sympathetic preganglionic nuclei in the spinal cord. The occurrence of enkephalin in presynaptic neurons suggests the possibility of coexistence of enkephalin and acetylcholine, similar to the coexistence of vasoactive intestinal peptide with acetylcholine (17) (page 398). It appears from these data that enkephalin may inhibit cholinergic transmission in addition to its inhibition of stimuli mediated or modulated by substance P.

Stengaard-Pederson and Larsson (11) find a striking similarity of distribution of enkephalin and cholecystokinin (page 389), particularly in hippocampus and amygdala (Fig. 9-2). In view of other findings of interaction between cholecystokinin-8 and opioid receptors, and of similar regional distribution of both kinds of receptors, it was felt that cholecystokinin may interact in many brain regions with enkephalin by reaction with different, yet functionally linked, receptors.

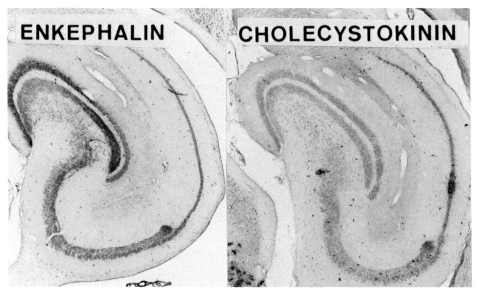

Figure 9-2. Enkephalin and cholecystokinin fibers and terminals are in identical regions in the hilus of the dentate gyrus and in the mossy fibers in regions CA3 of the hippocampus of the guinea pig. PAP method. ×16. [From Stengard-Pederson et al. (11).]

SUBSTANCE P

The undecapeptide, substance P, isolated and characterized by Chan and Leeman (18), has mainly excitatory functions related to nociception, but also mediates autonomic functions, such as blood pressure, smooth muscle contraction and salivary secretion. Hökfelt et al. (19) have shown by immunofluoescence that substance P is probably not present in more than 20% of primary sensory neurons originating in small cell bodies within the dorsal root ganglia. Substance P was seen in nerves related primarily to blood vessels or secretory cells in nearly every peripheral tissue. By pre-embedding staining electron microscopy with PAP technique, these authors revealed substance P-containing nerve endings in the spinal cord, the zona reticulata of the substantia nigra, and in the medial amygdaloid nucleus.

Di Figlia et al. (20) find that substance P axons originating from the dorsal root form frequent synapses on dorsal horn neurons which are also postsynaptic to other types of axons (Fig. 9-3). These results suggest that substance P modulates sensory inputs terminating in the outer dorsal lamina of the spinal cord, in part via axonal inputs onto secondary neurons in the dorsal root. Other transmitters and peptides exert modulating effects in the same area (page 366).

Other indication that substance P is intimately involved in the relay of pain stimuli comes from the observation of Pearson et al. (21) in familial dysautonomia (page 330). These patients have severely reduced sensitivity for pain and temperature, and indeed, exhibit near absence of substance P in the substantia gelatinosa (Fig. 9-4). There was, however, no diminution of substance P in the substantia nigra, indicating that familial dysautonomia does not involve a generalized defect in substance P synthesis.

SOMATOSTATIN

The first step in the isolation of new regulatory peptides is usually acid alcohol extraction of tissue. Under these conditions, small peptides are solubilized, while large proteins remain in the residue. The procedure has favored the early acceptance of small peptides as bioactive principles. The nature and degree of biologic activity of large molecular precursors of peptides was reserved for later explorations.

The 14-amino acid peptide, somatostatin, inhibits release of growth hormone, thyroid-stimulating hormone, insulin, glucagon, gastrin, cholecystokinin, vasoactive intestinal peptide, and many other secretions. It is, however, not an inhibitor of everything. It may be a stronger inhibitor in conditions of hypersecretion than during normal secretion. Given to normal individuals, somatostatin has only mild side effects. However, in the presence of insulin-secreting tumors, it increases blood sugar, and in the case of glucagon-secreting tumors it decreases it. Somatostatin reduces the toxicity of pentobarbital, but increases the toxicity of fluorophosphonate anticholinesteratic substances.

The RNA which encodes for somatostatin is translated into a 116 amino acid preprosomatostatin (22). Somatostatin itself consists of the 14 C-terminal amino acids of this preprohormone. A 28 amino acid somatostatin (consisting of the 28

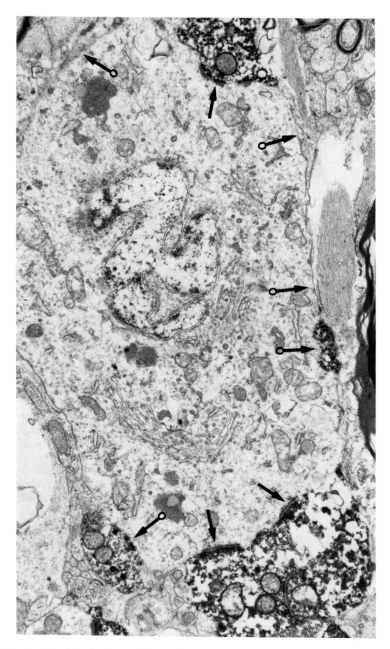

Figure 9-3. A cell body in lamina I of the monkey spinal cord is contacted by substance P-containing terminals (plain arrows). Regions in nearby sections where other substance P axons were found to form synapses are indicated by ringed arrows. PAP pre-embedding technique. ×15,000. [Reprinted with permission from *Neuroscience* **7:**1127, DiFiglia M., Aronin N., Lecman S. E., Light microscopic and ultrastructural localization of immunoreactive substance P in the dorsal horn of the monkey spinal cord, Copyright 1982, Pergamon Press, Ltd. (20).]

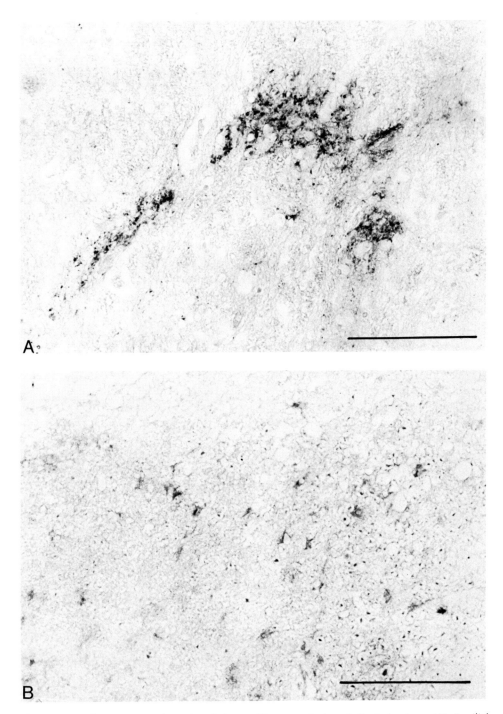

Figure 9-4. Substance P in substantia gelatinosa of human spinal cord. Control autopsy (A). Familial dysautonomia (B). Bar is 100 μm. [From Pearson et al. (21).]

C-terminal amino acids of the preprohormone) has been shown to be more potent biologically than the 14 amino acid somatostatin. Preprosomatostatin consists of an N-terminal leader sequence (amino acids 1-24), 64 amino acid prosequence, and the 28 amino acid C terminal sequence of somatostatin 28, from which somatostatin 14 is split enzymatically. Lechan et al. (23) prepared an antiserum to the 15 amino acid sequence corresponding to amino acid 63 to 77 of preprosomatostatin and belonging to its prosequence (antirat somatostatin cryptic peptide, RSCP). This antiserum provided an immunocytochemical tracer for the prohormone in distinction to antiserum to somatostatin 14, which provided a non-cross-reacting tracer for bioactive somatostatin. Exact correspondence of immunocytochemical localization with both antisera was found, showing that somatostatin is being processed post-translationally throughout its pathway of axonal transport. Most cell bodies reacting with RSCP and somatostatin 14 were in the periventricular nucleus and the parvicellular division of the paraventricular nucleus with some hypothalamic cell bodies also in the suprachiasmic nucleus (Fig. 9-5). Fibers from these cell bodies extended largely, but not exclusively, to the external zone of the median eminence for secretion into the portal pituitary circulation (Fig. 9-6). However, additional somatostatin cell bodies were widely distributed throughout the brain (Fig. 9-5, 9-7) and in peripheral organs where they appeared to form private (3) hormone-controlled relays (page 358).

Separate and distinct anatomical distributions of somatostatin pathways within the hypothalamus as compared to those of other peptides have been established by King et al. (24), Baker and Yu (25), and Krisch (26). Extensive extrahypothalamic networks for somatostatin fibers in the medulla and spinal cord have been mapped by Johannsson and Hökfelt (27) and Forssmann et al. (28). The majority of these projections originate in the hypothalamus, and, according to Krisch (29), form three main pathways: (1) along the stria terminalis and the fasciculus retroflexus to the interpeduncular nucleus, (2) along the medial forebrain bundle into the mammillary body, and (3) via the periventricular gray into the midbrain tegmentum. Significantly, similar extrahypothalamic pathways are occupied by most regulatory peptides that originate in the hypothalamus but project in separate fibers to lower regions of the brain. Many somatostatin projections form terminals on secondary neurons of somatic and visceral afferent systems. Third-order afferent neurons were also affected, but contacts with first-order neurons have not been seen. However, terminals were not exclusive to afferent systems. Limbic nuclei were prominent among other areas with somatostatin innervation.

Taking advantage of the higher resolution obtainable by light microscopy of semithin sections, Grube and Bohn (30) were able to form a three-dimensional reconstruction of cells immunocytochemically stained in serial sections (Fig. 9-8). By this method, they were able to show that only 15% of the pancreatic somatostatin cells (the D cells of the islets of Langerhans) lack contact with capillaries. They concluded that these cells function by secretion in a semiprivate (3), intrainsular circulation, reminiscent of the portal circulation between the median eminence and the anterior pituitary. Some cells contacted two capillaries, possibly revealing neurons with receptor and effector poles.

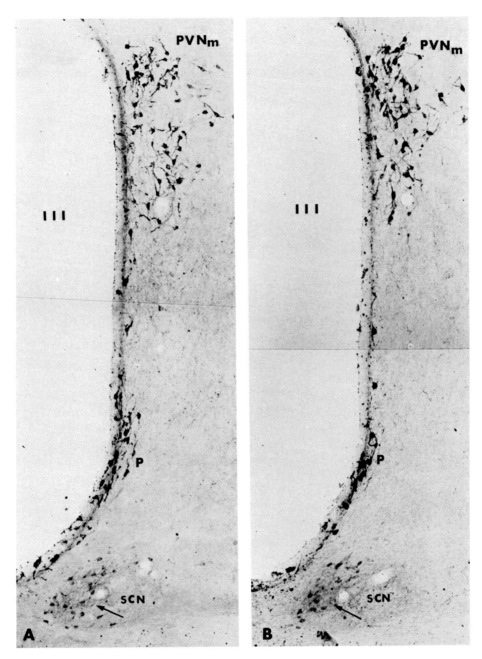

Figure 9-5. Serial coronal 60-μm-thick Vibratome sections of rat hypothalamus (colchicine-treated) show identical localization with antirat somatostatin cryptic peptide (RSCP) (A) and somatostatin 14 (B). P, periventricular nucleus. PV$_n$, parvocellular subdivision of the paraventricular nucleus. SCN, suprachiasmic nucleus. III, third ventricle. PAP method. ×140 [From Lechan et al. (23).]

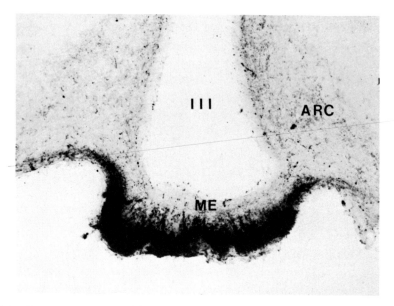

Figure 9-6. Somatostatin in external layer of rat median eminence. Vibratome section, 60 μm thick. Identical localization (not shown) was found for RSCP. ARC, arcuate nucleus. III, third ventricle. PAP method. ×135. [From Lechan et al. (23).]

CORTICOTROPIN-RELEASING FACTOR

The 41 amino acid peptide, corticotropin-releasing factor (CRF), possesses potent releasing activity for ACTH and β-endorphin. It may not be the only corticotropin-releasing factor, since equimolar doses of vasopressin (page 382) also release corticotropin in rats in which the CRF effects are pharmacologically

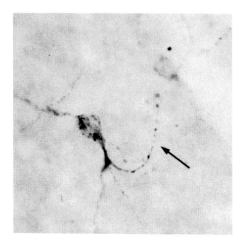

Figure 9-7. RSCP in a cerebrocortical neuron of layer II. Arrow indicates a bended axon originating from a first-order dendrite. [From Lechan et al. (23).]

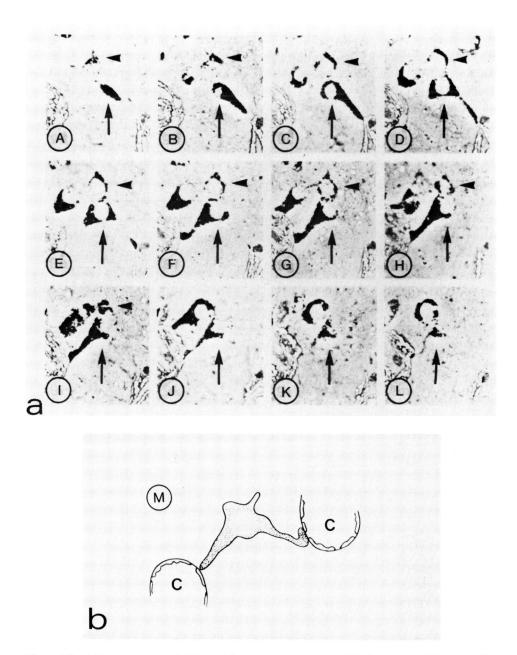

Figure 9-8. (a) Human pancreatic islet, serial plastic sections, 1 μm thick. Somatostatin is in three cells, one of them (arrows) has processes that contact two different capillaries. The cell is also in contact with two other somatostatin cells, of which one (arrowhead) has no vascular contact. PAP method. Phase optics. ×180. (b) Reconstruction of cell labeled by arrows in (a). Intensities of immunocytochemical staining are represented by dark spots. (c) Capillary. [From Grube and Bohn (30).]

blocked. Apparently, because of the importance of cortisone for survival, control of its trophic hormone, corticotropin, is assured by at least two, and conceivably more than two, releasing factors. The anatomic pathway of this release, like that of other pituitary factors, is the hypothalamo-pituitary tract, as revealed in the studies of Paull et al. (31), Merchenthaler et al. (32), and Kawata et al. (33).

Quite generally, when regulatory peptides are examined immunocytochemically, localization is weakest in the cell bodies, stronger in the projection axons, and strongest in the region of the axon terminals. Many peptide-secreting perikarya are entirely missed. A possible reason for this discrepancy could lie in the post-translational processing of peptides. When antibodies are produced to small molecular peptides, they react best with the peptides themselves, and with lesser affinity with precursors, even if the reactive epitopes are available in them. Apparently, forms with increasing immunocytochemical reactivity originate continually in post-translational processing during the course of axonal transport and accumulate in increasing concentrations as they approach the terminals. For instance, Paull et al. (31) observed a moderate distribution of CRF perikarya in the paraventricular nucleus of the hypothalamus (Fig. 9-9), none in the supraoptic nucleus, but intense localization in the external zone of the median eminence (Fig. 9-10) in contact with the capillaries of the hypothalamo-pituitary portal circulation which transfers secretory products to the pars distalis in a "semiprivate" release (3). In these studies, antibodies reacting with the C-terminal as well as the N-terminal portion of CRF were used. While antibodies to the C-terminal region visualized both, cell bodies and nerve terminals, those to the N-terminal

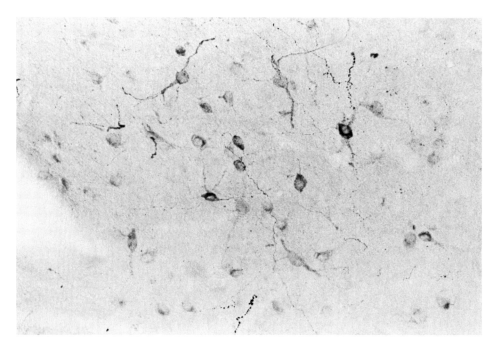

Figure 9-9. Corticotropin-releasing factor neurons in the sheep paraventricular nucleus. Vibratome section, 50 μm thick. Antiserum to C-terminal corticotropin-releasing factor. PAP method. Moderate staining is revealed without colchicine treatment or feedback stimulation. ×460. [From Paull et al. (31).]

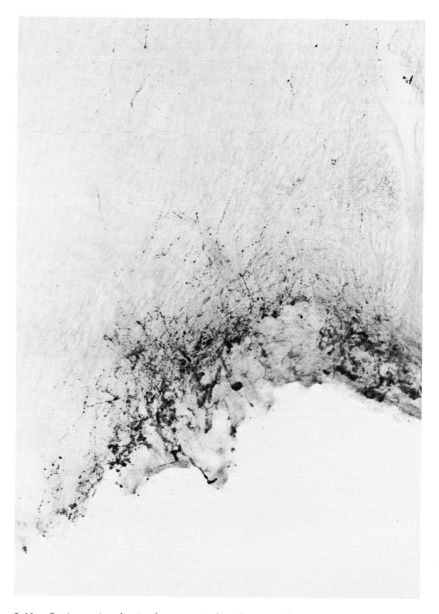

Figure 9-10.   Corticotropin-releasing factor terminals in the external zone of the sheep median entrance. Vibratome section, 50 μm thick. Antiserum to C-terminal corticotropin-releasing factor. PAP method. No colchicine treatment or feedback stimulation. Staining is heavier than in Figure 9-9. ×172. [From Paull et al. (31).]

portion revealed only nerve terminals. This finding provides direct evidence for the post-translational processing of neuropeptides during axonal transport. CRF, like many other peptides, constitutes the C-terminal portion of its ribosome-assembled preprohormone. Therefore, antibodies to the C-terminal portion will react with both the processed bioactive peptide as well as with its N-terminally extended precursors, although reactivity with the precursors may be lessened for steric reasons. On the other hand, antibodies to the N-terminal portion of the processed peptide will react only with the processed peptide. The antibodies will not react with precursor, because in the processed peptide the N-terminal amino acid is usually a pyroglutamate or otherwise altered amino acid, as for instance the deaminated serine (H-Ser) in CRF, while in the precursor the N-terminal amino acid is amidated with the adjacent precursor amino acid (usually a carboxy group of lysine or arginine).

In order to demonstrate perikarya that secrete regulatory peptides, it has generally been the practice to pretreat animals with colchicine to block neuropeptide transport. This treatment causes accumulation of the precursor peptides in perikarya, with concomitant decrease of staining intensity at the terminals. Apparently, the peptides are processed at the "ectopic" perikaryonal locations, thus making them detectable in locations in which normally only precursor is found. The frequent failure to localize peptides in perikarya may not be as much a question of sensitivity of the immunocytochemical method as the physiologic absence of processed peptide in this location. In a way, the colchicine-mediated acute biochemical lesion may resemble the chronic biochemical lesion of Alzheimer's disease (page 461), although the etiologic substrates of both lesions are different.

A more physiologic manner to depict CRF perikarya has been utilized by Merchenthaler et al. (32) who produced feedback stimulation of CRF secretion by hypophysectomy or adrenalectomy, the latter being more effective. Following these treatments, CRF perikarya were not only seen in the paraventricular nucleus but also in the supraoptic, dorsomedial, lateral, and posterior hypothalmic nuclei (Figs. 9-11, 9-12) from where projections curved in fan-like fashion to contribute to a medial, intermediate, and lateral bundle of fibers. Termination of these fibers was mainly in the external zone of the median eminence when

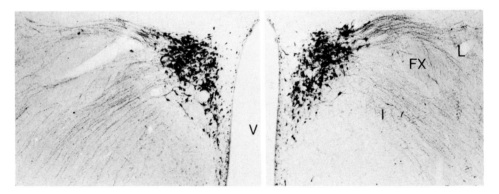

Figure 9-11. CRF perikarya and fibers in the paraventricular nucleus of the long-term adrenalectomized rat. The medial pathway of CRF secretion is seen in this coronal section in close approximation to the wall of the third ventricle (V). The lateral (L) and intermediate (I) pathways are separated by the fornix (FX). Vibratome section, 50 μm thick. Prior to staining by PAP method, sections were brought through 50%, 70%, and again 50% ethanol to facilitate penetration of reagents. The diaminobenzidine oxidation polymer was blackened by perchloric acid and a silver nitrate and formaldehyde-containing developer. The reaction was stopped by 1% acetic acid, "toned" with 0.2% yellow gold chloride (H_3AuCl_4) and further development of unreduced silver was terminated with sodium thiosulfate. ×125. [From Merchenthaler et al. (32).]

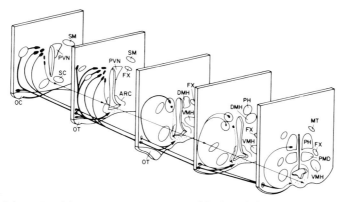

Figure 9-12. Schematics of the CRF containing portion of the hypothalamo-infundibular tract. SM, stria medullaris. PVN, paraventricular nucleus. SC, suprachiasmic nucleus. OC, optic chiasm. OT, optic tract. ARC, arcuate nucleus. FX, fornix. DMH, dorsomedial hypothalamic nucleus. VHM, ventromedial hypothalamic nucleus. P, posterior hypothalamic nucleus. MT, mammillo-thalamic tract. PMD, dorsal premammillary nucleus. [From the work of I Merchenthaler, MA Hynes, S Vigh, P Petrusz, and AV Schally.]

normal animals were used (Fig. 9-13). In addition, a small number of fibers passed through the internal zone to terminate in the pars nervosa. In hypophysectomized or adrenalectomized animals, an increase of staining was revealed in both external and internal zones, and appeared to be especially pronounced in the internal zone (Fig. 9-14) (see also page 382).

The perikarya of peptides that release pituitary hormones are located in the hypothalamus. The perikarya of peptides that affect gastrointestinal function are located in endocrine cells or intrinsic nerves of the gut. However, none of these peptides are functionally restricted to these regions. Many additional peripheral and central axons possess perikarya that produce the same peptides as the endocrine cells of the gut. In the brain, perikarya that secrete a given peptide may all be localized in a narrowly defined region, such as the anterior hypothalamus and may possess wide distribution throughout the brain. Peptides that follow this pattern are vasopressin, oxytocin, and luteinizing hormone-releasing hormone. The short axons of these peptides contribute toward the hypothalamo-pituitary tract. The extrapituitary functions of these peptides are mediated by long projection fibers. In other cases, the peptidergic perikarya themselves possess a wide distribution (33). As a consequence, the projection fibers of these peptides tend to be relatively short, often exhibiting a "private" (3), local distribution, which apparently is modulatory. Peptides that exhibit this pattern are somatostatin, enkephalin, and CRF. Merchenthaler et al. (32) have seen CRF perikarya in the bed nucleus of the stria terminalis and in the central nucleus of the amygdala, locations reminiscent of that of several other peptides (page 364). These perikarya were apparent without any pretreatment of animals, but were intensified by hypophysectomy or adrenalectomy. This suggests a functional relationship to corticosterone. Central ACTH neurons are largely restricted to the basal hypothalamus. Thus, it appears unlikely that the widely distributed CRF neurons act by release of ACTH. It is more likely that they mediate a stress-related function that does not involve ACTH as a trophic hormone or cortisone as an effector hormone, even though the activity is evoked or exacerbated when

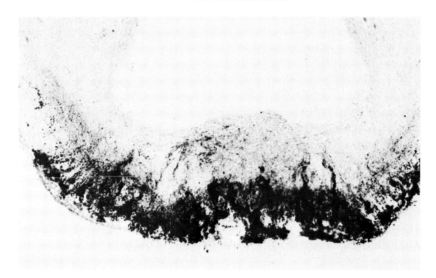

Figure 9-13. CRF fibers and terminals in the median eminence of the untreated rat. Vibratome section, 50 μm thick. PAP method with silver development. ×165. [From Merchenthaler et al. (32).]

these hormones are withdrawn from the peripheral circulation. The situation is reminiscent of the central function of luteinizing hormone-releasing hormone which involves sex behavior without the intermediate action of gonadotropins, but still requires "priming" by sex steroids (page 384).

CRF perikarya were also seen in many other regions of the brain, such as the neocortex, the olfactory bulb, the periaqueducal gray of the pons and mesencephalon, the nucleus cereleus, and the medial vestibular nucleus, but only if the animals were treated with colchicine (32). Staining in these areas was little affected by hypophysectomy or adrenalectomy.

Figure 9-14. CRF fibers and terminals in the median eminence of the long-term adrenalectomized rat. Vibratome section, 50 μm thick. PAP method with silver development. ×165. [From Merchenthaler et al. (32).]

OXYTOCIN AND VASOPRESSIN

The pars distalis of the pituitary is specialized for secretion of the neuron-produced nonapeptides, oxytocin and vasopressin, into the general circulation (2,3). Secreted vasopressin acts upon receptors in the distal convoluted tubules of the kidneys to mediate water retention. Vasopressin secretion is stimulated in dehydration. Vasopressin also has a central action on a broad range of structures of the limbic system. The anatomic pathways of these two divergent actions are different and have been elucidated by immunocytochemistry. Formation of vasopressin is stimulated by nicotine.

Oxytocin causes contraction of the uterus and helps in milk ejection. Formation of oxytocin is stimulated by estrogen.

Unphysiologic doses of oxytocin have vasopressin-like activity, and unphysiologic doses of vasopressin cause generalized smooth muscle contraction, resulting in hypertension. These phenomena are an expression of the structural similarity of both peptides and a phylogenetic origin from a single peptide. Thus, Goossens et al. (34) find only a single neurohypothalamic peptide in Lampetra, while teleosts, amphibians, and mammals possess both peptides. The two peptides are oxytocin and vasopressin in mammals,, and mesotocin and vasotocin in amphibians. All these peptides consist of nine amino acids and possess homology in seven of them. The peptides differ from one another only in amino acids 3 and 8. An intrachain disulfide bond exists between the common cysteines in position 1 and 6, thus making it possible to describe the peptides as consisting of a cyclic 6-amino acid N-terminal sequence and a linear 3-amino acid C-terminal sequence. The cyclic sequence is identical in oxytocin, mesotocin, and vasotocin with isoleucine in position 3. The vasopressin amino acid 3 is phenylalanine. The C-terminal sequence is Pro-Arg-Gly-amide in vasopressin and vasotocin. Since vasotocin is the amphibian equivalent of vasopressin, it appears that the C-terminal sequence is responsible for the functional similarity of both peptides. The corresponding sequence is Pro-Leu-Gly-amide in oxytocin and Pro-Ile-Gly-amide in mesotocin.

Neurophysins are 12,000-dalton proteins that act as carriers for oxytocin and vasopressin. There are two neurophysins in most species of higher vertebrates, called neurophysin I and II on the basis of their electrophoretic mobilities. In the rat, neurophysin I is associated with oxytocin, and neurophysin II with vasopressin; but in the ox, pig, and human, neurophysin II is associated with oxytocin and neurophysin I with vasopressin. Oxytocin and vasopressin are processed from different precursors. These precursors contain the corresponding neurophysins. Immunocytochemistry has generally localized oxytocin and vasopressin in the same locations as their associated neurophysins, confirming the assumed function of neurphysins as carriers for the nonapeptides. Although there is considerable homology among neurophysins of different species in amino acid sequences, radioimmunoassay revealed no significant cross-reactivity of porcine and ovine neurophysin II. However, Watkins (35) found immunocytochemical cross-reactions extensive (page 240).

Gainer (36) has established the processing of neurophysin and oxytocin from a precursor by incorporation into a 20-kDa protein of ^{35}S-methionine, injected

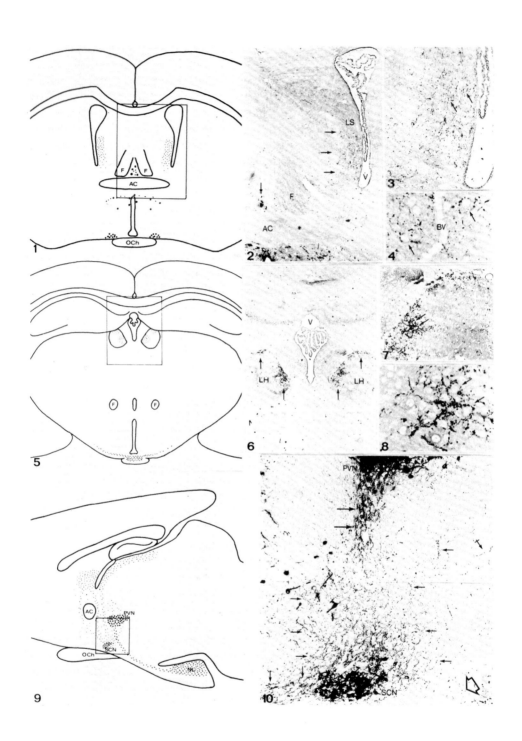

380

adjacent to the supraoptic nucleus, and transformation of the protein to neurophysin and oxytocin during axonal transport.

Studies by Vandesande et al. (37), Dierickx and Vandesande (38), Silverman (39), Krisch (40), Watkins (41–43), Wolf (44), and Sofroniew and Weindl (45) revealed PAP staining for oxytocin and vasopressin and their neurophysins in coarse fibers that leave stained perikarya of the magnocellular neurons of the supraoptic and paraventricular nuclei to converge toward the median eminence (Fig. 9-15) (1,9,10) and to pass caudally through its internal zone, ending in dilated nerve endings in the pars nervosa of the pituitary. This pathway is essentially identical in rat, guinea pig, man, ox, pig, sheep, mouse, quail, pigeon, tortoise, sturgeon, and lamprey.

By postembedding staining electron microscopy, Pelletier et al. (47–49), Koslowski et al. (50), Van Leeuwen and Swaab (51), Silverman (52), and Castel and Hochman (53) found oxytocin and vasopressin in secretion granules, less extensively in perikarya, more extensively in axonal dilations called Herring bodies, and most abundantly in nerve terminals. Castel and Hochman (53) observed a greater abundance of vasopressin-containing secretion granules in the wild mouse and particularly in the Dead Sea mouse than in the white laboratory mouse, apparently as an adaptation to arid climate. In general, no extragranular PAP complexes have been observed. Interestingly, Krisch (54) found that upon rehydration of long-term-dehydrated rats, a burst of vasopressin secretion is revealed not only by intragranular vasopressin, but also by presence of vasopres-

---

Figure 9-15. The drawings show the distribution of oxytocin (OT), vasopressin (VP), and neurophysin (Np) perikarya and fibers at different levels of the mouse brain. The micrographs reveal Np stained by the PAP method. These sections have been counterstained with toluidine blue to bring out background and reveal general cytoarchitecture. (1) Frontal section at the level of the anterior commissure (AC), columns of the fornix (F), optic chiasm (OCh), and septum. Magnocellular Np, OT, VP perikarya, and fibers are depicted as large dots in the supraoptic nucleus and scattered around the third ventricle below the AC. Some magnocellular OT and Np perikarya and fibers are found between the fornices in the triangular nucleus of the septum. Fine caliber VP and Np fibers in the lateral septum are depicted as fine dots. ×125. (2) Frontal section corresponding to the rectangle in (1). Magnocellular Np perikarya and fibers are present around the third ventricle below the AC and in the triangular nucleus (↓). Fine caliber fibers are concentrated (→) in the ventral portion of the lateral septum (LS). VL, ventricle. ×28. (3) Detail of (2). Fine caliber Np fibers in the LS. ⸜ cells in (4). ×71. (4) Detail of (3). Np fibers are clustered around the cell soma of septal neurons suggesting axo-somatic type contacts (↑). BV, blood vessel. ×280. (5) Frontal section at the level of the median eminence and habenulae. Fibers of magnocellular neurons are depicted as large dots in the median eminence. Fine caliber Np fibers in the median eminence. Fine caliber Np and VP fibers in the lateral habenulae are depicted as fine dots. ×12.5. (6) Frontal section corresponding to the rectangle in (5). Fine caliber NP fibers (↑) are clustered bilaterally in distinct medial and dorsal portions of the lateral habenulae (LH). V, ventricle. ×28. (7) Detail of (6). Fine caliber Np fibers in the LH. (⸝) cells in (8). ×80. (8) Detail of (7). Np fibers are clustered around the cell soma of neurons in the LH, suggesting axo-somatic type contacts (⸝). ×280. (9) Paramedian sagittal section. Magnocellular perikarya of the paraventricular nucleus (PVN) send their processes to the neural lobe (NL). Some parvocellular Np- and VP-producing perikarya of the suprachiasmatic nucleus (SCN) send their processes dorsally, and two main pathways can be traced to the lateral septum and lateral habenulae. ×12.5. (10) Paramedian sagittal section corresponding to the rectangle in (9). Larger caliber Np fibers (→) descending from magnocellular perikarya of the PVN are easily discernible from the fine caliber Np fibers ascending from the parvocellular neurons of the SCN (←). Fine caliber Np fibers leaving the SCN are directed rostrally (↓), as well as rostrodorsally, dorsally, and caudodorsally (←). No fibers appear to descend toward the median eminence (⸝). Most of the dorsally directed fibers ascend and can be traced on serial sections to the LS or LH as shown in (9). Some ascending fibers project caudally (⬂). ×71. [From Sofroniew and Weindl (46).]

sin in the axoplasmic reticulum, thus suggesting an extragranular transport of vasopressin that supplements the granular transport during periods of peak demand. The finding is important because it implies that a peptide may, at times, be secreted not only by exocytosis but also by other means (page 414).

In pre-embedding staining electron microscopy, Broadwell et al. (55) saw neurophysin within the cisternae of the nuclear envelope and rough endoplasmic reticulum and in Golgi vacuoles and secondary lysozomes.

Oxytocin and vasopressin and their associated neurophysins are produced in separate neurons and transported in separate fibers. Vandesande and Dierickx (56–62) immunized with neurophysin I and II, isolated by disk electrophoresis and electrophoretic focusing, and found both neurophysins in the bovine and rat supraoptic and praventricular nuclei in groups of neurons that were partially separated, yet often intermixed (56). With antiserum to vasopressin absorbed with insolubilized oxytocin, and with antioxytocin absorbed with insolubilized vasopressin, they found neurophysin I associated with oxytocin and neurophysin II with vasopressin. This demonstration depended on the use of adjacent serial sections. Similar separation of vasotocinergic and mesotocinergic fibers was observed by serial sectioning in the amphibian hypothalamus (58). Dierickx and Vandesande and their associates (60,62) extended these studies to serial ultrathin sections and again they found that in mesotocinergic fibers of the amphibian all granules contained mesotocin, and in vasotocinergic fibers all granules contained vasotocin. No mixed fibers or granules were seen. Similarly, complete separation of oxytocinergic and vasotocinergic fibers was observed in the rat (63). Vandesande and Dierickx (56,59) confirmed these results by double-staining technique (page 196).

Just as CRF, so does vasopressin secretion respond to adrenalectomy. Normally, vasopressin fibers course mainly in the internal zone of the median eminence toward the neurohypophysis. Few fine fibers are found in the external zone. However, after adrenalectomy, Dierickx et al. (64) find an increase of vasopressin fibers in the external zone of the median eminence, where they mediate secretion into the pituitary portal system to affect the adenohypophysis (Fig. 9-16). The findings support the physiologic significance of the corticotrophin-releasing function of vasopressin.

Sofroniew and Weindel (45,65) demonstrated, in the normal and the congenitally vasopressin-deficient Brattleboro rat, neurophysin and oxytocin-containing coarse fibers that originate from the magnocellular nuclei of the hypothalamus and pass through the stria medullaris to the central amygdala (Fig. 9-15). Their terminals are in a general area that also possesses terminals for LHRH and may be important in sexual behavior. That this pathway is mainly oxytocinergic was demonstrated with PAP staining by Buijs et al. (66) with antioxytocin absorbed with insolubilized vasopressin. Other fibers of the same origin descended through the posterior hypothalamus near the fornix, passed dorsal of the mammillary bodies to the substantia nigra to join the central gray. They have been found in the nucleus solitarius and in the dorsal and ventral horns of the spinal cord.

The hippocampus is one of the areas in which Buijs (67) found vasopressin projections from the paraventricular nucleus. As low doses of vasopressin increase reversibly the firing of neurons in the CA1 area of hippocampal slices (68)

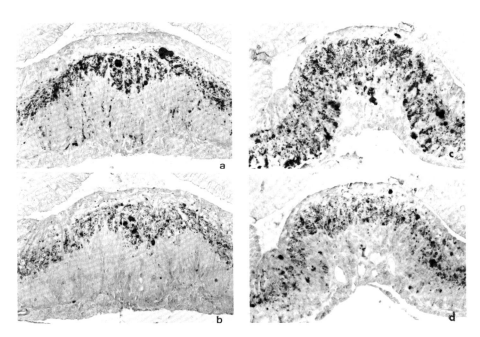

Figure 9-16. In a coronal section of normal rat immunostained with sepharose-4b-oxytocin-absorbed antivasopressin (a), vasopressin is seen primarily in the internal zone. Some fibers apparently coursing perpendicularly to those in the internal zone, enter the external zone to end, apparently, in próximity to capillaries of the pituitary portal circulation. An adjacent section (b) immunostained with sepharose-4b-vasopressin-absorbed antimesotocin reveals oxytocin only in the internal zone. Following bilateral adrenalectomy (c) vasopressin in the external zone is greatly increased, but an adjacent section (d) still reveals no oxytocin in this location. PAP method. ×144. [From Dierickx et al. (64).]

in normal and Brattleboro rats, these projection fibers are probably axons. The bi- and multipolarity of paraventriclar nucleus cells suggests that some cells may project to the neurohypophysis as well as to other regions. Some of these projection fibers may be dendrites, conceivably mediating release of vasopressin through axons into the general circulation via the neurohypophysis as observed upon stimulation of spinal cord, amygdala, and other regions of the brain.

The 20-kDa common neurophysin-vasopressin precursor described by Gainer (36) is probably itself the cleavage product of a still larger preprohormone. We will see that enkephalin colocalizes in the supraoptic nucleus and paraventricular nucleus with vasopressin and oxytocin (page 399). By affinity purification with antineurophysin, Lauber et al. (69) have isolated an 80-kDa peptide from neurohypophyseal extracts. Cleavage products of this peptide possess ACTH immunoreactivity and bioactivity, as well as β-endorphin, neurophysin, and vasopressin immunoreactivities. It appears to represent a common precursor of vasopressin and opioid peptides, larger in size than preproopiomelanocortin.

The analyzed genomic DNA for preproopiomelanocortin does not, however, code for neurophysin or vasopressin. Identification of genomic DNA depends on hybridization with cDNA, usually identified by radioactivity of chromatographically separated enzyme-cleaved DNA. Spots of highest activity compared to background are used for further investigation. If there existed a genomic DNA for neurophysin and parts of preproopiomelanocortin, it would hybridize with the preproopiomelanocortin cDNA probe with lesser efficiency and could be missed, because it might possess only little radioactivity above that of background. Such a situation could occur if most of ACTH-endorphin were indeed coded by preproopiomelanocortin cDNA as reported, and only the small fraction found in the supraoptic and paraventricular nuclei, by a cDNA coding for the 80-kDa peptide.

The analyzed genomic DNA for preproopiomelancortin does not code for neurophysin or vasopressin. Therefore, the 80-kDa precursor of neurophysin and vasopressin, while incorporating some of the proopiomelanocortin peptides, does not incorporate all of them. It, therefore, contributes to diversity of colocalization of identified preproopiomelanocortin products with other peptides not part of the classical preproopiomalanocortin sequence.

LUTEINIZING HORMONE-RELEASING HORMONE

The decapeptide, luteinizing hormone-releasing hormone (LHRH), affects release of both luteinizing hormone (LH) and follicle-stimulating hormone (FSH) from pituitary gonadotrophs. In addition, LHRH induces mating behavior (lordosis) in ovariectomized, estrogen-primed rats, even if they are hypophysectomized (70,71). Finally, LHRH stimulates testosterone production in purified Leydig cells in a direct, gonatropin-independent manner (72). All known functions of LHRH involve reproductive mechanisms.

As shown by King et al. (73), LHRH immunoreactive perikarya are found in a single region of the brain, although within this region their distribution is diffuse, so that no single anatomic nucleus can be described as being a major focus of origin of LHRH secretion. The distribution of these perikarya resembles the form of a V in the horizontal plane, in which the apex is directed rostrally toward the organum vasculosum of the lamina terminalis, while the arms of the V, bisected by the third ventricle, are directed ventrally and caudally toward the median eminence. The nuclei involved are the nucleus of the vertical limb of the diagonal band of Brocca, the medial nucleus of the septum, and the medial preoptic nucleus. From these areas, all LHRH fibers emanate, including not only those in the hypothalamo-pituitary tract, but those to other far-flung areas of the brain. There are no LHRH perikarya in the posterior hypohalamus.

As shown by King et al. (73–75), Baker et al. (76), Gross (77), and Ibata et al. (78), the majority of processes of LHRH immunoreactive fibers form two different systems which are separated by the midline hypothalamic nuclei over most of their course toward their termination in the external zone of the median eminence. The lateral fiber system contributes toward the median forebrain bundle, while the median system is closely associated with the third ventricle (Fig. 9-17).

A few LHRH immunoreactive fibers enter the internal zone of the median eminence. These fibers have been shown by Anthony et al. (80) to penetrate the neurohypophysis. Most of them terminate in proximity to the adenohypophysis and may affect the tuberal region of the organ which is especially rich in gonado-

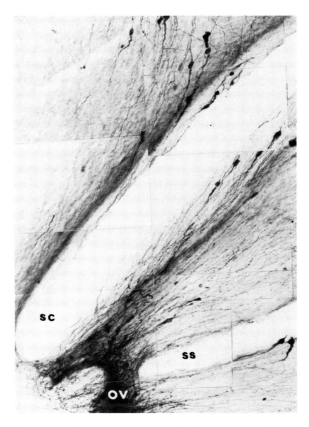

Figure 9-17. LHRH fibers ascending in close contact with the ependyma of the third ventricle. Photomontage of rat, saggital vibratome section near midline, 100 μm thick. PAP method. OV, organum vasculosum laminae terminalis. SC, suprachiasmic recess of third ventricle. SS, suprasellar recess of third ventricle. ×130. [From Burchanowski et al. (79).]

trophs. Conceivably, some of the LHRH is released into the general circulation and may directly affect receptors in such distant locations as in Leydig cells (72).

LHRH-immunoreactive neurons are usually bipolar. We have seen (79) many of these neurons directing one projection toward the organum vasculosum of the lamina terminalis of the median eminence, while the other ascended either within the stria medullaris, or in close association with the wall of the third ventricle toward the subfornical organ (Fig. 9-17). Silverman (81) has shown that LHRH-immunoreactive perikarya are the source of a wide system of LHRH fibers that terminate intracerebrally and represent, apparently, LHRH neurotransmitter fibers. In the guinea pig, two sets of profuse fibers descend to the preoptic and retrochiasmic portions of the suprachiasmic nucleus, respectively, passing close to non-LHRH-containing cells. Fine, scattered fibers ascend in the septum, while others pass through the stria medullaris to the habenula, are picked up in the fasciculus retroflexus, and become indistinct after having passed through the interpedunclar nucleus. A heavy bundle of fibers was also observed between the mammillary body and the interpeduncular nucleus.

Silverman (81) found that after lesions of the medial septal region, LHRH staining in the interpeduncular nucleus disappeared. Lesions in the organum vasculosum are inhibitory to staining of fibers in the medial preoptic area, in the mammillary body, and in the anterior interpeduncular nucleus.

The decapeptide, LHRH, possesses no free amino group capable of reacting with aldehyde fixative. The N-terminal amino acid is pyroglutamate, and the peptide is devoid of lysine amine. LHRH is highly soluble in water and fixatives do not attach it to tissue. One expects, therefore, that tissues processed for immunocytochemistry by fixation and washings should be devoid of LHRH. There exists, indeed, only a poor correlation of LHRH monitored by radioim-munoassay with that revealed by immunocytochemistry in various areas of the brain. We felt that LHRH could be detected by anti-LHRH in fixed tissue only if it were held by a receptor or carrier. To test this hypothesis, we treated Bouin-fixed paraffin sections with LHRH prior to immunocytochemical staining. Such treatment increases postembedding electron microscopic staining in the pitui-tary because of reaction of receptors with LHRH (page 403). In the median eminence, however, treatment of paraffin sections with LHRH, followed by extensive washings, prior to immunocytochemical staining for light microscopy by anti-LHRH, *abolished* the staining (82). We interpreted the findings by assum-ing that there exists a low-affinity carrier for LHRH and its precursors in the median eminence. Because of the solubility of LHRH, and the low affinity of the putative carrier, LHRH is lost from sections, and indeed never detected im-munocytochemically, as all immunocytochemistry involves extensive washings. However, LHRH may be detected by radioimmunoassay of fresh tissue in which no washing steps are involved. What is detected by immunocytochemistry ap-pears to be a precursor to LHRH which possesses higher affinity for the carrier than LHRH itself. Pretreatment of sections with high concentrations of LHRH exchanges the precursor for the decapeptide, which in turn is lost on subsequent washings because of its lower affinity, resulting in loss of LHRH immunocyto-chemical reactivity, at least in paraffin sections. When Bouin-fixed homogenates of hypothalamus were treated with LHRH, a peak was eluted that preceded LHRH in reverse-phase high-pressure liquid chromatography. No such peak was eluted by similar treatment of cerebellum.

These studies precipitated the search of an LHRH precursor in fresh hypo-thalamus. Basic to the approach was the consideration that the presumed pre-cursor possesses reactivity with LHRH, for otherwise, it would not have been possible to surmise its existence from immunocytochemical analysis of fixed tissue. Immunoreactivity permits use of affinity columns for purification, and has the advantage that material is concentrated by the column rather than di-luted, as in the case of gel filtration or ion-exchange purification. Concentration is especially effective if monoclonal antibodies are employed, because mono-clonal antibodies provide a narrow dissociation zone upon application of an elution gradient. We have, therefore, produced monoclonal antibodies to LHRH and isolated two clones which produced antibodies with affinities for LHRH of $10^{10}/M$ (83). Indeed, these antibodies provided some of the highest affinity antibodies ever produced, an important feature in the use of radioimmu-noassay at high sensitivity. The antibodies were found to be specific for the C-terminal sequence of LHRH.

The procedure for purification of precursor from hypothalamic extracts involved preliminary separation of LHRH from larger immunoreactive principles by dialysis through 2000 Da cutoff membranes. With these membranes, precursor was retained, while ^{125}I-LHRH added as a tracer was reduced to 0.0084%.

Affinity columns made with monoclonal anti-LHRH were standardized with [125]LHRH to determine the position of elution in acid gradients (84). When hypothalamic extracts were dialyzed and then passed through the columns, we found that 14 to 18% of the original LHRH immunoreactivity of rat hypothalami was present in the form of higher molecular weight material. On high-pressure liquid chromatography, this material formed a single peak that possessed immunoreactivity and was distinct from that of added LHRH tracer.

The projections of LHRH neurons to the midbrain central gray are of special importance as the site of facilitation of lordosis response in estrogen-replaced, gonadectomized female rats (70,71). LHRH released from the median eminence of the rat is dependent on gonadosteroids, and an increase of radioimmunoassayable LHRH in the pituitary portal circulation can be correlated with a decrease in immunocytochemical reactivity in the median eminence, suggesting accelerated release (85). Shivers et al. (86) quantified LHRH immunoreactivity contents in cell bodies by total cell counts and optical density of each PAP-stained cell body examined in a microspectrophotometer. LHRH-immunoreactive projections in the organum vasculosum of the lamina terminalis and in the median eminence were quantified by placing corresponding sections under a reticle consisting of 121 intersections and counting the number of PAP-stained fibers or beads. In the mesencephalic central gray, LHRH-immunoreactive fibers appeared in proximity to the ependymal lining of the cerebral aqueduct. The number of LHRH-immunoreactive fibers traversing cross-sections obtained at regular intervals was counted.

Gonadotropins or estrogen replacement did not affect the LHRH contents of the organum vasculosum of the lamina terminalis (Fig. 9-18). The contents of LHRH in the organum vasculosum were constant throughout the estrus cycle.

Gonadotropins in the male increased the release of LHRH into the pituitary portal circulation and decreased immunocytochemical reactivity in the median eminence as well as in the mesencephalic gray. The decrease may be attributable to depletion as the result of increasing release. Alternatively, the decrease of immunocytochemical reactivity may be due to accelerated post-translational processing of LHRH, considering that only the LHRH precursor is visualized immunocytochemically.

In the ovariectomized female, estrogen replacement increased the number of LHRH-immunoreactive fibers in the caudal median eminence, but decreased the number of these fibers in the mesencephalic gray that did *not* contact the ependyma. It is these fibers that may be of behavioral interest as they terminate in the gray matter in this area. The decrease of immunoreactive LHRH in fibers suggests an increased release, or alternatively an increased rate of processing of immunocytochemically reactive precursor to immunocytochemically unavailable LHRH. Infusion of LHRH into the mesencephalic gray facilitated lordosis response in ovariectomized estrogen-prime females, and infusion of anti-LHRH inhibited this response. The immunocytochemically revealed, increased LHRH release or the increased rate of LHRH processing following estrogen administra-

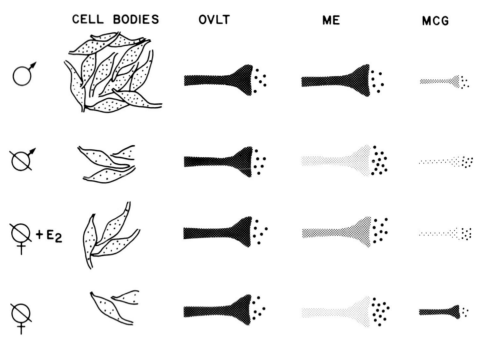

Figure 9-18. Effect of estrogen on LHRH in cell bodies, organum vasculosum of the lamina terminalis (OVLT), median eminence (ME), and mesencephalic gray (MCG) in normal and castrated male rats, and in ovariectomized and ovariectomized estrogen-(E_2)-replenished female rats. For each group, the relative number and optical density of stain in LHRH cell bodies are shown (indicated by number of dots), along with a representation of relative LHRH contents in terminals (indicating by variations in shading), and their presumed relative rates of LHRH release (indicated by dots adjacent to the terminals) in three brain regions. The small size of the terminals in mesencephalic gray relative to organum vasculosum of the lamina terminalis and the median eminence illustrates the lesser density of fibers in this terminal field. An increase of release (dots) is inferred from a decrease in LHRH immunoreactivity contents (shades), by results of radioimmunoassay studies of LHRH in the pituitary portal circulation, and LHRH immunocyto-chemical reactivity in the median eminence. Shaded symbols for male and female indicate gonadectomy. [From Shivers et al. (86).]

tion to ovariectomized females also shows that lordotic response can be attrib-uted to the action of LHRH.

THYROTROPIN-RELEASING HORMONE

The tripeptide, pyroglutamate-histidine-proline amide, besides acting as thyro-tropin-releasing hormone (TRH), possesses direct action on the central nervous system, such as L-dopa and serotonin potentiation, antidepressant properties, and inhibition of barbiturate poisoning. By radioimmunoassay and bioassay, it possesses a wide distribution in the human brain, with highest concentrations in the mammillary body, amygdala, and inferior olivary nucleus (87,88). Immuno-cytochemically, Hökfelt et al. (89,90) and Lechan and Jackson (91) found TRH nerve terminals not only in the medial part of the external layer of the median eminence, the dorsomedial nucleus, and the perifornical area but also in extrahypothalamic areas, such as the nucleus accumbens, the lateral septal nucleus, many cranial nerve nuclei, and motoneurons of the spinal cord.

Lechan et al. (92) found growth hormone not only in the adenohypophysis, but also in the neurohypophysis, in the hypothalamus, lateral septum, and many widespread regions involving extrahypothalamic areas of motor and sensory regulation of the autonomic nervous system. Some hypothalamic neurons also were found to project to extrahypothalamic regions. This distribution was strikingly similar to that of TRH. On serial sections, the distribution of both hormones was found identical. Similar results were obtained by staining sections brown with antigrowth hormone, PAP, and diaminobenzidine, eluting antibodies with potassium permanganate and finding the same localization on restaining sections blue with anti-TRH, PAP, and 4-chloro-naphthol. The consistent colocalization of growth hormone and TRH over a wide distribution of cells and fibers suggests that the coexistence is obligatory, that is, that both peptides are derived from a common precursor. The situation is reminiscent of the obligatory coexistence of ACTH peptides and β-endorphin, and differs from the occasional coexistence of other peptides in the same neuron but not in others, as for example, the coexistence of substance P with TRH in raphé nuclei of the medulla, but the separate existence of these peptides in most other locations (page 400).

CHOLECYSTOKININ

Gastrin stimulates secretion of gastric acid, pepsin, and intrinsic factor, of pancreatic enzymes, and of gastrointestinal water and bicarbonate. *Cholecystokinin* (CCK) has similar properties but also inhibits gastrin secretion. It is a powerful stimulant of gallbladder contraction and of pancreatic water and bicarbonate response to secretin. Gastrin possesses 17 amino acids and cholecystokinin 33. The biologic activity of both peptides resides in the carboxyterminal region. Identity of the five carboxyterminal amino acids in both peptides suggested to Larsson and Rehfeld (93) a common ancestral origin. Antisera reactive with the five carboxyterminal amino acids will detect both gastrin and cholecystokinin. However, an antiserum specific to the 25-30 region of cholecystokinin will detect cholecystokinin, but not gastrin. By the use of these two antisera, Larsson and Rehfeld (93) found that some cells of the mammalian gastrointestinal mucosa, especially in the duodenum and jejunum, only reacted with anticholecystokinin[25-30] in PAP staining and were, therefore, cholecystokinin cells. Other cells, especially in the antral mucosa, reacted with anti-C-terminal pentapeptide but not with the anticholecystokinin and were, therefore, gastrin cells. In the frog, however, all cells, whether in the gastrointestinal mucosa or in the median eminence, which reacted with anticholecystokinin[25-30] also reacted with the antipentapeptide. Therefore, more than the carboxyterminal pentapeptide sequence must have been shared by the polypeptide in all the cells, suggesting greater homology, if not identity of gastrin and cholecystokinin-like peptide in the amphibian and demonstrating that both peptides, indeed, have developed from a common ancestor.

In the alligator antrum and small intestine, however, Buchan et al. (94) detected immunocytochemical reactivity of mucosal endocrine cells only with antiserum to the C-terminus of gastrin. Antisera to the N-terminal sequence of gastrin did not react. Neither did antiserum specific to the 9-20 sequence of CCK. Therefore, in the alligator, the single peptide sharing carboxyterminals with gastrin and CCK is diverted from the gastrin-like structure found in frogs and mammals. Furthermore, in contrast to frogs and mammals, intrinsic nerves of the intestine were devoid of CCK-like C-terminal immunoreactivity. These findings illustrate the conservative inheritance of the carboxyterminal end of a bioactive peptide and the increased genetic flexibility that is permitted as we move toward the amino terminals of the preprohormone. One may conceive that the principal action of a group of peptides that can be assembled from a preprohormone resides in the C-terminus, but that bioactive precursors of larger size may have more specific function that permits greater variability or greater discriminatory power.

Larsson and Rehfeld (95) showed that a number of antisera reacting with gastrin and CCK detected widely distributed neurons and fibers that were most numerous in the neocortex, hippocampus, amygdala, hypothalamus, spinal cord, and the submucosal and myenteric plexus of the colon. Reactivity was also found in other visceral nerves, but to lesser extents. In the urinary system, rich CCK innervation was only to the bladder. As mucosal, endocrine gastric cells did react with all these sera, the neuronal substances are related to CCK and its breakdown products. By gel filtration of extracts of regions rich in immunocytochemical reactivity, Larsson and Rehfeld (95) found five immunoreactive components of which four corresponded to the 33 amino acid peptide CCK and the C-terminal dodeca-, octa-, and tetrapeptide portions of CCK, respectively. Apparently, the tetrapeptide was quantitatively the most important among these components.

Despite differences in structure, the sharing of bioactive carboxyterminal sequences between the gastrointestinal endocrine cell peptide, gastrin, and the neuropeptide, CCK, confers to both peptides a functional similarity, in that both peptides are usually, but not always, excitatory. This, as well as their origin from a common ancestral form (93), provides yet another illustration of the Scharrer concept (1,2) of the close relation between endocrine and neurosecretory systems. In the cerebral cortex, CCK excites cortical neurons. Peters et al. (96) compared the shape of immunocytochemically stained neurons with Golgi preparations (page 320) to identify which type of cortical neurons contain CCK. The peptide was found in layer I neurons, bipolar cells (Fig. 9-19, 9-20, 9-21) and other nonpyramidal cells with either multipolar or bitufted dendritic trees. CCK was not found in pyramidal cells. The axons of bipolar cells commonly arise from one of the primary dendrites some distance from the cell body, which like the dendrites are vertically oriented. The axonal boutons form asymmetric synapsis. They are presumably excitatory neurons (97). In contrast, the CCK-containing bitufted and multipolar neurons are probably inhibitory (98).

By radioimmunoassay, Handelman et al. (99) found high concentrations of CCK in the hippocampus. Immunocytochemically, most CCK cell bodies were in the middle to upper third of the stratum radiatum of the CA1 subfield. Cells had multiple, long processes reaching into the pyramidal layer where immunoreactive terminals were located. Bilateral, laser deafferentation of the hippocampus

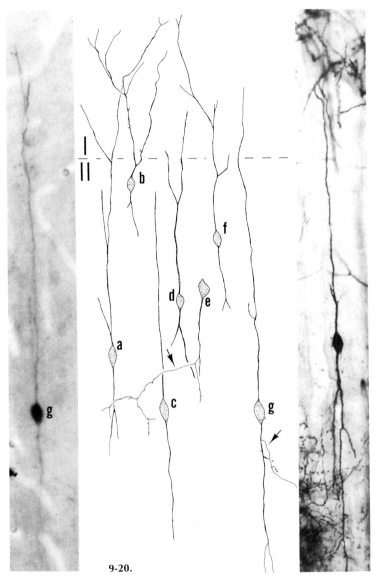

9-19.　　　　　　　　9-20.　　　　　　　　　　　　　　　9-21.

Figure 9-19. Cholecystokinin in bipolar neurons of the cerebral cortex. Some pieces of axon, which do not belong to this neuron, are passing parallel to its ascending dendrite. Vibratome section, 25–30 μm thick. PAP method. [Reprinted with permission from *Neuroscience* **8**:431, A. Peters, M. Miller, L. M. Kimerer, Cholecystokinin-like immunoreactive neurons in rat cerebral cortex, Copyright 1983, Pergamon Press, Ltd. (96).]

Figure 9-20. Camera lucida drawings of examples of cholecystokinin-positive bipolar cells encountered in cortical layers II/III. The boundary between layers I and II is indicated. The bipolar cell, g (shown also in Figure 9-19), as well as the bipolar cell, e, have axons that extend their descending primary dendrites. [Reprinted with permission from *Neuroscience* **8**:431, A. Peters, M. Miller, L. M. Kimerer, Cholecystokinin-like immunoreactive neurons in rat cerebral cortex, Copyright 1983, Pergamon Press, Ltd. (96).]

Figure 9-21. Golgi-impregnated cell from cortical area 17. Compare with Figures 9-20 and 9-21. [From Peters et al. (97).]

391

was controlled for completeness by absence of acetylcholinesterase-containing terminals from the nucleus basalis (pages 317 and 461). Despite completeness of deafferentation, hippocampal CCK contents remained essentially unaffected, thus suggesting that the hippocampal CCK neurons are intrinsic, presumably acting as interneurons that modulate action of pyramidal and granule cells.

We have seen that some peptides, such as LHRH, vasopressin, and ACTH, act primarily via long projection fibers. CCK appears to belong to the group of peptides that act as neuromodulators via interneurons, resembling in arrangement the local circuits of enkephalin (page 364) or substance P (page 367). In the intestine too, Malmfors et al. (100) have shown that substance P, vasoactive intestinal peptide, enkephalin and somatostatin are primarily intrinsic to nerve plexuses of the gut wall, even though these peptides are also found in fibers of the vagus nerve. Following complete extrinsic denervation of the gut, adrenergic fibers have disappeared, but immunocytochemistry for Leu-enkephalin, somato-statin, substance P, and vasoactive intestinal peptide remained unaffected. In addition, Leander et al. (101) found CCK, gastric-releasing peptide, and β-endorphin in cell bodies in myenteric and submucosal ganglia, showing that these peptides, too, are intrinsic to the gut wall. The stimulating effect of CCK C-terminal octapeptide on contraction of isolated taenia coli was reduced by tetrodotoxin, showing that it is mediated via neurotransmission and not by direct effects on the smooth muscle. However, atropine also reduced the CCK-induced response, showing that at least partially it is mediated via cholinergic nerves and suggesting that the peptide acts as a neuromodulator rather than a neurotrans-mitter.

VASOACTIVE INTESTINAL PEPTIDE

As emphasized by Adler and Grube (102), vasoactive intestinal peptide (VIP) possesses much structural homology with secretin, glucagon, glicentin, and gastric inhibitory peptide. Like glucagon, VIP causes hyperglycemia by increas-ing hepatitic glycogenolysis. VIP has general vasodilator effects, inhibiting gas-tritic secretion and stimulating release of insulin and glucagon. Roberts et al. (103) found a wide distribution of VIP in the central nervous system, primarily in the cortex, hippocampus, amygdala, suprachiasmic nucleus, and brainstem. As in many other neuropeptides, the stria medullaris was also an important pathway for VIP fibers. The strong representation in the cortex resembles that of CCK, and contrasts with most other peptides which are usually more promi-nent in deeper nuclei. While many of the VIP neurons may be interneurons, long fiber projects were also seen, mainly in the stria medullaris. As shown by transection, these represent pathways from the amygdala to the bed nucleus, preoptic area, and hypothalamus. Stimulation of the amygdala causes ovulation, decreases ACTH, blood pressure, and gastric acid secretion. Conceivably, these effects may be mediated by stria medullaris fibers, possibly, but not necessarily containing VIP. Interestingly, this central action of VIP in the amygdala re-sembles its peripheral action of lowering blood pressure and gastric acid se-cretion.

POLYPEPTIDE YY

Six hormones have been localized by PAP technique in the pancreas. The relative distribution of these hormones within islets has beeun studied with double-staining immunocytochemistry and serial sectioning by Erlandsen et al. (104). B cells, which contain *insulin,* fill the bulk of the interior of the islets (Fig. 3-63). Rickert et al. (105) have shown that cyproheptadine, which causes reversible lesions of B-cells, depletes these cells of most of their secretory granules, and those remaining had no recognizable PAP complexes.

Glucagon, in the hands of Erlandsen et al. (104), was confined to A cells in the periphery of the islets (Fig. 3-63). Serial sections showed that the A cells contained a second hormone, *gastric inhibitory polypeptide,* which is known to potentiate secretion of insulin and glucagon.

Somatostatin was contained in D cells (104), a third group of islet cells that are also found at the islet periphery, except in smaller number than A cells (Fig. 3-64).

D cells possess fine cellular processes that form a "semiprivate" system of hormone secretion (3), apparently affecting the rest of pancreatic islet cells (page 358).

Pancreatic polypeptide and *polypeptide YY* possess 36 amino acids and share much of their sequences, including a C-terminal tyrosine. Pancreatic polypeptide appears to stimulate hepatic glycogenolysis and lipid synthesis, to relax the gallbladder, and to inhibit pentagastrin-stimulated gastric acid secretion. Pancreatic polypeptide is seen in pancreatic islets and exocrine parenchyma. In the islets, pancreatic polypeptide is seen in a fourth type of cells, distinct from A, B, and D cells. El Salhy et al. (106) found that polypeptide YY-containing intestinal mucosal cells are of the open type, that is, they extend from the basal lamina of the crypts of Lieberkuhn to the gut lumen (Fig. 9-22). These cells increase in number toward the lower part of the intestine, being most frequent in the rectum, absent in the human, and rare in the monkey jejunum and ileum (107). Serial plastic sections have shown that these cells are distinct from intestinal pancreatic polypeptide cells, demonstrating that antisera to polypeptide YY and pancreatic

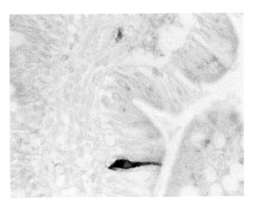

Figure 9-22.   Polypeptide YY cell in the lower part of the ileum. Plastic section, 1 μm thick. PAP method. ×650. [From El Salhy et al. (106).]

polypeptide reveal different peptides rather than immunocytochemical cross-reaction of a common peptide. The distribution of goblet cells is similar to that of polypeptide YY cells. Polypeptide YY cells were shown to emit cytoplasmic processes to neighboring goblet cells, suggesting that polypeptide YY cells may exert a "private" secretory signal on mucus-secreting goblet cells.

FMRF-AMIDE

The molluscan peptide, FMRF-amide, possesses sequence homology with enkephalin (page 112) and also shares an arginine and an amidated aromatic amino acid with pancretic polypeptide. Triepel and Grimmelhikhuijzen (108) have shown that much of the widespread immunoreactivity in the rodent brain with antisera to FMRF-amide can be absorbed with pancreatic polypeptide, and, therefore, it is not clear whether the reactivity observed is due to FRMF-amide, pancreatic polypeptide, or still another peptide, or whether it is due to yet unknown precursors displaced by the peptides used for blocking immunocyto-chemical visualization (page 386). Cross absorption did not occur, however, in some hypothalamic structures, central gray, reticular formation, and spinal cord, thus not precluding that the molluscan peptide does indeed occur in mammals.

EVOLUTIONARY ASPECTS

Neurosecretion as a universally important mechanism of cellular communication received one of its earliest confirmations from the findings of Berta Scharrer (109) on the analogy of neurohemal organs in insects, such as corpora allata and corpora cardiaca, with neurosecretory areas of the vertebrate brain, such as the median eminence, the neurohypophysis, and the organum vasculosum of the lamina terminalis. The wide distribution of neuropeptides in the nervous system of organisms which date back to early evolutionary times and possess relatively simple nervous systems, suggests that endocrine functions of nerve cells must have taken precedence to interneuronal synaptic functions. The conservative inheritance of individual peptide sequences alludes to their essentiality to bio-logic functions. Even prior to appearance of discernible nervous systems, bioactive peptides have existed that resemble in composition and manner of assembly those of higher vertebrates. Thus, LeRoith et al. (110) find both, corticotropin and β-endorphin immunoreactivity in extracts of protozoa. The size of these peptides corresponds to those of authentic mammallian corticotropin and β-endorphin, respectively, which suggests that they are similar if not identical. Furthermore, LeRoith et al. (110) isolated a high molecular weight material which possessed both, ACTH and β-endorphin immunoreactivities, indicating that processing of these hormones from a common precursor in unicellular organisms resembles that of vertebrates.

Stefano et al. (111) demonstrated in insect midgut homogenates high-affinity, saturable neuropeptide-binding sites for an enkephalin analogue known to possess stable physiologic activity upon binding sites in the vertebrate myenteric plexus. The insect receptor also possessed high-affinity binding for the opioid antagonist, naloxone. Denervated insect midgut exhibited reduced binding to the enkephalin analogue that was no longer affected by naloxone. In vertebrates, enkephalin seems to act primarily on interneurons. The loss of receptors on denervation in the insect may suggest a similar role.

Hansen et al. (112) found material that shared immunocytochemical reactivity with oxytocin, vasopressin, met-enkephalin, and β-endorphin predominantly in the central release area of the insect corpus allatum, suggesting that these peptides are of central origin. On the other hand, immunocytochemical reactivity for somatostatin, substance P, and bombesin was found primarily in areas rich in graunlar cells, suggesting that these substances are synthesized in these cells. The former location is somewhat similar to that of the mammallian posterior pituitary, while the latter resembles that of the mammallian endocrine pancreas. El Salhy et al. (113) revealed neurosecretory cells in the brain of insects that possessed immunoreactivity for insulin B chains, somatostatin, C- and N-terminal glucagon, pancreatic polypeptide, secretin, vasoactive intestinal peptide, C-terminal cholecystokinin, α- and β-endorphin, substance P, and calcitonin. All these neurons emitted fibers to the corpus cardiacum, and in some cases, also to the corpus allatum.

In vertebrates, many peptides are localized in the brain, peripheral nervous system such as myenteric plexus, and in endocrine cells such as those of the intestinal mucosa. Nishiitsutsuji-Uwo et al. (114, 115) and Dube and Thorpe (116) revealed pancreatic polypeptide, vasoactive intestinal peptide, and somatostatin in the insect brain, in the gut-associated ganglia, and in separate gut endocrine cells, thus providing some degree of analogy to the mammallian distribution.

Not all peptides seem to have accompanied the whole evolution of the animal kingdom. Reinecke et al. (117) visualized the C-terminal sequence of neurotensin in open-type (page 393) intestinal mucosal endocrine cells. The peptide seems to appear in sparsely distributed patterns in higher developed invertebrates and has exhibited a wider distribution in the earliest vertebrates (such as cartilagineous fish). It becomes more numerous in bony fish, amphibia, reptiles, and birds and is found in these species, particularly in the antral, pyloric, and duodenal regions. In mammals, it appears at high density in the ileum.

CHEMOARCHITECTONIC PATTERNS

A large part of the roof of the vertebrate mesencephalon, the *optic tectum,* is devoted to the elaboration of visual input. The area is especially well developed in frogs and other nonmammalian vertebrates. The large neuropil of retinal projections into the tectum delineates a number of characteristic layers, distinguishable by Golgi impregnation and similar silver stains. The number of layers described on morphologic basis varies with different authors, but exceeds, in many cases, the classic description of 15 layers. Electrophysiologic studies confirm a layered distribution of projections of different functional classes of retinal neurons into the tectum. However, correlation of anatomy and physiology has been elusive. The first approach toward a functional understanding of the layers of the tectum was provided by the enzyme histochemical studies of Scharrer and

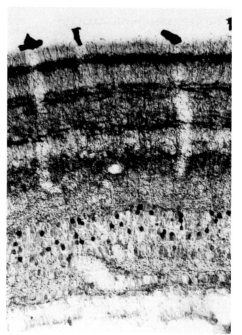

Figure 9-23. Cholecystokinin octapeptide reactivity in a coronal, frozen section of frog optic tectum. Cholecystokinin-containing perikarya in layer 6 exhibit processes that ramify in layers in the superficial neuropil, which receives most of its contributions from these perikarya and is, therefore, intrinsic in origin. PAP method. [From Kuljis and Karten (119).]

Figure 9-24. Leu-enkephalin reactivity in a coronal frozen section of the frog optic tectum. Leu-enkephalin perikarya in layer 6 send processes to the neuropil, which receives most of its Leu-enkephalinergic innervation from these cell bodies, and is, therefore, intrinsic in origin. [From Kuljis and Karten (119).]

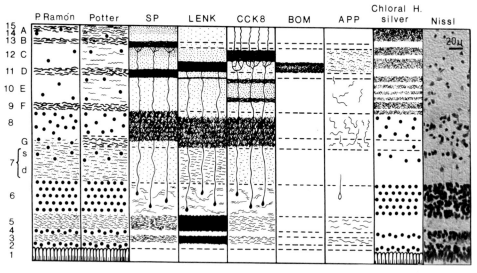

Figure 9-25. Laminar organization of the frog optic tectum as depicted by tinctorial staining and by peptide immunocytochemistry. Numbers designate tectal organization according to Cajal, letters according to Potter. s, superficial (cell containing) portion of layer VII. d, deep (cell devoid) portion of layer 7. SP, substance P. LENK, Leu-enkephalin. CCK8, cholecystokinin C-terminal octapeptide. APP, avian polypeptide. The projections from neurons in layer 6 pass through layers 8 to 11 and, therefore, immunoreactive layers falling in these zones are probably of extrinsic origin as are the immunocytochemically visualized bands in the deeper layers. [From Kuljis and Karten (119).]

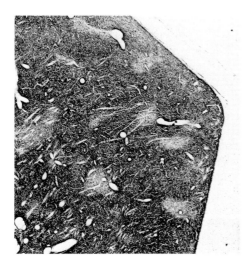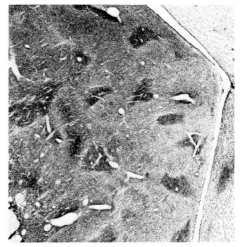

Figure 9-26.   Serial section through cat caudate nucleus. Left, acetylcholinesterase, enzyme histochemistry. Right, metenkephalin, PAP method. [From Graybiel (120).]

Sinden (118). This work has provided the first correlation of enzyme chemistry with histologic structure in the brain and coined the concept of *chemoarchitectonics*. By immunocytochemistry for bioactive peptides, Kuljis and Karten (119) were able to arrive at an even more exquisite laminar differentiation which was particularly elaborate throughout the superficial neuropil of the optic tectum, a major retino-recipient zone. Substance P, cholecystokinin C-terminal octapeptide (Fig. 9-23), Leu-enkephalin (Fig. 9-24), bombesin, and avian pancreatic polypeptide displayed unique laminar distributions, differing in number of layers formed. By double staining immunocytochemistry, substance P, Leu-enkephalin, bombesin, and avian pancreatic polypeptide were seen to be segregated into separate bands. Thus, by immunocytochemistry, the laminar segregation of the optic tectum is even more elaborate than that observed by tinctorial staining or by enzyme histochemistry (Fig. 9-25). In contrast to bioactive peptides, aminergic neurotransmitters had a reticular distribution without suggestion of laminar organization.

Afferent fibers to the mammallian *striatum* terminate in characteristic mozaic patterns. By histochemistry for acetylcholinesterase, Graybiel (120) has revealed enzyme-poor zones, or *striosomes,* which, in the cat, are avoided by efferent projections, and filled or avoided by afferent projections. The striosomes are rich in met-enkephalin (Fig. 9-26). In the neocortex, afferent fibers of a particular type terminate only in restricted layers and sublayers. A similar restriction of zones of termination in the striatum raises the question whether the strict functional differentiation of neocortex and striatum can be conceptually maintained.

COLOCALIZATION

We have already seen (page 317) that more than one neurotransmitter can be elaborated by the same neuron. With regard to bioactive peptides, we expect that the cell may contain more than one peptide. These peptides are the product of a common precursor. We consider this an obligatory colocalization. Thus, in proopiomelanocortin cells, we will find β-endorphin along with ACTH in cases in which ACTH is not further processed, such as in the anterior pituitary and many other locations in which β-endorphin is found. In the intermediate lobe of the pituitary, the same situation prevails except that ACTH is further processed into α-MSH and the C-terminal bioactive portion of ACTH. However, in addition to such expected, obligatory colocalization, we often encounter in the same cell the presence of a number of peptides that are not related to a known common precursor. For instance, we have already alluded to the presence of β-endorphin in the same cell as vasopressin (page 383). In this case, the unexpected colocalization could be attributed to a common precursor that was distinct from proopiomelanocortin.

In our enumeration of examples of colocalization, we consider only those in which no common precursor has yet been described for the peptides found in the same cell. It leaves open the question whether these are situations in which known peptides are processed from yet unknown, single precursors that incorporate their sequences, or whether they are, indeed, the products of independently expressed multiple genes for known precursors. In either event, the existence of colocalization of bioactive peptides different from those expected from the structure of known precursors, increases the variety by which a number of peptides can be coexpressed in a given neuron.

Regulatory peptides are transported in large, dense core vesicles, while classical neurotransmitters (aminergic transmitters such as noradrenalin, serotonin, dopamine, and acetyl choline, as well as γ-amino butyric acid and taurine) are found in small clear vesicles in axon terminals, where "dense" and "clear" refers to their appearance in conventional electron microscopy, but not necessarily to their protein contents as revealed by immunocytochemistry. Most cells that express small, clear vesicles also have large, dense core vesicles. Thus, it is not surprising that neurons of known neurotransmitter contents also possess one or more regulatory peptides. In these cells, the peptides are probably modulators of the neurotransmitter action. It is possible that some neurons are devoid of classical neurotransmitters and only contain regulatory peptides. In these cases, the peptides may have to be designated as neurotransmitters or neurosecretory principles, depending on whether the axons end upon other neurons or upon vascular space.

As classical neurotransmitters are released from small, clear vesicles, the mere demonstration of these vesicles in a peptidergic nerve ending suggests colocalization of the peptide with a classical neurotransmitter. Thus, the demonstration of vasoactive intestinal peptide immunoreactivity in dense core vesicles of typical cholinergic-type endings in cat exocrine glands by Johannsson and Lundberg (121) and in dog and snake nerve terminals at the precapillary space of the pancreatic islet cells by Fujii et al. (122) provides suggestions of coordinated functions between classical transmitters and bioactive peptides. Lundberg and Hökfelt (123) indeed found simultaneous release of acetylcholine and vasoactive intestinal peptide into the venous effluent of electrically stimulated submandibular gland of the cat. At low-stimulation frequency, both secretion and vasodilation were potentiated by acetylcholinesterase inhibition and abolished by atropine. Thus, it is apparent that both effects require acetylcholine. However, at high-stimulation frequency, vasodilation became atropine-resistant. Apparently under these conditions, the effect was caused by vasoactive intestinal peptide. Acetylcholine infusion promotes most vasodilation and secretion. Vasoactive intestinal peptide alone causes only vasodilation. However, addition of vasoactive intestinal peptide to acetylcholine prolongs the secretion response to acetylcholine. Thus, it is likely that regulatory peptides alone do not usually promote a physiologic response, at least at nerve endings in which they coexist with classical neurotransmitters, but rather act as modulators of the neurotransmitter response. The modulatory effect of bioactive peptides may explain why blockade of classical neurotransmitters at times only partially abolishes the effect of nerve stimulation.

Hökfelt et al. (124) described the coexistence of cholecystokinin C-terminal octapeptide with dopamine in the mesolimbic system. This coexistence may be important because of involvement of these neurons in Parkinson's disease.

Bowker et al. (125) found that 82% of medullary raphé neurons, retrogradally labeled by injection of wheat germ agglutinin in the lumbosacral spinal cord, were serotonergic. The remaining cells were morphologically distinct. They were larger and multipolar and did not react for serotonin, substance P, enkephalin, and thyroid-releasing hormone. Instead, they contained choline acetyl transferase. No other cells were labeled by wheat germ agglutinin. However, a large proportion of the smaller, labeled cells contained substance P, enkephalin, or thyrotropin-releasing hormone. Therefore, these peptides must coexist with serotonin. Direct evidence for coexistence of serotonin and substance P in the small cells in the raphé was obtained by Chan-Palay et al. (126).

Pelletier et al. (127) found that in both raphé nuclei and dorsal horn of the spinal cord, not more than 20% of serotonin-containing nerve terminals were positive for substance P. By postembedding staining electron microscopy of serial sections, both peptide and neurotransmitter were found in the same large secretion granules (Fig. 9-27), suggesting that both substances are released simultaneously. This release may be exocytotic rather than synaptic, as the terminals were devoid of synaptic junctions. The results do not preclude the possibility that serotonin immunoreactivity in the small, clear vesicles has escaped the detection by postembedding staining electron microscopy.

The coexistence of peptides with classical neurotransmitters may permit a subdivision of neurotransmitter systems. Peptides act slower than transmitters, they exhibit different mechanisms of release, and unlike classical neurotransmitters do not undergo reuptake at nerve endings. Peptides may be released under different circumstances than neurotransmitters and may not necessarily be released to the same extent along with neurotransmitters at each terminal of arborization of a given axon. They may tune the response to variations in stimuli. The diversity of response may further be increased by the presence of multiple peptides within a single neuron. Martin and Voigt (128) found metenkephalin invariably in oxytocin nerve terminals in the neurohypophysis, and Leu-enkephalin often in vasopressin terminals. These peptides could be inhibitory, as opiates seem to inhibit release of oxytocin and vasopressin. Furthermore, dynorphin and α-neoendorphin (129) have been found to coexist with vasopressin in the same hypothalamic neurons. The Leu-enkephalin localization in vaso-

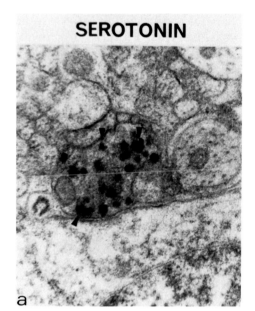

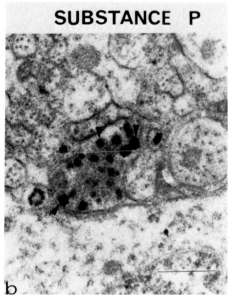

Figure 9-27. Serotonin (a) and substance P (b) immunoreactivity in the same dense core vesicle of adjacent sections of the anterior horn of the spinal cord. PAP postembedding staining technique. Bar is 0.5 μm. [From Pelletier et al. (127).]

pressin neurons was elicited after tryptic digestion (130), suggesting the presence of Leu-enkephalin in the form of a dynorphin or α-neoendorphin-like precursor (Table 9-1). On the other hand, met-enkephalin in oxytocin neurons required no such treatment, suggesting its presence as free pentapeptide. Cholecystokinin octapeptide was also found in oxytocin terminal, but not in vasopressin terminals. These colocalizations occurred in the same secretion granules as evident from postembedding electron microscopic staining of serial sections. Since cloned cDNA coding for vasopressin-neurophysin does not contain the enkephalin code, it is likely that a single secretion granule may contain different gene products. Grube et al. (131) found glucagon and α-endorphin in the same secretion granules in rat pancreatic α-cells. Since glucagon cells were devoid of ACTH, they concluded that the biosynthetic pathway of endorphin in the pancreas was not the same as in the pituitary. The findings suggest the existence of additional, still unknown preprohormones to known peptides that would diversify the potential of their colocalization with other peptides.

C-terminal ACTH does coexist, however, with LHRH in the same secretion granule in the median eminence (Fig. 9-28), as shown by Beauvillain et al. (132).

Lechan et al. (133) found growth hormone immunoreactivity in cell bodies in the periventricular and paraventricular nucleus of the hypothalamus and a wide fiber distribution to the neurohypophysis, thalamus, amygdala, and brainstem. Throughout this distribution, growth hormone was associated with thyrotropin-releasing hormone (Fig. 9-29), thus suggesting a common precursor that leads to obligatory coexistence of the two peptides. In contrast, substance P colocalized with thyrotropin-releasing hormone only in raphé nuclei of the medulla (126),

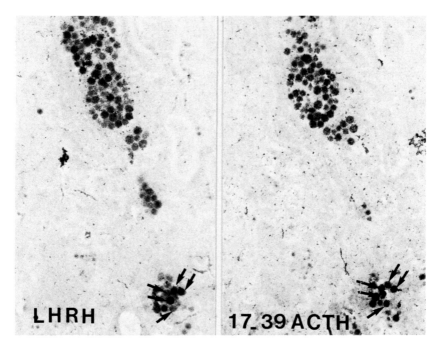

Figure 9-28. Serial sections through a fiber in the median eminence of the guinea pig revealed LHRH and 17-39 ACTH in the same secretion granules (arrows). Postembedding staining PAP technique. ×20,000. [From Beauvillian et al. (132).]

suggesting either a different precursor in this location or assembly from independently expressed genes.

HORMONE RECEPTORS

Peptide hormone receptors are localized on plasma membranes with such regularity that they are often referred to as *membrane receptors*. Evidence for this localization depends upon saturable, high-affinity ligand binding to isolated plasma membrane fractions and finding in these fractions the enzymes necessary for initiating the physiologic consequences of ligand-receptor interaction. The most common intercellular *second messenger effects* of this interaction involve promotion or suppression of protein activation through phosphorylation mediated by cyclic AMP- or cyclic GMP-dependent kinases. In secretory cells, certain ligand-receptor interactions may lead to release of hormones stored in secretion granules via exocytosis or to neosynthesis of new secretion granules, or both. The exocytotic effect may not always be cyclic nucleotide-dependent.

Support of the physiologic significance of plasma membrane receptors comes from studies on the effect of insolubilized ligands. Thus, Conn et al. (134) have shown that a luteinizing hormone-releasing hormone (LHRH) agonist analogue made impermeable to the interior of the cell by attachment to sepharose, was nevertheless capable to effect luteinizng hormone (LH) release. The analogue was chosen because unlike LHRH itself, it was resistant to enzymatic degradation

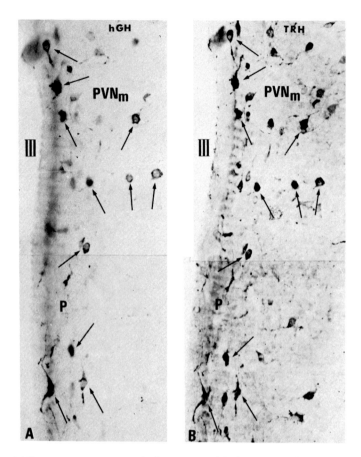

Figure 9-29.   A Vibratome section, 50 μm thick, was stained for human growth hormone by PAP method with 4-chloro-naphthol as substrate and the section was photographed (A). The soluble enzyme reaction product, the antibodies, and the PAP were removed by acid potassium permanganate, and the section was restained for thyrotropin-releasing hormone by PAP method with diaminobenzidine as substrate (B). Both hormones were found in the same cell (arrows) in the periventricular (P) and medial paraventricular nuclei (PV_N). Control sections in which antithyrotropin-releasing hormone was omitted failed to react with diaminobenzidine, thus showing that removal of antibodies was complete. III, third ventricle. $\times 390$. [From Lechan et al. (133).]

and because it possessed a free amino group that was utilized for reaction with sepharose. LHRH itself was able to stimulate LH release only as long as it was applied to gonadotrophs in culture. Secretion returned to baseline levels upon washing. There was no continued effect of the ligand.

The results with sepharose-conjugated, stable LHRH analogue can be interpreted as indicating that all the events for induction of secretion occur on the cell membrane where the presumed primary interaction of LHRH and receptor takes place. However, the results do not preclude that a primary LHRH-receptor interaction may not also occur elsewhere, inside the cell, and that the ensuing complex may be inactivated after interaction.

The overall evidence suggests that plasma membrane receptors are important for peptide hormone action. The evidence does not exclude the existence of additional intracellular receptors.

Studies on plasma membrane receptors are usually carried out by radioligand assays in which, in general, a fraction of tissue homogenate, such as the plasma membrane fraction, is isolated prior to the binding studies. In contrast, immuno-cytochemistry visualizes the whole cell, rather than a fraction of it, although some components of the cell may have been destroyed before the tissue came to immunocytochemical processing. By immunocytochemistry, peptide hormone receptors have regularly been observed intracellularly. By electron microscopy, they were revealed at the inner membrane of secretion granules. When we treated sections of picric acid-paraformaldehyde-fixed rat pituitary with anti-LHRH at 1:1000 or higher dilutions as first antibody, secretion granules in gonadotrophs were sometimes stained and sometimes unstained (135). Staining, when it occurred, was usually of moderate degree with absorbence indices of 0.1 to 0.2 (Fig. 9-30). An immunoabsorbent was prepared by insolubilizing LHRH on cyanogen bromide-activated sepharose via a ribonuclease spacer (136). When anti-LHRH treated with this immunoabsorbent was used as first antibody, stain-ing of the gonadotroph granules was abolished (Fig. 9-31), suggesting that it was due to LHRH.

When the anti-LHRH was admixed with LHRH in solution, the staining did not become blocked as expected. Instead, it became intensified, even if the LHRH concentration for blocking was high (1μg/μl). This suggested that the added LHRH binds with the tissue section at a higher overall affinity than with the antibody, and that similar intensification could be obtained if the section were treated with LHRH and anti-LHRH in sequence rather than with a LHRH-anti-LHRH mixture. Indeed, following pretreatment with LHRH, staining be-came regularly intensified to high or maximal absorbence indices, ranging from 0.35 to 0.6 (Fig. 9-32,a,b). The degree of intensification varied from 2-fold to more than 23-fold total immunoreactivity. The lower the degree of staining without pretreatment, the greater was the degree of intensification.

The staining reaction was confined to gonadotroph secretion granules. The large granules stained stronger than the small ones. No cell of the pituitary other than the gonadotroph reacted with LHRH. No organelle within the gonado-troph, except the secretory granules, reacted with LHRH. However, the plasma membrane did exhibit a weak reaction provided it had been exposed to LHRH *prior* to embedding. The plasma membrane is invisible in picric acid-paraformal-dehyde-fixed material processed immunocytochemically after embedding.

The affinity for LHRH of gonadotroph secretion granules was high. Pretreat-ment with as little as 4 pg LHRH/μl yielded significant staining enhancement compared to buffer pretreatment. Levels close to saturation were reached with 60 pg/μl. Staining intensity of gonadotroph granules did not significantly in-crease with increasing concentrations of LHRH pretreatment to 1μg/μl, thus indicating saturability. At the same time, increase of LHRH concentration to 1μg/μl did not confer background staining to the section.

The concentration of 4 pg LHRH/μl still is an order of magnitude higher than that found in the pituitary-portal circulation during LH surge. However, it should be recalled that unlike in vivo, the immunocytochemical binding after application of LHRH in vitro is only revealed following a 48-hour staining

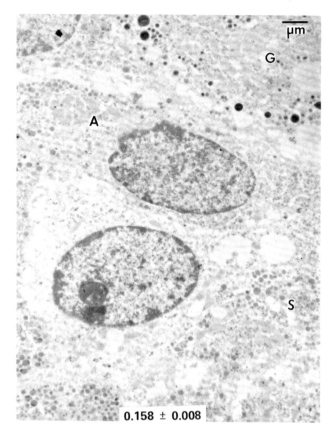

Figure 9-30.   Rat pituitary Araldite section, pretreated with buffer and stained with the use of anti-LHRH, 1 : 1000, as first antiserum in the PAP method. Number represents absorbence index of the large gonadotrophs + SEM (page 148) [From Sternberger et al. (136).]

procedure that includes six further additions of immunoreagents and four further washes in excess buffer prior to the actual diaminobenzidine and hydrogen peroxide staining. This procedure would have provided ample opportunity for dissociation if the binding of LHRH were weak.

These data indicate that there exists a high-affinity receptor for LHRH on gonadotroph secretion granules. Unlike in radioligand assay, there were no low-affinity binding substances that would have yielded background staining especially at high-ligand concentration. Conceivably, material binding with low affinity is lost during the extensive immunocytochemical staining and washing procedures.

The data also show that LHRH bound on receptor is not sterically hindered from reacting with antibodies, despite the relatively small size of the peptide. This would seem to indicate that the clefts in receptor and antibody binding sites are not as deep as hitherto thought.

When anti-LHRH is absorbed with insolubilized LHRH, no staining occurs even if the section is pretreated with LHRH. In order to show that the LHRH immunoabsorbent binds only LHRH, rather than being destructive to antibodies

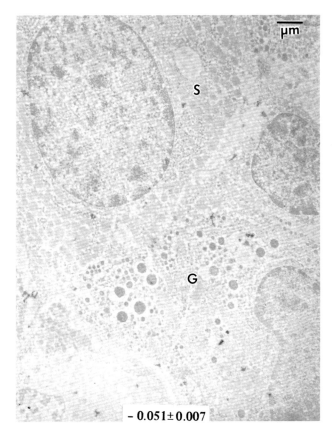

Figure 9-31.   Section near that of Figure 9-30, pretreated with buffer and stained with the use of anti-LHRH, 1:1000, absorbed with insolubilized LHRH, as first antiserum in the PAP technique. Number represents absorbence index of the large gonadotrophs ± SEM. [From Sternberger et al. (136).]

in a nonspecific manner, sections of rat pituitary were stained with mixtures of anti-LHRH an anti-ACTH[17-39], both at dilutions of 1:1000. With buffer pretreatment, the mixtures stained the ACTH granules, but failed to stain gonadotroph granules (Fig. 9-32a). Following pretreatment with LHRH, the absorbence indices of the gonadotroph granules approached those of the ACTH granules (Fig. 9-32b). If after LHRH pretreatment, a serum mixture absorbed with LHRH immunoabsorbent was used as first antibody, staining in the gonadotroph granules was abolished, but that in the ACTH granules was not significantly affected (Fig. 9-32c).

These data show that there exists an intracellular receptor for the peptide hormone, LHRH, and that it is confined to the secretory granules of gonadotrophs. This receptor is capable of binding LHRH in vitro. Small amounts of receptor have also been seen on the plasma membrane, provided the material was processed by pre-embedding immunocytochemistry. However, the bulk of receptors was revealed on the secretion granules and not on the plasma membrane.

Immunocytochemically detectable LHRH receptors are not limited to the

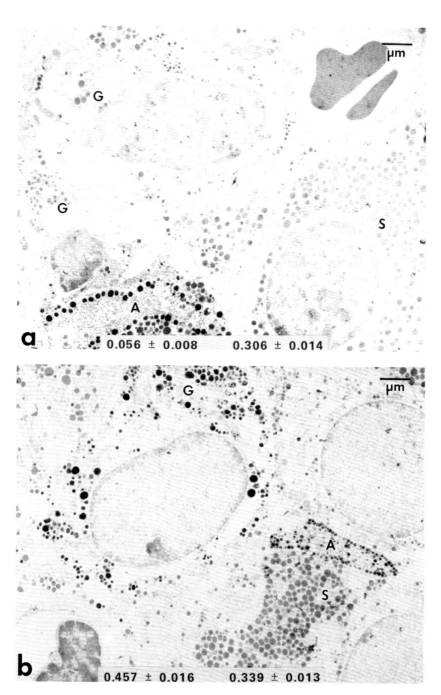

Figure 9-32. Rat pituitary. Araldite section, PAP-stained with mixture of anti-LHRH and anti-ACTH[17-39] as first antiserum. (a) Buffer pretreatment, unabsorbed serum mixture. (b) LHRH pretreatment, unabsorbed serum mixture. (c) LHRH pretreatment, serum mixture absorbed with LHRH immunoabsorbent. First number under each micrograph is absorbence index of large gonadotroph granules, second number is index of ACTH granules ± SEM. A, corticotroph, G, gonadotroph, S, somatotroph. [From Sternberger et al. (136).]

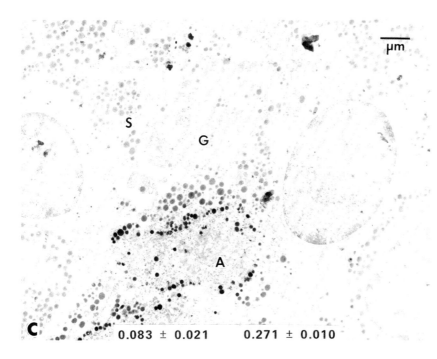

pituitary gonadotrophs. Seppälä et al. (137) disclosed them on pancreatic islet cells and confirmed the presence of LHRH in this location by extraction procedures. In the pituitary, as well as in the pancreas, LHRH seemed to be bound to receptor by its N-terminal end, leaving the C-terminal sequence free (135,137). Similar intracellular LHRH receptors were suggested from the observations of Seppälä et al. (138) on human syncytiotrophoblasts and trophoblastic tumors. The preservation of staining in these tissues after admixture of excess LHRH with anti-LHRH could have been due to reaction of the cells with receptors or due to Fc receptors in the tissue. The latter is unlikely since antisera absorbed with insolubilized LHRH did not reveal staining, even though PAP alone is an excellent reagent for Fc receptors (page 145). LHRH-anti-LHRH will react preferentially with tissue sections over free LHRH (page 235).

We also demonstrated intracellular LHRH binding in the zona fasciculata and reticularis of the adrenal (139). Castel and Hochman (53) revealed PAP staining of secretion granules of pars intermedia cells with antivasopressin, suggesting a receptor site for endogenous vasopressin at this location. Characteristically the immunocytochemical reaction was not blocked by addition of vasopressin to the antiserum, even though this did abolish staining in the pars nervosa and the hypothalamus (Fig. 9-33). Vasopressin could conceivably reach the pars intermedia through the zona externa of the median eminence or by diffusion from the pars nervosa.

Vasopressin receptors have also been localized in the cytoplasm of the distal convoluted tubules of rat kidney. Moderate staining was intensified when paraf-

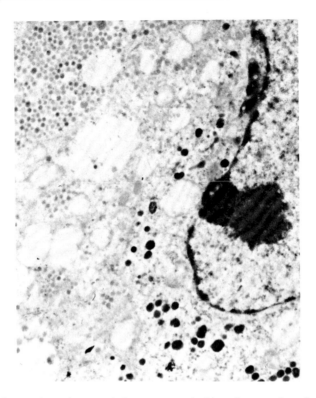

Figure 9-33. When sections of mouse pituitary are treated with antivasopressin as first antiserum in the PAP postembedding staining technique, secretory granules in nerve endings of the pars nervosa and in the cells of the pars intermedia are stained. The micrograph shows the staining pattern when antivasopressin pretreated with an excess of vasopressin was used. The pretreatment blocked the staining in the pars nervosa (left upper), but failed to block and possibly enhanced the staining the pars intermedia (right), thus suggesting a specific vasopressin-binding site in this location. [From Castel and Hochman (53).]

fin sections were treated with vasopressin prior to application of antivasopressin and the reagents of the PAP method (Figs. 9-34, 9-35).

Witorsch (140,141) was able to demonstrate intracellular binding sites for prolactin in male rat accessory sex organs by application of hormone to tissue sections followed by staining with antiprolactin. In the epithelial cells of the ventral prostate, prolactin binding was in distinct supranuclear locations. In the coagulating gland, it was in the apical portions of the epithelial cells and in the dorsolateral prostrate, it was in the apical region of some, and in the whole cytoplasm of other epithelial cells.

Hypophyseal prolactin enhances androgen-induced prostatic enlargement. Witorsch (142) has demonstrated intracellular binding sites in autopsy and biopsy specimens of normal, hyperplastic, and neoplastic human prostates (Fig. 9-36). Immunocytochemical demonstration was dose dependent upon preapplication of the ligand.

Dunaif et al. (143) found intracellular receptors for prolactin in the cytoplasm of luteal and theca interna cells of ovaries from cycling virgin rats. Cytoplasm of developing ova and stroma cells were also reactive, as were granulosa cells of

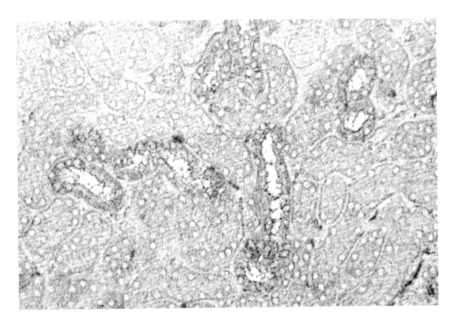

Figure 9-34. Moderate staining, primarily in the distal convoluted tubules, is obtained when paraffin sections of rat kidney are treated with buffer and antivasopressin as first antiserum in the PAP method. [From the work of K. M. Mills, J. P. Petrali, and L. A. Sternberger.]

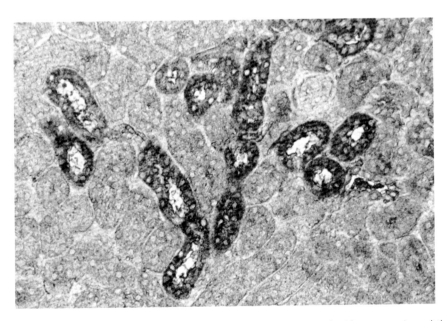

Figure 9-35. When a section adjacent to that of Figure 9-34 was treated with vasopressin and then processed in analogous manner, staining in the cytoplasm of distal convoluted tubules was intensified. [From the work of K. M. Mills, J. P. Petrali, and L. A. Sternberger.]

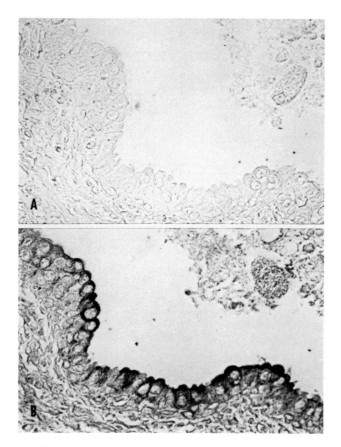

Figure 9-36.   Biopsy of benign prostatic hypertrophy. Section treated with buffer (A) and human prolactin (5 ng/μl) before staining with antihuman prolactin (1 : 3200) and PAP method. ×160. [From Witorsch (142).]

very mature follicles. On application of antiprolactin as first antiserum, staining was weak. When instead of antiprolactin, antiserum to isolated receptor protein was used, staining was strong and in the same location. This suggested, as we have seen in the pituitary that only some of the receptors were occupied by endogenous prolactin. Much more receptor was able to react with antireceptor serum. Indeed, when the sections were treated with prolactin in concentrations as low as 10 pg/μl before application of antiprolactin, staining became increased to the same intensity as that obtained with antireceptor serum. Furthermore, pretreatment with antireceptor serum blocked the enhancement of antiprolactin staining after prolactin treatment.

Even though in many cases, the immunocytochemically disclosed receptors were shown to be saturable and of high affinity, it is often felt that they should be called binding sites before their existence is confirmed by radioligand methods similar to those used for the studies of membrane receptors and before the functional significance of the immunocytochemically detected receptors has been established. Wagner et al. (144) found by radioligand studies the majority of gonatroph LHRH receptors on secretion granules and not on the plasma membrane. Receptors of only a single affinity were revealed, even though some of the binding observed was due to membrane constituents as well as secretion granules. Hence, it is likely that the binding substances of membranes and granules are identical, and that, indeed, both are receptors. Zolman and Valenta (145) could also find considerable amounts of receptor on isolated secretion granules. Again by radioligand studies, Miller et al. (146) found high-affinity LHRH receptors in purified nuclei of rat pituitary, thus alluding to a possible nuclear translocation of LHRH-receptor complex conceivably related to LH and FSH neosynthesis. Finally, Dular and LaBella (147) have shown that isolated secretion granules of bovine pituitary release prolactin and growth hormone upon stimulation by thyrotropin-releasing hormone or partially purified prolactin-releasing factor. The affect was promoted by calcium and inhibited by somatostatin, thus suggesting a functional capability of granule receptors.

The immunocytochemical studies, especially those performed by postembedding staining electron microscopy, suggest the existence of bioactive peptide receptors on the inner membrane of secretion granules. However, these studies do not negate the existence of membrane receptors. Postembedding staining immunocytochemistry only reveals antigens in secretion granules. Antigens on other membranes are missed (page 117). Thus, by combining information from radioligand studies and from immunocytochemistry, we would be able to conclude that receptors exist both, on the plasma membrane and secretion granules, were it not for the occasional studies, discussed below, that seem to raise doubts about the functional significance of receptors at either of these locations.

The presence of membrane receptors has generally been thought to be a logical place for receptors, because it is the plasma membrane where interaction of the cell with its environment takes place. Indeed, macromolecules do not enter living cells passively. However, hydrophobic molecules, such as steroids, do penetrate the cell membrane to interact with cytosolic receptors. Regulatory peptides are small molecules that are soluble in acid alcohol and not as insoluble in lipids as large proteins. Their conformation tends to be circular. They generally possess masked C- and N-terminal amino acids. All these are properties that favor penetration of cell membranes. It is not necessary, a priori, for them to act on receptors solely on the cell membrane. They could conceivably penetrate the cell without membrane interaction. Secretion of granule contents is by exocytosis. The granule membrane is identical to the plasma membrane and fuses with it during the process. Since cells are often virtually studded with granules, continuous secretion would eventually result in an enormous plasma membrane. It is obvious that a mechanism must exist to prevent this from happening.

After it had been reported that secretion granules contained receptors (135), many studies appeared that showed that ligand-receptor interaction stimulates membrane reuptake or *endocytosis*. Ligands were usually found on the plasma membrane early, and in lysozomes late after application (148), thus suggesting that ligand-stimulated endocytosis is a degradative mechanism. It follows that receptors on the plasma membrane will not recirculate.

Regulation of receptors is an important feature of hormone-receptor interaction, and in the case of LHRH action may determine the relative proportions of FSH and LH secreted during the pulsatile release of LHRH from the hypothalamus in the ovarian cycle. In the initial stages after interaction of gonadotrophs with LHRH, Loumaye and Catt (149) observed a decrease of LHRH receptors concomitant with LH release. The findings suggested that exocytosis did not, by itself, restore receptors to the cell membrane and that endocytosed receptor was indeed degraded. It would appear, from these data, that secretion granule receptors are without significant function. Duello et al. (148) found that after a pulse of tritiated LHRH agonist analogue, there was, indeed, accumulation of the tracer in secretion granules. However, while membrane tracer disappeared and lysozomal tracer appeared during a 2-hour period, tracer in secretion granules appeared immediately after application and remained unchanged during the period of observation. These studies do not suggest an important contribution of granule receptors to the changes in membrane receptors observed after LHRH stimulation.

On the other hand, Kuhl and Baumann (150) found that LHRH binding sites on gonadotroph plasma membranes are probably related in size and binding affinity to an LHRH-degrading enzyme which is also found in the hypothalamus. Binding affinity was comparable to that attributed to receptors. These studies would suggest that the usual membrane receptors in nonstimulated cells are not functional receptors at all. The findings explain why highly active LHRH analogues that are resistant to enzymatic degradation, compete less effectively for membrane binding sites than LHRH itself. The data also tend to suggest that membrane receptors are unimportant for LHRH action relative to intracellular receptors.

It seems that much of these conflicting lines of evidence can be resolved by the discovery of Farquhar (151,152) of a pathway from the plasma membrane to the Golgi complex, the site of origin of secretion granules. Through this pathway, recirculation of the plasma membrane is established. Previously it had been thought that endocytosis mainly leads to degradation in lysozomes and, indeed, this mechanism may prevail in most nonsecretory cells. In many cases, the pathway to lysozomes may have been favored by the nature of the tracer employed. Bioactive peptides or other ligands for receptors, such as cholera toxin, have usually been labeled with ferritin, horseradish peroxidase, or fluorescent dyes. Once the ligands have interacted with plasma membrane receptors, the fate of the complex may largely be determined by the labels, and as these are foreign to the intracellular environment, they may be degraded in lysozomes. Using uncharged polysaccharide molecules or cationic ferritin as tracer, Farquhar (152) found that, at least in secretory cells, endocytotic traffic from the plasma membrane was heaviest to the dilated rims of trans-Golgi cisternae, where secretory packaging usually takes place. That this pathway, in all likelihood, represents recirculation of secretion granule membranes following exocytosis is suggested from its preponderance in secreting cells during active phases of secretion.

The recirculating pathways may involve both receptors for agonistic and antagonistic releasing hormones. Somatostatin is a peptide antagonistic to many forms of secretion (page 367). The bulk of pancreatic islet receptors was found by Sussman et al. (153) on secretion granules and not on the plasma membrane, but both receptors had equal affinities. Glucose-stimulated insulin release causes concomitant accumulation of somatostatin receptor on the plasma membrane, thus providing downregulation for insulin secretion. Receptor neosynthesis does not appear to partake in this downregulation. However, colchicine and deuterium oxide, which interfere with microtubule function and vesicle migration, did interfere with receptor downregulation. These findings, along with the presence of cyclic AMP-stimulated protein kinase activity in secretion granules, as well as the generally observed similarity of receptors of plasma membrane and secretion granules, suggest not only a strong interaction of secretion granules with plasma membrane, but also the possibility that both can mediate simultaneously or independently the totality of functions that follow ligand-receptor interaction.

Several pathways of interaction are feasible. One is by direct action of ligand on plasma membrane, which in all likelihood is the only mechanism available for large molecular hormones. Even if we accept that most of the binding substance on the cell membrane, at least in the case of gonadotrophs, is an LHRH-degrading enzyme rather than a receptor, there remain two pathways of ligand action. In one of them, the ligand could enter the cell passively to interact with secretion granule receptors, leading to immediate release of their contents and fusion of the ligand-receptor complex with the plasma membrane. Release may be inhibited by antagonistic receptors, as postulated by Sussman et al. (153). Thus, it is feasible that after interaction of LHRH, only some secretion granules are released while others remain in the cytoplasm. The released granules would no longer be available for observation, but the retained granules would maintain immobilized LHRH as has been observed by Duello et al. (148) after a pulse administration of LHRH. Conn et al. (134) have shown that continuous administration of LHRH is needed to maintain LH secretion.

Pituitary cultures reveal a baseline release of LH that contributes a considerable proportion of the release which can be stimulated by LHRH. Thus, nonstimulated LH release brings, by exocytosis, unoccupied LHRH receptors from the secretion granules to the plasma membrane and may be responsible for the amounts of LHRH receptors normally observed on plasma membranes. After LHRH stimulation, fusion of secretion granules with the plasma membrane will deliver receptors already occupied by LHRH, although the process of endocytosis will prevent the total cell membrane from enlarging excessively. As a result of fusion of LHRH-occupied receptors with the plasma membrane, any unoccupied receptor in this location would be diluted. When measuring remaining LHRH receptors after LHRH stimulation, one would observe, therefore, an effective LHRH receptor downregulation on the plasma membrane. Consequently, the decrease of LHRH receptors on the plasma membrane during early stages of secretion does not necessarily indicate that secretion granules are devoid of LHRH receptors (134).

Another mechanism postulated by Sussman et al. (153) does not require passive entry of bioactive peptides into the cytosol, yet still involves participation of secretion granules. These authors have been able to dissociate the penultimate event of membrane fusion from the ultimate event of membrane lysis and hormone discharge. This mechanism involves dual effects on a cell, like glucose and somatostatin on insulin cells, or conceivably, the basal nonstimulated release that can be enhanced by a releasing hormone such as in the case of gonadotrophs in culture. In this two-stage mechanism, secretion granules are first stimulated to fuse with the plasma membrane, whereupon a second ligand interacts specifically at the junction of secretion granules with the plasma membrane, conceivably prior to actual release of secretory product. This mechanism would preclude, at least in the case of LHRH, degradation of the ligand by plasma membrane enzymes.

A further explanation for the downregulation of receptors on the plasma membrane could be inferred from the studies of Krisch (54) on secretion of vasopressin in hyperstimulated animals (page 381), if we consider the usual experimental in vitro exposure to releasing hormones a form of hyperstimulation. Under conditions of hyperstimulation, hormones may not be solely released by exocytosis. While exocytosis would co-release, in the case of gonadotrophs, luteinizing and follicle-stimulating hormones for export and LHRH receptor for plasma membrane incorporation, nonexocytotic release would liberate the hormones without receptor, thus explaining downregulation of plasma membrane receptors during early phases of artificially induced hormone release.

DIABETES MELLITUS

Intolerance to glucose is a symptom of a heterogeneous group of disorders with varying etiologies. It is not surprising, therefore, that diabetes is a common disease not only in humans but also in many other mammallian species, in which progression or spontaneous recovery, as the case may be, may differ decisively.

The pathology of human juvenile onset, insulin-dependent diabetes presents many pathognomonic changes. Most islets are composed of narrow, easily missed cores of small cells, which in the past have been considered atrophic. However, Gepts and Lacompte (154) have show that these cells consist of two-

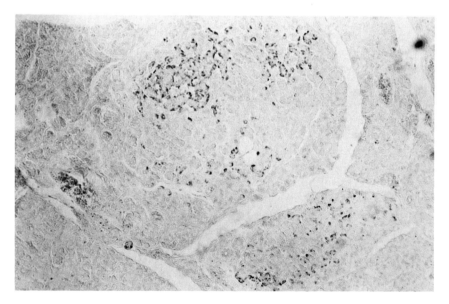

Figure 9-37. Long-standing juvenile diabetes. Glucagon cells are partially in islets and partially in exocrine tissue. PAP method. ×65. [From Gepts and Lecompte (154).]

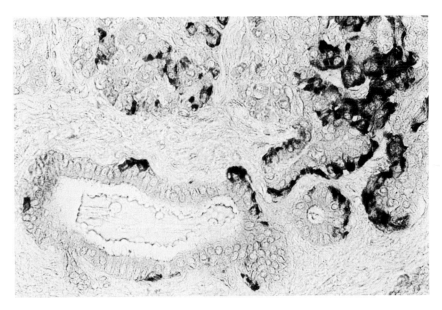

Figure 9-38. Pancreatic polypeptide in one type of long-standing juvenile diabetes. PAP method. ×134. [From Gepts and Lecompte (154).]

third glucagon cells and one-third somatostatin cells (Fig. 9-37). The islets are often found in the neighborhood of medium sized ducts. In some cases, there is continuity of duct epithelium with islet cell cores and in these cases the islets are predominantly composed of pancreatic polypeptide cells (Fig. 9-38). The abnormal glucagon cells may well account for the abnormal glucagon secretion patterns in juvenile diabetes.

In contrast to juvenile diabetes, the immunocytochemical patterns of adult onset diabetes was extremely variable, and not pathognomonic (154).

ENDOCRINE TUMORS

Tinctorially cells of the normal and neoplastic adenohypophysis have been classified into acidophils (prolactin and growth hormone cells), basophils (gonadotrophs, corticotrophs and thyrotrophs), and chromophobe cells. Staining with orange G and erythrosin and carmoisine was thought to distinguish growth hormone from prolactin cells, in that the former stained with orange G, while the latter stained with erythrosin and carmoisine. However, only prolactin cells from pregnant or lactating women were consistently found to be positive with these stains, thus leaving the presence or absence of prolactin cells in other pituitaries open to question. Halmi (155,156,157) re-examined the classification of pituitary adenomas with PAP staining and found that among acidophil tumors, those staining with orange G and not with carmoisine were indeed growth hormone-secreting tumors. Furthermore, those that were negative with orange G, but did stain with carmoisine were, indeed, prolactin tumors. However, a large number of tumors reacted unequivocally with these stains or failed to stain at all. More than half of these were found to be prolactin tumors. The orange G-negative tumors, whether they stained with carmoisine or not, would generally have been described as "chromophobe." This situation is reminiscent of the normal pituitary (not pregnant or lactating) in which prolactin-immunostained cells failed to stain with carmoisine (156).

Kovacs et al. (158) found that 6 out of 45 chromophobe adenomas contained prolactin. Also, unlike previous contention, based on tinctorial procedures, PAP staining showed that in old age prolactin-secreting cells do not involute, but remain numerous and well developed (158). Their secretory activity is apparently independent of steroid deficiency.

The studies of pituitary adenomas suggest that classification of these tumors into acidophil, basophil, and chromophobe has outlived its usefulness.

Functional classification on the basis of the hormones they secrete seems to be more informative than tinctorial staining or electron microscopy. It is conceivable that especially in poorly preserved material, tinctorial staining is greatly compromised, while reactivity with sensitive PAP staining is maintained.

Most pituitary tumors are benign and secrete the hormones normally found in the gland. Multiple hormone secretion is common, representing multiple neoplastic cells, rather than secretion of multiple hormones from a single clone.

Endocrine tumors that secrete hormones normally found in the pituitary often arise from endocrine cells in *ectopic* locations outside the pituitary. Heitz et al. (159) described eight patients with ectopic tumors producing Cushing's syndrome. ACTH secretion caused symptoms in pancreatic endocrine tumors, medullary thyroid carcinoma, and a gastric, thymic, and mediastinal carcinoid. In six of these cases, ACTH secretion was demonstrated immunocytochemically, and it was usually associated with β-lipotropin immunoreactivity, suggesting assembly from proopiomelanocortin. As the symptoms of ectopic hormone secretion may precede other signs of tumor, it is important to search by immunocytochemistry for existence of such ectopic hormone-producing sites.

These ectopic ACTH-producing tumors provided a striking contrast to the 125 cases of pancreatic endocrine tumors described by Heitz et al. (160) which produce symptoms attributable to hormones normally present in the pancreas. These secreted hormones included insulin, pancreatic polypeptide, gastrin, vasoactive intestinal peptide, and glucagon. Often a number of hormones were secreted simultaneously. Ectopic hormones, such as proopiomelanocortin products, secretin, parathyroid hormone, calcitonin, and cholecystokinin were not found in the tumors. Since the morphology of these tumors was variable, they are best classified by the symptoms they cause. By histology of the primary tumors, it was impossible to determine whether they were malignant or benign, and malignancy was only diagnosed if they were metastatic or locally infiltrating. Because of the difficulty in treating these tumors on the basis of morphology, their immunocytochemical diagnosis is important, for most insulinomas and all pancreatic polypeptideomas were benign, while most glucagonomas, gastrinomas, and vasoactive intestinal peptidomas were malignant. However, some insulinomas were malignant (Fig. 9-39).

An unusual pancreatic carcinoma with ectopic hormone production was described by Asa et al. (161). The patient presented with Zollinger-Ellison syndrome but later developed Cushing's syndrome. The case is interesting since all

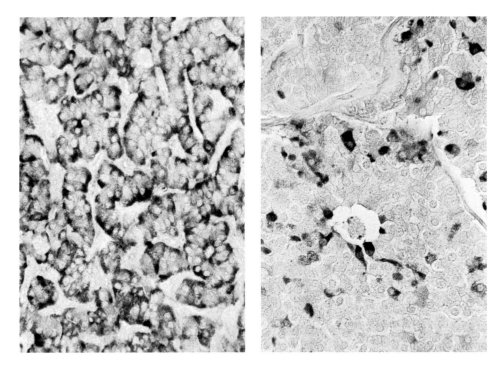

Figure 9-39. Malignant insulinoma. Bouin fixation, paraffin section. Left, trabecular growth pattern with many cells containing insulin. Right, solid growth pattern and many pancreatic polypeptide cells in liver metastasis. PAP method. ×450. [From Heitz et al. (160).]

of five hormones, gastrin, ACTH, α-endorphin, somatostatin, and calcitonin, were produced by the same cell, suggesting a genetic linkage between the prohormone for these peptides as well as perhaps for all hormones in the chromosome and malignant reversion to a stage of differentiation prior to segregation of specific hormone-secreting functions.

Pancreatic somatostatinoma has been identified from autopsy material by Larsson et al. (162). The symptoms of these cases had been steatorrhoea, achlorhydria, and impaired glucose tolerance. In the extract of the tumor from one recent patient, four components reacted with antisomatostatin by radioimmunoassay. One of these components corresponded to the quadridecapeptide, while all of them possessed biologic activity of somatostatin. It is interesting that the patients did not have severe symptoms of glucose metabolism derangement. This seems to support the notion that somatostatin has strong antisecretory activity only under conditions of hypersecretion (page 367).

Ectopic production of α-subunit of glycoprotein hormones and of LHRH was described by Wahlström and Seppälä in 22 carcinoid tumors (163) and in 6 out of 11 ductal carcinomas of the mammary gland (164). The LHRH immunocytochemical reactivity was blocked by admixture of antiserum with LHRH. Therefore, the activity in all likelihood was due to LHRH produced by the tumors rather than due to receptor binding of exogenous LHRH. We have found (165) that some cells in the intact pituitary, which are not gonadotrophs, as well as in

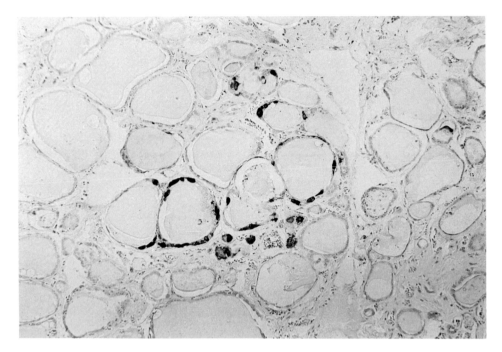

Figure 9-40.   Increase of thyroid C cells in C-cell hyperplasia. Stain for calcitonin. PAP method. Tinctorial counterstain. ×90. [From Ulbright et al. (167).]

pituitary cultures are able to synthesize LHRH *de novo,* thus providing an additional pathway for releasing hormone stimulation.

Medullary thyroid carcinoma originates from thyroid C-cells which produce the hypocalcemic polypeptide, calcitonin. DeLellis et al. (166) used sequential increase in calcitonin response to provocative calcium and pentagastrin infusion to identify family members of high risk of development of medullary thyroid carcinoma. By morphologic electron microscopy and with PAP-stained paraffin sections from thyroidectomy material, a spectrum of C-cell proliferative abnormalities ranging from C-cell hyperplasia to invasive medullary carcinoma could be identified. Both normal and hyperplastic C-cells occupied an intrafollicular location, being separate from the interstitium by the follicular basal lamina and from the luminal colloid by extensions of the follicular cell cytoplasm. In advanced hyperplasia, they often encircled and displaced follicular epithelium, but the relationship to intersitium and luminal colloid remained intact. In nodular hyperplasia, in which the follicular space was completely obliterated, occasional defects in basal lamina were seen.

The sporadic form of medullary carcinoma is more common than the familial tumor. Patients who have undergone incomplete thyroid resection for the nonfamilial disease are still at risk for developing C-cell proliferaion and possible medullary carcinoma. Ulbright et al. (167) have demonstrated a marked C-cell hyperplasia in a thyroid remaining after primary resection (Fig. 9-40).

REFERENCES

1. Scharrer E, Scharrer B: Secretory cells within the hypothalamus. *Res Publ Am Res Nervous Mental Diseases* **20**:170, 1939.

2. Scharrer E, Scharrer B: *Neuroendocrinology.* New York, Columbia University Press, 1963.

3. Scharrer B: Neuroendocrinology and Histochemistry, in Stoward PJ, Polak JM (eds): *Histochemistry: The Widening Horizons.* New York, Wiley, 1981.

4. Mains RE, Eipper B, Ling BL: Common precursor to corticotropins and endorphins. *Proc Natl Acad Sci USA* **74**:3014, 1977.

5. Nakanishi S, Inoue A, Kita T, Nakamura M, Chang ACY, Cohen SN, Numa S: Nucleotide sequence of cloned cDNA for bovine corticotropin-β-lipotropin precursor. *Nature* **278**:423, 1979.

6. Krieger D: Presence of corticotropin in brain of normal and hypophysectomized rats. *Proc Natl Acad Sci USA* **74**:648, 1977.

7. Liotta A, Gildersleeve D, Brownstein MJ, Krieger DT: Biosynthesis in vitro of immunoreactive 31000-dalton corticotropin/β-endorphin-like material by bovine hypothalamus. *Proc Natl Acad Sci USA* **76**:1448, 1979.

8. Watson SJ, Richard CW III, Barchas JD: Adrencorticotropin in rat brain: Localization in cells and axons. *Science* **200**:1180, 1978.

9. Sofroniew MV: Immunoreactive β-endorphin and ACTH in the same neurons of the hypothalamic arcuate nucleus in the rat. *Am J Anat* **154**:283, 1979.

10. Cuello AC: Central distribution of opoid peptides. *Brit Med Bull* **39**:11, 1983.

11. Stengaard-Pedersen K, Tredens K, Larsson L-I: Comparative localization of enkephalin and cholecytoskinin immunoreactivities and heavy metals in the hippocampus. *Brain Res* **273**:81, 1983.

12. Hökfelt T, Elde R, Johannsson D, Terenius L, Stein L: The distribution of enkephalin-immunoreactive cell bodies in the rat central nervous system. *Neurosci Lett* **5**:25, 1977.

13. Glazer EJ, Basbaum AI: Immunohistochemical localization of leucine-enkephalin in the spinal cord of the cat: Enkephalin-containing marginal neurons and pain modulation. *J Comp Neurol* **196**:377, 1981.

14. Ruda MA: Opioid and pain pathways: Demonstration of enkephalin synapses on dorsal horn projection neurons. *Science* **215**:1523, 1982.

15. Cuello AC: Nonclassical neuronal communication. *Fed Proc* **42**:2912, 1983.

16. Delsgaard C-J, Hokfelt T, Elfrin L-G, Terenius L: Enkephalin containing sympathetic preganglionic neurons projecting to the inferior mesenteric ganglion: Evidence from combined retrograde tracing and immunohistochemistry. *Neuroscience* **7**:2039, 1982.

17. Lundberg JM Hökfelt T, Schultzberg M, Urnas-Wallensten K, Kohler C, Said SI: Occurrence of vasoactive intestinal peptide-like immunoreactivity in certain cholinergic neurons of the cat: Evidence from combined immunohistochemistry and acetyl cholinesterase staining. *Neuroscience* **4**:1539, 1979.

18. Chang MM, Leeman SE: Isolation of a sialogogic peptide from bovine hypothalamic tissue and its characterization as substance P. *J Biol Chem* **245**:4784, 1970.

19. Hökfelt T, Johannsson O, Kellert J-O, Ljungdahl Å, Nilsson G, Nygårds A, Pernow B: Immunohistochemical distribution of substance P, in Leuler US, Pernow B (eds): *Substance P.* New York, Raven Press, 1977.

20. DiFiglia M, Aronin N, Leeman SE: Light microscopic and ultrastructural localization of immunoreactive substance P in the dorsal horn of the monkey spinal cord. *Neuroscience* **7**:1127, 1982.

21. Pearson J, Brandeis L, Cuello AC: Depletion of substance P axons in the substantia gelatinosa of patients with diminished pain sensitivity. *Nature* **295**:5844, 1982.

22. Taylor WL, Collier, KJ, Deschener RJ, Weith HC, Dixon JE: Sequence analysis of a cDNA coding for a pancreatic precursor of somatostatin. *Proc Natl Acad Sci* **78**:6694, 1981.

23. Lechan RM, Goodman RH, Rosenblatt M, Reichlin S, Hubener JF: Prosomatostatin-specific antigen in rat brain: Location by immunocytochemical staining with an antibody to a synthetic sequence of preprosomatostatin. *Proc Natl Acad Sci* **80:**2780, 1983.

24. King JC, Gerall AA, Fishback JB, Elkind KE, Arimura A: Growth hormone-releasing-inhibiting hormone pathway of the rat hypothalamus revealed by unlabeled antibody peroxidase-antiperoxidase method. *Cell Tiss Res* **160:**423, 1975.

25. Baker Bl, Yu Y-Y: Distribution of growth hormone release-inhibiting hormone in the rat brain as observed by immunocytochemistry. *Anat Rec* **186:**343, 1976.

26. Krisch B: Morphological equivalent of the bifunctional role of somatostatin. *Cell Tiss Res* **174:**211, 1977.

27. Johannsson O, Hokfelt T: Thyrotropin-releasing hormone, somatostatin and enkephalin distribution studied using immunohistochemical technique. *J Histochem Cytochem* **28:**364, 1980.

28. Forssmann W-G, Burnweit C, Shehab T, Triepel J: Somatostatin-immunoreactive nerve cell bodies and fibers in the medulla oblongata spinalis. *J Histochem Cytochem* **27:**1391, 1979.

29. Krisch B: Somatostatin-immunoreactive fiber projections into the brain stem and the spinal cord of the rat. *Cell Tiss Res* **217:**531, 1981.

30. Grube D, Bohn R: The microanatomy of the human islet of Langerhans with special reference to somatostatin (D)-cells. *Arch Histol Japon* **46:**327, 1983.

31. Paull WK, Scholer J, Arimura A, Meyers CA, Chang JK, Chang D, Shimiza M: Immunocytochemical localization of CRF in the ovine hypothalamus. *Peptides* **1:**183, 1983.

32. Merchenthaler I, Vigh S, Petrusz P, Schally AV: The paraventricular-infundibular corticotropin-releasing factor pathway as revealed by immunocytochemistry and adrenalectomized rats. *Reg Peptides* **5:**295, 1983.

33. Kawata M, Hashimoto K, Takahara T, Sano Y: Differences in distributional patterns of CRF-, oxytocin and vasopressin-immunoreactive nerve fibers in the median eminence of the rat. *Cell Tiss Res* **230:**247, 1983.

34. Goossens N. Dierickx K, Vandesande F: Immunocytochemical demonstration of the hypothalamo-hypophysial vasotocinergic system of Lampetra fluriatilio. *Cell Tiss Res* **177:**317, 1977.

35. Watkins WB: Localization of neurosecretory pathways. *Prog Neuropathol* **3:**383, 1976.

36. Gainer H, Sarne Y, Brownstein MJ: Neurophysin biosynthesis: Conversion of a putative precursor during axonal transport. *Science* **195:**1354, 1977.

37. Vandesande F, De Mey J, Dierickx K: Identification of neurophysin-producing cells. I. The origin of the neurophysin-like substance containing nerve fibers of the external region of the median eminence of the rat. *Cell Tiss Res* **151:**187, 1974.

38. Dierickx K, Vandesande E: Immune-enzyme cytochemical demonstration of mesotocinergic nerve fibers in the pars intermedia of the amphibian hypophysis. *Cell Tiss Res* **174:**25, 1976.

39. Silverman AJ: The hypothalamic magnocellular neurosecretory system of the guinea pig. II. Immunohistochemical localization of neurophysin and vasopressin in the fetus. *Am J Anat* **144:**445, 1975.

40. Krisch B: Immunohistochemical and electron microscopic study of the rat hypothalamic nuclei and cell clusters under various experimental conditions. *Cell Tiss Res* **174:**109, 1976.

41. Watkins WB: Immunocytochemical study of the hypothalamo-neurohypophysial system. I. Localization of neurosecretory neurons containing neurophysin-I and neurophysin-II in the domestic pig. *Cell Tiss Res* **175:**165, 1976.

42. Watkins WB, Choy VJ: Immunocytochemical evidence for the association of neurophysin-I with vasopressin and neurophysin-II with oxytocin in the pig hypothalamus. *Neurosci Lett* **3:**293, 1976.

43. Watkins WB, Choy VJ: Immunocytochemical study of the hypothalamo-neurohypophysial system. III. Localization of oxytocin- and vasopressin-containing neurons in the pig hypothalamus. *Cell Tiss Res* **180:**491, 1977.

44. Wolf G: Immunohistological identification of neurophysin and neurophysin-like substance in different vertebrates. *Endokrinologie* **68:**288, 1976.

45. Sofroniew MV, Weindl A: Extrahypothalamic neurophysin-containing perikarya, fiber pathways and fiber clusters in the rat brain. *Endocrinology* **102**:334, 1978.

46. Sofroniew MV, Weindl A: Immunohistochemical evidence of projections from the vasopressin and neurophysin-producing neurons of the suprachiasmic nucleus to the lateral septum, dorsal thalamus and lateral habenulae. *Am J Anat* **153**:391, 1978.

47. Pelletier G, Leclerc R, Labrie F, Puviani R: Electron microscopic immunohistochemical localization of neurophysin in the rat hypothalamus and pituitary. *Mol Cell Endocrinol* **1**:157, 1974.

48. Pelletier G, Leclerc R, Puviani R: Localization ultrastructurale d'hormones hypothalamiques. *Union Med Can* **104**:355, 1975.

49. Leclerc R, Pelletier G: Ontogeny of neurophysin in the rat pituitary gland. An electron microscope immunohistochemical study. *Brain Res* **129**:275, 1977.

50. Kozlowski GP, Frenk S, Brownfield MS: Localization of neurophysin in the rat supraoptic nucleus. I. Ultrastructural immunocytochemistry using the postembedding technique. *Cell Tiss Res* **179**:467, 1977.

51. Van Leeuwen FW, Swaab DF: Specific immunelectronmicroscopic localization of vasopressin and oxytocin in the neurohypophysis of the rat. *Cell Tiss Res* **177**:493, 1977.

52. Silverman AJ: Ultrastructural studies on the localization of neurohypophysial hormones and their carrier proteins. *J Histochem Cytochem* **24**:816, 1976.

53. Castel M, Hochman J: Ultrastructural immunohistochemical localization of vasopressin in the hypothalamic-neurohypophysial system of three murids. *Cell Tiss Res* **174**:69, 1976.

54. Krisch B: Nongranular vasopressin synthesis and transport in early stages of rehydration. *Cell Tiss Res* **207**:89, 1980.

55. Broadwell RD, Oliver L, Brightman MW: Localization of neurophysin within organelles associated with protein synthesis and packaging in the hypothalamo-neurohypophyseal system: An immunocytochemical study. *Proc Natl Acad Sci* **76**:5999, 1979.

56. De Mey J, Vandesande F, Dierickx K: Identification of neurophysin-producing cells. II. Identification of the neurophysin I and the neurophysin II-producing neurons in the bovine hypothalamus. *Cell Tiss Res* **153**:531, 1974.

57. Vandesande F, Dierickx K, De Mey J: Identification of the vasopressin-neurophysin II and the oxytocin-neurophysin I producing neurons in the bovine hypothalamus. *Cell Tiss Res* **156**:184, 1975.

58. Vandesande F, Dierickx K: Immunocytochemical demonstration of separate vasotocinergic and mesotocinergic neurons in the amphibian hypothalamic magnocellular neurosecretory system. *Cell Tiss Res* **175**:289, 1976.

59. Vandesande F, Dierickx K: Immunocytochemical demonstration, in the external region of the amphibian median eminence, of separate vasotocinergic and mesotocinergic nerve fibers. *Cell Tiss Res* **177**:37, 1977.

60. Van Vossel A, Dierickx K, Vandesande F, Van Vossel-Daeninck J: Electron microscopic immunocytochemical demonstration of separte vasotocinergic and mesotocinergic nerve fibers in the neural lobe of the amphibian hypophysis. *Cell Tiss Res* **173**:461, 1976.

61. Vandesande F, Dierickx K: Identification of the vasopressin-producing and the oxytocin-producing neurons in the hypothalamic magnocellular neurosecretory system of the rat. *Cell Tiss Res* **164**:153, 1975.

62. Van Vossel A, Van Vossel-Daeninck J, Dierickx K, Vandesande F: Electron-microscopic immunocytochemical demonstration of separate mesotocinergic and vasotocinergic nerve fibers in the pars intermedia of the amphibian hypophysis. *Cell Tiss Res* **178**:175, 1977.

63. Aspeslagh M-R, Vandesande F, Dierickx K: Electron microscopic immunocytochemical demonstration of separate neurophysin-vasopressinergic and neurophysin-oxytocinergic nerve fibers in the neural lobe of the rat hypophysis. *Cell Tiss Res* **171**:31, 1976.

64. Dierickx K, Vandesande F, De Mey J: Identification in the external region of the median eminence of the rat, of separate neurophysin-vasopressin and neurophysin-oxytocin containing nerve fibers. *Cell Tiss Res* **168**:141, 1976.

65. Weindl A, Sofroniew MV: Neurohormones and circumventricular organs. An immunohisto-chemical investigation, in Scott DE, Kozlowski GP, Weindl A (eds): *Brain-Endocrine Interaction. III. Neural Hormones and Reproduction.* Basel, Karger, 1978.

66. Buijs RM, Swaab DF, Dogterom J, Van Leeuwen FW: Intra- and extrahypothalamic vasopressin and oxytocin pathways in the rat. *Cell Tiss Res* **186**:423, 1978.

67. Buijs RM: Intra- and extrahypothalamic vasopressin and oxytocin pathways in the rat. Pathways to the limbic system, medulla oblongata and spinal cord. *Cell Tiss Res* **192**:423, 1978.

68. Mühlenthaler M, Dreifuss JJ, Gahwiler BH: Vasopressin excites hippocampal neurons. *Nature* **296**:749, 1982.

69. Lauber M, Nicolas P, Bousetta H, Fahy C, Beguin P, Camier M, Vaudry H, Cohen P: The Mr common forms of neurophysin and vasopressin from bovine neurohypophysis have cortico-tropin- and endorphin-like sequences and liberate by proteolysis biologically active cortico-trophin. *Proc Natl Acad Sci* **78**:6086, 1981.

70. Pfaff DW: Luteinizing hormone-releasing factor potentiates lordosis behavior in hypophysec-tomized ovariectomized female rats. *Science* **182**:1148, 1973.

71. Moss RL, McCann SM: Action of luteinizing hormone-releasing factor in the initiation of lordosis behavior in the estrone-primed ovariectomized female rat. *Neuroendocrinology* **17**:309, 1975.

72. Browning JY, D'Aguta R, Steinberger A, Grotjun HE, Steinberger E: Biphasic effect of gonadotropin-releasing hormone and its agonist analogue (HOE 766) on in vitro testosterone production by purified rat Leydig cells. *Endocrinology* **113**:985, 1983.

73. King JC, Tobert SA, Snavely FC, Arimura AA: LHRH-immunopositive cells and their projections to the median eminence and the organum vasculosum of the lamina terminalis. *J Comp Neurol* **209**:287, 1982.

74. King JC, Parsons JA, Erlandsen SL, Williams TH: Luteinizing hormone-releasing hormone pathway of the rat revealed by the unlabeled antibody peroxidase-antiperoxidase method. *Cell Tiss Res* **153**:211, 1974.

75. King JC, Elkind KE, Gerall AA, Millar RP: Investigation of the LHRH system in the normal and neonatally steroid-treated male and female rat, in Scott DF, Kozlowski GP, Weindl A (eds): *Brain Endocrine Interaction. III. Neural Hormones and Reproduction.* Basel, Karger, 1978.

76. Baker BL: Distribution of gonadotropin-releasing hormone in the rat brain as observed with immunohistochemistry. *Endocrinology* **97**:125, 1975.

77. Gross DS: Distribution of gonadotropin-releasing hormone in the mouse brain as revealed by immunohistochemistry. *Endocrinology* **98**:1410, 1976.

78. Ibata Y, Wanatabe K, Kinoshita H, Kubo S, Sano Y, Sin S, Hashimura E, Imagawa K: The location of LHRH neurons in the rat hypothalamus and their pathways to the median eminence. Experimental immunohistochemistry and radioimmunoassay. *Cell Tiss Res* **198**:381, 1979.

79. Burchanowski BG, Knigge KM, Sternberger LA: Rich ependymal investment of luliberin (LHRH) fibers revealed immunocytochemically as image like that from Golgi stain. *Proc Natl Acad Sci* **76**:6771, 1979.

80. Anthony ELP, King JC, Stopa E: Immunocytochemical localization of LHRH in the median eminence, infundibular stalk and neurohypophysis. Evidence for multiple sites of releasing hormone secretion in humans and other mammals. *Cell Tiss Res* **236**:5, 1984.

81. Silverman AJ: Distribution of luteinizing hormone releasing hormone in the guinea pig brain. *Endocrinology* **99**:30, 1976.

82. Sternberger LA, Greenwals JC, Hock D, Elger K-H, Forssmann W-G: A new hypothalamic substance and not luteinizing hormone-releasing hormone is detected immunocytochemi-cally by antibody to luteinizing hormone-releasing hormone. *Proc Natl Acad Sci* **78**:5216, 1981.

83. Knapp RJ, Sternberger LA: A monoclonal antibody to luteinizing hormone-releasing hormone. Preparation and binding studies. *J Neuroimmunol* **6**:361, 1984.

84. Knapp RJ, Sternberger LA: Heterogeneity of luteinizing hormone-releasing hormone studied with a monoclonal antibody. *Soc Neurosci Abst* **13**:138, 1983.

85. Fink G: Feedback action of target hormones on hypothalamus and pituitary with special reference to gonadal steroids. *Ann Rev Physiol* **41**:571, 1979.

86. Shivers BD, Harlan RE, Morrell JI, Pfaff DW: Immunocytochemical localization of luteinizing hormone-releasing hormone in male and female rat brains. Quantitative studies on the effect of gonadal steroids. *Neuroendocrinology* **36**:1, 1983.

87. Brownstein MJ, Palkovitz M, Saavedra JM, Bassiri RM, Utiger RD: Thyrotropin-releasing hormone in rat brain membranes. *Brain Res* **92**:309, 1975.

88. Kubek MJ, Lorincz MA, Wilbur JF: The identification of thyrotropin-releasing hormone in hypothalamic and extrahypothalamic loci of the human nervous system. *Brain Res* **126**:196, 1977.

89. Hökfelt T, Fuxe K, Johannsson O, Jeffcoate S, White N: Thyrotropin-releasing hormone-containing nerve terminals in certain brain stem nuclei and in the spinal cord. *Neurosci Lett* **1**:133, 1975.

90. Hökfelt T, Fuxe K, Johannsson O, Jeffcoate S, White N: Distribution of thyrotropin-releasing hormone in the central nervous system as revealed by immunohistochemistry. *Eur J Pharmacol* **34**:389, 1975.

91. Lechan RM, Jackson IMD: Immunohistochemical localization of thyrotropin-releasing hormone in the rat hypothalamus and pituitary. *Endocrinology* **111**:55, 1982.

92. Lechan RM, Molitch ME, Jackson IMD: Distribution of immunoreactive growth hormone-like and thyrotropin-releasing hormone in the rat central nervous system. Evidence for their coexistence in the same neurons. *Endocrinology* **112**:877, 1983.

93. Larsson LI, Rehfeld JF: Evidence for a common evolutionary origin of gastrin and cholecysto-kinin. *Nature* **269**:335, 1977.

94. Buchan AMJ, Lance V, Polak JM: Regulatory peptides in the gastrointestinal tract of Alligator missisipiensis. An immunocytochemical study. *Cell Tiss Res* **231**:439, 1983.

95. Larsson LI, Rehfeld JF: Localization and molecular heterogeneity of cholecystokinin in the central and peripheral nervous system. *Brain Res* **165**:201, 1979.

96. Peters A, Miller M, Kimerer LM: Cholecystokinin-like immunoreactive neurons in rat cerebral cortex. *Neuroscience* **8**:431, 1983.

97. Peters A, Kimerer LM: Bipolar neurons in rat visual cortex: a combined Golgi-electron-microscopic study. *J Neurocytol* **10**:921, 1983.

98. Peters A, Regidov J: A reassessment of the forms of nonpyramidal neurons in area 17 of the visual cortex. *Neuroscience* **5**:2079, 1980.

99. Handelmann GE, Meyer DK, Beinfeld MC, Oertel WH: Cholecystokinin-containing terminals in the hippocampus are derived from intrinsic neurons: an immunohistochemical and radioimmunological study. *Brain Res* **224**:180, 1981.

100. Malmfors G, Leander S, Brodie E, Håkenson R, Holmin T, Sundler F: Peptide-containing neurons intrinsic to the gut wall. An experimental study in the pig. *Cell Tiss Res* **214**:225, 1981.

101. Leander S, Ekman R, Uddman R, Sundler F, Håkenson R: Neuronal cholecystokinin, gastrin-releasing peptide, neurotensin and β-endorphin in the intestine of the guinea pig. Distribution and possible motor function. *Cell Tiss Res* **235**:521, 1984.

102. Adler G, Grube D: Die Neuroendokrinologie des Magen-Darm-Trakts. *Internist* **23**:23, 1982.

103. Roberts GW, Woodhams PL, Bryant MG, Crow TJ, Bloom SR, Polak JM: VIP in the rat brain: Evidence for a major pathway linking the amygdala and hippocampus via stria terminalis. *Histochemistry* **65**:103, 1980.

104. Erlandsen SL, Hegre OD, Parsons JA, McEvoy RC, Elde RP: Pancreatic islet cell hormones. Distribution of cell types in the islet and evidence for the presence of somatostatin and gastrin within the D cell. *J Histochem Cytochem* **24**:883, 1976.

105. Rickert DE, Fischer LF, Burke JP, Redick JA, Erlandsen SL, Parsons JA, Van Orden LS III: Cryptoheptadine-induced insulin depletion in rat pancreatic B cells. Demonstration by light and electron microscopic immunocytochemistry. *Horm Metab Res* **8**:430, 1976.

106. El-Salhy M, Grimelius L, Wilander E, Ryberg B, Terenius L, Lundberg JM, Tatemoto K: Immunocytochemical identification of polypeptide YY cells in the human gastrointestinal tract. *Histochemistry* **77**:15, 1983.

107. El-Salhy M, Grimelius L: Immunocytochemical demonstration of polypeptide YY in the gastrointestinal tract of the monkey, Macacca rhesus: A light and electron-microscopic study. *Biomed Res* **4:**284, 1983.

108. Triepel J, Grimmelikhuijzen CJP: A critical examination of FMRFamide immunoreactivity in the brain of guinea pig and rat. *Histochemistry* **80:**63, 1984.

109. Scharrer B: Peptidergic neurons. *Acta Morphol Neerland-Scand* **20:**219, 1982.

110. LeRoith D, Liotta AS, Roth J, Shiloach J, Lewis ME, Pert CB, Krieger DT: Corticotropin and β-endorphin-like materials are native to unicellular organisms. *Proc Natl Acad Sci* **79:**2086, 1982.

111. Stephano GB, Scharrer B, Assana P: Demonstration, characterization and localization of opioid binding sites in the midgut of the insect Leucophaea maderne (Blattaria). *Brain Res* **253:**205, 1982.

112. Hansen BL, Hansen GN, Scharrer B: Immunoreactive material resembling vertebrate neuropeptides in the corpus cardiacum and corpus allatum of the insect, Leucophaea maderne. *Cell Tiss Res* **225:**319, 1982.

113. El-Salhy M, Falkmer S, Kramer KJ, Speirs RD: Immunohistochemical investigation of neuropeptides in the brain, corpora allata and corpora cardiaca of an adult lepidopteran insect, Manduca sexta (L). *Cell Tiss Res* **232:**295, 1983.

114. Nishiitsutsuji-Uwo J, Endo Y: Gut endocrine cells in insects: The ultrastructure of the endocrine cells in the cockroach midgut. *Biomed Res* **2:**30, 1981.

115. Iwanaga T, Fujitat T, Nishiitsutsuji-Uwo J, Endo J: Immunohistochemical demonstration of pancreatic polypeptide-, somatostatin-, enteroglucagon-, and VIP-like immunoreactivities in the cockroach midgut. *Biomed Res* **2:**202, 1981.

116. Dube H, Thorpe A: The distribution of pancreatic polypeptide in the nervous system and gut of the blowfly, Calliphora vomitoria (Diptera). *Cell Tiss Res* **227:**67, 1982.

117. Reinecke M, Larraway RE, Falkmer S, Feurle GE, Forssmann W-G: Occurrence of neurotensin-immunoreactive cells in the digestive tract of lower vertebrates and deuterostomian invertebrates. A correlated immunohistocytochemical and radioimmunochemical study. *Cell Tiss Res* **212:**173, 1980.

118. Scharrer E, Sinden J: A contribution to the "chemoarchitectonics" of the optic tectum of the brain of the pigeon. *J Comp Neurol* **91:**331, 1949.

119. Kuljis RO, Karten HJ: Laminar organization of peptide-like immunoreactivity in the anuran optic tectum. *J Comp Neurol* **212:**188, 1982.

120. Graybiel AM: Compartmental organization of the mammalian striatum. *Progr Brain Res* **58:**247, 1983.

121. Johannsson O, Lundberg JM: Ultrastructural localization of VIP-like immunoreactivity in large dense core vesicle of "cholinergic-type" nerve terminals in cat exocrine glands. *Neuroscience* **6:**847, 1981.

122. Fujii S, Kobayashi SU, Fugita T, Yannihara N: VIP-immunoreactive nerves in the pancreas of the snake, Elaphe quadrivirgata (Boie). Another model for insular neurosecretion. *Biomed Res* **1:**180, 1980.

123. Lundberg JM, Hökfelt T: Coexistence of peptides and classical neurotransmitters. *Trends Neurosci* **6:**1, 1983.

124. Hökfelt T, Rehfeld JF, Skirboll L, Ivemark B, Goldstein M, Mackey K: Evidence for coexistence of dopamine and cholecystokinin in mesolimbic nerves. *Nature* **285:**476, 1980.

125. Bowker RM, Westlund KN, Sullivan M, Wilber JF, Coulter JP: Transmitters of the raphé-spiral complex: Immunocytochemical studies. *Peptides* **3:**291, 1982.

126. Chan-Palay V, Jonsson C, Palay SL: Serotonin and substance P coexist in neurons of the rat central nervous system. *Proc Natl Acad Sci* **75:**1582, 1978.

127. Pelletier G, Steinbusch HWM, Verhofstad AAJ: Immunoreactive substance P and serotonin present in the same dense core vesicles. *Nature* **293:**71, 1981.

128. Martin R, Voigt KH: Enkephalin coexists with oxytocin and vasopressin in nerve terminals of rat neurohypophsis. *Nature* **289:**502, 1981.

129. Weber E, Roth KA, Barchas JD: Colocalization of α-neo-endorphin and dynorphin immuno-reactivities in hypothalamic neurons. *Biophys Biochem Res Commun* **103**:951, 1981.

130. Martin R, Geis R, Holl M, Schafer M, Voigt KH: Coexistence of unrelated peptides in oxytocin and vasopressin terminals of rat neurohypophysis: Immunoreactive methionine-enkephalin, Leu-enkephalin and cholecystokinin-like substances. *Neuroscience* **8**:213, 1983.

131. Grube D, Voigt KH, Weber E: Pancreatic glucagon cells contain endorphin-like immuno-reactivity. *Histochemistry* **59**:75, 1978.

132. Beauvillain JC, Tramu C, Dubois MP: Ultrastructural immunocytochemical evidence of the presence of a peptide related to ACTH in granules of LHRH terminal in the median eminence of the guinea pig. *Cell Tiss Res* **218**:1, 1981.

133. Lechan RM, Molitch ME, Jackson IMD: Distribution of immunoreactive human growth hormone-like material and thyrotropin-releasing hormone in the rat central nervous system: Evidence for their coexistence in the same neurons. *Endocrinology* **112**:877, 1983.

134. Conn PM, Hsueh AJW, Crowley WF: Gonadotropin-releasing hormone: molecular and cell biology, physiology and common applications. *Fed Proc* **43**:2351, 1984.

135. Sternberger LA, Petrali JP: Quantitative immunocytochemistry of pituitary receptors for luteinizing hormone-releasing hormone. *Cell Tiss Res* **162**:141, 1975.

136. Sternberger LA, Petrali JP, Joseph SA, Meyer HG, Mills KR: Specificity of the immunocyto-chemical LHRH receptor reaction. *Endocrinology* **102**:63, 1978.

137. Seppälä M, Wahlström T, Leppaluoto J: Luteinizing hormone-releasing factor-like immuno-reactivity in rat pancreatic islet cells. *Life Sci* **25**:1489, 1979.

138. Seppälä M, Wahlstrom T, Lehovirta R, Lee JN, Leppaluoto J: Immunohistochemical demonstration of luteinizing hormone-releasing factor-like material in human syncytiotiophoblastic and trophoblastic tumors. *Clin Endocrinol* **12**:441, 1980.

139. Sternberger LA, Petrali JP: Quantitative immunocytochemistry of pituitary receptors for luteinizing hormone-release hormone. *Cell Tiss Res* **162**:141, 1975.

140. Witorsch RJ: Immunohistochemical demonstration of prolactin binding sites in some sex accessory organs of the male rat. Fifty Ninth Annual Meeting, The Endocrine Society, Chicago, 1977, p 281.

141. Witorsch RJ: Immunohistochemical studies of prolactin binding in male sex accessory organs. *J Histochem Cytochem* **26**:565, 1978.

142. Witorsch RJ: The application of immunoperoxidase methodology for the visualization of prolactin-binding sites in human pancreatic tissue. *Hum Path* **10**:521, 1979.

143. Dunaif AE, Zimmerman EA, Frantz AG, Friesen HG: Prolactin and its receptor: Intracellular localization in the ovary by immunoperoxidase technique. *Clin Res* **25**:293A, 1977.

144. Wagner TOF, Adams TE, Nett TM: GNRH interaction with anterior pituitary. I. Determination of the affinity and number of receptors for GNRH in ovine anterior pituitary. *Biol Reprod* **20**:140, 1979.

145. Zolman JC, Valenta LJ: Gonadotropin-releasing hormone receptor binding in bovine anterior pituitary. *Biophys Biochim Acta* **627**:172, 1980.

146. Millar RF, Rosen H, Badminton M, Pasqualini C, Kordelhue B: Luteinizing hormone-releasing hormone binding to purified rat pituitary nuclei. *FEBS Lett* **153**:382, 1982.

147. Dular R, LaBella F: Action of releasing factors on isolated secretory granules mediated by calcium. *Life Sci* **21**:1527, 1977.

148. Duello TM, Nett TM, Farquhar MG: Fate of gonadotropin-releasing hormone internalized in rat pituitary gonadotrophs. *Endocrinology* **112**:1, 1983.

149. Loumaye E, Catt KJ: Agonist-induced regulation of pituitary receptors for gonadotropin-releasing hormone. *J Biol Chem* **258**:12002, 1983.

150. Kuhl H, Baumann R: New aspects of the physiological significance of LHRH receptors of pituitary plasma membranes. *Acta Endocrinol* **96**:36, 1981.

151. Farquhar MG: The Golgi Apparatus (complex) (1954–1981)—From artifact to center stage. *J Cell Biol* **91**(Suppl):775, 1981.

152. Farquhar MG: Multiple pathways of exocytosis, endocytosis and membrane recycling: validation of a Golgi route. *Fed Proc* **42**:2407, 1983.

153. Susman KE, Draznin B, Leitner JW, Mehler PS: The enzyme secretion granule revisited—Postulated new functions. *Metabolism* **31**:959, 1982.

154. Gepts W, LeCompte PM: The pancreatic islet in diabetes. *Am J Med* **70**:105, 1981.

155. Halmi NS, Parsons JA, Erlandsen SL, Duello T: Prolactin and growth hormone cells in the human hypophysis: A study with immunoenzyme histochemistry and differential staining. *Cell Tiss Res* **158**:497, 1975.

156. Halmi NS, Duello T: "Acidophilic" pituitary tumors. A reappraisal with differential staining and immunocytochemical techniques. *Arch Pathol Lab Med* **100**:346, 1976.

157. Halmi NS: The current status of human pituitary cytophysiology. *NZ Med J* **80**:551, 1974.

158. Kovacs K, Corenblum B, Sirek AMT, Penz G, Ezrin C: Localization of prolactin in chromophobe pituitary adenomas: study of human necropsy material by immunoperoxidase technique. *J Clin Pathol* **29**:250, 1976.

159. Heitz PU, Kloppel G, Polak JM, Staub J-J: Ectopic hormone production by endocrine tissues: Localization of hormones at the cellular level by immunocytochemistry. *Cancer* **48**:2029, 1981.

160. Heitz PU, Kasper M, Polak JM, Kloppel G: Pancreatic endocrine tumors: Immunocytochemical analysis of 125 tumors. *Hum Path* **13**:263, 1982.

161. Asa SC, Kovacs K, Killinger DW, Marcon N, Platt M: Pancreatic islet cell carcinoma producing gastrin, ACTH, α-endorphin, somatostatin and calcitonin. *Am J Gastroenterol* **74**:30, 1980.

162. Larsson LI, Hursch MA, Holst, JJ, Ingemansson S, Kuhl C, Lindkaer Jensen S, Lundquist G, Rehfeld JF, Schwartz TW: Pancreatic somatostatinoma. Clinical features and physiological implications. *Lancet,* March 26, 1977, p 666.

163. Wahlstrom T, Seppälä M: Immunologic evidence for the occurrence of luteinizing hormone-releasing factor and the α-subunit of glycoprotein hormones in carcinoid tumors. *J Clin Endocrin Metab* **53**:209, 1981.

164. Seppälä M, Wahlstrom T: Identification of luteinizing hormone-releasing factor and subunits of glycoprotein hormone in ductal carcinoma of the mammary gland. *Int J Cancer* **26**:267, 1980.

165. Li Y, Knapp RM, Sternberger LA: Immunocytochemistry of a "private" luteinizing hormone-releasing hormone system in the pituitary. *Cell Tiss Res* **235**:263, 1984.

166. DeLellis RA, Nunemacher G, Wolfe HJ: C-cell hyperplasia. An ultrastructural analysis. *Lab Invest* **36**:237, 1977.

167. Ulbright TU, Kraus FT, O'Neal LW: C-cell hyperplasia developing in residual thyroid following resection of sporadic medullary carcinoma. *Cancer* **48**:2076, 1981.

Chapter Ten

Neuronal Diversity

We have seen that a neurosecretory cell can express a variety of combinations of bioactive principles. Every neuron seems to be a neurosecretory cell that coexpresses, besides classical neurotransmitters, one or more peptidergic substances which may modulate nervous function in response to different demands.

We have also seen that many neurons have their cell bodies in limited regions of the brain from whence they innervate wide areas of the nervous system through extensive arborizations (pages 316 and 379). When we view an area as small as an electron microscopic section, we can see a large number of synaptic contacts within its confines. If we consider the thinness of an electron microscopic section and the wide anatomical ramifications of some neurons, we must arrive at an enormous number of synapses that mediate the communicative functions of a single neurons. It is unlikely that all the synapses fire simultanelusly in anything but a convulsive attack. We may speculate that the coexistence of conventional transmitters and several peptidergic principles may determine a degree of functional specialization to individual synapses of a given neuron. However, mere coexistence does not, in itself, determine which synapse should be activated and which deactivated at a single instance. To this end, we may assume that the neuron possesses a second system of discrimination that may conceivably direct a given transmitter or peptide to a given terminal in its arborization and exclude it from other segments. This could be a transport function, since transport could extend over the wide range of neuronal projections. Thus, neuritic elements that form the anatomic substrate to this arborization are prime candidates for this function. In order to gate given peptides among a variety of peptides to individual sites, the cytoskeleton itself must have functional diversity.

Besides diversity in peptidergic transmission and cytoskeleton-associated transport function, a neuron may possess a third element of diversity. Neurons are genetically endowed to make similar connections in different individuals of the same species. The chemical mediators of the specificity of neuronal connectivity are unknown, although nonspecific growth and plasticity factors have been described. The establishment of neuronal connectivity is thought to be a function of constituents of the cell membrane, since the cell membrane is what makes the contact of one neurite with another.

Beyond a limited number of peptides that have been described so far, it is safe to assume that the majority of peptidergic transmitters have not yet been discovered. The biochemical basis of diversity that may distinguish either the cytoskeleton or the cell membrane of one neuron from another is even more obscure. This is not surprising. The isolation of peptide principles shared by many cells, such as luteinizing hormone-releasing hormone (LHRH), required thousands of brains in the original work from Schally's and Guilleman's groups (1,2). The isolation of LHRH was guided by the knowledge of existence of a hypothalamic principle that liberates gonadotropins from the pituitary. Bioassay for this principle directed the separation and purification procedure. Without knowledge of this action, LHRH could not have been isolated.

Newer bioactive peptides have also been isolated on the basis of bioassay, even if the bioassay did not necessarily provide an indication of the principal action of the peptide eventually obtained. Many preparations from brain produce contraction of the isolated ileum, and this bioassay has led to a number of important new discoveries in neuroendocrinology. Of special interest is the isolation of neurotensin performed by Leeman et al. (3) on the basis of bioassay of peaks as well as troughs obtained on chromatographic separation of brain extract. The activity was not associated with a measurable peak, but was found in a trough containing amounts of material below those detectable by UV absorption.

If we consider the difficulty of isolating principles that are shared by a large number of neurons, it becomes easy to understand why we have not yet found a substance, be it a peptide or a cytoskeleton or membrane constituent or any other substance, characteristic of only a single neuron or a group of few selected neurons. This difficulty is compounded by the fact that a search for such a substance would lack a proper mode of assay in its isolation. How can we discover a new substance, which we suspect to exist, but whose action we do not know and for which no bioassay exists? It is easy to understand, therefore, that most substances that may determine neuronal diversity and any possible individuality that distinguishes one neuron from another, still await discovery.

A fresh approach to this problem became possible with the use of monoclonal antibodies in immunocytochemistry. We know that a monoclonal antibody will react only with a single epitope or cross-react with epitopes very similar to it. If we use, in immunocytochemistry, an antiserum to an impure antigen, we may at best localize the immunizing antigen plus a lot of other substances. If we look for antibodies to a constituent of a single neuron and we immunize with whole brain, our antiserum reacts immunocytochemically throughout the brain as well as in peripheral tissues. If the serum contains any antibodies specific to only a single neuron or a single group of neurons, we would miss them in immunocytochemical localization. We cannot absorb from the serum the irrelevant antibodies, leaving behind any antibodies specific to individual neurons, because we cannot prepare an absorbent containing all the irrelevant substances profusely found throughout the brain and lacking the unknown substance in which we are presumed to be interested. Even if we could do this, the absorption would be ineffective, because it is technically difficult to remove the majority of antibodies from a serum and leave behind only a rare idiotype.

With the advent of monoclonal antibodies, however, the search for antibodies to minor constituents in an impure antigen has become realistic. If we immunize a mouse with whole brain homogenate or any other crude neural tissue preparation, the animal again will produce a large array of antibodies most of them probably directed to antigens shared among many neuronal and non-neuronal constituents, and a few of them, conceivably, specific to individual neurons. Each of these antibodies is a product of different cell lines (page 246). The production of monoclonal antibodies involves selections of clones derived from individual cells of the immunized host (page 250). Each antibody obtained will, therefore, be specific to an epitope in a single antigen of the immunizing crude homogenate. Only rarely is such epitope shared with other antigens (page 246). Hence, we can use monoclonal antibodies to detect and eventually isolate and characterize putative antigens specific to individual neurons. The only requirement is the proper selection procedure. Conventionally, monoclonal antibodies are selected by immunologic reactions of the cell culture supernate. The common techniques, such as radioimmunoassay or enzyme-linked immunosorbent assay, require the antigen we are interested in. They are, therefore, not useful for discovering new and unknown antigens. Immunocytochemistry, however, is capable of distinguishing unknown antigens of interest from those we wish to discard. If we immunize with whole brain extract, we would discard those antibodies that react with all brain tissue, and would retain those that react with only specific structures among neurons, or perhaps only with individual neurons or groups of neurons. The approach to select monoclonal antibodies to neuronal constituents depends somewhat on the objective to be achieved. Earlier search for neuron-specific antibody in the work of Zipser and McKay (4) was aimed at identification of functional groups of neurons in the nervous system of the leech. Antibodies were selected by immunofluorescence of fixed whole mount preparations of the leech nervous system. No embedding was necessary, because of the simplicity of the leech nervous system which, when spread directly on a slide, exposes most nerve cells to the antibodies. Antibodies to cell surface and intracellular constituents could be localized. Individual neurons in the leech are relatively few and are well mapped anatomically. Some antibodies, indeed, detected exclusively pairs of neurons in a given ganglion known to be related to reproductive function. Others were specific to sensory stimuli and identified as such by retrograde transport of lucifer yellow (page 187) from cutaneous sites. Trisler et al. (5) used immunofluorescence of frozen sections to select antibodies cloned from fused mouse spleen cells immunized with retina. This analysis will preferentially reveal antibodies to cell surface antigens. One of the antibodies distributed itself in a gradient over the retina. Matthew et al. (6), using the PAP method, were the first to describe by light and electron microscopy monoclonal antibodies specific to synaptic structures. Lampson (7) produced monoclonal antibodies to selected neurons of the retina and obtained improved localization by the use of paraffin sections.

We used sagittal paraffin sections of rat brain to evaluate supernates of hybridoma clones obtained after immunization with rat brain homogenate (8). With paraffin sections, we were likely to miss most antibodies specific to cell surface antigens. We would also miss antibodies to epitopes destroyed by embedment. However, the use of these sections had the advantage that it was relatively easy to

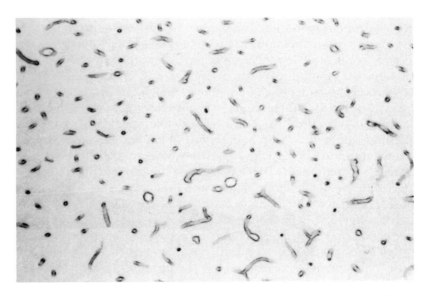

Figure 10-1. Antibody 02-132 is specific for rat nervous system endothelium. It may be a specific reagent for the blood-brain barrier. ClonoPAP. ×265. [From the work of Nancy Sternberger.]

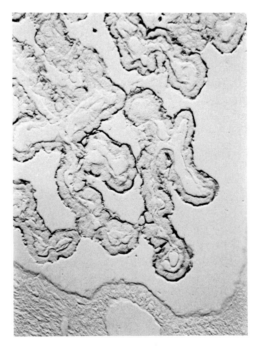

Figure 10-2. Cilia of choroid plexus, antibody 06-69. ClonoPAP. ×180. [From Östermann et al. (9).]

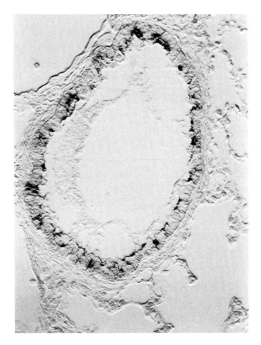

Figure 10-3. Cilia of bronchial epithelium, antibody 06-69. ClonoPAP. ×180. [From Östermann et al. (9).]

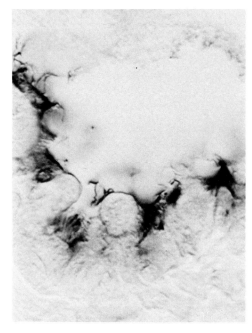

Figure 10-4. Cilia of bronchial epithelium, antibody 06-69. ClonoPAP. ×1900. [From Östermann et al. (9).]

distinguish antibodies that reacted with epitopes common to nervous and non-nervous tissue from those specific for neurons. Among 135 monoclonal antibodies produced, we found that 81 were specific to individual structures. The remaining antibodies reacted with neural and non-neural structures and were discarded. Among the 81 retained antibodies, 37 were neuron-specific. Among the 44 other antibodies from the retained 81, many were specific to selected cells in the anterior pituitary. One antibody reacted with endothelium in central and peripheral nerves of the rat, but not with endothelium in other tissues (Fig. 10-1). One antibody was specific for cilia in the chorid plexus and in respiratory epithelium (Figs. 10-2, 10-3, 10-4).

IDENTIFICATION OF NEWLY DETECTED ANTIGENS

We found that 37 of the 135 monoclonal antibodies selected after immunization with whole brain were neuron-specific. Each of these antibodies had a slightly different staining distribution (8). However, it was possible to classify these antibodies into groups on the basis of major staining differences that excluded appreciable overlap from one group to another. Within each group, individual antibodies still exhibited minor but characteristic staining differences.

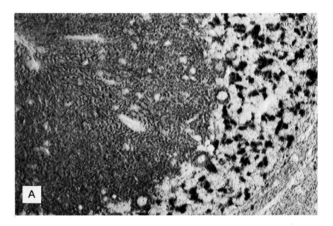

Figure 10-5.   Rat cerebellum sagittal paraffin sections. In the adult, antibody 02-24 stains glomeruli in the granular layer stronger than it stains the molecular layer (A). Purkinje cells and their dendrites are also stained. In contrast, antibody 02-29 stains in the adult (B) the molecular layer stronger than the glomeruli of the granular layer, and Purkinje cells and their unstained dendrites are outlined in negative image. At 15 days of age, antibody 02-24 stains, in contrast to the adult, Purkinje cells and their dendrites stronger than glomeruli (C). Antibody 02-29 at 15 days of age, stains glomeruli and molecular layer strongly, but leaves Purkinje cells unstained (D). Staining of cerebellar white matter is stronger at 15 days of age (D) than in the adult (B). In the newborn, staining with antibody 02-24 is restricted to a band (E) that will become the Purkinje cell layer in the adult. Staining by antibody 02-29 in the newborn (F) is more extensive than that of antibody 02-24 and includes what will be white matter fibers and the Purkinje cell layer. Throughout development, staining of Purkinje cell bodies is more common with antibody 02-24 than with antibody 02-29. Only with antibody 02-29 is the cell body staining destined to disappear with progressive development. Antibody 02-29, but not 02-24, outlines a rim around developing neurons, which disappears in the adult. ClonoPAP. ×265. [From Sternberger et al. (10).]

Antibodies of group I acted predominantly with gray matter. On the basis of morphologic appearance of staining, these antibodies were thought to react with synaptic contacts (Fig. 10-5). On immunoblots (page 20), they revealed few bands in electrophoresed synaptic preparations, while multiple bands were apparent upon nonspecific staining for protein by Coomassie blue (Fig. 10-6). Most antibodies from this group had slightly different staining distributions. In all likelihood, they reacted with different proteins in synaptosomal preparations. Antibody 02-24 and 02-29 also revealed distinct developmental patterns (page 458). Antibodies from group I were called antisynapse-associated antibodies (8,9).

Antibodies of *group II* reacted with basket cell fibers in the cerebellum, tangential fibers in the cerebral cortex, white matter fibers in the cerebellum, and many long axonal projections in the brainstem. These antibodies never visualized cell bodies, dendrites, or proximal axons in the central nervous system (Fig.

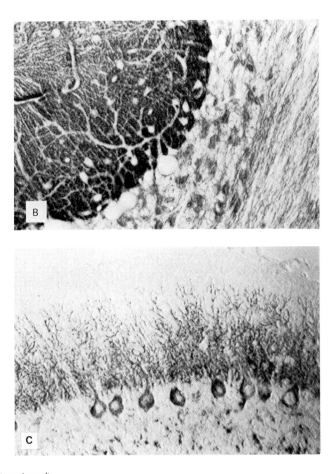

Figure 10-5.   (continued)

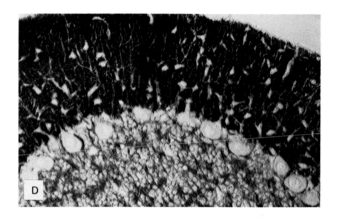

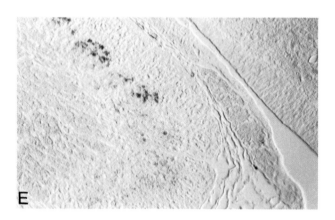

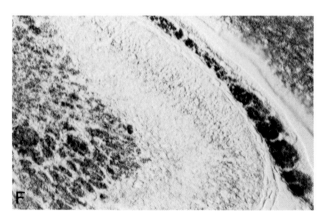

Figure 10-5. (continued)

434

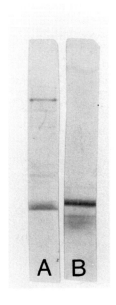

Figure 10-6. Electrophoresis immunoblot of synaptosomal preparation. Lane A, monoclonal antibody, 02-24. Lane B, monoclonal antibody 02-29. Stained with ClonoPAP. [From Sternberger et al. (10).]

3-45). On purely morphologic grounds, it appeared that they react with neurofibrils. Basket cell fibers and long axons, indeed, are rich in neurofibrils. Electrophoresis-immunoblot analysis confirmed this suspicion.

When electrophoresed and electroblotted neurofilaments prepared by the axonal flotation method of DeVries et al. (11) were stained with Coomassie blue, the three strongest bands corresponded to the 200-, 150-, and 68-kDa molecular weight subunits of the neurofilament triplet. Cytoskeletal preparations made according to Chiu and Norton (12) or Eng et al. (13) disclosed six bands that included the neurofilament triplet, tubulin, vimentin, and fodrin. Neurofilaments are cytoskeletal components characteristic of the nervous system, but vimentin and tubulin occur in non-neuronal cells as well. Brain tubulin is more heterogeneous than peripheral tubulin (14) and, as shown by Matus et al. (15), high molecular weight microtubule-*associated* protein may be specific for dendrites (Fig. 10-7).

When the electroblotted preparations were stained with monoclonal antibodies of group II, either the 200-kDa band or this band as well as the 150-kDa band plus occasional degradation bands were stained, depending on the antibody used and the amount of cytoskeletal preparation applied to the gel (Fig. 10-10). The 68-kDa neurofilament band or the vimentin, tubulin, or fodrin bands were never revealed. When instead of axonal flotation or cytoskeletal preparations, whole brain extracts were electrophoresed in amounts of 75 µg/stack, electroblotted and stained with antibodies from group II, the same bands were revealed, and no additional bands were visualized. Thus, the antibodies of group II were specific to neurofilament subunits and their breakdown products, and did not cross-react with other components of brain homogenate. For these reasons, antibodies from group II were called *antineurofibrillar antibodies* (8,9).

Antibodies from *group III* reacted with selected neuronal cell bodies (perikarya), with dendrites, and with proximal axons. In the cerebellum, the cell bodies usually included Purkinje cells, Lugaro cells, and cells in the fastigial nucleus, but

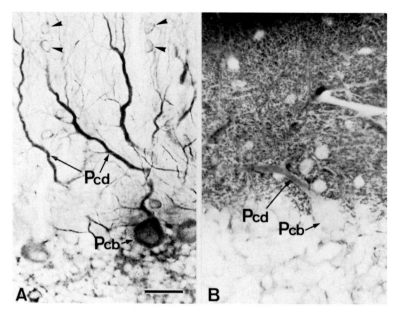

Figure 10-7. Rat cerebellum Vibratome section reacted with antiserum to high molecular weight micro-tubule-associated protein (A) reveals Purkinje cell bodies (Pcb) and dendrites (Pcd), but no axons. Antiserum to tubulin (B), on the other hand, stains axons (transversely cat parallel fibers shown) and glia (radial fibers of Bergmann glia shown). PAP method. 4-chloro-1-naphthol. Bar is 25 μm. [From Matus et al. (15).]

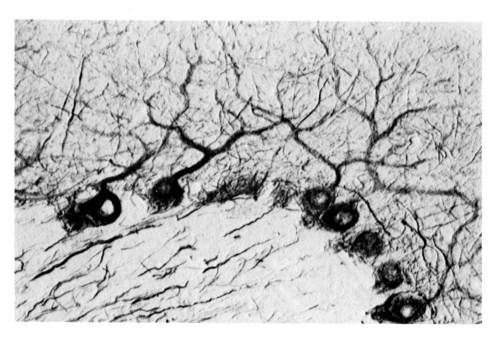

Figure 10-8. Rat cerebellum sagittal paraffin section. Staining with the antiperikaryonal-neurofibrillar, monoclonal antibody 02-135 reveals Purkinje cell bodies, their dendrites, and proximal axons. Basket cell fibers are unstained. Compare with Fig. 3-45. ClonoPAP. ×311. [From the work of Ludwig and Nancy Sternberger.]

basket cells, granule cells, or other neurons of the cerebellum were unstained (Fig. 10-8). In the brainstem, many large neurons were stained, usually including those of the red nucleus, trapezoid body, vestibular, and motor nuclei. In the spinal cord, motor neurons were usually most prominent. In the cerebral cortex, pyramidal cells as well as their dendrites and proximal axons were stained. Basket cell fibers in the cerebellum or transverse fibers in the cerebral cortex, as well as many axons prominent with antibodies from group II, were not stained by antibodies from group III (Fig. 10-9). Thus, there was little overlap in staining between antibodies from group II and antibodies from group III.

When the antibodies from group II were used for staining electrblots from brain homogenate, or from cytoskeletal or neurofilament preparations, they stained, to our surprise, the 200- and a 180-kDa neurofilament component, and occasional degradation bands were also stained (Fig. 10-10). The 150- and 68-

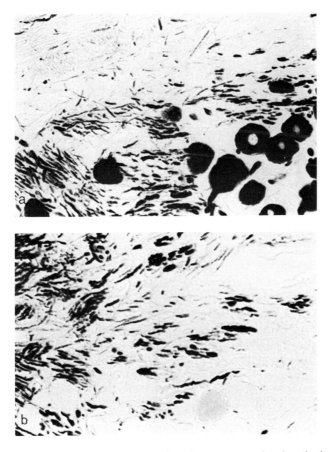

Figure 10-9. Paraffin section through the rat facial nucleus. (a) Monoclonal antibody 06-53 from the antiperikaryonal-neurofibrillar group stains perikarya and proximal axons, but leaves fibers passing through the nucleus unstained. (b) Monoclonal antibody 07-5 from the antineurofibrillar group stains fibers passing through the nucleus, but leaves cell bodies and their proximal axons unstained. There is no overlap in staining of antibodies from the antiperikaryonal-neurofibrillar group and the neurofibrillar group. ClonoPAP. ×200. [From the work of Ludwig and Nancy Sternberger.]

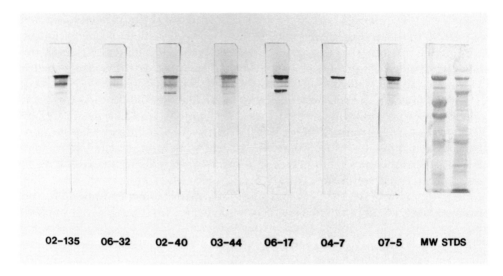

Figure 10-10. Lanes 1–8, electroblots of cytoskeletal preparations (25 μg/ml) stained with the monoclonal antibodies indicated. Group III antibodies: 02-135, 06-31. Group IV antibody: 02-40. Group II antibodies: 03-44, 06-17, 04-7, 07-5. ClonoPAP. Lanes 8 and 9, molecular weight standards stained with Coomassie blue. [From Goldstein et al. (18).]

kDa neurofilament bands or vimentin, tubulin, or fodrin were not revealed. Thus, despite lack of significant overlap of staining between antibodies from groups II and III, both reacted with the 200-kDa subunit of neurofilaments as defined electrophoretically according to molecular weight.

The antibodies from group III were called *antiperikaryonal-neurofibrillar antibodies* (8,9).

Group IV consisted of a single antibody, 02-40, that incorporated both, staining characteristics of the antineurofibrillar and antiperikaryonal-neurofibrillar antibodies. Thus, in the cerebellum, both basket cell fibers and Purkinje cell bodies were stained, and in the cerebral cortex, both pyramidal cell bodies and transverse fibers. Therefore, the antibody was called *broadly reacting neuron-specific antibody*. On electroblots with brain homogenate, axonal flotation or cytoskeletal preparations, this antibody revealed the 200-, 180-, and 150-kDa components as well as degradation bands strongly (Fig. 10-10). The 68-kDa neurofilament band was not detected.

HETEROGENEITY OF NEUROFILAMENTS

Since there is little overlap in staining between antibodies from groups II and III, there must exist a major heterogeneity in the neurofilament proteins revealed. Similarly, the broad staining reactivity of antibody 02-40 (group IV) compared to that of groups II and III, also defines a major heterogeneity of these proteins. This *macroheterogeneity* is distinct from the lesser differences or *microheterogeneity*, observed for every antibody in groups II and III.

All antibodies from groups II, III, and IV recognized the 200-kDa neurofilament protein (Fig. 10-10). None reacted with the 68-kDa protein. One antibody from group II (06-17) also reacted with the 150-kDa protein, and one (04-7) revealed this protein weakly. No other antibodies from group II and none of those from group III reacted with the 150-kDa protein. The antibodies from groups III and IV, but not those from group II, also reacted with a 180-kDa protein. This protein seems to be a nonphosphorylated form of the 200-kDa protein (page 441) and is not seen by Coomassie blue staining of electroblotted cytoskeletal preparations. In addition, antibodies from all groups reacted with two to three minor bands, not seen by Coomassie blue staining, which appear to represent degradation products of the 200- and 150-kDa proteins. Some may be products of partial dephosphorylation (pages 448 and 455).

These data alone are merely a reflection of the expectation that each antibody has a different specificity and reacts with a different epitope. Each macromolecule possesses many epitopes, some of which may or may not be shared among the 200- and 150-kDa proteins and their related degradation forms. The stronger reaction with the 200-kDa protein than with the 150-kDa protein may either be due to a higher frequency of the relevant epitopes in the former, or more likely due to only partial homology of epitopes of both forms, the antibodies being more specific for the 200-kDa epitope. In any event, the sodium dodecyl sulfate gel electroblot data do not differentiate between the possibility that the differences of reactivity among the antibodies may be due to epitopic diversity within single neurofilament proteins or that the single neurofilament proteins themselves may be heterogeneous, consisting of a family of proteins that share molecular weight, but differ in primary structure.

We arrived at the suggestion that the antibodies, indeed, reveal macroheterogeneity as well as microheterogeneity in neurofilaments by comparison of electrophoretic patterns with immunocytochemical staining distribution (8,16) and by two-dimensional electrophoresis immunoblot patterns (17).

All antibodies from the neurofibrillar groups (group II) react in the cerebellum with basket cell fibers and white matter fibers, in the cerebral cortex with predominantly tangential fibers, in the brainstem and spinal cord with prominent long axonal projections, and in the adrenal medulla with nerve fibers. Microheterogeneity of reactive neurofilaments was indicated, however, in the relative intensities of localization of these structures with the varying antibodies from group II. Thus, antibody 07-4 stained basket cell fibers in the same section stronger or equally strong as cerebellar white matter (Fig. 3-54), while antibodiy 04-7 stained basket cell fibers weaker than the white fibers (Fig. 3-58). Such quantitative discrepancy in the same section can only be explained by differences in proportional distribution of microheterogeneous neurofilaments in different regions. Similarly, in the periphery, nerves in the thymus were only detected by group II antibodies 03-44, 06-17, and SMI 31, but not by antibody 06-68. Developmental studies also point to microheterogeneity (18). Thus, antibody 06-17 stains neurofibrils from the sixth postnatal day onwards, and staining becomes more widespread as the brain develops. Only fibrillary structures are stained throughout development. Antibody 03-44, on the other hand, stains a few fibers already at birth. In addition, on the sixth postnatal day, Purkinje cell bodies are transiently stained. This is the only instance in which we saw perikaryonal staining with an antibody from group II in normal animals. The staining disappears in the adult. Neurofibrillar staining becomes widespread for a while with antibody 03-44, but from day 20 on, staining in the cerebellar white matter decreases while that in the basket cell fibers increases in prominence. This contrasts with the parallel development of both staining distributions in the case of antibody 06-17, again alluding to microheterogeneity of the neurofilaments visualized. Apparently, neurofilaments revealed by antibody 03-44 are more specific than those revealed by 06-17. The specificity seems to reflect a selective process during differentiation, leading in the case of some neurofilaments to their elimination in one area and retention in another.

Another fundamental difference in neurofilaments detected by antibodies from group II exists between reaction of antibody 06-68 and the rest of antibodies of the antineurofibrillar groups. Antibody 06-68 is not entirely brain specific, in that it reacts, in peripheral organs, also with diffuse cell nuclei. In the adult brain, however, it reacts only with neurofibrils. In the early developing brain, on the other hand, it reacts with nuclei of cells lining the ventricular and dural surfaces and growing toward deeper structures (Fig. 10-11). Only late in development does neurofibrillar staining appear (Fig. 10-12). Interestingly, developing areas that reveal neurofibrillar staining patterns become devoid of nuclear staining. In the adult brain, no nuclear staining is seen. It is conceivable that this phenomenon is merely a reflection of accidental sharing of a neurofibrillar epitope with a transient, developmental nuclear epitope. However, mutual exclusion of localization of neurofibrils and nuclear antigen, in a single region of brain, suggests that both localizations may represent a developmental sequence. Kornguth et al. (19) have observed filamentous structures in nuclei of developing brains. If some neurofibrils, such as those revealed by monoclonal antibody 06-68, are developing from a skeletal structure of early nuclei, while those reacting with other antibodies from group II do not, it would constitute another suggestion of microheterogeneity of antigens reactive with antineurofibrillar antibodies.

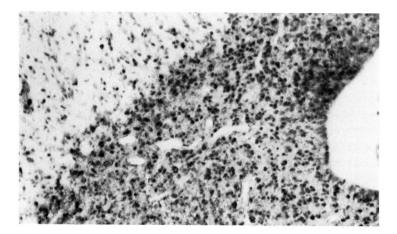

Figure 10-11.   In this 6th postnatal day rat cerebellum, monoclonal antibody 06-68 from the antineurofibrillar group (group II) reacts with nuclei. ClonoPAP. ×200. [From the work of Ludwig and Nancy Sternberger.]

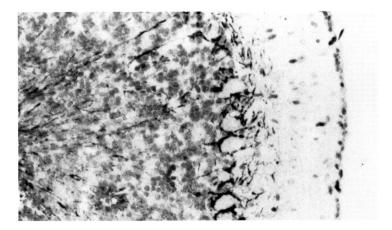

Figure 10-12.   In the 28-day-old rat brain, monoclonal antibody 06-68 reveals cell nuclei and neurofibrils. Neurons with stained neurofibrils are devoid of nuclear staining. ClonoPAP. ×200. [From the work of Ludwig and Nancy Sternberger.]

As we have seen, electrophoretic separation, according to molecular weight only, is insufficient for demonstrating neurofibrillar microheterogeneity unless the data are evaluated in conjunction with immunocytochemical morphology. On the other hand, electrophoresis in two dimensions followed by electroblotting, did separate neurofilaments into distinct moieties, of which some do and some do not react with given monoclonal antibodies, thus revealing microheterogeneity. When separation was carried out according to charge in the horizontal direction and according to molecular weight in the vertical direction, we found (17) that antibody 04-7 only reacted with forms of the 200- and 150-kDa protein with isoelectric points ranging from pH 5.1 to 5.2 (Fig. 10-13). Antibody 06-17 revealed, in addition, a 180-kDa form at this pH range. Antibody 07-5 revealed five bands separated according to molecular weight. These included components of the 200-kDa peptides, ranging in isoelectric point from pH 5.1 to 6.3. In addition to the pH 5.1 form of the 163-, 141-, and 123-kDa proteins, more acidic forms were also revealed. Finally, antibody 03-44 stained the same peptides as antibody 07-5, but in addition revealed a group of peptides that lose molecular weight as they become more basic, as revealed by a sweeping line in the electroblot. Dephosphorylation would be a mechanism by which peptides could become more basic. Julien and Mushynski (20) have reported multiple phosphorylation sites in neurofilament peptides and have shown that with gradual removal of phosphate from the 200-kDa protein, the apparent molecular weight approaches 180 kDa. We will see (page 448) that antibodies from group II are specific for phosphate-containing epitopes in neurofilaments. It is to be expected that each antibody from group II reacts with a different phosphorylated epitope and that only one, and almost certainly not more than two phosphate groups, form part of a single epitope. The 200-kDa neurofilament protein processes multiple phosphorylation sites. Partially phosphorylated 200-kDa components would occupy intermediate positions on the electrophoresis-electroblot between pH 5.1 and 6.3, and between 200 and 180 kDa, thus accounting for the sweep in one of the bands obtained with antibody 03-44. Different phosphate sites in

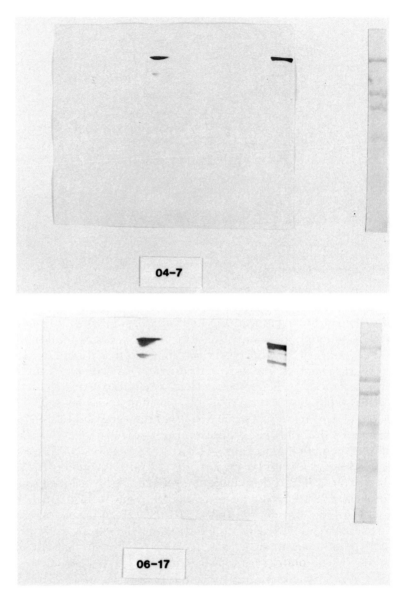

Figure 10-13. A cytoskeletal preparation (25 μg/ml) was electrofocused in the horizontal dimension and electrophoresed in the presence of sodium dodecyl sulfate in the vertical dimension (center of gel sheets). Sodium dodecyl sulfate electroblots without prior electrofocusing on the right side of the gel sheets. The gels have been electroblotted and stained with monoclonal antineurofilament antibodies of group II diluted 1 : 5000, antimouse IgG and ClonoPAP. Separate strips on the far right side of the figures represent Coomassie blue-stained molecular weight standards (200, 160, 92, and 66 kDa). The antibodies used are indicated on the bottom of the figures. [From Goldstein et al. (17).]

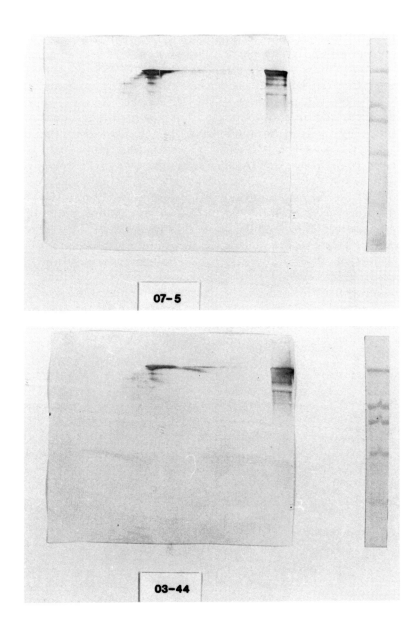

07−5

03−44

443

neurofilaments vary in their susceptibility to dephosphorylation as detected by antibodies from group II. The site detected by antibody 03-44 is the most resistant one observed, thus suggesting that it reacts with a buried phosphate site. This antibody detects at least the more acidic side of the sweeping line which approaches the 180-kDa position as its isoelectric point increases. Apparently, it reacts with a partially dephosphorylated component. Interestingly, the phosphate epitope with which the antibody reacts and for which other evidence suggests that it is buried, is also less susceptible to dephosphorylation, and thus is still present in proteins that occupy an intermediate position between pH 5.1 and 6.3 and 200 and 180 kDa.

Antibodies from the perikaryonal-neurofibrillar group (group III) also reveal quantitative differences in immunocytochemical distribution in the brain. For instance, antibody 06-32 stained Purkinje cells stronger than those of the nucleus ruber, while antibody 02-135 stained cells of the nucleus ruber stronger than Purkinje cells (Fig. 10-14). This suggests microheterogeneity of the neurofilament peptides localized.

Microheterogeneity is also evident from developmental studies (18). With monoclonal antibody 02-135, staining in Purkinje cell perikarya, dendrites, and proximal axons increases concomitantly with age. Monoclonal antibody 06-32 reveals a similar staining pattern until the 20th day of age. However, from then

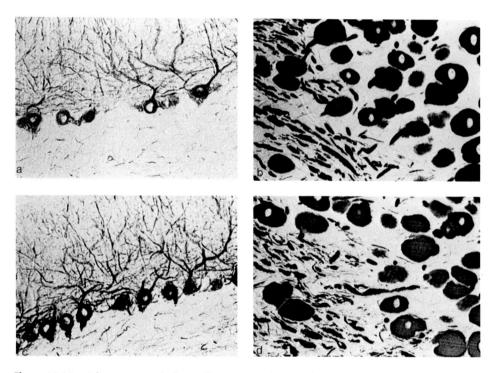

Figure 10-14. Adjacent 7-μm-thick paraffin sections of rat cerebellum (a,c) and facial nucleus (b,d) reacted with monoclonal antiperikaryonal-neurofibrillar antibody 06-32 diluted 1 : 2000 (a,b) or with 02-135 diluted 1 : 2000 (c,d). ClonoPAP. ×200. [From the work of Ludwig and Nancy Sternberger.]

on, staining in Purkinje dendrites and axons diminishes. Again, developmental pressure seems toward specialization and selection of only given forms of neurofilaments in specialized areas.

Among the antibodies from the antiperikaryonal-neurofibrillar group (group III), antibody 02-135 and 06-32 reveal similar, two-dimensional electrophoretic patterns (Fig. 10-15). The neurofilament proteins reactive with these antibodies consist of a variety of species varying from a more acidic 200-kDa component to

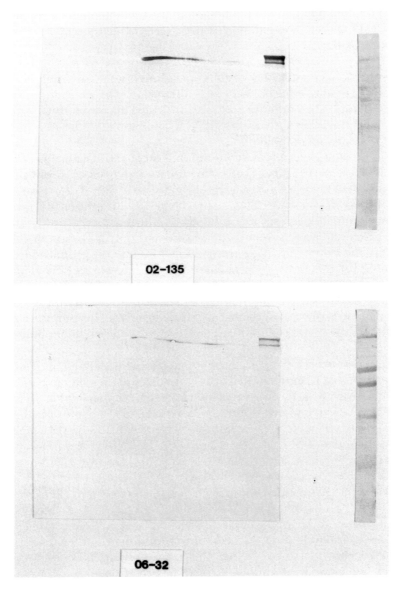

Figure 10-15. Two-dimensional electrophoresis electroblots of cytoskeletal preparations reactive with monoclonal antibodies from the perikaryonal-neurofibrillar group (group III). ClonoPAP. One-dimensional electroblots on right side of gel sheets. Coomassie blue-stained molecular weight standards on separate strip on right side of figures. The antibodies used are indiciated. [From Goldstein et al. (17).]

a more basic 180-kDa component, the latter apparently representing the de-phosphorylated 180-kDa component of Julien and Mushynski (20). The electrophoresis reveals a macroheterogeneity that distinguishes the reaction of the antiperikaryonal-neurofibrillar antibodies (group III) from the antineurofibrillar antibodies (group II). However, the similarity of electrophoresis patterns for antibodies 02-135 and 06-32 precludes conclusion with regard to microheterogeneity within group III, at least as far as electrophoretic separation is concerned.

ANTIGENICITY OF EPITOPES FROM HETEROGENEITY REGIONS OF NEUROFILAMENTS

When one produces antisera to organs, including brain, most antibodies are not very specific. It may appear, therefore, surprising that we found 63% of our monoclonal antibodies brain specific and 27% specific to neuronal constituents of brain, and that, furthermore, this 27% of antibodies delineated highly variable, heterogeneous components.

The fusion of spleen cells of an immunized mouse with myeloma cells usually involves about 2×10^8 pairs of cells. The number of antibody-producing hybridomas obtained from a fusion is rarely more than 80, if the total fusion is utilized. This is an efficiency of less than 0.00004%. The efficiency is low because only a portion of spleen cells are antibody-producing B cells, only a portion of cells are fused and have survived the fusion, and only a portion of cells retain throughout the cloning life both, the genome for antibody production, as well as the genome for the recovery pathway during the hypoxanthine-aminopterin-thymidine phase of clone selection. Finally, many successful antibody-producing clones may be missed by the method of selection. The narrow specificity of monoclonal antibodies requires that we present in our selection system the appropriate epitope for selection in a form reactive with antibodies in the culture supernate.

Our selection procedure was aimed at detecting intracellular antigens of high heterogeneity, that is, antigens that are found only in some, but not all, neuronal contituents. Furthermore, we were interested in antibodies that had a broad interspecies reactivity, so that the antibodies can be used not only for the staining of rat brains, but also for surgical and retrospective human pathologic material. To favor obtainment of the desired antibodies, we chose the following procedural details:

1.   We selected antibody-producing clones by immunocytochemistry on paraffin sections. Because of poor preservation of cell membranes, but good penetration of tissue, we favored, thereby, detection of intracellular antigens.

2.   We discarded all hybridomas that gave uniform, rather than a discrete, immunocytochemical reaction when first assayed on paraffin sections. By this maneuver, we eliminated antibodies to widely distributed antigens, as well as antibodies crossreactive with many antigens. Geisler et al. (21) reported a homology in excess of 40% of amino acid residues for the 68-kDa neurofilament peptide and the nonneuronal cytoskeletal proteins, vimentin, and desmin. We

would expect, therefore, that many antibodies to the 68-kDa peptide cross-react with peripheral tissues or with nonneuronal brain components. Such antibodies would have been discarded by us in the primary assay for hybridoma selection. This may explain why we describe only neurofilament antibodies reactive with the 200- and 150-kDa neurofilament peptides or their degradation products, but not with the 68-kDa peptide.

The linear arrangement of neurofilaments in the axon in the same direction in which materials are transported raised the possibility that neurofilaments may be involved in transport. However, many primitive axons, such as those of the ventral cord of the crayfish, lack neurofilaments (22). Peters and Vaughn (23) find no neurofilaments in the newborn optic nerve, even though it must depend on axonal transport for development. Levine et al. (24) find retinal ganglion cell axonal transport even in the absence of electrophoretically demonstrated neurofilaments. Developmental studies with our monoclonal antibodies that react primarily with the 200-kDa neurofilament polypeptide, to a lesser extent with the 150-kDa polypeptide, and not at all with the 68-kDa peptide, revealed little or no neurofilaments in the newborn rat (18), depending on the antibody used, with the gradual and relatively slow development until the 20th postnatal day. Nevertheless, axonal transport occurs well before that. However, the developmental studies also show that some neurofilament epitopes are more widely distributed in the 15- to 20-day period than in the period from 28 days to adulthood. Apparently, developmental heterogeneity is a selective process. Early in development, heterogeneous neurofilaments may be widely distributed, and only with specialization will their distribution become more restricted, presumably by a selective process. Thus, it seems that neurofilaments, while not essential for transport in primitive or early developing neurons, may become in differentiated organisms an aid in transport, that might perhaps, by virtue of extensive heterogeneity, mediate a selective mode, gating given constituents to active transport in some neurons, while perhaps arresting the transport of other constituents in other neurons.

The situation is reminiscent of the immune response. Antibodies have been relatively late in phylogenetic appearance, being present abundantly only in birds and mammals. Nevertheless, more primitive species still mount an effective response against noxious microorganisms. Immunoglobulins are latecomers in defense of the host, making it more specific and perhaps more effective. The phenomenon is repeated in development. The newly hatched chick has an undeveloped immune response, but even though it is raised gnodobiotically in ovo, it is quite well prepared for defense against environmental microorganisms. The newborn rat transports neurotransmitter principles as well as organelles to its axon terminals. However, it is not yet a coordinated organism that responds rapidly and with discrimination to environmental stimuli. Perhaps a more mature response that requires not only acceleration of transport of essential principles, but perhaps also a simultaneous retardation of transport of inhibitory principles, requires a specific gating structure that could be, conceivably, supplied by neurofilaments. With this in mind, we concentrated our succeeding efforts to the nature of neurofilament heterogeneity and its possible functional significance.

MONOCLONAL ANTIBODIES DISTINGUISH PHOSPHORYLATED AND NONPHOSPHORYLATED FORMS OF NEUROFILAMENTS IN SITU

Heterogeneity may be pretranslational or post-translational. Amino acid composition studies of the 200-, 150-, and 68-kDa neurofilament triplet polypeptides by DeVries et al. (25) and peptide mapping studies by Chiu et al. (26) and Brown et al. (27) have shown that each of the peptides are products of different genes. Furthermore, studies on the cell-free biosynthesis of the neurofilament triplets by Czosnek et al. (28) indicate that the polypeptides do not derive from a common precursor. Autilio-Gambetti et al. (29) have shown that polyclonal antisera to individual neurofilament peptides contain cross-reacting antibodies, suggesting that short sequences may be shared among the neurofilament triplet polypeptides, and that perhaps they may have evolved from a common ancestral gene (see also page 389). The larger neurofilament peptides are, therefore, not oligomers of the smaller ones. Genomic variations occur independently in them by excision and insertion of exon regions.

Post-translational modifications in proteins generally involve glycosylation, phosphorylation at serine or threonine groups, amino-terminal pyroglutamate formation, carboxy-terminal acetylation, as well as addition of amino acids. The latter may be quite specifically mediated via axonal 4S/RNA, which is chromatographically indistinguishable from perikaryonal tRNA, and is, according to Lindquist et al. (30), the predominant species of RNA in axons despite absence of ribosomes. Other post-translational changes are dephosphorylation, deglycosylation, as well as specifically controlled proteolytic cleavage.

Gainer's group (31) were the first to show that neurofilaments are phosphorylated. Julien and Mushynski (20) found that in vivo administered ^{32}P attaches to 22 sites in the 200-kDa neurofilament polypeptide, to 9 sites in the 150-kDa peptide, and to 3 sites in the 68-kDa peptide. The high phosphate content was confirmed by treating neurofilaments with alkaline phosphatase *prior* to separation into the triplet subunits.

As discussed by Kennedy (32) and Willard (33), phosphorylation is usually related to other steric changes and to high-energy transport mechanisms. The strong association of neurofilaments with a magnesium-dependent, cyclic AMP independent protein kinase reported by Julien et al. (34), suggests that phosphorylation, in particular, may be an important post-translational modification of neurofilaments that conceivably might have physiologic significance. For these reasons, we have decided to examine whether some of our monoclonal antineurofilaments react with phosphorylated epitopes in neurofilaments and whether some of the heterogeneity disclosed by these antibodies may be, indeed, due to post-translational phosphorylation. To this end, we electrophoresed cytoskeletal preparations in sodium dodecyl sulfate polyacrylamide gel and electroblotted them onto cellulose nitrate paper (35). Pairs of strips cut out from the electroblots were either incubated in phosphatase or in buffer and then stained immunocytochemically with monoclonal antibodies, goat antimouse immunoglobulin, and ClonoPAP (peroxidase-antiperoxidase complex prepared from monoclonal antiperoxidase). Phosphatase treatment abolished the staining with all antibodies from the antineurofibrillar group (group II, including monoclonal antibodies 06-17, 03-44, 06-68, 04-7, and 07-5) and suggested that these antibodies are specific for phosphorylated epitopes and unreactive with them once they have been dephosphorylated (Fig. 10-16). Since neurofilaments are extensively phosphorylated as shown by Julien and Mushyinski (20) and since the antibodies from the antineurofibrillar group react with different microheterogeneous neurofilament polypeptides, it is unlikely that the phosphorylated epitopes detected by these antibodies are identical.

Staining of electroblots with antibodies from the antiperikaryonal-neurofibrillar group (group III, including antibodies 02-135, 06-32, and 06-53) became enhanced after treatment with phosphatase. This finding is amenable to two interpretations. Conceivably, the antibodies react with phosphorylated as well as nonphosphorylated epitopes of neurofilaments, but better with the latter. Alternatively, cytoskeletal preparations contain mixtures of phosphorylated and nonphosphorylated neurofilament peptides and the antibodies react only with the nonphosphorylated form which increases in amount upon digestion with phosphatase. As we will see below, the latter interpretation appears to be more likely.

Phosphatase had no effect on the electroblot staining with the broadly reactive, neurofilament-specific monoclonal antibody 02-40.

Dephosphorylation in these experiments was carried out on electroblot strips obtained from cytoskeletal preparations separated into components by sodium dodecyl sulfate. The detergent, undoubtedly, improved accessibility of sites to

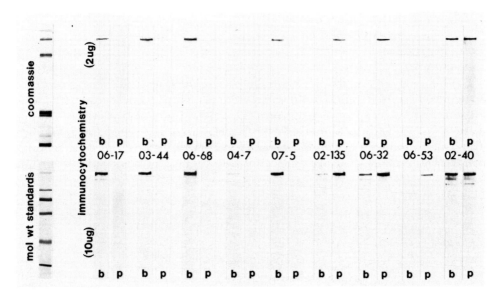

Figure 10-16. Electroblots of cytoskeletal preparations. The far left lanes have been stained with Coomassie blue after electroblotting of the electrophoresis gels loaded with 10 μg cytoskeletal preparation (*upper left lane*) or with molecular weight standards (top to bottom, 200, 160, 92, 66, 45, and 31 kDa) (*lower left lane*). The remaining lanes were stained immunocytochemically with the monoclonal antibodies listed between the upper and lower lanes. Prior to immunocytochemical staining, lanes *b* were treated with buffer and lanes *p* with phosphatase. The electroblots were obtained from electrophoresis gels loaded with 2 μg (*upper lanes*) and 10 μg (*lower lanes*) of cytoskeletal preparations. ClonoPAP [From Sternberger and Sternberger (35).]

phosphatase, which may be inaccessible in intact neurofilaments. Indeed, digestion of paraffin-embedded brain sections with even larger doses of phosphatase
had no effect on immunocytochemical staining with any of the monoclonal
antibodies. With antibodies of the neurofibrillar group (group II), digestion of
sections with trypsin, again had no effect. However, when sections were first
treated with trypsin and then with phosphatase, staining became diminished (Fig.
10-17). Prolonged incubation times and concentrations of phosphatase, generally nine times higher than those used on the electroblots, were needed for the
effect to become pronounced. Differences in phosphorylation sites detected by
each of the antineurofibrillar antibodies was suggested by difference in susceptibility to phosphatase. Diminution of staining was apparent within 2½ hours of
incubation with monoclonal antibody 04-7, even if the phosphatase concentration was relatively low, but required 5 to 18 hours with antibodies 06-17, 07-5
and SMI 31. Diminution of staining could not be established by a single series of
trypsin-phosphatase treatments with antibodies 03-44 and 06-68. This, again,
alludes to heterogeneity of neurofilaments themselves, or to heterogeneity of
position of phosphorylation sites in given forms of neurofilaments, which determine differences of accessibility to phosphatase, even after digestion with
trypsin.

Entirely different effects were noted when enzyme-treated sections were
stained with antibodies from the perikaryonal-neurofibrillar group (group III,
monoclonal antibodies 02-135, 06-32, 06-53, and SMI 32). These antibodies, we
recall, react with cell bodies, their dendrites, and thick proximal axons, including
Purkinje cells in the cerebellum, and pyramidal cells in the cerebral cortex. They
do not react with thin axons, or axon terminals, as for instance, basket cell fibers
in the cerebellum or tangential fibers in the cerebral cortex. In contrast to
antibodies from the neurofibrillar group, when sections were treated with trypsin, all staining with antibodies from the perikaryonal-neurofibrillar group disappeared (Figs. 10-18 and 10-19). When tryptic digestion was followed by phosphatase, staining reappeared, but now the perikaryonal-neurofibrillar staining
pattern was replaced by a neurofibrillar pattern. In other words, the antibodies
that had reacted with nonphosphorylated epitopes now gave the same staining
pattern as normally observed with antibodies of the antineurofibrillar group

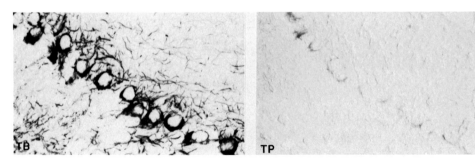

Figure 10-17. Rat cerebellar cortex. Paraffin sections were stained with antineurofibrillar monoclonal
antibody 06-17 diluted 1 : 20,000. ClonoPAP. TB, preincubation in trypsin followed by incubation in
buffer. TP, preincubation in trypsin followed by incubation in phosphatase. ×200. [From Sternberger and
Sternberger (35).]

reactive with phosphorylated epitopes. There was no overlap of staining observed with these antibodies in untreated or buffer-treated sections and in sections treated with trypsin and then with phosphatase. In the cerebellum, we now stained basket cell fibers, but no Purkinje cell bodies, dendrites, and proximal axons. In the cerebral cortex, we now stained thin fibers, most of them coursing tangentially, but no pyramidal cells, their dendrites or radially coursing thick axons.

The ease of digestibility with trypsin of neurofilaments reactive with antibodies of the perikaryonal-neurofibrillar group (group III) and lack of effect on staining of neurofilaments reactive with antibodies of the neurofibrillar group (group II) suggests that nonphosphorylated forms of neurofilaments are less compact than phosphorylated forms. This conclusion is strengthened by the fact, that the neurofibrillar staining patterns which were obtained after trypsin and phosphatase digestion with antibodies from the antiperikaryonal-neurofibrillar group, disappear readily upon a second treatment with trypsin, while the same patterns, obtained with antibodies from the antineurofibrillar group were resistant to tryptic digestion.

The effects of phosphatase were abolished when digestion was carried out in phosphate buffer showing that they were indeed due to phosphatase and not a contaminant in the enzyme preparation. Staining with the monoclonal antibod-

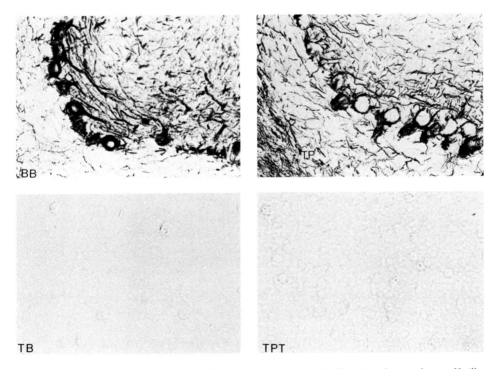

Figure 10-18. Rat cerebellar cortex. Paraffin sections were stained with antiperikaryonal-neurofibrillar monoclonal antibody 02-135 diluted 1 : 2000. ClonoPAP. BB, preincubation in buffers. TB, preincubation in trypsin followed by incubation in buffer. TP, preincubation in trypsin followed by incubation in phosphatase. TPT, preincubation in trypsin, followed by incubation in phosphatase and again by incubation in trypsin. ×200. [From Sternberger and Sternberger (35).]

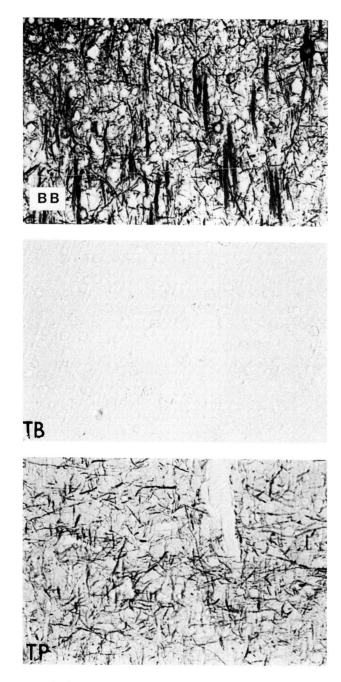

Figure 10-19. Rat cerebral cortex. Paraffin sections are stained with antiperikaryonal-neurofibrillar monoclonal antibody SMI 32 diluted 1:2000. ClonoPAP. BB, preincubation in buffers. TB, preincubation in trypsin followed by incubation in buffer. TP, preincubation in trypsin, followed by incubation in phosphatase. TPT, preincubation in trypsin followed by incubation in phosphatase and again in trypsin. ×200. [From the work of Ludwig Sternberger, Nancy Sternberger, and Howard Meyer.]

TPT

ies of the neurofilamentous group (except for antibody 03-44) was also diminished when the antibodies were diluted in phosphate buffer instead of the usual Tris buffer (Fig. 10-20), showing that they reacted with a phosphorylated epitope. Relatively high concentrations of the inhibiting hapten, inorganic phosphate, are provided by phosphate buffer. The need for such high concentrations is expected because of the relatively poor similarity of inorganic phosphate with the total reactive site of the phosphorylated epitope. Phosphate buffer had no affect on staining of antibodies from the antiperikaryonal-neurofibrillar group (group III) and on staining with antibody 02-40.

Immunocytochemistry is more sensitive for appearance of staining in an unstained section, than for disappearance of staining in a stained section. In fact if antibody is in excess, minor changes of concentration of the reactive antigen will not be apparent. In this case, staining is maximal, whether the antigen concentration is high or moderately low. Therefore, for visualization of decrease of staining, nonsaturating concentrations of antibody are needed. These concentrations should be in the range that falls under the steep portion of the curve obtained when blotting staining intensity or sensitivity against antibody concentration (page 176). The reappearance of staining with antibodies of the antiperikaryonal-neurofibrillar group after trypsin and phosphatase treatments is more dramatic than its disappearance with antibodies from the antineurofibrillar group, because difference of stain against no stain is more readily apparent than diminution of a pre-existing strong stain.

The immunocytochemical data on dephosphorylation permit conclusions only with regard to epitopes with which each monoclonal antibody reacts. Since some forms of neurofilaments are extensively phosphorylated, it is feasible that the immunocytochemically detected, dephosphorylated forms are only partially devoid of phosphate. It is possible that they still contain phosphorylated epitopes unreactive with or inaccessible to the monoclonal antibodies used. That, indeed, dephosphorylation is only partial, is illustrated by the data with antibodies to the antiperikaryonal-neurofibrillar group. When staining with these antibodies has been converted to a neurofibrillar pattern (Fig. 10-19 TP), it is easily reabolished

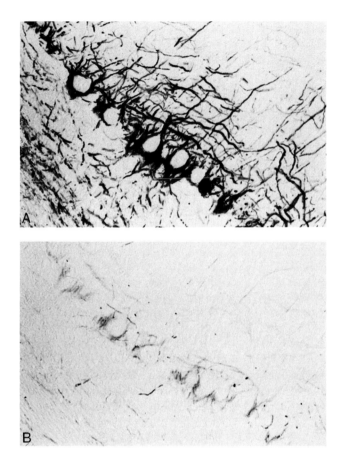

Figure 10-20.   Rat cerebellar cortex. Paraffin sections were stained with antineurofibrillar monoclonal antibody 07-5 diluted 1:40,000. ClonoPAP (A) antibody diluted in Tris buffer (pH 7.6); (B) antibody diluted in phosphate buffer (pH 7.6). ×200. [From Sternberger and Sternberger (35).]

by a second trypsin treatment (TPT), in line with the less compact structure of dephosphorylated neurofilaments. However, when treated with phsophatase a second time, some neurofibrillar staining reappears, albeit with lessened intensity. This shows that the dephosphorylation after the first phosphatase treatment was not complete.

The electroblot data (page 449) left it open whether or not the antiperikaryonal-neurofibrillar monoclonal antibodies (group III) reacted with both dephosphorylated and phosphorylated forms of neurofilaments, albeit better with the former. However, the fact that tryptic digestion retained the staining with antineurofilament antibodies but abolished that with antiperikaryonal-neurofibrillar antibodies shows that the latter do not stain phosphorylated epitopes. Hence, the enhancement of electroblot staining of the antibodies of the antiperikaryonal-neurofibrillar group by phosphatase digestion shows that cytoskeletal preparations consist of mixtures of phosphorylated and nonphosphorylated forms of neurofilaments.

The overall data show that neurofilaments in cell bodies, dendrites, and proximal thick axons are nonphosphorylated, either completely or partially, and that neurofilaments in long fiber projections and thin terminal axons are largely phosphorylated. Phosphorylation seems to be a post-translational process that accompanies neurofilaments on their transport (36) to nerve terminals.

MICROHETEROGENEITY OF POST-TRANSLATIONAL CHANGE

Many proteins become functional only after post-translational change. Complex proteins require assembly from subunits. Antibodies will react with antigens only after light and heavy chains have combined. Keratin and neurofilaments are assembled from three helically intertwined polypeptides, with the smallest forming the core and the two larger ones partially inserted in the core and partially protruding as whiskers (37–39). In contrast, neurosecretory polypeptides become bioactive peptides only after controlled proteolytic breakdown (page 360). Neurofilaments are closely associated with calcium-dependent proteinases and Nixon et al. (40) have shown that the 150-kDa neurofilament peptide can be selectively processed into slightly smaller components in vivo. Both phosphorylated and nonphosphorylated forms seem to be subject to such limited proteolysis.

Bioactive peptides often are inactive unless their amino-terminal or carboxy-terminal groups are masked. Glycosylation is essential to some proteins prior to secretion, while deglycosylation may be necessary for their insertion into the cell membrane. Differences in composition of sugars, as well as their enzymatic removal, contributes to microheterogeneity of secretory proteins.

Phosphorylation mediates dramatic changes in the activity of proteins. Other steric changes resulting from phosphorylation determine the activity state of some enzymes. Protein phosphorylation is often an effector step in the reaction mediated by the action of hormones. Phosphorylation of neurofilaments may be important in their yet unknown function, whether or not such function may be related to slow axonal transport. The presence of multiple phosphorylation sites (20) and their microheterogeneity (35) suggests high specificity or discriminating capacity for neurofilaments. As Julien and Mushyinski have shown (41) that the multiple phosphorylation sites of the 200- and 150-kDa neurofilaments peptides are restricted to the proximal portion of the whisker projections in the structured neurofilament, and since our data suggest that phosphorylation mediates compactness of neurofilaments (35), it may be conceivable that selected phosphorylation and dephosphorylation may mediate a gating effect of neurofilaments in axonal transport, accelerating selected substances and retarding others. Such gating would give the neuron increased functional specialization, permitting different functions at different times by the same neuron. These effects may be a primary function of neurofilaments or may be carried out in conjunction with associated microtubules (42).

Immunocytochemistry with monoclonal antibodies characteristic to epitopes altered post-translationally can, therefore, be used to trace in situ post-translational modifications in a cell. Such tracing should be especially suitable for neurons, because their long projections permit histologic differentiation of different parts of the same cell. A requirement for such study is, of course, not only availability of monoclonal antibodies to a post-translational addition alone, such as acetate or phosphate, but monoclonal antibodies to such addition in a specific protein. The monoclonal antibodies to phosphorylated neurofilaments fulfill this requirement: They do not react with any phosphorylated protein but are highly specific to phosphate in neurofilaments (9) and even within neurofilaments to phosphate in individual heterogeneous sites (17).

The scope of immunocytochemistry of post-translational modification is further enhanced when there are in a single antigen various sites of post-translational change, or alternatively, the antigen itself is heterogeneous, provided one has antibodies that distinguish between these sites. In the case of antibodies to phosphorylated neurofilament epitopes, it may be possible to distinguish more or less accessible epitopes, or epitopes more readily or less readily phosphorylated, in relation to distance in an axon from the cell body or perhaps in distinction of one neuron from another.

Finally, immunocytochemistry may help to study the mechanism of post-translational change itself. Julien et al. (34) have shown that neurofilament preparations contain a bound, magnesium-dependent cyclic AMP-independent protein kinase. The activity is associated with the neurofilament backbone and would be expected to phosphorylate preferentially those phosphorylation sites that are proximal to the backbone over those more distal on the projection whiskers. As shown by Leterrier et al. (43), neurofilaments can also be phosphorylated by the cyclic AMP-dependent protein kinase associated with the projection domain of microtubules that may contact other organelles, including neurofilaments (42). It is conceivable that this kinase phosphorylates preferentially the more distant sites of the neurofilament projections, at least those of the 150-kDa protein. Perhaps the cyclic AMP-dependent protein kinase promotes fast transport, and a neurofilament-associated kinase slow transport. If it is possible to phosphorylate neurofilaments in situ, the choice of appropriate enzyme and substrate added to tissue sections may help to utilize immunocytochemistry with monoclonal antibodies for detecting which mechanism participates in neurofilament phosphorylation at a given site within a neuron. By electron microscopic immunocytochemistry, it may also be possible to determine which portion of the neurofilament preparation may phosphorylate by neurofilament-associated protein kinase and which by microtubule-associated kinase.

Such studies require a degree of functional intactness of embedded and sectioned material that may differ from the epitopic intactness that is necessary for immunocytochemistry alone. We have examined whether in Bouin-fixed paraffin-embedded material neurofilament-associated kinase activity is preserved (44). When sections of such material were treated with ATP or with a cytoskeletal preparation from rat brain plus ATP, immunocytochemical staining with antibodies from the neurofibrillar group became slightly increased. A stronger effect was noted when the neurofilaments in the section were dephosphorylated by trypsin followed by phosphatase, prior to treatment with ATP or with cytoskeletal preparation plus ATP (Fig. 10-21). Cytoskeletal preparations alone had no effect.

The rephosphorylation of neurofilaments in situ illustrates that neurofilament protein kinase activity may be preserved during fixation, at least under

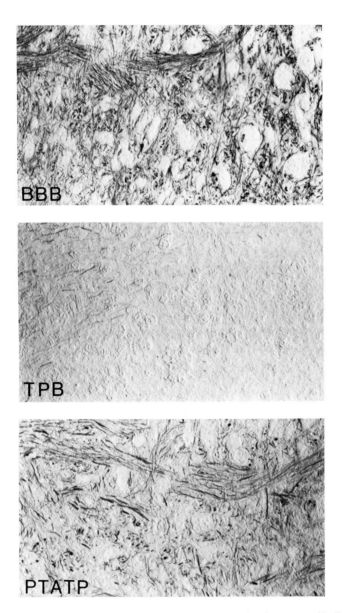

Figure 10-21. Rat lateral vestibular nucleus. Paraffin sections stained with antineurofibrillar monoclonal antibody 04-7 diluted 1 : 2000. ClonoPAP. BBB, Preincubation in buffers (identical picture is obtained if preincubated in trypsin followed by buffer). TPB, preincubation in repeat cycles of trypsin and phosphatase followed by buffer has diminished the staining. PTATP, similar preincubation followed by ATP/0.01 *M* magnesium chloride/0.05 *M* 4-morphorlinoethane sulfonic acid, pH 6.5, has restored some of the staining. ×200. [From Nancy Sternberger et al. (44).]

certain circumstances. However, certain areas that normally are not phosphory-lated, such as perikarya or dendrites stainable with antibodies of the perika-ryonal-neurofibrillar group, but not with antibodies of the neurofibrillar group, do not become stainable with the latter upon treatment with ATP. The neurofi-laments in these sites may not contain associated kinase, or the structure of neurofilaments in these sites is so loose that the kinase, apparently associated with the core of neurofilaments (34), is too distant from the phosphorylation sites.

Studies on rephosphorylation indicate how immunocytochemistry with mono-clonal antibodies can be used to probe into the mechanism of post-translational change. Here immunocytochemistry does not merely indicate that a change takes place and where it does, which is still an anatomical problem, but what factors mediate such a change in given tissue locations, which is a biochemical problem. One may hope that by such investigations the gap between anatomy and biochemistry or molecular biology becomes bridged.

In our studies on dephosphorylation (35), trypsin was used to make phos-phorylated forms of neurofilaments accessible to phosphatase. It is unlikely that a trypsin-like enzyme is physiologically active on neurofilaments. However, cal-cium-dependent proteinases have been shown to mediate in vitro as well as in vivo limited, and thus apparently highly specific, neurofilament breakdown, which, for these very reasons, may have physiologic significance. Nixon et al. (40) have shown, by injection of radioactive precursors, that appearance of 140- and 143-kDa neurofilament occurs concomitantly with decrease in the 145-kDa form (corresponding to the 150-kDa form in other studies) and that this process may involve phosphorylated and nonphosphorylated neurofilaments, suggesting concomitant post-translational dephosphorylation and limited proteolysis in vivo.

As shown by Schlaepfer (45), calcium influx into transected nerve initiates degradation of neurofilaments. There exist a number of calcium-activated neurofilament proteases. Some are soluble, requiring minimole levels of calcium ions, and seem to degrade a variety of cytoskeletal proteins. Other proteinases which have been shown by Ishizaki et al. (46) to be tightly associated with neurofi-laments, require only 0.2 mM calcium for complete activation and degrade the 160-kDa component (equivalent to the 150 or 145 kDa of other workers) prefer-entially. When this protease was dissociated from the cytoskeleton by 0.6 M potassium chloride, it reversibly reassociated on reduction of ionic strength. The close association of this protease with neurofilaments and its full activity at 0.2 mM calcium ion concentration suggests that it may be physiologically active in intact axons, possibly altering the composition of the 150-kDa component and making it more accessible to physiologic phosphorylation. Monoclonal antibod-ies to epitopes unraveled by proteinase would be needed to study the effects in situ.

EPITOPES OF EARLY AND LATE APPEARANCE IN DEVELOPMENT

We have seen that during development, reaction of tissues with some antineuro-fibrillar and antiperikaryonal-neurofibrillar monoclonal antibodies increases as

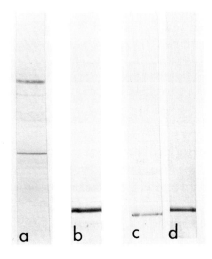

Figure 10-22. Electroblots of brain homogenates from developing (a,b) and adult (c,d) rats reacted with anti-synapse-associated monoclonal antibodies 02-24 (a,c) and 02-29 (b,d). ClonoPAP [From Sternberger et al. (10).]

the brain develops. However, reaction with other antibodies remains more restricted (page 439) while still other antibodies may react with different structures in developing than in adult animals (page 440). This divergence is especially well illustrated with two of the antibodies from the antisynapse-associated group, monoclonal antibodies 02-24 and 02-29 (10). Antibody 02-29 reacts on brain homogenate electroblots with a 25-kDa single band, both in adult and developing rats (Fig. 10-22). Antibody 02-24, on the other hand, reacts in the newborn with two bands of 40 and 140 kDa, respectively. With development, reactivity of these two bands gradually disappears, and from 11 days of age to adulthood only one band reacts, but this band represents a different protein corresponding to the 22-kDa region.

On tissue sections, antibody 02-29 exhibited widespread reaction. In the cerebellum, developing white matter was darkly stained, while the Purkinje cell layer was less intense (Fig. 10-5). During development, the changing patterns of staining included dark membrane staining of neurons and their processes, along with weak perikaryonal staining and a gradual lessening of staining in the white matter. In the cerebellum, reaction with the molecular layer and the glomeruli of the granular layer increased after 6 days of age. In the adult, staining was darkest in the molecular layer, and Purkinje cells were unstained.

Antigens reacting with antibody 02-24 were less widely distributed in the newborn. In the cerebellum, staining was confined to the developing Purkinje cell layer. During development and in the adult, Purkinje cell bodies were stained. The darkest area in the adult were the glomeruli of the granular layer of the cerebellum.

The visualization of membrane antigens on cell bodies early in development even before formation of the membranes for which they are destined has previously been established by Nancy Sternberger et al. (47) for myelin proteins (page 343). In the case of myelin basic protein, once myelin has formed and has acquired rich immunocytochemical reactivity, reaction for myelin basic protein in cell bodies diminishes, but does not disappear (48). Apparently, a similar situation prevails with synaptic constituents. Antibody 02-29 seems to react with a more specialized, less prevalent protein than antibody 02-24. This protein may be formed very slowly in a restricted number of cell bodies during adulthood and may have escaped, therefore, immunocytochemical detection in cell bodies. Antibody 02-24 reacts with a more widely distributed and more prevalent synaptic protein. Perhaps localization, albeit weak, even in adult cell bodies, may reflect the continued formation and rapid turnover of this synaptic membrane protein throughout life.

CHEMOARCHITECTONICS AND THE SCOPE OF MODERN IMMUNOCYTOCHEMISTRY

One of the main problems in biochemistry is to integrate, into intact organisms, mechanisms that have been discovered by the study of isolated components. One of the main problems in anatomy is to understand in biochemical terms the structural details that have been observed. Solutions of these problems have been slow to come. Tinctorial staining provided a primitive tool. Yet fundamental discoveries have been made on the basis of tinctorial staining alone. Pioneering in this regard was the discovery by the Scharrers of secretory cells in the nervous system (49) which heralded the advent of regulatory peptides (page 358). Enzyme histochemistry provided additional dimensions which, although limited in application, did enable Scharrer and Sinden (50) to refine the morphology of the optic tectum. Hence, Scharrer coined the word *chemoarchitectonics* for expression of morphology in biochemical terms.

A broad spectrum of differentiation of structure by virtue of their chemical composition is provided by immunocytochemistry because antibodies are more specific than enzymes and because nearly all tissue constituents provide epitopes, while only few are functional enzymes salient to enzyme histochemistry. To fulfill its mandate for chemoarchitectonics, immunocytochemistry had to grow to become reliable. First, methods had to become sensitive and free of background. Then attention could be placed to the specificity of antibodies. We have seen that only upon the use of monoclonal antibodies did it become possible to evaluate specificity of immunocytochemistry with some reliability.

Yet, even with monoclonal antibodies and reliable methods, immunocytochemistry as such only determines constituents in tissue at fixed instances. It does not monitor biochemical processes. Thus, while adding new refinements to histology and pathology, immunocytochemistry by itself does not provide the information on the relation of structure and function postulated by the concept of chemoarchitectonics.

However, we hope we have been able to show in this chapter how the use of batches of suitable monoclonal antibodies and appropriate tissue processing, in conjunction with immunocytochemistry, may monitor biochemical processes in situ. The examples outlined above describe post-translational changes, dependent on the utilization, in this particular instance, of monoclonal antibodies specific to a variety of phosphorylated and nonphosphorylated forms of a given family of proteins. In another application, antibodies could actually be used to monitor a biochemical process in the tissue section revealed by changing epi-

topes upon application of suitable substrate (Fig. 10-21). Conceivably, procedures similar or perhaps quite different from those described, using immunocytochemistry with appropriate monoclonal antibodies, may help eventually to
describe biochemical processes as they occur in intact tissue and to synthesize
thereby the chemoarchitectonics of individual reactions that cooperate in a complex functional pathway.

ALZHEIMER'S DISEASE

Excessive loss of memory and cognitive functions prior to the sixth decade of life
defines *Alzheimer's disease* clinically. Excessive loss of these functions after the
sixth decade is considered *senile dementia of the Alzheimer type*. The pathologic
correlary of these symptoms is the formation of *neurofibrillary tangles* and of *senile
plaques*. Tangles are the result of a degenerative process in neuronal perikarya.
They consist of neurofilaments that possess unusually high resistance to solubilization by detergents and appear on negative staining in electron microscopy as
paired helical filaments. Plaques appear to be the result of degenerative processes
in neurites. They contain paired helical filaments in an amyloid matrix.

Abundance of these changes, especially when found in the hippocampus and
other cortical areas as well, provides a pathologic diagnosis of Alzheimer's disease. Loss of cognitive function and memory is a general symptom that may not
necessarily be a reflection of these pathologic changes in every case. While most
patients afflicted with these symptoms excessively will demonstrate the lesions,
other disorders, not associated with plaques and tangles, may also lead to loss of
memory, although less frequently. Furthermore, aging itself, even when associated with mild degrees of loss of cognitive function or memory, will reveal
occasional plaques and tangles, but again with lesser frequency and density. In
these cases, lesions are usually confined to the hippocampus. Other disorders,
such as Down's syndrome, exhibit lesions similar to those of Alzheimer's disease.

The cholinergic system has been incriminated as a major mediator of memory. In primates, the most significant source of origin of cholinergic projections
to the cerebral cortex are the magnocellular neurons of the nucleus basalis of
Meynert. Whitehouse et al. (51) and Nagai et al. (52) have shown by immunocytochemistry that deletion of choline acetyl transferase associated with degeneration of projections from the nucleus basalis, precedes in severity and extent the
development of Alzheimer plaques and tangles, thus suggesting that the cholinergic lesion is primary. The suggestion is worth serious consideration, because it
may provide an avenue for eventual therapy of the disease, especially in early
stages, reminiscent to the L-Dopa treatment of Parkinson's disease, where the
striatal lesion has been shown to be secondary to deficiency in dopaminergic
neurons of the substantia nigra.

We have already seen (page 450) that in the central nervous system of the rat
monoclonal antibodies to phosphorylated rat neurofilament epitopes stain long
projection axons, particularly thin axons. These antibodies never stain central
nervous system cell bodies or dendrites. In contrast, monoclonal antibodies to
nonphosphorylated epitopes stain cell bodies, dendrites, and thick, proximal

axons, but not thin axonal projections. The antibodies to phosphorylated epitopes (06-17, 07-5, 04-7, 03-44, 06-68, also stain axonal projections in normal human autopsy material. Again, cell bodies are unstained.

In Alzheimer's disease, normally appearing areas beyond the confines of the lesion reveal with these antibodies axonal staining and no staining in cell bodies. In the lesion itself, however, Nancy Sternberger et al (53) and Cork et al (54) observed that antibody 07-5, reactive with a phosphorylated epitope, stained tangles even though they are perikaryonal constituents, and even though perikarya are normally devoid of phosphorylated neurofilaments (Fig. 10-23).

Aluminum poisoning in rabbits induces extensive perikaryonal tangle formation. Again, these tangles, despite their perikaryonal location, reacted as shown by Nancy Sternberger et al (55) and by Troncoso et al (56), with antibodies to phosphorylated epitopes (Fig. 10-24). However, only antibodies 06-17 and 03-44 stained, while antiphosphoepitope antibodies 07-5, 06-68 and 04-7 failed to

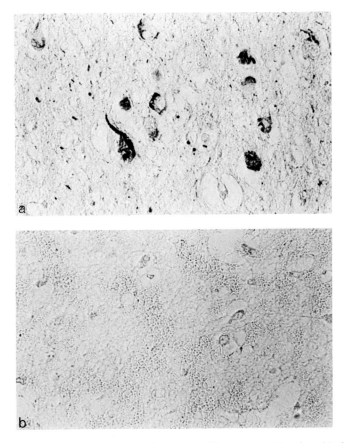

Figure 10-23.   Alzheimer's disease. Formalin fixation. Paraffin section. (a) Incubated in four changes of buffer and stained with monoclonal antibody 07-5 specific for phosphorylated neurofilament epitopes, diluted 1 : 2000, and ClonoPAP. (b) Incubated in tryspin 10 minutes, phosphatase 2½ hours, and again in trypsin 10 minutes and phosphatase overnight, and stained with monoclonal antibody 07-5, diluted 1 : 2000 and ClonoPAP. All staining has disappeared. ×200. [From Nancy Sternberger et al. (53).]

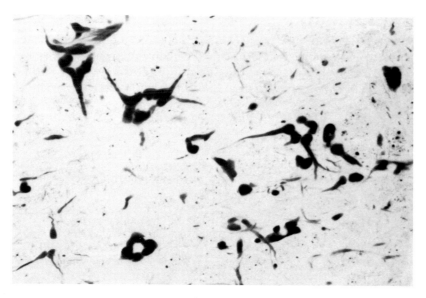

Figure 10-24. Rabbit cerebellum. Aluminum poisoning. Bouin fixation. Paraffin section. Monoclonal antibody to phosphorylated neurofilament epitope, 06-17, diluted 1 : 1000. ClonoPAP. ×265. [From Nancy Sternberger et al. (55).]

stain. Thus, tangles, whether in Alzheimer disease or in aluminum poisoning, exhibit premature neurofilament phosphorylation in the perikaryonal location. However, the lesions are not merely the result of damming up of the phosphorylation process. They are specific in that they involve only the 07-5 epitope in Alzheimer disease, and only the 06-17 and 03-44 epitopes in aluminum poisoning. Thus, both lesions can be considered the result of aberrant neurofilament phosphorylation. They may reflect hyperactivity of specific and different neurofilament kinases.

Dephosphorylation by trypsin and phosphatase treatments (53) was more readily accomplished in Alzheimer tangles than in normal axonal neurofilaments (Fig. 10-23). It appears, therefore, that at least with regard to the regions within Alzheimer tangles that present the 07-5 epitope, tangles are less compact than normal neurofilaments, even though they are more compact than normal perikaryonal, nonphosphorylated neurofilaments.

The results suggest that both Alzheimer and aluminum tangles are specific metabolic lesions that involve neurofilament kinases. The kinases are different in both cases, even though the morphologic end result is similar.

Phosphorylation mediates compacting of neurofilaments. Orderly compacting of the multiple phosphorylation sites in neurofilaments may lead to assembly of a normal, axonal neurofilament. The unbalanced phosphorylation of the 07-5 epitope in Alzheimer disease may result in the disorderly compacting of neurofilaments characteristic of tangles, and in a consequent arrest of neurofilament transport. While the 07-5 site in tangles may be less compact than in normal neurofilaments, the disorderly assembly of the total tangles may yield a highly insoluble structure, as described by Selkoe et al (57).

It remains to be established whether the specific involvement of the 07-5 epitope in Alzheimer disease is the result of a specific, metabolic lesion exhibited as hyperactivity of the 07-5 kinase, either primary or compensatory to certain deficiencies, or whether there are alterations in the structure of neurofilaments themselves that result in preferential phosphorylation of the 07-5 site.

REFERENCES

1. Matsa H, Baba Y, Nair RM, Arimura A, Schally A: Structure of the porcine LH- and FSH-releasing hormone. I. The proposed amino acid sequence. *Biochem Biophys Res Commun* **43**:1334, 1971.

2. Burgus R, Amoss M, Brazeau P, Brown M, Ling N, Rivier C, Rivier J, Vale W, Villarreal J: Isolation and characterization of hypothalamic peptide hormones, in Labrie F, Meites J, Pelletier G (eds): *Hypothalamus and Endocrine Functions*. New York, Plenum Press, 1976, p. 355.

3. Leeman SE, Mroz E, Carraway RE: Substance P and neurotensin, in Gaines H (ed): *Peptides in Neurobiology*. New York, Plenum Press, 1977.

4. Zipser B, McKay R: Monoclonal antibodies distinguish identifiable sites of neurons in the leech. *Nature* **289**:549, 1981.

5. Trisler GD, Schneider MD, Nirenberg M: A topographic gradient of molecules in retina can be used to identify neuron positions. *Proc Natl Acad Sci USA* **78**:2149, 1981.

6. Matthew D, Reichardt LF, Tsaraler L: Monoclonal antibodies to synaptic membranes and vesicles, in *Monoclonal Antibodies to Neural Antigens*. Cold Spring Harbor Laboratory, Cold Spring Harbor, 1981, p 163.

7. Lampson LA: Molecular basis of neuronal individuality. Lessons from anatomical and biochemical studies with monoclonal antibodies, in Kenneth RH (ed): *Monoclonal Antibodies. Progress and Applications*. New York, Plenum Press, 1984.

8. Sternberger LA, Harwell LW, Sternberger NH: Neurotypy: Regional individuality in rat brain detected by immunocytochemistry with monoclonal antibodies. *Proc Natl Acad Sci USA* **79**:1326, 1982.

9. Östermann E, Sternberger NH, Sternberger LA: Immunocytochemistry of brain-reactive monoclonal antibodies in peripheral tissue. *Cell Tiss Res* **228**:459, 1983.

10. Sternberger LA, Osterhout DJ, Sternberger NH: A study of synaptogenesis using monoclonal antibodies. *Transact Amer Soc Neurochem* **15**:118, 1984.

11. DeVries GH, Norton, WT, Raine CS: Axons: Isolation from mammalian central nervous system. *Science* **175**:1370, 1972.

12. Chiu F-C, Norton WT: Bulk preparation of CNS cytoskeleton and the separation of individual neurofilament proteins by gel filtration: Dye-binding characteristics and amino acid composition. *J Neurochem* **39**:1252, 1982.

13. Eng LF, DeArmond SJ: Immunochemistry of the glial fibrillary acidic protein, in Zimmerman HM (ed): *Progress in Neuropathology*. New York, Raven Press, 1983.

14. Von Hungen K, Chin CR, Baxter CF: Braintubulin microheterogeneity in the mouse during development and aging. *J Neurochem* **37**:511, 1981.

15. Matus A, Bernardt R, Hugh-Jones T: High molecular weight microtubule-associated proteins are preferentially associated with dendritic microtubules in brain. *Proc Natl Acad Sci USA* **78**:3010, 1981.

16. Goldstein ME, Sternberger LA, Sternberger NH: Microheterogeneity of neurofilament proteins. *Proc Natl Acad Sci USA* **80**:3101, 1983.

17. Goldstein ME, Sternberger LA, Sternberger NH: Phosphorylation protects neurofilaments against proteolysis. *Transact Amer Soc Neurochem* **16**:247, 1985.

18. Goldstein ME, Sternberger NH, Sternberger LA: Developmental expression of neurotypy revealed by immunocytochemistry with monoclonal antibodies. *J Neuroimmunol* **3**:203, 1982.

19. Kornguth S, Andrews J, Scott Z: Observations on the ultrastructure of developing cerebellum of Macacca. *J Comp Neurol* **130**:1, 1967.

20. Julien J-P, Mushynski WE: Multiple phosphorylation within mammalian neurofilament polypeptides. *J Biol Chem* **257**:10467, 1982.

21. Geisler N, Plessman U, Weber K: Related amino acid sequences in neurofilaments and non-neuronal intermediate filaments. *Nature* **296**:448, 1982.

22. Samson FE: Mechanism of oxoplasmic transport. *J Neurobiol* **2**:347, 1971.

23. Peters A, Vaughn JE: Microtubules and microfilaments in the axons and astrocytes of early postnatal optic nerves. *J Biol Chem* **32**:113, 1967.

24. Levine J, Simon C, Willard M: Mechanistic implication of the behavior of axonally transported protein, in *Axoplasmic Transport*. Berlin, Heidelberg, Springer-Verlag, 1982.

25. DeVries GH, Eng LF, Lewis DC, Hadfield MG: The protein composition of bovine myelin-free axons. *Biochem Biophys Acta* **439**:133, 1976.

26. Chiu F-C, Korey B, Norton WT: Intermediate filaments from bovine, rat and human central nervous system. Mapping analysis of the major proteins. *J Neurochem* **34**:1179, 1980.

27. Brown BA, Nixon RA, Srouchi P, Morotta CA: Characterization and comparison of neurofilaments from rat and mouse central nervous system. *J Neurochem* **36**:143, 1981.

28. Czosnek H, Soifer D, Wisniewski H: Studies on the biosynthesis of neurofilament proteins. *J Cell Biol* **85**:726, 1980.

29. Autilio-Gambetti L, Velasco ME, Sipple J, Gambetti P: Immunochemical characterization of antisera to rat neurofilament subunits. *J Neurochem* **37**:1760, 1981.

30. Lindquist TD, Ingoglia NA, Gould RM: 4S RNA is transported axonally in normal and regenerating axons of the sciatic nerve of rats. *Brain Res* **230**:181, 1981.

31. Pant HC, Shecket J, Gainer H, Lasek RJ: Neurofilaments are phosphorylated in the squid giant axon. *Cell Biol* **78**:R23, 1978.

32. Kennedy MB: Experimental approach to understanding of the role of phosphorylation in the regulation of neuronal function. *Ann Rev Physiol* **6**:493, 1983.

33. Willard M: Neurofilaments and axonal transport, in Marotta LA (ed): *Neurofilaments*. Minneapolis, Univ. Minnesota Press, 1983.

34. Julien J-P, Smolak, CD, Mushinski WE: Characterization of the proteinkinase activity associated with rat neurofilament preparations. *Biophys Biochem Acta* **775**:25, 1983.

35. Sternberger LA, Sternberger NH: Monoclonal antibodies distinguish phosphorylated and non-phosphorylated forms of neurofilaments in situ. *Proc Natl Acad Sci* **80**:6126, 1983.

36. Black MM, Lasek RJ: Slow component of axonal transport. Two cytoskeletal networks. *J Cell Biol* **86**:616, 1980.

37. Steinert PM: Structure of the three-chain unit of the bovine epidermal kerntin filament. *J Mol Biol* **123**:49, 1978.

38. Willard M, Simon C: Antibody decoration of neurofilaments. *J Cell Biol* **89**:198, 1981.

39. Nirokana N, Flicksmen MA, Willard M: Organization of mammalian neurofilament polypeptide within the axonal cytoskeleton. *J Cell Biol* **96**:236(abs), 1982.

40. Nixon RA, Brown BA, Marotta CA: Post-translational modification of a neurofilament protein during oxoplasmic transport: Implications for regional specialization of CNS axons. *J Cell Biol* **94**:150, 1982.

41. Julien J-P, Mushynski WE: The distribution of phosphorylation sites among identified proteolytic fragments of mammalian neurofilaments. *J Biol Chem* **258**:4019, 1981.

42. Range MS, Lane TM, Yphantis DA, Lifsics MR, Saito A, Altin M, Reintra K, Williams RC: ATP-induced formation of an associated complex between microtubules and neurofilaments. *Proc Natl Acad Sci USA* **78**:1431, 1981.

43. Leterrier J-F, Liem KH, Shelanski MC: Preferential phosphorylaion of 150000 mol wt components of neurofilaments by cyclic AMP-dependent microtubule-associated protein kinase. *J Cell Biol* **90**:755, 1981.

44. Sternberger NH, Vögtli S, Sternberger LA: Monoclonal antibodies monitor neurofilament-associated protein kinase activity in situ. In preparation.

45. Schlaepfer WW: Experimental alterations of neurofilaments and neurotubules by calcium and other ions. *Exp Cell Res* **36**:367, 1971.

46. Ishizaki Y, Tashiro T, Kurakawa M: A calcium activated protein kinase which preferentially degrades the 160 kDa component of the neurofilament triplet. *Eur J Biochem* **131**:41, 1983.

47. Sternberger NH, Itoyama Y, Kies MW, Webster H deF: Myelin basic protein demonstrated immunocytochemically in oligodendrocytes prior to myelin sheath formation. *Proc Natl Acad Sci USA* **75**:2521, 1978.

48. Sternberger NH, del Cerro C, Herndon RE: Myelin basic protein demonstrated immunocytochemically in adult oligodendrocytes. *J Neuroimmunol* **7**:355, 1985.

49. Scharrer E, Scharrer B: Secretory cells within the hypothalamus, in Scharrer E, Scharrer B (eds): *The Hypothalamus and Central Levels of Autonomic Function.* Baltimore, Williams and Wilkins, 1970.

50. Scharrer E, Sinden J-A: A contribution to the "chemorachitectonics" of the optic tectum of the brain of the pigeon. *J Comp Neurol* **91**:331, 1949.

51. Whitehouse PJ, Price DL, Struble RG, Clark AW, Coyle JT, DeLong MR: Alzheimer's disease and senile dementia: Loss of neurons in the forebrain. *Science* **215**:1237, 1982.

52. Nagai T., McGeer PL, Peng JH, McGeer EG, Dolman CE: Choline acetyl transferase immuno-histochemistry in brain of Alzheimer disease patients and controls. *Neurosci Lett* **36**:195, 1983.

53. Sternberger, NH, Sternberger LA, Ulrich J: Aberrant neurofilaments phosphorylation in Alzheimer disease. *Proc Natl Acad Sci USA,* **82**:4274, 1985.

54. Cork LC, Sternberger NH, Sternberger LA, Casanova MF, Struble RG, Price DL. Phosphorylated neurofilament antigens in neurofibrillary tangles in Alzheimer's disease. *J Neuropath Exp Neurol,* in press.

55. Sternberger NH, Gambetti L, Bizzi A, Sternberger LA, Gambetti P: Premature neurofilament phosphorylation in aluminum intoxication, *Proc Natl Acad Sci USA,* submitted.

56. Troncoso JC, Sternberger NH, Sternberger LA, Hoffman PN, Price DL: Immunocytochemical studies of neurofilament antigens in the neurofibrillary pathology induced by aluminum. *Brain Res,* in press.

57. Selkoe DJ, Ihara Y, Salaza FJ: Alzheimer's disease: Insolubility of partially purified paired helical filaments in sodium dodecyl sulfate and urea. *Science* **215**:1243, 1982.

Chapter Eleven

Prospective Pathology

The classification of tumors by tissue of origin and degree of differentiation is no longer of mere academic interest. Treatment of lymphomas of different classification, dependent on the nature or amount of specific proteins they may or may not secrete, is not identical. In adenocarcinoma, the presence of specific hormone receptors, such as estrogen receptors in mammary tumors; or in metastatic tumors of unknown origin, the presence of organ-specific substances, such as prostatic acid phosphatase, may provide important clues to specific hormonal therapy. The finding that undifferentiated tumors may possess substances characteristic to the corresponding differentiated tissues, or alternatively may contain substances characteristic to embryonic tissues, is permitting differentiation of tumors that present morphologically similar appearance. This differentiation has resulted in new classifications that have helped the selection of patients in whom aggressive chemotherapy has been life-prolonging and even life-saving.

It has been found that secretion of specific substances into fluid compartments of the body is not an adequate criterion for their production by tumors, since secretion is erratic and often difficult to distinguish from normal levels of the same substances. Instead, examination of biopsy material by immunocytochemistry has proven to be a reliable indicator for future managment. This approach to diagnosis, called *prospective pathology* by Mansour et al. (1) has proved to be an important adjunct to the modern management of malignancy. For appropriate analysis, sensitive immunocytochemical technique is needed. It has been found by Wagener et al. (2), Jautzke and Altenaehr (3), Bentz et al. (4), Taylor (5), and others that the unlabeled antibody PAP method provides appropriate sensitivity while immunofluorescence, peroxidase-conjugated antibody methods as well as the four-stage unlabeled antibody method (page 183) yielded erratic results.

The adoption of immunocytochemistry for prospective analysis of biopsy specimens has required the experience gained from autopsy pathology for many decades and the correlation of recorded clinical history and morphologic histopathology with immunocytochemistry. Even though sensitive immunocytochemistry is of relatively recent origin, use of immunocytochemistry in pathology has been expedited after Di Stefano et al. (6), Halmi et al. (7), Taylor (8), and Mason and Taylor (9) have noted that the PAP method is sensitive enough to detect antigens in routinely fixed, paraffin-embedded material. Because of the high sensitivity of the method, it does not matter, apparently, if most epitopes are destroyed during fixation and embedding. A few resistant epitopes will suffice for detection by PAP immunocytochemistry. By immunocytochemistry, Halmi and Duello (10) were able to reclassify pituitary adenomas on the basis of secreted hormones, using autopsy material stored for years. In these studies, even patients could be used from whom no paraffin blocks had been kept and only sections stained with hematoxylin and eosin were available. After destaining, such sections still reacted immunocytochemically for growth hormone. Even more remarkable was the successful immunostaining of prolactin of a section previously stained with aldehyde-thionin-periodic acid Schiff-orange G, considering that these sections had been subject to permanganate oxidation prior to initial staining.

These observations opened the way to re-examine the wealth of pathologic material that has been kept in jars, blocks, and sections for decades. Use of such retrospective material was responsible for making available cases that are rarely encountered in current practice. Consequently, progress in reclassification of disease, especially of malignancy, has been rapid.

Two general results of these efforts of reclassification were fortunate:

Firstly, it has been found that in problem tumors that have been difficult to differentiate, such as highly anaplastic fibrosarcomas from gliomas, immunocytochemistry in general confirmed the opinion of the leading experts guided only by morphology. Consequently, immunocytochemistry did not force a dramatic re-evaluation of tumor classification. At best, it provided additional, more rapid, and more generally available criteria for classification.

Secondly, the use of immunocytochemistry for establishment of the tissue of origin of metastatic tumors and for more accurate grading of malignancy coincided with availability of an increasing armamentarium of chemotherapeutic agents, and has provided new data for the selection of proper management of given tumors. Consequently, prognosis of highly anaplastic tumors has been greatly improved during recent years, even though the prognosis of well-differentiated adenocarcinomas has remained essentially unchanged.

We have already discussed in previous chapters the immunocytochemistry of lymphomas (page 288), of endocrine tumors (page 415), and the diagnosis and grading of tumors of neural origin (page 339). In the present chapter, we will restrict ourselves to the utility of prospective immunocytochemistry in the diagnosis and management of tumors originating from other tissues.

ANTIGENIC EXPRESSION OF TUMOR DIFFERENTIATION

Differentiation of a cell can be considered a process of specialization. In normal development, organ-specific cells are selected from pluripotential cells, and when these selected cells have multiplied sufficiently to form a specialized organ, they stop dividing and produce substances characteristic to their adulthood function. Peptide or protein growth factors are needed to promote cell division.

We have seen, with the use of immunocytochemistry by monoclonal antibodies (page 439) that developing neurons express a variety of heterogeneous epitopes of the neurofilament proteins. As adulthood is reached, the cells become more selective. Epitopes that are found in the majority of neonatal neurons become restricted to neurons of only given regions of brain and excluded from other regions.

Adult neurons are incapable of division. Apparently, they have completed most of their genetic switch to producing only adulthood proteins and no longer embryonic growth factors. Nevertheless, it cannot be excluded that such cells may not undergo additional specialization even at the genetic level along with training and experience. Other cells, such as epithelial cells, liver cells, or mononuclear blood cells maintain their potential for cell division in adulthood and, along with it, the capability of production of growth factors, as exemplified by the high level of epidermal growth factor in the submandibular gland demonstrated immunocytochemically by Gresik and Barka (11). We have seen (page 285) that final differentiation in B cells occurs only after exposure to antigenic stimulation and after a period of cell division (clonal expansion). Only then is immunoglobulin secreted and the cell is no longer able to divide. Apparently at some step during differentiation, the capability of production of growth or cell division factors has ceased. The cessation of production of cell division factors may merely be part of a general process of allelic exclusion (page 11), of which exclusion of production of all immunoglobulin types except that designated for secretion is another part.

To the extent that growth factors are important for cell division, we can consider them along with other proteins characteristic of rapidly dividing cells as *embryonic antigens.*

Insertions into the genome, such as infection by some rheoviruses, or other genetic alterations, may lead to re-expression of proteins excluded in the differentiated cell. While the re-expressed proteins can be considered embryonic proteins, not all these proteins are growth factors. It appears reasonable that only as long as growth factors are co-expressed with embryonic proteins does a cell become malignant. Nevertheless, immunocytochemistry of proteins not normally expressed by a cell has become an important *index of malignancy,* irrespective of whether they are functional growth factors or other proteins co-expressed with growth factors. *Oncofetal antigens* that have become diagnostically important in this respect include carcino-embryonic antigen and α_1-antitrypsin.

Even when reverting to expression of embryonic antigens, cells can still produce antigens characterisic of their normal counterpart. However, the relative amounts of adulthood proteins decrease, presumably because of limits of total production capacity by a cell in a situation where embryonic proteins compete with adulthood proteins. In some cases (page 165), absence or decrease of adulthood proteins may be of significant value in estimating degree of malignancy. By the same token, we will see below that presence or increase of certain embryonic antigens may also be an index of malignancy.

Hyperstimulated pituitary cells form tumors that secrete the same hormones that are formed by their normal counterparts. These cells have not undergone re-expression of embryonic antigens. As a consequence, most pituitary tumors are benign. However, when hormones mainly produced by the pituitary, such as corticotropin or prolactin, are expressed in ectopic locations, such as in pancreas, the tumors are usually malignant. Here, the expression of these hormones appears to be the result of genetic interference that leads to the production of multiple principles not expressed by the normal counterparts of the involved cells. The hormones are presumably co-expressed with other growth factors that promote cell division and invasiveness.

Espinoza et al. (12) emphasized that even in highly undifferentiated tumors some adulthood proteins can usually be detected, thus permitting diagnosis by immunocytochemistry when routine histopathologic examination is equivocal. The immunocytochemical diagnosis becomes particularly important when a tumor first presents itself in metastatic location. Among adulthood antigens that were of particularly general importance in the hands of these authors was keratin. Immunocytochemistry with antikeratinin distinguished most carcinomas, regardless of site of origin or degree of differentiation from lymphoid, mesenchymal, or carcinoid tumors, or from melanomas.

CARCINOEMBRYONIC ANTIGEN

A typical oncofetal antigen, carcinoembryonic antigen (CEA), is found in a number of adenocarcinomas as well as in normal fetal epithelia. It is most abundant in colonic carcinoma and has, prior to development of sensitive immunocytochemical technique, indeed, been considered as specific for tumors of gastrointestinal origin and absent from other tumors and from normal gastrointestinal epithelia. With the PAP method, a wider range of distribution has been established. On examination of paraffin-embedded specimens, Wagener et al. (2) found CEA in normal adult colonic mucosa as well as in colonic carcinoma. In the tumor specimens, staining was at the apical border of the cells, intraluminal, and usually also throughout the cytoplasm of the cells. In the normal mucosa, staining was mainly at the apical border of the adluminal and to a lesser extent at the apical borders of intraglandular cells.

Sehested et al. (13) conducted a prospective immunocytochemical study on lung tumor biopsies and found that patients with strongly positive tumors had a longer survival rate than those negative for CEA.

In contrast, Jautzke and Altenaehr (3) found, in the case of urinary bladder carcinoma, a positive correlation of invasiveness with CEA immunocytochemistry of urinary specimens of transitional cell carcinoma. It has been important in these studies to use immunocytochemistry of fixed specimens, rather than cytologic urinary preparations or radioimmunoassay determination of CEA in urine, because reactive non-neoplastic tissue infiltrates about the tumor may also contain the oncofetal antigen.

Such prospective studies are desirable in carcinoma of relatively low malignancy, because in contrast to highly malignant mesenchymal tumors, the prognosis of such adenocarcinomas has changed little during recent decades. In this connection, Mansour et al. (1), in prospective studies on primary and metastatic biopsies of mammary carcinoma, again found a positive correlation between CEA immunocytochemistry and invasiveness.

It appears, therefore, that the predictive value of CEA immunocytochemistry depends on the tissue of origin. Conceivably, such tissues as colon or lung epithelia which have a high regenerative capacity under normal physiologic conditions maintain considerable potential for production of embryonic antigen, even in adulthood, a situation reminiscent of the potential for immunoglobulin production other than IgM and IgD by B cells (page 11). Thus, a moderate stimulus that expresses only few embryonic antigens may include expression of CEA in colon or lung epithelia, leading to a positive correlation with relatively low malignancy. A stronger stimulus that produces a highly anaplastic tumor may re-express so many additional antigens that the capacity of CEA production is competitively diminished.

In contrast, transitional epithelium undergoes less cellular turnover than lung or intestinal epithelia, while mammary epithelium exhibits increased turnover only episodically after estrogen and prolactin binding. These tissues do not normally produce immunocytochemically detectable CAE. The antigen seems to be, however, produced after a carcinogenic stimulus that produces highly anaplastic tumors accompanied by extensive re-expression of oncofetal antigens, including CEA.

EXTRAGONADAL GERM CELL CANCER SYNDROME

Poorly differentiated carcinomas are a histologically heterogenous group that often are first detected at metastatic sites. Usually they have a dismal prognosis. However, a few of these tumors may, in fact, be treatable, some with specific hormones and others with antimitotic therapy, if the nature of the tumors or their tissues of origin were better known. Immunocytochemistry has provided the means of detecting whether a poorly differentiated carcinoma or adenocarcinoma is, indeed, a treatable neoplasm, such as prostatic, breast or gastric carcinoma, or whether in fact it is a sarcoma or lymphoma.

Richardson et al. (14) and Greco et al. (15) have shown that some patients under the age of 50 presenting with mediastinal or retroperitoneal tumors or with multiple pulmonary nodules or lymphadenopathy, possess poorly differentiated tumors that stain immunocytochemically for human chorionic gonadotropin β-subunit or for α-fetoprotein. Because of these markers, the tumors were considered to be of germinal cell origin. α-fetoprotein is an indicator of malignancy, as it represents an antigen associated with re-expression of deleted proteins as a result of the malignant process. Chorionic gonadotropin may be the same, when produced at ectopic locations, if the tumors are considered to be the result of conversion of somatic cells to germinal cells. Alternatively, chorionic gonadotropin may be an expression of germinal rest cells.

It is important to diagnose these extragonadal germ cell tumors by immunocytochemistry, because they are highly susceptible, if not curable, by aggressive combined chemotherapy consisting of cisplatin, vinblastin, and bleomycin with or without adriamycin. Sometimes, α-fetoprotein and chorionic gonadotropin are also secreted into the serum, but in many cases these constituents were confined to the cells, thus making immunocytochemistry a life-saving necessity.

METASTATIC TUMORS

Nadji et al. (16), Li et al. (17), and Shaw et al. (18) established that immunocyto-chemistry for prostatic acid phosphatase is specific for normal and neoplastic prostatic tissue. The enzyme is absent from other tissues. Therefore, immunocyto-chemical positivity of a metastatic tumor for prostatic acid phosphatase estab-lishes it as a *prostatic carcinoma.* Serum levels of prostatic acid phosphatase are not reliable indicators (16,17) since abnormal levels of the enzyme may also occur in patients with noncancerous prostatic conditions. Furthermore, prostatic acid phosphatase in serum is evident in only 75% of patients with disseminated prostatic carcinoma (16). The immunocytochemical diagnosis is important, be-cause prostatic carcinoma frequently presents itself as bone marrow or supracla-vicular lymph node metastasis, and because the diagnosis indicates institution of specific estrogen therapy.

Bentz et al. (4) found that only 2 out of 98 prostatic carcinomas were negative for prostatic acid phosphatase by immunocytochemistry. Well-differentiated and poorly differentiated tumors were stained with comparable intensity, not only attesting to the sensitivity of the technique, but also making it useful for diagnosis of the most malignant cases.

Winkler et al. (19) were able to identify by immunocytochemistry the prostatic origin of a tumor presenting itself as orbital metastasis. The patient had been admitted because of a blind, proptic, and painful eye. An additional physical finding was an enlarged prostate. An intravenous pyelogram revealed invasion of the bladder wall by a tumor. Even though the orbital tumor was well differen-tiated, the suggestion of prostatic origin of the tumor had been met with skepti-cism prior to immunocytochemical examination, and indeed the coexistence of a second metastatic carcinoma along with the carcinoma of the prostate had been considered.

Sarcomas are rare among malignant neoplasms of the prostate. While the coexistence of sarcoma and carcinoma in the same tumor may occur, the inclu-sion of sarcomatous elements in carcinoma in the form of a *carcinosarcoma* is a more frequent event than the presence of two independent tumors. Ordonez et al. (20) reported two cases of such prostatic carcinosarcomas and found that both, the sarcomatous and carcinomatous elements, were immunocytochemi-cally positive for prostatic acid phosphatase, thus establishing the epithelial ori-gin of the sarcomatous components. Significantly, these cases progressed poorly and were essentially resistant to estrogen therapy.

In addition to prostatic acid phosphatase, there exists a prostate-specific anti-gen (PSA) which appears to be found mainly or exclusively in the prostate, at least within the range of sensitivity of gel diffusion tests. Importantly, and unlike prostatic acid phosphatase, this antigen was present in the immnocytochemical studies of Stein et al. (21) in all cases of well-differentiated prostatic carcinoma, but not in all cases of poorly differentiated tumors. Thus, absence of PSA and the presence of prostatic acid phosphatase may help in the diagnosis of poorly differentiated cases.

Mammary tumors have been described as expressing several antigens includ-ing carcinoembryonic antigen, casein, lactalbumin, chorionic gonadotropin, pregnancy-specific β_1-glycoprotein, placentolactogen, and milk-fat globule membrane antigen. Gugliotta et al. (22) found that only the latter was specific for mammary tumors, and only this antigen as well as carcinoembryonic antigen was present in the majority of mammary tumors. Accordingly, the combined presence of these antigens in bone marrow appears to be the most useful immunocytochemical identification of neoplastic cells originating from carcinoma of the breast.

REFERENCES

1. Mansour EG, Hasterd M, Park CH, Koehler KA, Petrelli M: Tissue and plasma carcinoembryonic antigen in early breast cancer. *Cancer* **51:**1243, 1983.

2. Wagener C., Csaszar H, Totoric T, Breuer H: A highly sensitive method for the demonstration of carcinoembryonic antigen in normal and neoplastic colonic tissue. *Histochemistry* **38:**1, 1978.

3. Jautzke G, Altenaehr E: Immunohistochemical demonstration of carcinoembryonic antigen and its correlation with grading and staging of tissue sections of urinary bladder cancers. *Cancer* **50:**2052, 1982.

4. Bentz MS, Cohen C, Demers LM, Budgeon LR: Immunohistochemical acid phosphatase level and tumor grade in prostatic carcinoma. *Arch Path Lab Med* **106:**476, 1982.

5. Taylor CR: Immunohistochemical approach to tumor diagnosis. *Oncology* **35:**189, 1978.

6. Di Stefano HS, Marucci AA, Dougherty RM: Immunohistochemical demonstration of avian leukosis virus antigens in paraffin embedded tissue. *Proc Soc Exp Bio Med* **142:**1111, 1973.

7. Halmi NS, Parsons JA, Erlandsen SL, Duello T: Prolactin and growth hormone cells in the human hypophysis: A study with immunoenzyme histochemistry and differential staining. *Cell Tiss Res* **158:**497, 1975.

8. Taylor CR: The nature of Reed-Sternberg cells and other malignant "reticulum" cells. *Lancet,* Oct. 5, 1974, p. 802.

9. Mason DY, Taylor CR: The distribution of muramidase in human tissues. *J Clin Pathol* **28:**124, 1975.

10. Halmi NS, Duello T: "Acidophilic" pituitary tumors. A reappraisal with differential staining and immunocytochemical techniques. *Arch Path Lab Med* **100:**346, 1976.

11. Gresik E, Barka T: Immunocytochemical localization of epidermal growth factor in mouse submandibular gland. *J Histochem Cytochem* **25:**329, 1977.

12. Espinoza CG, Pillavisetti SG, Azar HA: Some applications of immunoperoxidase techniques in surgical pathology. *Ann Clin Lab Sci* **13:**240, 1983.

13. Sehested M, Hirsch FR, Hon-Jensen K: Immunoperoxidase staining for carcinoembryonic antigen in small cell cancer of the lung. *Eur J Cancer* **17:**1125, 1981.

14. Richardson RL, Schoumacher RA, Fer MF, Hande KR, Forbes JT, Oldham RK, Greco FA: The unrecognized extragonadal germ cell cancer syndrome. *Ann Int Med* **94:**181, 1981.

15. Greco FA, Oldham RK, Fer MF: The extragonadal germ cell cancer syndrome. *Sem Oncol* **9:**448, 1982.

16. Nadji M, Rabei SZ, Castro A, Chu TM, Morales AR: Prostatic origin of tumors. *Am J Clin Path* **73:**735, 1980.

17. Li C-Y, Lam WKW, Yam LT: Immunohistochemical diagnosis of prostatic cancer with metastasis. *Cancer* **46:**706, 1980.

18. Shaw LM, Yang N, Neat M, Croop W: Immunological and clinical specificity of immunocytochemical detection of prostatic acid phosphatase. *Ann NY Acad Sci* **390:**73, 1982.

19. Winkler CF, Goodman GK, Eiferman RA, Yam LT: Orbital metastasis from prostatic carcinoma. Identification by an immunoperoxidase technique. *Arch Ophthalmol* **99:**1406, 1981.

20. Ordonez NG, Ayala AG, von Eschenbach AC, Mackay B, Hanssen G: Immunoperoxidase localization of prostate-specific antigen. *Am J Clin Path* **6:**553, 1982.

21. Stein BS, Petersen RO, Vangove S, Kendell AR: Immunoperoxidase localization of prostate-specific antigen. *Am J Clin Path* **6:**553, 1982.

22. Gugliotta P, Botta C, Bussolati G: Immunocytochemical detection of tumor markers in bone marrow metastases of cancer of the breast. *Histochem J* **13:**953, 1981.

Chapter Twelve

Autoimmune Diseases

Ranging from disorders with widespread manifestations, such as systemic lupus erythematosus, to fairly organ-specific disorders, such as primary hypothyroidism, nearly every organ exhibits one or more types of chronic inflammatory diseases that appear to be associated with immunity against its own constituents. Evidence for deposition of antiorgan antibodies rests mainly on immunocytochemistry. The presence of immunoglobulin in a location in which it normally is absent, such as in the alveolar basement membrane, is presumptive evidence that an immunologic reaction has taken place in the lesion. The finding does not by itself suggest that the antibodies are etiologically related to the lesion, nor does it suggest that the antibodies are directed against constituents of basement membrane of normal human lung. Evidence for true autoantibodies, though not their role in etiology of a lesion, can be obtained by dissociation of antibodies from the tissue of the diseased host (page 27) and their specific reattachment to homologous tissue of a normal host examined immunocytochemically. Another method for differentiation between specifically reacting immunoglobulin and nonspecific deposits depends on the restricted heterogeneity of specific antibody compared to that of total host immunoglobulin (page 5). A lesser number of H-chain subgroups in the dissociated antibodies than in serum immunoglobulin suggests that the antibodies have been produced by a limited number of B-cells: their formation is, therefore, the result of a specific process. This test does not, however indicate whether the antibodies have been reactive with the tissue from which they were isolated, or with microorganisms infecting such tissues, or whether they represent antigen-antibody complex formed elsewhere in the host and secondarily deposited in the tissue under examination.

Normally, an individual does not form antibodies to one's own organ constituents or does so in only limited amounts. *Immune tolerance* is acquired in embryonic life and maintained by the persistence of the antigen in later life. Neonatal thymectomy perpetuates tolerance into adulthood, even in the absence of large amounts of persisting antigen. Autoimmunity seems to be the replacement of a tolerance response by a hyperimmune response. This shift in response may be caused by *deficiency in T suppressor cells* (page 283). In some cases, anti-immunoglobulin autoimmunity may conceivably involve *idiotypic antibodies.*

DEFICIENCY OF T SUPPRESSOR CELLS

Under certain circumstances, immunologic tolerance (page 283) can be abrogated by injection of a cross-reactive antigen. Thus, rabbits tolerant of bovine serum albumin will form antibovine serum albumin following injection of bovine serum albumin coupled with diazotized *p*-aminophenyl-arsanilic acid. Similarly, immunization with conjugated thyroglobulin abrogates the natural tolerance of thyroglobulin in homologous hosts.

Many autoimmune diseases are associated with infections, such as β-hemolytic streptococcal infection, and often with long-lasting infections, such as slow virus infections. Mice of the New Zealand Black (NZB) strain develop autoimmune hemolytic anemia spontaneously. This is confirmed by the direct antiglobulin *Coombs test* in which binding of immunoglobulin to erythrocytes is demonstrated by their agglutination with anti-IgG. Certain hybrid progeny strains of NZB mice develop, however, a fulminating glomerulonephritis and circulating antinuclear antibodies associated with edema, ascites, pleural effusion, pulmonary edema, and gastrointestinal hemorrhage. The syndrome mimics human lupus erythematosus (page 482) in many respects. These mice, like several other mouse strains, harbor type C leukemia virus thoughout life in extracts of normal organs, as well as in malignant lymphomas developing spontaneously with high frequency. The type C soluble antigen (CSA) is one of the nonvirion antigens specified by the leukemia virus. Mellors (1) found that the production of CSA coincides closely with the appearance of a positive, direct antiglobulin Coombs test. Unlike other strains of mice bearing type C leukemia virus, NZB mice are not tolerant to type C antigens. The break in tolerance, apparently, is the starting point for the massive antibody production, resulting in the lupus erythematosus-like syndrome. Thus, autoimmune disease in this case is, apparently, caused by a genetic immunologic deficiency. The tolerance itself may have been abrogated by membrane fusion of viral antigen with autologous cell surface antigen.

The deposition of extensive electron-dense material in the peripheral capillary loops and mesangia is characteristic of the electron microscopic morphology of lupus erythematosus and of NZB mouse glomerulonephritis. These deposits consist of antigen, antibody, and complement. Using peroxidase-conjugated antibodies, Imamura et al. (2) demonstrated murine type C viral envelope glycoprotein in the same location in NZB mouse kidneys, suggesting an immune response to this antigen. The antigen may, however, be only one component of a massive, more generalized group of antigen-antibody complexes resulting from abrogation of tolerance to host-homologous antigens secondary to an in vivo interaction of viral glycoprotein with host proteins.

In normal mice, injection of a hapten, such as trinitrophenol, conjugated to a homologous carrier does not necessarily abrogate tolerance of the carrier. Instead, it may induce tolerance of the hapten. In mice, trinitrophenol conjugated to mouse red cells (homologous carrier) are a B-cell antigen, which invokes a limited IgM response to trinitrophenol. Trinitrophenyl sheep red cells (heterologous carrier) are a T-cell antigen, which invokes an extensive antitrinitrophenol response, at least in young mice. Noar et al. (3) have shown that in old mice of a long-lived strain (page 283), the antitrinitrophenol response to the homologous carrier conjugate is stronger than that to the heterologous carrier. In addition, old mice produced a carrier response after injection of trinitrophenyl-mouse red cells, displayed by antibodies of poor specificity that cross-reacted with sheep red cells. Apparently, older mice exhibit a repression of T suppressor cells resulting in an abrogated tolerance to the homologous red cells upon injection of trinitrophenyl-modified carrier.

The majority of antibodies in NZB mice are autoimmune antibodies. Those to type C viral glycoprotein are only a small fraction of total antibodies, not responsible for the massive tissue deposition of immunoglobulin. As in lupus erythematosus (page 483), most antibodies are autoimmune antibodies, reactive largely with nucleic acids and nucleoproteins. Borel et al. (4) found that injection of adenosine, guanosine, cytosine, and thymidine conjugated to homologous immunoglobulin into young NZB mice prevented the development of the usual glomerulonephritis upon aging. Apparently, immunization with the tolerogen (page 281) into young animals prior to development of sensitization to the nucleosides induced a state of tolerance that was specific to the antigens used. The treatment seemed to result in a strong state of tolerance that could no longer be abrogated by subsequent type C virus infection.

Aleutian mink disease is caused by a slow virus and manifested by plasmacytosis, hypergammaglobulinemia, and glomerulonephritis. Autoimmunity is expressed by antibodies to DNA and homologous erythrocytes.

Fudenberg (5) emphasizes the association of "adult onset" hypogammaglobulinemia, a genetic disorder, with a high incidence of autoimmune disease and malignancy. A genetically determined T-cell defect may only be partial in that it affects only the response to few specific antigens, such as staphylococcal antigens or a single synthetic polypeptide antigen. As a result, antigens could accumulate that alter autologous proteins and abrogate the pre-existing tolerance of these proteins. Similarly, specific deficiencies may permit proliferation of slow viruses that insidiously could abrogate a pre-existing organ immune tolerance. Also, antinuclear antibodies, normally absent from circulation because of immune tolerance, could be induced by viral DNA and RNA via a mechanism reminiscent of the induction of antibodies to single-stranded DNA or RNA by carrier-conjugated bases.

IDIOTYPIC ANTIBODIES

Mouse plasmocytoma protein 315 (a myeloma IgA) binds dinitrophenol with a high degree of specificity. The protein bears BALB/c allotype on its α-chain. Nevertheless, immunization of BALB/c mice produces antibodies against the protein 315. Binding of the antibodies and the protein is inhibited by dinitrophenol. Hence, the antigenic determinants of protein 315 that evoke antibodies in the BALB/c mice are in or near its specific combining sites: the antibodies are idiotypic. Animals are normally tolerant of allotypic determinants of their own proteins. Indeed, no antibodies are evoked in BALB/c mice against determinants of protein 315 except those at the specific combining sites. Idiotypic determinants in the immunized host's own immunoglobulins are, apparently, present in too small quantities to induce tolerance. Hence, injection of the large amounts of these determinants provided by isologous immunoglobulins, such as protein 315 (the product of a single clone of plasma cells), may provoke an immune response. Similarly, production of large amounts of antibodies in an overwhelming infection may provide immunoglobulins of restricted heterogeneity that, in turn, could induce autoimmune idiotypic antibodies—that is, anti-immunoglobulin autoimmunity.

PATHOGENICITY

Tissue damage in autoimmune disease is due to cell or antibody-mediated cytotoxicity. *Cell-mediated cytotoxicity* is manifested by infiltration into tissue of mononuclear cells and is proved by transfer of the specific lesion to isogeneic hosts by such cells. Another test is provided by inhibition of macrophage (capillary tube) migration by lymphocytes from the autoimmune donor in the presence of the antigen responsible for autoimmunity. The presence of specific immunoglobulin in the lesion or circulation of the diseased animal or patient may be of diagnostic value but has no bearing on the production of the cell-mediated lesion, and indeed, may inhibit it.

Antibody-mediated cytotoxicity in autoimmunity is due to reaction of large amounts of antigen and antibody. As a result, antigen-antibody complexes deposit both in the organs of the primary lesion as well as in the capillary beds of distant location, such as the renal glomeruli. If these complexes consist of antigen and specific IgG or IgM, they fix complement leading to a cytotoxic reaction with the cells on which they are deposited.

GLOMERULONEPHRITIS

Immunofluorescence of affected glomeruli with anti-IgG reveals two patterns of localization. A linear deposit (Fig. 12-1) is characteristic of Goodpasture's disease, a rapidly fatal illness manifested by hemoptysis, anemia, hematuria, renal failure, and pulmonary hemorrhages, and restricted pathologically to lungs and kidneys. Linear deposits are also found in less fulminating instances, such as in a large number of subacute and chronic glomerulonephritides of adults. Granular deposits—that is, discrete irregular and lumpy deposits (Fig. 12-2)—are characteristic of the nephritis following β-hemolytic streptococcal infections (such as tonsillitis, scarlet fever, or pyodermia), of the nephritis associated with acute and subacute bacterial endocarditis and lupus erythematosus, and of the nephrosis accompanying quartan malaria. The lesions in both linear and granular immunofluorescence reveal infiltration of polymorphonuclear leukocytes and absence of mononuclear cells. This excludes cellular cytotoxicity as the mechanism of renal pathogenesis.

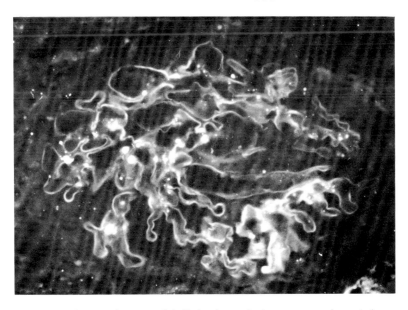

Figure 12-1. Linear deposit of immunoglobulin in glomerular basement membrane in human glomerulonephritis. Immunofluorescence. ×650. [From the work of G. A. Andres.]

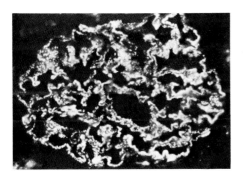

Figure 12-2. Granular deposit of immunoglobulin in glomerular basement membrane. Immunofluorescence. ×700. [From the work of G. A. Andres.]

GOODPASTURE'S SYNDROME

The immunoglobulin revealed by immunofluorescence in Goodpasture's syndrome can be eluted from glomeruli or alveoli by treatment at pH 3.2 at 37°C for 2 hours. The eluted material binds specifically with human alveolar and renal tissue as revealed by immunofluorescence. The material fails to bind with other tissues. The eluate also binds with glomerular basement membrane of the mouse and other species but not with alveolar basement membrane of the mouse. The findings suggest that the immunoglobulin found in Goodpasture's syndrome is an autoantibody or a group of autoantibodies cross-reactive with lung and kidney. The cross-reactivity is species specific. At least some of the antibodies are organ specific, but not species specific—that is, they react with basement membrane of the kidneys in many species, but not with basement membrane of other organs. The antibodies are not homogeneous: in one patient described by Poskitt (6), postmortem glomerular tissue is stained by anti-IgG$_1$, anti-IgG$_2$, and anti-IgG$_4$, but not by anti-IgG$_3$. Hence, the antibodies have not been produced by a restricted clone of immunocompetent cells. Their specificities may not be identical, and it is feasible that some types are cross-reactive with human lung, while others are cross-reactive with mouse kidney. The failure to find IgG$_3$ is additional evidence that the IgG is deposited in the basement membrane as a result of an antigen-antibody reaction, and not merely resorbed from serum as a nonspecific sequella of another renal lesion that may have increased accessibility of the basement membrane to circulating proteins.

Sometimes complement can be revealed in the affected kidney by immunocytochemistry with antibodies to complement components. Whether this can be demonstrated or not, the antibody eluted from glomeruli fixes complement with basement membrane antigen in vitro. Moreover, immunoglobulins eluted from affected kidneys and localized specifically in the glomerular basement membrane of injected mice, sheep, and squirrel monkeys cause in the latter two species fulminating glomerulonephritis with evidence of glomerular deposition of complement components.

The circulation of patients with linear deposit type of nephritis does not reveal antikidney antibodies. However, Lerner et al. (7) observed that following nephrectomy prior to renal transplantation there is a rapid rise in circulating antikidney antibodies. After transplantation, the circulating antibodies disappear again, being bound by the transplant along with complement. Apparently, renal tissue acts as a sink for a large amount of autoimmune antibody absorbing all detectable antibody from circulation. The large amount of antigen supplied by any tissue in autoimmune diseases may thus evoke a massive antigen-antibody reaction capable of the close packing of IgG on the tissue that is necessary for fixation of complement.

The massive antigen-antibody reaction observed in Goodpasture's syndrome, the ability to transfer the nephritis to experimental animals by eluted antibodies (rather than by cells), and the fixation of complement, suggests that the antibody observed by immunocytochemistry in this disease is responsible for its pathogenesis. The damage to tissue is by antibodies via complement. Cellular cytotoxicity does not play an important role in the pathogenesis.

Injection of renal basement membrane material produces linear immunofluorescence deposit nephritis in heterologous as well as homologous hosts. This reproduction of autoimmune nephritis in experimental animals suggests but does not prove an autoimmune etiology of the spontaneous disease in man. The fact that experimental nephritis has been produced by injection of lung tissue and that injection of kidney tissue does not induce a pulmonary disease may perhaps suggest, by inference, that in Goodpasture's syndrome the lung lesion is primary. The course of the disease in which initial symptoms are confined to the lungs seems to support this assumption.

IMMUNE COMPLEX DISEASE

When a large amount of foreign protein is injected into an experimental animal, renal pathology does not result if the immune response is efficient or if the animal is immune tolerant. Transient renal pathology, as revealed by granular deposits on immunofluorescence with anti-immunoglobulin, results only if the immune response is moderate. In the case of an efficient response, antibody is in excess, and the antigen precipitates. The precipitates are taken up by the reticuloendothelial system, and no renal pathology ensues. However, if the immune response is moderate, the antigen-antibody complexes are formed in antigen excess. These complexes are caught in the filtering system of the kidneys and can be detected by immunocytochemistry. Their predilection for the kidney is apparently due to the large circulatory volume passing through the renal arteries and to direct accessibility of the glomerular basement membrane to the capillary lumen via breaks in the endothelial surface. Complexes of three antigen and two specific IgG molecules, and larger antigen-IgG complexes, fix complement as they contain more than one IgG subunit (8). When such complexes localize at the renal basement membrane, damage to surrounding tissue results.

If the immune response is poor, no antibodies form, or their amounts are so small that they combine with antigen in such high antigen excess that the resulting complexes consist of two antigen and one antibody molecule. Complexes of two antigens and one IgG molecule do not fix complement. They cause no cytotoxic pathology.

Complement disappears from circulation during the development of kidney lesions after injection of antigen into experimental animals. The lesions mimic *serum sickness* of man in all respects. The renal pathology is transitory, and recovery is complete.

Circulating antigen-IgG complexes that are too small for elimination by phagocytosis do not in themselves become entrapped in the filtering system of the glomeruli despite breaks in the endothelial surface. Entrapment only occurs once capillary permeability is increased. Henson and Chochrane (9) find that glomerulonephritis develops only in rabbits that form specific IgE in addition to IgG after injection of antigen. In the presence of antigen, basophil-bound IgG (page 26) releases an intermediate that clumps platelets and mediates liberation of vasoactive amines from the aggregated platelets. The resulting increased vascular permeability appears to be the cause of entrapment of the cytotoxic, soluble antigen-IgG complexes (the basophil intermediate appears to be independent of basophil histamine and degranulation).

Progressive renal lesions characterized by granular immunofluorescence may appear as sequellae or accompanying manifestations of severe infections or severe, chronic autoimmune diseases. Experimental immune thyroiditis (see below) is normally confined to a purely thyroid pathology. However, if the afflicted thyroid is damaged by radioiodine, there may be extensive leakage of thyroglobulin from the gland into circulation. Circulating complexes of thyroglobulin and autoimmune antibodies form, and progressive glomerulonephritis may ensue.

The glomerulonephritis that follows β-hemolytic streptococcal infection reveals granular deposits by immunofluorescence after reaction with anti-IgG, anticomplement, as well as antiserum against type 12 streptococcal products.

One may ask why soluble antigen-antibody complexes entrapped in the glomeruli in chronic immune complex disease should persist so long in this location as part of a chronic, often progressive lesion. Most soluble complexes can exist only in the presence of excess of antigen. In most antigen-antibody systems, the required excess is large. Complexes may well be entrapped in a soluble state, while the concentration of circulating antigen is high. Upon subsequent immune elimination of circulating antigen, the entrapped complexes re-equilibrate by release of antigen and formation of complexes of lower antigen-antibody ratios. If the antibody affinity is high, such as in chronic immune complex disease, the re-equilibrated complexes form immune precipitates and are revealed as persisting lesions by immunofluorescence. On the other hand, if the affinity is low, such as in serum sickness type of lesions produced by single immunizing injections, dissociation of antigen from the complexes continues to completion and the entrapped antibody is released as well. The lesions demonstrated by immunofluorescence are transitory.

The size of circulating antigen-antibody complexes responsible for renal lesions is usually measured by gradient sedimentation using radiolabeled antigens. The serum is placed as a zone on top of the gradient. During sedimentation, the complex moves toward the bottom of the gradient, away from the free antigen that remains close to the top. As a result, the sedimenting complex re-equilibrates and releases antigen continually. A complex of low-affinity antibodies releases antigen faster and, thus, falsely appears lighter than a complex of high-affinity antibodies. Hence, correlation of pathology with size of complexes as determined by zonal sedimentation should be evaluated with caution.

AUTOIMMUNE THYROIDITIS

Antibodies reactive with thyroglobulin and sometimes with two other thyroid antigens are found in the circulation of patients afflicted with *lymphocytic thyroiditis*. The antibodies are usually IgG, occasionally IgM, or IgA. The amount and frequency of detection of antibodies apparently parallels severity of various forms of lymphocytic thyroiditis. As much as 19 mg/ml or precipitating antithyroglobulin has been isolated from a case of a fibrous variant of goiterous, diffuse, lymphocytic thyroiditis (Hashimoto's disease). Circulating antibodies can also be demonstrated with high frequency in severe atrophic thyroiditis (myxedema). Mild atrophic thyroiditis, which is a common disorder exhibiting mild hypothyroidism, is occasionally associated with circulating antibodies in low levels. Pathologic diagnosis depends primarily on immunocytochemistry of thyroid tissue with anti-immunoglobulin. Complement is bound in the lesion. The circulating antibodies are cytotoxic to cultured thyroid cells. These are, of course, properties expected of IgG and IgM. The findings are consistent with antibody-mediated cytotoxic etiology of autoimmune thyroiditis but do not prove it as the main mechanism.

Matsuta (10) has shown immunocytochemically that 63% of cells in the infiltrate in Hashimoto's thyroiditis contain immunocytochemically immunoglobulin of which 90% is IgG. These cells seem to secrete autoimmune antibodies. Dense deposits, apparently antigen-antibody complexes, were observed electron microscopically in the basement membrane of thyroid follicles.

LUPUS ERYTHEMATOSUS

Lupus erythematosus is a progressive, multiorgan disease initiating with articular and cutaneous involvement and presenting during the course of the disease, in addition to these manifestations, fever, renal, pleuritic, pericarditic, and neuropsychiatric manifestations, along with anemia, leukopenia, and elevated immunoglobulins. The disease may be self-limited, or it may be relentlessly progressive, nephritis being often diagnosed within one year after initial symptoms. Renal failure is the usual cause of death.

Characteristic of lupus erythematosus is the presence of serum antibodies reactive with the patient's cells, with cells from normal individuals, or even with cells of animal origin. At least five different groups of antigens that react with the sera of various patients are described by Tan and Lerner (11). Some patients' sera react with only one of these antigen groups. Others react with many. However, all lupus erythematosus sera possess antibodies that are reactive with widely distributed antigens—that is, antigens that are neither organ-specific nor species-specific. DNA is characteristically such an antigen. Possessing only four different nucleotides, the number of antigenic determinants that can be specified by a DNA sequence is much less than the number of determinants specified by a peptide incorporating permutations of 22 amino acids. Consequently, antibodies to proteins are likely to be highly specific, and diseases with autoimmune antibodies to proteins are usually restricted to few organs. Thus, autoimmune thyroiditis with antibodies to thryoglobulin is usually manifested in the thyroid only. On the other hand, in lupus erythematosus with antibodies to DNA, there is no organ or even species specificity of reaction. Consequently, clinical manifestations are widespread and involve multiple organ systems. Diagnosis of lupus erythematosus depends on reaction of patient's serum with cells, such as cultures of SIL_2 cells and immunocytochemical detection of this reaction with antiimmunoglobulin.

The five groups of antigens that react with lupus erythematosus serum by immunocytochemistry are native DNA, single-sranded DNA, nucleoprotein, a protein antigenically not dependent on nucleic acid determinants, and a nuclear ribonucleoprotein.

Single- or double-stranded DNA as well as RNA or histone are poor antigens. Apparently, tolerance to these antigens is found in most species. The similarity of structure of the polynucleotides per unit length within the confines of the maximum size of an epitope (page 16), and perhaps the richness of basic groups in histone, may ensure that tolerance is not species specific. Consequently, it is not possible to simulate lupus erythematosus in experimental animals, even when complete Freund's adjuvants are given with heterologous antigen. This contrasts with the organ-specific thyroiditis or organ-specific encephalitis that can be produced by immunization with thyroglobulin or with nervous tissue and Freund's adjuvants. The strong tolerance normally encountered against antigens reactive with lupus erythematosus serum is undoubtedly related to their ubiquitousness. However, once antibodies to these antigens are formed, the autoimmune reaction is widespread, and the manifestations of the disease involve many organ systems.

Slow virus infection is sometimes suspected as cause of lupus erythematosus. It is implicit in this assumption that part of the nucleotide sequence in these viruses is sufficiently different from mammalian polynucleotides, as to be recognized as immunogens or, alternatively, that the viral nucleic acids are complexed with a protein carrier other than a histone, thus making the nucleotide antigenic by a hapten carrier mechanism (page 16).

Nephritis is the most serious manifestation of lupus erythematosus. This is an immune complex nephritis that reveals granular immunofluorescence deposits with antibodies against IgG, third component of complement, and nucleo-protein.

Lupus erythematosus is characterized by frequent, febrile exacerbations and remissions. During remissions, the patient's serum usually contains free antibod-ies. During exacerbations, the serum contains excess antigen. It is during these periods that antigen is released, reacting with all available antibody and exacer-bating the deposits of immune complexes in the kidneys. Serum sickness mani-fests itself when soluble antigen-antibody complexes of smaller size, formed in antigen excess, are caught in the subendothelial filtering system of the renal glomeruli.

Damage in lupus erythematosus is due to antibody-mediated, and not to cell-mediated cytotoxicity. Gottlieb et al. (12) found that patients with system lupus erythematosus mounted a poor blastogenic response following immunization with tetanus toxoid, as measured by thymidine incorporation. The findings sug-gest that T-cell functions have been impaired. Nevertheless, the patients exhib-ited a circulating antibody response, albeit to a lesser degree than control sub-jects. Blastogenic response to antigen is characteristic of all kinds of T cells, including helper and suppressor cells. It is conceivable, that in lupus erythema-tosus a poor T suppressor cell response may trigger excessive production of circulating antibodies.

MYASTHENIA GRAVIS

Abnormal fatigability, rapid exhaustion, and loss of voluntary muscle strength are the chief manifestations of myasthenia gravis. Partial restoration of muscle strength with anticholinesteratic drugs incriminates the myoneural junction as the main site of the affliction.

Lindstrom et al. (13) found antibodies that reacted with human acetyl choline receptor, in the sera of 87% of patients with myasthenia gravis. The receptor had been isolated from amputated leg muscle and was assayed by binding of ^{125}I-bungarotoxin, a specific, high-affinity inhibitor of acetyl choline binding sites. Binding of labeled receptor with antibodies in patients' sera was assayed by precipitation with antiimmunoglobulin. The fact that bungarotoxin did not in-hibit the reaction of patients' antibodies with receptor suggests that the antibod-ies are directed to sites in the receptor other than the specific acetyl choline-binding site. Also, serum from patients with myasthenia gravis did not inhibit the binding of acetylcholine or even the larger α-bungarotoxin to plasma mem-branes of denervated muscle. Hence, the autoimmune pathogenesis of myasthe-nia gravis does not, apparently, involve an inhibition of neuromuscular transmis-sion by blockage of receptors with antibodies.

Transient myasthenia gravis can be transmitted into mice by transfer of either serum or lymphocytes from patients with myasthenia gravis, thus suggesting cytotoxic and cellular mechanisms of pathogenesis.

In some cases of myasthenia gravis, a large number of germinal centers are seen in the thymus. Whether or not germinal centers are seen, thymectomy often induces remission of the muscular symptoms. Interestingly, Perlo et al.

(14) find that thymectomy in cases without germinal centers induces early remission, while in cases with many germinal centers remission is delayed.

The existence of a shared antigen between thymus and acetyl choline receptor is evident from reaction of the majority of thymocytes with sera of patients with myasthenia gravis. In addition, Kamo et al. (15) succeeded in producing a monoclonal antibody to acetyl choline receptor from B cells obtained from the *thymus* of a patient with myasthenia gravis. The cells were established in culture by transformation with Epstein-Barr virus. Pizzighella et al. (16) have studied the thymic lesion often encountered in myasthenia gravis patients with neuromuscular pathology and found polyclonal IgG-containing cellular infiltrates within septa and close to perivascular spaces. These cells were, apparently, of extrathymic origin and have invaded the thymus through septa and blood vessels, from where they passed into the medulla. The cortex appear to be infiltrated later by immunoglobulin-positive cells and showed signs of atrophy. The findings suggest identity or similarity of antigens in thymus and acetyl choline receptor and leave it open to question whether the autoimmunity is primary to the thymic or the neuromuscular antigen.

MULTIPLE SCLEROSIS

The presence of increased concentrations of immunoglobulin in cerebrospinal fluid and brain tissue of patients with multiple sclerosis has focused attention to autoimmunity as an eitologic factor (17). Aggressive demyelination has been produced experimentally in animals in the form of experimental allergic encephalitis (EAE) by repeat immunizations with brain homogenate or myelin basic protein in Freund's complete adjuvants. The histopathology of EAE, especially in its chronic, relapsing form, is essentially indistinguishable from that of clinical multiple sclerosis and includes perivascular cuffing and removal of myelin sheaths by macrophages. Yet these end-products of a pathologic process suggest little about a similar etiology of both diseases.

The sera of cases of multiple sclerosis are myelotoxic to normal myelin. Tabira et al. (18,19) succeeded in producing lesions in tadpole optic nerves 48 hours after injection of cerebrospinal fluid from patients with multiple sclerosis. The activity correlated better with duration and severity of the disease than with immunoglobulin levels, suggesting that if immunoglobulin is a mediator of the lesion, it is not the only causative factor. This suspicion received confirmation, at least as far as EAE is concerned, by the studies of Stoner et al. (20,21), who produced retinal demyelination in rabbits upon intraocular injection of mixtures of supernates from activated lymphocytes and antisera. The normal lymphocytes had been activated either by nonbrain antigens or by a nonspecific mitogen (concanavalin A-Sepharose). Antisera alone or supernates alone induced no demyelination (primary myelin stripping), although they did produce other cellular responses, such as induction of a mononuclear cell infiltration. The serum factor was shown to be immunoglobulin. These results established an antibody-dependent, cell-mediated mechanism for primary demyelination. The antibody must be myelin specific, but the cells may be activated by nonspecific factors that cause mononuclear infiltration, a mechanism that may involve NK cells.

Esiri (22) found immunoglobulin-containing cells with higher frequency in multiple sclerosis plaques than in nonplaque areas from the same patients, and again more frequently in recent plaques than in old plaques. More cells contained light chains than heavy chains. In cells of recent plaques, but not of old plaques, the ratio of light to heavy chains was significantly higher than in cells from nonplaques. This suggests a restricted heterogeneity of antibody produced by these cells, and, therefore, an active response to an antigen in their immediate confines. The immunoglobulin-containing cells were clustered closely within plaques. Much smaller numbers of immunoglobulin-containing cells were seen in the normally myelinated tissue even if closely surrounding the plaques. However, even within the plaques, the immunoglobulin-containing cells did not constitute the majority of mononuclear cells.

By affinity purification with measles virus (page 27), Vandevick et al. (23) isolated measles-specific antibodies from cerebrospinal fluids and brain extracts of all patients with subacute sclerosing panencephalitis and some patients with multiple sclerosis. These antibodies again were electrophoretically homogeneous, in contrast to antimeasles antibodies isolated from sera of other patients after measles infection. Antibodies of restricted heterogeneity are generally produced after prolonged antigenic stimulation. The data in subacute sclerosing panencephalitis and to some extent in multiple sclerosis suggest perhaps an autoimmunity that occurs locally after prolonged antigenic stimulation by a virus, acting here as a slow virus (page 476).

Even though demyelinating lesions can be produced by specific antibodies and activated lymphocytes, and even though antibodies to viruses have been demonstrated in multiple sclerosis plaques, we still cannot conclude that multiple sclerosis is caused by autoimmunity, by immunity to a virus, or by abrogation of tolerance as a result of virus infection. Indeed, demyelinating lesions can be produced by the direct effect of neurotropic viruses. Thus, Herndon et al. (24) have produced demyelinating lesions in 4-week-old mice by intracerebral inoculation of a neurotropic strain of mouse hepatitis virus (JHM virus). The pathologic process was associated with death of oligodendrocytes, the cells required for myelination (page 341). Recovery of one-half of the inoculated mice was associated with remyelination, reminiscent of the frequent, transitory nature of individual signs in multiple sclerosis. With the use of tritiated thymidine, Herndon et al. (24) have shown that the cells associated with remyelination were newly generated oligodendroglia.

The totality of data from spontaneous demyelinating diseases of the mutliple sclerosis type suggests that demyelination is a frequent end result from injury that may have multiple causes, perhaps often associated with chronic or slow virus infection. Autoimmunity seems to be a common accompaniment of chronic lesions. Autoimmunity alone could simulate the lesion, as evident from studies of experimental allergic encephalomyelitis. Whether or not autoimmunity is the primary cause of multiple sclerosis, it appears that autoimmunity may exacerbate or perpetuate the disease. Confirmation of this supposition requires immunocytochemical studies of the lesions themselves rather than evaluation of circulating antibodies or T-cell subsets in circulation, because if autoimmune, the disease is organ-restricted to the nervous system. In contrast to a generalized autoimmune disease, such as lupus erythematosus, it is unlikely that an organ-restricted disorder, such as multiple sclerosis, provides a major imbalance in the totality of proportions of circulating lymphocyte subsets. In addition, the nervous system behaves much as a *privileged site,* well separated from the general circulation by the blood-brain barrier, which does not only seem to affect diffusion of solutes, but also of cellular elements involved in such phenomena as transplant rejection (brain transplants between nonhistocompatible animals appear to have good survival times). Indeed, while autoimmunity, such as that of NZB mice or of lupus erythematosus, is associated with a decrease in T suppressor cells relative to T helper cells, recent data by Rice et al. (25) and Compston and Hughes (26) suggest that in multiple sclerosis there are no fluctuations in the ratios of these cells beyond those expected in the normal population. More significant evaluation of the immunologic contribution to the exacerbation and perpetuation of the lesion in multiple sclerosis can be obtained by immunocytochemical examination, such as that carried out by Traugott et al. (27) who found that active progression of the lesion was associated with dense infiltration of T helper cells that extended from the lesion itself into nearby, normally appearing white matter, thus suggesting that it mediated early events in a progressive immunologic reaction. In contrast, T suppressor cells were confined to the margin of the lesion itself and to perivascular spaces. It seems, therefore, that the immunosuppressor reaction lagged behind the immunologic insult. These data point to an immunologically perpetuated lesion, whether or not autoimmunity has been its primary cause. Also, Ia-positive cells (macrophages and B cells) were present in the active lesion as well as in adjacent white matter, suggesting possible antigen presentation to the T cells (page 282) or, alternatively, macrophage involvement in demyelination.

The antibodies involved may be specific for myelin constituents, as they are in experimental allergic encephalomyelitis. However, it is conceivable that other antibodies, such as antibodies to bioactive peptides or peptide-receptor complexes, may also be involved, at least in some cases, as suggested by the immunocytochemical studies of Hansen et al. (28).

Both the acute and chronic forms of canine distemper present demyelinating lesions which resemble human paramyxovirus-associated disorders. Vandevelde et al. (29,30) found no immunologic component in the acute lesion. However, the chronic lesion presented heavy infiltration of mononuclear cells producing polyclonal antibodies, thus suggesting the association between chronic demyelination and local immune responses.

EXPERIMENTAL ALLERGIC ENCEPHALOMYELITIS

The progression of acute allergic encephalitis (EAE) to a chronic lesion, with remissions and exacerbations that resemble multiple sclerosis, can be produced by *repeat* injections of myelin basic protein or other myelin constituents along with Freund's adjuvants to susceptible strains of mice, guinea pigs, or rabbits. Within myelin basic protein, only certain loci possess pathogenic epitopes. The disease is mediated and transferred by cells.

It appears to be surprising that autoimmune diseases, such as multiple sclerosis or EAE should occur at all. Normally the brain is free of mononuclear blood cells. Circulating antibodies do not penetrate the blood-brain barrier. Hetero-transplants in brain possess a remarkable survival time even without immuno-suppressive treatment, and indeed, it has been shown that they become functional and make specific neuronal connections with host tissue that resemble in location and transmitter contents those of normal tissue replaced by the transplant. The long survival of brain transplants contrasts sharply with the aggressive rejection of other transplants, such as skin transplants.

It is probable that one can explain the autoimmunity in multiple sclerosis on the assumption that it is secondary to a chronic infection, such as a virus infection, which may have damaged the blood-brain barrier and thus exposed antigens to circulating mononuclear cells. Tolerance to these antigens may never have been established, because even in early development they have been excluded from contact with the general circulation. From these considerations, it would appear that multiple sclerosis of necessity would be an autoimmune reaction secondary to a nonimmunologic insult, rather than a disease caused by immune mechanisms, such as a deficiency of T-suppressor cells. Existence of autoimmune demyelination secondary to viral infection seems to be corroborated by the studies of Vandevelde et al. (29,30) on canine distemper.

Nancy Sternberger et al. (31) have shown that, indeed, blood-brain barrier must be destroyed prior to development of the lesion of EAE. With a monoclonal antibody specific to central and peripheral nervous system endothelia (Fig. 10-1), all endothelia of nervous tissue are stained, while endothelia in other tissues are unstained. Within lesions of EAE (Figs. 12-3, 12-4), staining of endothelium has disappeared (Fig. 12-5), suggesting that the blood-brain barrier has been damaged. Significantly, in areas adjacent to the lesion, which appear normal on hematoxylin and eosin staining (Fig. 12-6) and were devoid of demyelination as indicated by immunocytochemistry with antimyelin basic protein (Fig. 12-7), a number of blood vessels have also been devoid of the antigen reactive with the monoclonal antibody to blood-brain barrier (Fig. 12-8). This finding suggests that damage to blood-brain barrier precedes development of the autoimmune pathology that results in demyelination.

How is this damage to blood vessels in EAE produced? We may recall that it was necessary to use repeat injections of myelin basic protein along with Freund's adjuvants to produce chronic relapsing EAE. Brain emulsions or myelin basic protein without adjuvants do not produce the lesion. In fact, even frequently repeated injections of spinal cord emulsion along with precipitants, but without Freund's adjuvants, as was the practice in rabies immunization with early vaccines, resulted in demyelinating encephalitis in only 1 case in 10,000, despite the fact that the emulsions contained live virus which could have damaged the blood-brain barrier prior to eliciting autoimmunity. Furthermore, a single injection of brain emulsion or myelin basic protein along with Freund's adjuvants again produces only acute disease, but no recurrent, chronic demyelination that resembles multiple sclerosis. Apparently, what is needed is the effect of the adjuvants, which alone, even without antigens, may produce a syndrome called adjuvant disease. Conceivably, the adjuvants have a dual effect in production of autoimmune demyelinating encephalitis, one to induce damage to blood vessels, and the other to produce a macrophage reaction to promote presentation of the immunizing antigen to lymphocytes. It is of interest, in this

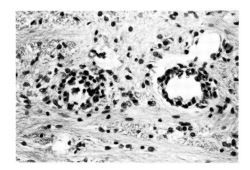

Figure 12-3. The lesion in acute allergic encephalitis. Bouin fixation. Paraffin section, hematoxylin, and eosin. Perivascular infiltration of inflammatory cells. ×265. [From Nancy Sternberger et al. (31).]

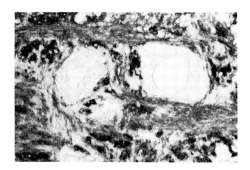

Figure 12-4. Serial section of the same area as that in Figure 12-3. Antiserum to myelin basic protein. PAP method. The region of staining reveals areas of demyelination. ×265. [From Nancy Sternberger et al. (31).]

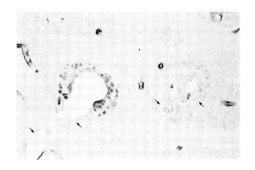

Figure 12-5. Serial section of the same area as that in Figures 12-3 and 12-4. Monoclonal antibody to blood-brain barrier, 02-132. ClonoPAP technique. Blood vessels surrounded by the lesion (arrows) no longer stain with the monoclonal antibody. Staining pattern with the antibodies is normal (see Figure 10-1) in blood vessels not affected by the lesion. ×265. [From Nancy Sternberger et al. (31).]

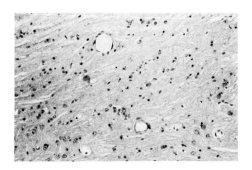

Figure 12-6. Normally appearing area adjacent to that depicted in Figure 12-3. Hematoxylin and eosin. ×265. [From Nancy Sternberger et al. (31).]

489

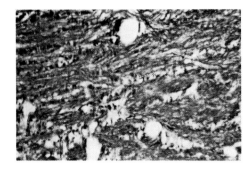

Figure 12-7. Section adjacent to that of Figure 12-6. Antibody to myelin basic protein. PAP method. Area appears normal. There is no evidence of demyelination. ×265. [From Nancy Sternberger et al. (31).]

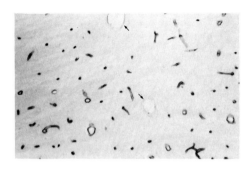

Figure 12-8. Section adjacent to that of Figure 12-7. Monoclonal antibody to blood-brain barrier, 02-132. ClonoPAP technique. Two blood vessels (arrows) no longer react with the antibody, suggesting that deletion of the recognized antigen (protein doublet in the 41 to 46 kDa range) occurs as an initial event in the breakdown of the blood-brain barrier. ×265. [From Nancy Sternberger et al. (31).]

connection, that the antibody to blood-brain barrier itself was selected from clones obtained from fusions with spleen cells of a mouse immunized with brain extract *along with Freund's adjuvants.*

DEMYELINATING POLYNEUROPATHY

Characteristic to Waldenstrom's paraproteinemia is secretion of a monoclonal IgM resulting from a diffuse tumor of plasma cells. Frequently the disease is a prodrome to multiple myeloma. Different paraproteinemias produce different idiotypes. Occasionally the disease is associated with a peripheral neuropathy. Meier et al. (32–34) described two cases in which the monoclonal IgM was an antibody to myelin-associated glycoprotein as detected by electroblot immunocytochemistry. The antibody stained oligodendrocytes in culture, as evident by dual color immunocytochemistry along with glial fibrillary acidic protein, as a marker for astrocytes, and along with antimyelin basic protein, as a marker for oligodendrocytes. The autoimmune nature of the paraproteinemia was evident by staining of nerve biopsies from the patients with anti-IgM in a pattern characteristic of that of myelin-associated glycoprotein (page 348), that is, staining was periaxonal, and compact myelin itself was generally not stained (Fig. 12-9). Only rare fibers in the milder case, and somewhat more frequent fibers in the more severe case, also exhibited staining of the whole myelin sheath.

Periaxonal staining patterns, characteristic of myelin-associated glycoprotein, were also obtained when patient serum was reacted with normal human sural nerve.

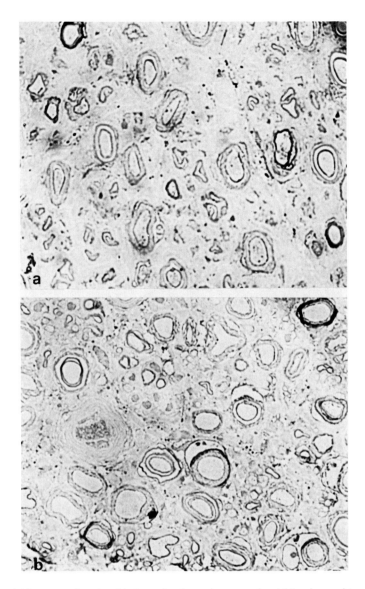

Figure 12-9. IgM paraproteinemia with demyelinating polyneuropathy. (a) Sural nerve biopsy. Osmium tetroxide fixation. Plastic section. Rabbit antihuman IgM. PAP method. IgM is localized adaxonally and periaxonally in a pattern corresponding to the distribution of myelin-associated glycoprotein. The occasional staining of whole myelin sheaths appears to be a pathologic alteration. (b) Sural nerve biopsy of normal control, first treated with patient serum and then stained as in (a). [[From Meier et al. (32).]

If the paraproteinemia is considered primary, it remains to be established how IgM, which is normally intravascular, produced the demyelinating lesion. On the other hand, if a specific peripheral nerve defect is primary, one wonders how autoimmunity can be that extensive as to produce a monoclonal hyperplasia of plasma cells.

Electron microscopically, the patients' nerves revealed evidence of repeat demyelination and remyelination, along with abnormal spacing of the myelin major dense lines and also occasional vesicular disintegration of myelin lamellae. Apparently these degenerative and regenerative changes are responsible for occasional staining of the whole myelin sheath with anti-IgM, rather than only adaxonal and periaxonal regions characteristic of the normal myelin-associated glycoprotein distribution.

REFERENCES

1. Mellors R: Leukemia virus and autoimmune disease of NZB mice. *Ann NY Acad Sci* **183**:221, 1971.

2. Imamura M, Melors RC, Steand M, August JT: Murine type C viral envelope glycoprotein gp 69/71 and lupus-like glomerulonephritis of New Zealand mice. An immunoperoxidase study. *Am J Pathol* **86**:375, 1977.

3. Naor D, Bonavida B, Walford RL: Autoimmunity and aging: The age-related response of mice of a long-lived strain to trinitrophenylated syngeneic mouse red blood cells. *J Immunol* **117**:2204, 1976.

4. Borel Y, Lewis RM, Stollar BD: Prevention of murine lupus nephritis by carrier-dependent induction of immunologic tolerance to denatured DNA. *Science* **182**:76, 1973.

5. Fudenberg HH: Genetically determined immune deficiency as the predisposing cause of "autoimmunity" and lymphoid neoplasia. *Am J Med* **51**:295, 1971.

6. Poskitt TR: Immunologic and electron microscopic studies in Goodpasture's syndrome. *Am J Med* **49**:250, 1970.

7. Lerner RA, Glassrock RJ, Dixon FJL: The role of antiglomerular basement membrane antibody in the pathogenesis of human glomerulonephritis. *J Exp Med* **133**:554, 1971.

8. Mayer MM, Miller JA, Shin HS: A specific method for purification of the second component of guinea pig complement and a chemical evaluation of the one-hit theory. *J Immunol* **105**:237, 1970.

9. Henson PM. Chochrane DG: Acute immune complex disease in rabbits. The role of complement and of a leukocyte-dependent release of vasoactive amines from platelets. *J Exp Med* **133**:554, 1971.

10. Matsuta M: Immunohistochemical and electron-microscopic studies on Hashimoto's thyroiditis. *Acta Path Jpn* **32**:41, 1982.

11. Tan EM, Lerner RA: An immunological approach to the fate of nuclear and nucleolar macromolecules during the cell cycle. *J Mol Biol* **68**:107, 1972.

12. Gottlieb AB, Lahita RG, Chiorazzi N, Kunkel HG: Immune functions in systemic lupus erythematosus. Impairment of in vitro T-cell proliferation and in vivo antibody response to exogenous antigen. *J Clin Invest* **63**:885, 1979.

13. Lindstrom JM, Seybold ME, Lennon VA, Whittingham S, Dunne DD: Antibody to acetylcholine receptor in myasthenia gravis. *Neurology* **26**:1054, 1976.

14. Perlo VP, Arnason B, Poskanzer D, Castleman B, Schwab RS, Osserman DE, Papatestis A, Alpert L, Kark A: The role of thymectomy in the treatment of myasthenia gravis. *Ann NY Acad Sci* **183**:308, 1971.

15. Kamo I, Furukawa S, Tada A, Mano Y, Iwasaki Y, Furuse T, Ho N, Hayashi K, Satoyoshi E: Monoclonal antibody to acetyl choline receptor: Cell line established from throid of patient with myasthenia gravis. *Science* **215**:995, 1982.

16. Pizzighella S, Riviera AP, Tridente G: Thymic involvement in myasthenia gravis. Study by immunofluorescence and immunoperoxidase staining. *J Neuroimmunol* **4**:117, 1983.

17. Link H: Immunoglobulin abnormalities in multiple sclerosis. *Ann Clin Res* **5**:330, 1973.

18. Tabira T, Webster H deF, Wray SH: Multiple sclerosis cerebrospinal produces myelin lesions in tadpole optic nerves. *N Engl J Med* **295**:644, 1976.

19. Tabira T, Webster H deF, Wray SH: In vivo test for myelinotoxicity of cerebrospinal fluid. *Brain Res* **120**:103, 1977.

20. Stoner GL, Fildes Brosnan C, Wisiniewski HM, Bloom BR: Studies in demyelination by activated lymphocytes in the rabbit eye. I. Effects of a mononuclear cell infiltrate induced by products of activated lymphocytes. *J Immunol* **118**:2094, 1977.

21. Fildes Brosnan C, Stoner GL, Bloom BR, Wisniewski HM: Studies in demyelination by activated lymphocytes in the rabbit eye. II. Antibody-dependent cell-mediated demyelination. *J Immunol* **118**:2103, 1977.

22. Esiri MM: Immunoglobulin-containing cells in multiple sclerosis plaques. *Lancet* Sept 3, 1977, p 478.

23. Vandvick B, Norrby E, Nordal HG, Degre M: Oligoclonal measles virus-specific antibodies isolated from cerebrospinal fluids, brain extracts, and sera from patients with multiple sclerosis and subacute encephalitides. *Scand J Immunol* **5**:427, 1976.

24. Herndon RM, Price DL, Weiner LP: Regeneration of oligodendroglia during recovery from demyelinating disease. *Science* **195**:693, 1977.

25. Rice GPA, Finney D, Braheny SL, Knobler RL, Sipe JC, Oldstone MBA: Disease activity markers in multiple sclerosis—Another look at suppressor cell deficiency by monoclonal antibodies OKT4, OKT5, and OKT8. *J Neuroimmunol* **6**:75, 1984.

26. Compston DAS, Hughes PJ: Peripheral blood lymphocyte populations and multiple sclerosis. *J Neuroimmnol* **6**:105, 1984.

27. Traugott U, Reinherz EL, Raine CS: Multiple sclerosis: Distribution of T-cell subsets within active chronic lesions. *Science* **219**:308, 1983.

28. Hansen BL, Hansen GN, Hagen C, Brodersen P: Autoantibodies against pituitary peptides in sera from patients with multiple sclerosis. *J Neuroimmunol* **5**:171, 1983.

29. Vandevelde M, Kristensen F, Kristensen B, Steck AJ, Kihm U: Immunologic and pathologic findings in demyelinating encephalitis associated with canine distemper virus infection. *Acta Neuropath* **56**:1, 1982.

30. Vandevelde M, Higgins RJ, Kristensen R, Kristensen F, Steck AJ, Kihm U: Demyelination in experimental canine distemper infection: Immunologic, pathologic and immunohistochemical studies. *Acta Neurpath* **56**:285, 1982.

31. Sternberger NH, Murant FG, Parkinson JA, Kies MW: An immunocytochemical study of EAE in the Lewis rat. *Am Assn Neuropath* **60**:154, 1984.

32. Meier C, Vandevelde M, Steck A, Zurbriggen A: Demyelinating polyneuropathy associated with monoclonal IgM-parproteinemia. Histologic, ultrastructural and immunocytochemical studies. *J Neurol Sci* **63**:353, 1984.

33. Steck AJ, Murray N, Meier C, Page N, Porruissean G: Demyelinating neuropathy and monoclonal IgM antibody to myelin-associated glycoprotein. *Neurology* **33**:19, 1983.

34. Meier C, Steck A, Vandevelde M: Immunopathogenese der Polyneuropathien bei Paraproteinämie. *Deutsche Med Wchschr* **109**:828, 1984.

Author Index

Abdelfattahged, M., 110, 167, 203, 206
Abel, J.H., Jr., 164, 205
Abo, T., 272, 301
Abraham, S., 135, 136, 204
Abrahams, S., 283, 303
Abrahams, S.J., 186, 207
Adams, T.E., 410, 425
Ades, E.W., 52, 87, 274, 301
Adler, G., 392, 423
Agarwal, H.C., 348, 355
Ahmad, D., 298, 304
Ahren, B., 168, 206
Aitu, M., 271, 301
Alexander, E.L., 52, 87, 145, 205, 273, 301
Alm, P., 168, 206
Alpert, L., 485, 492
Altanaehr, E., 171, 206, 467, 470, 473
Altin, M., 455, 456, 465
Altschuler, R.A., 129, 130, 204
Alumets, J., 107, 168, 202, 206
Alvord, E.C., Jr., 135, 204
Amanten, A., 271, 301
Amoss, M., 428, 464
Anderson, M.J., 339, 355
Anderson, R.E., 165, 205
Anderton, B.J., 340, 355
Andrews, J., 440, 465
Anthony, E.L.P., 216, 223, 384, 422
Anthony, R., 109, 203
Aoki, T., 261, 269
Araneo, B.A., 284, 303
Arends, J., 61, 88
Arimura, A., 370, 375, 420, 428, 464
Armin, A., 335, 354
Armstrong, D.M., 265, 269
Arnason, B., 485, 492
Aronin, N., 367, 368, 419

Asa, S.C., 416, 426
Aspeslagh, M.-R., 382, 421
Assana, P., 394, 424
Atkins, R.C., 259, 269
Atweh, S.F., 265, 269
Aufdemorte, T.B., 295, 304
August, J.T., 476, 492
Autilio-Gambetti, L., 340, 355, 448, 462, 463, 465, 466
Avrameas, S., 28, 31, 59, 60, 63, 68, 88, 185, 207
Axelrod, F., 331, 354
Ayala, A.G., 472, 474
Azar, H.A., 470, 473

Baba, Y., 428, 464
Backmann, J., 185, 207
Badminton, M., 411, 425
Bajen, A.S., 33, 86
Baker, B.L., 168, 172, 206, 370, 384, 420, 422
Baker, H., 152, 205
Baklien, K., 294, 303
Balazs, R., 167, 206
Banerjee, D., 298, 304
Barandum, S., 28, 31
Barbarash, G.R., 348, 356
Barber, R.P., 183, 207, 317, 322, 323, 353
Barchas, J.D., 364, 399, 419, 425
Barcos, M., 295, 304
Barka, T., 469, 473
Basbaum, A.I., 193, 208, 364, 419
Baskin, D.G., 212, 221, 223, 241, 244
Basler, V., 350, 356
Bassiri, R.M., 388, 423
Basten, A., 278, 302
Baumann, N.A., 351, 356
Baumann, R., 412, 425
Baxeranis, C.N., 282, 302

Baxter, C.F., 435, 464
Beauvillain, J.C., 400, 401, 425
Bechtel, P.J., 183, 184, 207
Becker, G.J., 259, 269
Beguin, P., 383, 422
Beinfeld, M.C., 390, 423
Beitz, A.J., 189, 208
Bellone, C.J., 279, 302
Benjamin, D.C., 283, 303
Bennik, J.R., 282, 302
Benno, R.H., 146, 147, 148, 149, 155, 205
Bentz, M.S., 467, 472, 473
Berenstein, E.H., 256, 268
Bernardt, R., 435, 436, 464
Bessis, M.C., 285, 303
Bestetti, G., 115, 122, 123, 203
Biberfeld, P., 210, 223
Bigbee, J.W., 71, 89, 106, 202, 336, 354
Bignami, A., 335, 354
Bigner, D.D., 110, 111, 203, 240, 244
Binz, H., 171, 183, 206
Bizzi, A., 462, 463, 466
Björklund, A., 310, 353
Black, C.M., 52, 87, 274, 301
Black, M.M., 455, 465
Blennerhassett, J.B., 296, 304
Bloch, B., 222, 224
Bloom, B.R., 485, 493
Bloom, S.R., 216, 223, 392, 423
Bloth, B., 26, 31
Blume, K.G., 299, 301, 304
Bocker, W., 165, 167, 172, 205
Bode, G., 340, 355
Bohn, R., 370, 373, 420
Bohn, W., 80, 83, 89
Bollum, F.J., 293, 302
Bonavida, B., 283, 302, 477, 492
Bondi, A., 66, 88
Bonk, A., 286, 287, 288, 289, 303
Boorsma, D.M., 60, 62, 64, 88
Bore, A.T., 308, 314, 315, 352
Borel, Y., 477, 492
Botta, C., 473, 474
Bousetta, H., 383, 422
Bowker, R.M., 188, 189, 208, 325, 328, 353, 354, 399, 424
Boyse, E.A., 261, 269
Bradfield, J.W.B., 220, 224
Braheny, S.L., 487, 493
Brandeis, L., 316, 318, 319, 329, 331, 332, 333, 353, 354, 367, 369, 419
Brandon, C., 132, 204
Brandon, L., 315, 353
Brandtzaeg, P., 44, 51, 55, 86, 194, 196, 209, 292, 204, 303
Brazeau, P., 428, 464
Breuer, H., 467, 473
Brightman, M.J., 335, 354, 382, 421
Brinkley, B.R., 54, 87

Broadwell, R.D., 382, 421
Brodersen, P., 487, 493
Brodie, E., 392, 423
Broodtaerts, L., 79, 82, 89
Bross, K.J., 259, 269, 299, 301, 304
Brownfield, M.S., 381, 421
Browning, J.Y., 384, 387, 422
Brownstein, J.J., 364, 419
Brownstein, M.J., 379, 388, 420, 423
Brown, B.A., 448, 455, 458, 465
Brown, D., 80, 89
Brown, J.C., 172, 173, 197, 206
Brown, L.P., 20, 30
Brown, M., 428, 464
Brucker, J.-M., 339, 355
Brusco, A., 133, 204, 310, 313, 352
Bryant, M.G., 216, 223, 392, 423
Buchan, A.M.J., 172, 173, 197, 206, 389, 423
Budgeon, L.R., 467, 472, 473
Buetti, G., 171, 206
Bugnon, C., 222, 224
Buijs, R.M., 382, 422
Bulman, A.S., 66, 88
Bu'Lock, A.J., 216, 223
Bu'Lock, J.D., 216, 223
Burchanowski, B.G., 385, 422
Burgisser, E., 171, 206
Burgus, R., 428, 464
Burke, J.P., 180, 207, 393, 423
Burns, J., 100, 103, 105, 114, 167, 168, 202
Burnweit, C., 370, 420
Burton, H., 317, 353
Bussolati, G., 66, 88, 169, 206, 473, 474

Camier, M., 383, 422
Campbell, I.C., 335, 354
Cancino, M., 295, 304
Capra, J.D., 3, 4, 13, 29, 30
Carbonara, A., 169, 206
Carillo, C., 298, 304
Carnegie, J.A., 214, 223
Carpenter, A.-M., 148, 152, 153, 154, 205
Carraway, R.E., 107, 202, 428, 464
Carrel, S., 28, 31
Casanova, M.F., 462, 466
Casey, S.M., 219, 224
Castel, M., 381, 407, 408, 421
Castleman, B., 485, 492
Castro, A., 472, 473
Catt, K.J., 412, 425
Cebra, J.J., 46, 51, 87
Celio, M.R., 171, 183, 206
Cerny, J., 284, 303
Chain, M.M., 271, 301
Chalon, M.P., 21, 30
Chang, A.C.Y., 361, 419
Chang, D., 374, 375, 420
Chang, J.K., 374, 375, 420
Chang, M.M., 367, 419

Chan-Palay, V., 313, 314, 316, 328, 353, 354, 399, 400, 424
Charukian, C.J., 49, 87
Chieregatti, G., 66, 88
Chiller, J.M., 281, 302
Chin, C.R., 435, 464
Chiorazzi, N., 484, 492
Chiu, F.-C., 435, 448, 464, 465
Chochrane, D.G., 481, 492
Choy, V.J., 381, 420
Chu, T.M., 472, 473
Clark, A.W., 461, 466
Clark, C., 187, 197, 207
Cleveland, L., 255, 268
Clyne, D.H., 59, 88
Cocchia, D., 137, 138, 204, 271, 301, 335, 354
Cohen, C., 467, 472, 473
Cohen, J., 167, 206
Cohen, P., 383, 422
Cohen, S.N., 361, 419
Cohn, M., 15, 30
Collier, K.J., 367, 419
Compston, D.A.S., 487, 493
Conde, F.P., 21, 30
Conley, E.K., 167, 206
Conn, P.M., 401, 425
Connelly, E.M., 335, 354
Coon, J.S., 165, 167, 205
Coons, A.H., 33, 49, 86, 211, 223
Corenblum, B., 416, 426
Cork, L.C., 462, 466
Corson, R.L., 17, 30
Cossman, J., 271, 301
Coulter, J.D., 117, 188, 189, 203, 208, 220, 224, 325, 326, 327, 328, 353, 354, 399, 424
Cowan, K.M., 168, 206
Coyle, J.T., 127, 128, 131, 203, 204, 316, 320, 353, 461, 466
Crabbe, P.A., 194, 195, 208
Cram, L.S., 47, 87
Crawford, G.D., 317, 322, 323, 353
Cristina, M.L., 169, 206
Croop, W., 472, 473
Cross, A.M., 278, 302
Crow, T.J., 216, 223, 392, 423
Crowley, W.F., 401, 425
Csaszar, H., 467, 473
Cuculis, J.J., 93, 95, 97, 100, 101, 102, 114, 116, 167, 201, 203, 258, 269
Cuello, A.C., 187, 188, 207, 260, 261, 269, 310, 352, 364, 366, 367, 369, 419
Cunningham, B.A., 5, 7, 30
Curry, P.M., 76, 77, 84
Czosnek, H., 448, 465

Dacheux, F., 107, 117, 118, 120, 121, 126, 202, 203
D'Aguta, R., 384, 387, 422
Dancis, J., 331, 354

Daniels, D.C., 270, 301
Dannenberg, A.M., Jr., 58, 87, 107, 202, 270, 301
Daviderits, G., 47, 87
Davies, D.R., 8, 10, 30
Davis, D.A., 57, 87
Dean, G., 348, 355
Dean, L., 293, 302
DeArmond, S.J., 336, 338, 354, 435, 464
DeBrabander, M., 33, 86
Decke, J., 274, 301
Degre, M., 486, 493
de Harven, E., 261, 269
Delaunoy, J.P., 348, 355
del Cerro, C., 136, 347, 348, 355, 459, 460
DeLellis, R.A., 418, 426
DeLong, M.R., 461, 466
Delsgaard, C.-J., 366, 419
DeLuka, D., 274, 301
de Magistris, L., 196, 208
Demers, L.M., 467, 472, 473
DeMey, J., 33, 79, 82, 86, 89, 381, 382, 383, 420, 421
Demoulin-Brahy, L., 270, 301
Denk, H., 110, 167, 203, 206
De Pasquale, A., 197, 209
DePetris, S., 45, 87, 277, 301
Derby, M.A., 47, 87
Dermody, W.C., 168, 172, 206
De St. Groth, S.F., 253, 268
Deschener, R.J., 367, 419
DeVries, G.H., 435, 448, 464, 465
DeWaele, M., 79, 82, 89
Dickler, H.B., 279, 302
Diener, E., 281, 302
Dierickx, K., 196, 208, 379, 381, 382, 383, 420, 421
DiFiglia, M., 367, 368, 419
Dihome, A., 191, 192, 208
DiMeo, P., 183, 207
DiStefano, H.S., 100, 103, 186, 201, 207, 468, 473
Dixon, F.J.L., 480, 492
Dixon, J.E., 367, 419
Dixon, R.G., 215, 223
Dockray, G.J., 216, 223
Doerr-Schott, J., 119, 203
Dogterom, J., 382, 422
Doherty, P.C., 282, 302
Dolman, C.E., 462, 466
Donati, E.J., 33, 72, 86
Donato, R., 335, 354
Dougherty, R.M., 100, 103, 142, 143, 144, 186, 201, 202, 207, 468, 473
Douglass, R.D., 13, 30
Downs, E., 187, 197, 207
Drammond, R.J., 348, 355
Draznin, B., 412, 413, 426
Dreesman, G. R., 282, 302
Dreifuss, J.J., 382, 422
Drenkhahn, D., 137, 139, 204

Dreskin, R.B., 183, 207
Dube, H., 395, 424
Dubois, M.P., 107, 117, 118, 119, 120, 121, 183, 202, 203, 207, 400, 401, 425
Dubois, P.M., 117, 118, 119, 203
Duello, T.M., 100, 103, 164, 202, 411, 412, 413, 415, 425, 426, 468, 473
Duffus, P.H., 45, 87
Dular, R., 411, 425
Dunaif, A.E., 408, 425
Dunne, D.D., 484, 492
Dupouey, P., 351, 356
Dura, W.T., 297, 298, 304
Dyer, S.A., 47, 87
Dyle, R.A., 12, 30

Eardley, D., 284, 303
Edelman, G.M., 5, 7, 30
Edmison, P., 308, 314, 315, 352
Eichner, R., 262, 263, 264, 269
Eiferman, R.A., 472, 473
Eipper, B., 360, 419
Eisenberg, L., 298, 304
Ek, J., 294, 303
Ekman, R., 392, 423
Elde, R., 364, 419
El Etreby, M.F., 183, 207
Elfrin, L.-G., 366, 419
Elger, K.-H., 386, 422
Elias, J.M., 93, 98, 202, 251, 268
Elkind, K.E., 370, 384, 420, 422
El-Salhy, M., 393, 395, 423, 424
Elu, H., 169, 170, 206
Endo, T., 335, 354
Endo, Y., 395, 424
Eng, L.F., 71, 89, 106, 202, 215, 216, 223, 335, 336, 338, 339, 340, 341, 354, 355, 435, 448, 464, 465
Engelhard, M., 13, 30, 282, 302
Erlandsen, S.L., 100, 103, 117, 122, 148, 152, 153, 154, 164, 180, 181, 202, 203, 205, 207, 212, 220, 221, 223, 224, 384, 393, 415, 422, 423, 426, 468, 473
Erlanger, B.F., 255, 268
Erlich, P.H., 17, 30
Esiri, M.M., 486, 493
Espinoza, C.G., 470, 473
Estess, P., 3, 13, 29, 30
Ettinger, W.H., Jr., 270, 301
Eusebi, V., 66, 88
Ewinstein, B.W., 282, 302
Ezrin, C., 416, 426
Ezzell, R., 274, 301

Facer, P., 220, 224
Faherty, D.A., 283, 302
Fahy, C., 383, 422
Fair, D.S., 12, 30

Fajardo, M., 336, 355
Falck, B., 310, 352, 353
Falkmer, S., 168, 206, 395, 424
Fanger, H., 68, 85, 88, 89, 172, 206
Farquhar, M.G., 46, 87, 411, 412, 413, 425, 426
Farrel, C., 273, 274, 276, 301
Faulk, W.P., 77, 89
Feldmann, M., 277, 301
Fellman, D., 222, 224
Fer, M.F., 471, 473
Ferrarini, M., 26, 31
Feurle, G.E., 395, 424
Fey, H., 171, 183, 206
Fey, J., 129, 130, 204
Figliewicz, D.A., 348, 356
Fildes Brosnan, C., 485, 493
Fink, G., 387, 423
Finney, D., 487, 493
Fischer, L.F., 393, 423
Fishback, J.B., 370, 420
Fistel, S.H., 54, 87
Fitzgerald, T.J., 180, 207
Flang, F.-M.S., 308, 314, 315, 352
Flaster, M.S., 2, 29
Flecko, B., 135, 204
Flicksmen, M.A., 455, 465
Foidaut, J.M., 147, 177, 179, 180, 205
Forbes, J.T., 471, 473
Forsland, J.C., 47, 87
Forssmann, W.-G., 370, 386, 395, 420, 422, 424
Fox, P.C., 256, 268
Franklin, R., 298, 304
Frantz, A.G., 408, 425
Frater, W., 109, 203
Fredens, K., 364, 366, 419
Freedman, M.H., 12, 30
Frenk, S., 381, 421
Frens, G., 79, 89
Fresen, K.O., 76, 89
Friesen, H.G., 408, 425
Fudenberg, H.H., 12, 30, 477, 492
Fugita, T., 398, 424
Fujii, S., 398, 424
Fujimoto, W.Y., 241, 244
Fujita, T., 307, 308, 352, 395, 424
Fukai, K., 183, 207
Fukunaga, T., 183, 207
Fulcheri, E., 66, 88
Furcht, L.T., 147, 177, 179, 180, 205, 207
Furukawa, S., 485, 492
Furuse, T., 485, 492
Fuxe, O., 230, 244, 388, 423

Gadden, C.A., 191, 208
Gahwiler, B.H., 382, 422
Gailbraith, G.M., 50, 87
Gailbraith, R.M., 50, 87
Gainer, H., 379, 420, 448, 465

Gall, W.E., 5, 7, 30
Gallotta, F., 341, 355
Gallyas, F., 67, 88
Gambetti, P., 340, 355, 448, 462, 463, 465, 466
Garver, F.A., 348, 355
Gay, C.V., 165, 205
Gearhart, P.J., 13, 30
Geis, R., 400, 425
Geisler, N., 446, 465
Gepts, W., 414, 415, 426
Gerall, A.A., 370, 384, 420, 422
Gerdes, J., 286, 287, 288, 289, 303
Gerstl, B., 335, 354
Geuze, H.J., 77, 89
Gibson, S.J., 220, 224
Gilbert W., 11, 30
Gildersleeve, D., 364, 419
Gillis, S., 282, 302
Gjeruldsen, S.T., 294, 303
Glaser, L., 47, 87
Glassrock, R.J., 480, 492
Glazer, E.J., 193, 208, 317, 353, 364, 419
Gleich, G.J., 12, 30
Glowinski, J., 310, 352
Goebel, H.H., 340, 355
Goldenberg, D.M., 169, 206
Goldin, E.M., 76, 77, 84
Goldrosen, M.H., 12, 30
Goldstein, M., 194, 208, 316, 318, 319, 329,
   331, 332, 333, 353, 354, 399, 424
Goldstein, M.E., 290, 303, 438, 439, 441, 442,
   444, 447, 456, 464
Goltermann, N., 196, 208
Gonatas, N.K., 46, 87, 339, 355
Goodman, G.K., 472, 473
Goodman, R.H., 370, 371, 372, 420
Goodwin, F.K., 335, 354
Goossens, N., 379, 420
Gordon, D.S., 52, 87, 274, 301
Gordon, J., 20, 30, 242, 244
Goren, T., 135, 204
Gores, T., 67, 88
Gorray, R.C., 241, 244
Gottlieb, A.B., 13, 30, 282, 302, 484, 492
Gottlieb, P.D., 5, 7, 30
Gouget, A., 222, 224
Gould, R.M., 448, 465
Grabb, A.O., 197, 198, 209
Graham, R.C., Jr., 57, 87
Gramsch, Ch., 171, 206
Granatik, C.H., 76, 77, 84
Graybiel, A.M., 320, 322, 324, 353, 397, 424
Graziadei, G.A.M., 333, 334, 354
Graziadei, P.P.C., 333, 334, 354
Greco, F.A., 471, 473
Green, C., 279, 302
Greenwald, J.C., 386, 422
Gresik, E., 469, 473

Griffith, W.P., 217, 224
Grimelius, L., 168, 206, 393, 423, 424
Grimmelikhuijzen, C.J.P., 394, 424
Gröschel-Stewart, U., 137, 139, 204, 240, 244
Gross, D.S., 384, 422
Grotjun, H.E., 384, 385, 422
Grubb, A., 197, 199, 209
Grube, D., 370, 373, 392, 400, 420, 423, 425
Grzanna, R., 127, 128, 131, 203, 204, 316, 320,
   353
Guesdin, J.-C., 68, 88
Gugliotta, P., 473, 474
Gu, J., 220, 224

Hackenthal, E., 156, 158, 205, 241, 244
Hadfield, M.G., 448, 465
Hagen, C., 487, 493
Håkenson, R., 168, 206, 392, 423
Hakenson, S., 107, 202, 306, 352
Halmi, N.S., 100, 103, 164, 202, 237, 238, 244,
   415, 426, 468, 473
Hamagachi, Y., 65, 88
Hamilton, J.A., 281, 302
Hammer, R.A., 107, 202
Hammerling, U., 261, 269, 271, 284, 301, 303
Han, T., 295, 304
Hancock, M.G., 167, 205
Hancock, W.W., 259, 269
Hande, K.R., 471, 473
Handelmann, G.E., 390, 423
Hanker, J.S., 33, 58, 72, 86, 87
Hansen, B.L., 395, 424, 487, 493
Hansen, G.M., 487, 493
Hansen, G.N., 395, 424
Hanssen, G., 472, 474
Hansson, H.-A., 63, 88
Hansson, V., 44, 51, 55, 86
Hara, K., 335, 354
Hardin, J.W., 333, 354
Hardy, P.H., Jr., 50, 53, 87, 93, 95, 97, 100,
   101, 102, 114, 116, 167, 201, 203, 258, 269
Harlan, R.E., 191, 208, 387, 388, 423
Harmison, G.G., 129, 130, 204
Harris, C., 109, 203
Hartman, B.K., 42, 86, 348, 355
Hartman, K.-U., 259, 269
Harwell, L.W., 17, 24, 30, 252, 268, 429, 432,
   433, 435, 438, 439, 464
Hashimoto, K., 374, 377, 420
Hashimura, E., 384, 422
Haskill, J.S., 53, 87
Hasterd, M., 467, 470, 473
Hastie, A.T., 270, 301
Hauw, J.J., 351, 356
Hay, J.B., 285, 303
Hayashi, K., 485, 492
Hayward, J.A., 279, 302
Hegre, O.D., 180, 181, 207, 393, 423

Heises, G.R., 129, 130, 204
Heitz, P.U., 121, 203, 350, 356, 416, 417, 426
Helic, H., 169, 170, 206
Helms, C.M., 220, 224
Henderson, E., 295, 304
Henson, P.M., 481, 492
Heremans, J.F., 194, 195, 208
Herndon, R.M., 136, 347, 348, 355, 459, 460, 486, 493
Herzenberg, L.A., 46, 51, 87
Heusser, C., 284, 303
Heydermann, E., 66, 88
Hideka, H., 335, 354
Higgins, 488, 493
Higgins, D., 317, 353
Hill, T.A., 109, 203
Hillarp, N.-A., 310, 352
Hinton, D.M., 115, 116, 127, 146, 150, 200, 203, 204
Hirsch, F. R., 470, 473
Ho, A., 335, 354
Ho, N., 485, 492
Hobbs, J., 135, 136, 204
Hochman, J., 381, 407, 408, 421
Hock, D., 386, 422
Hoffman, M.K., 271, 301
Hoffman, P.N., 462, 466
Hoffman, R., 47, 87
Hohenberg, H., 80, 83, 89
Hökfelt, T., 194, 208, 230, 244, 364, 366, 367, 370, 388, 398, 399, 419, 420, 423, 424
Holl, M., 400, 425
Hollt, V., 171, 206
Holmin, T., 392, 423
Holst, J.J., 417, 426
Honjo, T., 4, 11, 12, 29
Hon-Jensen, K., 470, 473
Hood, L., 13, 30
Horisberger, M., 79, 89
Horobin, R.W., 222, 224
Houser, C.R., 317, 322, 323, 353
Hoyama, Y., 219, 224
Hozumi, N., 11, 30
Hsu, K.C., 165, 172, 205
Hsu, P.-L., 26, 31
Hsu, S.-M., 26, 31, 68, 85, 88, 89, 172, 206, 271, 294, 301, 303
Hsueh, A.J.W., 401, 425
Huang, W.M., 220, 224
Hubener, J.F., 370, 371, 372, 420
Hughes, P.J., 487, 493
Hughes-Jones, N.C., 79, 89
Hugh-Jones, T., 435, 436, 464
Humphrey, D.M., 295, 304
Hurlimann, J., 295, 296, 304
Hursch, M.A., 417, 426

Iacovitti, L., 317, 353
Ibata, Y., 384, 422

Ihara, Y., 463, 466
Imagawa, K., 384, 422
Imagawa, M., 65, 88
Imamura, M., 476, 492
Imperiale, M.J., 283, 302
Inagami, T., 156, 158, 205
Inenaga, K., 190, 208
Ingemansson, S., 417, 426
Ingman-Baker, J., 172, 173, 197, 206
Ingoglia, N.A., 448, 465
Inman, F.P., 25, 30, 31
Inoue, A., 361, 419
Iremnck, B., 194, 208
Isaacson, P., 213, 214, 223, 294, 303
Isac, R., 279, 302
Ishiguro, Y., 335, 354
Ishikawa, E., 65, 88
Ishizaka, K., 26, 31
Ishizaka, T., 26, 31
Ishizaki, Y., 458, 466
Ito, S., 307, 308, 352
Itoh, G., 145, 204, 273, 279, 301, 302
Itoyama, Y., 103, 108, 109, 123, 136, 153, 202, 203, 204, 341, 342, 343, 344, 345, 346, 347, 348, 355, 356, 459, 466
Ivemark, B., 399, 424
Iverson, J.-G., 280, 302
Iwanaga, T., 307, 308, 352, 395, 424
Iwasaki, Y., 485, 492

Jackson, I.M.D., 388, 389, 400, 402, 423, 425
Jacobson, S., 189, 208
Jaffe, E.S., 271, 301
Jancer, H., 350, 356
Jarvinen, M., 262, 263, 269
Jasiewisz, M.L., 68, 88
Jautzke, G., 171, 206, 467, 470, 473
Jay, G., 138, 139, 204
Jeffcoate, S., 230, 244, 388, 423
Jenkins, K.A., 167, 206
Jerrome, D., 214, 215, 223
Jirkowski, G., 315, 353
Joh, T.H., 146, 147, 148, 149, 152, 155, 205, 317, 322, 324, 353
Johannsson, D., 364, 367, 398, 419, 424
Johannsson, O., 134, 185, 204, 207, 230, 244, 370, 322, 324, 353
Johnsen, T.A., 93, 98, 202, 251, 268
Johnson, D., 348, 356
Johnson, N.D., 13, 30
Jones, D.B., 213, 214, 223
Jones, P., 46, 51, 87
Jones, T.R., 110, 111, 203, 240, 244
Jonsson, C., 399, 400, 424
Joosten, H.W.J., 133, 204, 308, 311, 352
Joseph, K.C., 46, 87
Joseph, S.A., 28, 31, 146, 149, 196, 205, 208, 238, 241, 244, 309, 352, 403, 404, 405, 406, 425
Judd, M.A., 213, 214, 223

Julien, J.-P., 441, 446, 448, 449, 455, 456, 458, 465
Juretic, A., 282, 302

Kahn, J., 340, 355
Kamo, I., 485, 492
Kanazana, R., 65, 88
Kaplan, M.H., 33, 49, 86, 211, 223
Kappler, J.W., 284, 303
Kark, A., 485, 492
Karnovsky, M.J., 57, 58, 87, 107, 202
Karten, H.J., 396, 397, 424
Karush, F., 3, 4, 29
Kasper, M., 350, 356, 416, 417, 426
Kato, K., 335, 354
Kataoka, T., 4, 11, 12, 29
Katoh, Y., 109, 203
Kawamoto, S., 335, 354
Kawaoi, A., 64, 88
Kawata, M., 190, 208, 374, 377, 420
Keefer, C.A., 183, 207
Keefer, D.A., 217, 223
Kellert, J.-O., 367, 419
Kelsoe, G., 15, 30
Kendell, A.R., 472, 474
Kennedy, M.B., 448, 465
Kennedy, R.C., 282, 302
Keren, D.F., 220, 224
Kies, M.W., 103, 107, 108, 109, 135, 136, 153, 202, 204, 219, 224, 242, 244, 342, 343, 344, 345, 346, 347, 355, 459, 466, 488, 489, 490, 493
Kihm, U., 488, 493
Killinger, D.W., 416, 426
Kimerer, L.M., 390, 391, 423
Kimura, H., 167, 206, 311, 353
Kimura, S., 271, 301
King, B., 169, 206
King, J.C., 216, 223, 370, 384, 420, 422
Kinoshita, H., 384, 422
Kirchanski, S.J., 47, 87
Kita, T., 361, 419
Klaus, G.G.B., 278, 302
Klein, J., 282, 302
Kloppel, G., 416, 417, 426
Knapp, R., 17, 24, 29, 30, 251, 262, 268, 386, 387, 417, 422, 426
Knigge, K.M., 385, 422
Knobler, R.L., 487, 493
Kobayashi, S.U., 398, 424
Koehler, K.A., 467, 470, 473
Kohler, C., 366, 419
Kohler, G., 247, 268
Konigsberg, W.H., 17, 30, 277, 301
Kopin, I.J., 315, 353
Kordelhue, B., 411, 425
Korey, B., 448, 465
Kornguth, S., 440, 465
Korsrud, F., 294, 303

Kosek, J.C., 106, 202
Kovacs, K., 416, 426
Kozlowski, G.P., 164, 205, 381, 421
Kraft, N., 259, 269
Kraus, F.T., 418, 426
Krieger, D.T., 237, 238, 244, 364, 394, 419, 424
Krisch, B., 370, 381, 414, 420, 421
Kristensen, B., 488, 493
Kristensen, F., 488, 493
Krueger, R.G., 12, 30
Kubek, M.J., 388, 423
Kubo, S., 384, 422
Kugel, G., 216, 223
Kuhl, C., 417, 426
Kuhl, H., 412, 425
Kuljis, R.O., 396, 397, 424
Kumagi, K., 272, 301
Kumar, S., 340, 355
Kunkel, H.G., 4, 10, 13, 14, 29, 30, 282, 302, 484, 492
Kurakawa, M., 458, 466
Kuusela, P., 18, 19, 30
Kwon, E.E., 349, 356

Labaume, S., 145, 167, 204, 273, 274, 285, 299, 301
Labaw, L.W., 8, 10, 30
LaBella, F., 411, 425
Labrie, F., 381, 421
Laemmli, U.K., 20, 30
Laender, S., 306, 352
Lahita, R.G., 484, 492
Lam, D.M.K., 315, 353
Lam, W.K.W., 472, 473
Lambert, A.M., 33, 86
Lampson, L.A., 429, 464
Lance, V., 389, 423
Lande, S., 28, 31
Landquist, I., 168, 206
Lane, T.M., 455, 456, 465
Langrari, I., 135, 204
Lanyon, H.C., 259, 269
Larraway, R.E., 395, 424
Larsson, L.-I., 196, 208, 364, 366, 389, 390, 417, 419, 423, 426
Lasek, R.J., 187, 207, 323, 353, 448, 455, 465
Lau, D.M.K., 132, 204
Lauber, M., 383, 422
Lauder, J.M., 191, 192, 208, 311, 312, 353
LaVia, M.F., 52, 87, 274, 301
Lazarus, G.S., 52, 87
Leander, S., 392, 423
Lebovitz, R.M., 312, 353
Lechan, R.M., 189, 208, 216, 223, 370, 371, 372, 388, 389, 400, 402, 420, 423, 425
Leclerc, R., 381, 421
LeCompte, P.M., 414, 415, 426
Lee, J.N., 407, 425
Lee, S.T., 284, 303

Lee, V.M.-Y., 265, 267, 269, 290, 303
Leeman, S.E., 107, 202, 367, 368, 419, 428, 464
Lehtovirta, R., 407, 425
Lehy, T., 169, 191, 206, 208
Leitner, J.W., 412, 413, 426
Leknes, A.K., 308, 314, 315, 352
Lennet, K., 286, 287, 288, 289, 303
Lennon, V.A., 349, 356, 484, 492
Lenys, D., 222, 224
Leonardelli, J., 194, 196, 208
Leppaluoto, J., 407, 425
Lerner, R.A., 480, 483, 492
LeRoith, D., 394, 424
Leterrier, J.-F., 456, 465
Leuin, L., 66, 88
Levey, A.I., 265, 269
Levine, J., 447, 465
Levine, R.R., 333, 354
Levitt, P., 336, 337, 355
Levy, J., 172, 173, 197, 206
Lewis, D.C., 448, 465
Lewis, E.A., 180, 207
Lewis, M.E., 394, 424
Lewis, R.M., 477, 492
Li, C.-Y., 472, 473
Li, J.Y., 117, 118, 119, 203
Li, Y., 417, 426
Liem, K.H., 456, 465
Lietz, H., 165, 167, 205
Lifsics, M.R., 455, 456, 465
Lin, C., 17, 30
Linder, E., 107, 202
Lindkaer Jensen, S., 417, 426
Lindquist, T.D., 448, 465
Lindstrom, J.M., 484, 492
Lindstrom, P.B.-M., 186, 207
Lindwall, J., 310, 353
Ling, B.L., 360, 419
Ling, N., 428, 464
Link, H., 485, 492
Liota, A., 364, 419
Liotta, A.S., 394, 424
Liposits, Z., 135, 204
Lithicum, D.S., 279, 280, 302
Littlefield, J.W., 248, 268
Ljundberg, O., 168, 206
Ljungdahl, Å., 367, 419
Lofberg, H., 197, 198, 199, 209
Lord, B.A.P., 193, 208
Lord, E., 15, 30
Lorincz, M.A., 388, 423
Louis, J., 281, 302
Loumaye, E., 412, 425
Ludwin, S.K., 349, 356
Luk, D.C.M., 333, 354
Lundberg, J.M., 134, 204, 366, 393, 398, 419, 423, 424
Lundquist, G., 168, 206, 417, 426
Lutz, H., 171, 183, 206

McCann, S.M., 384, 387, 422
McCarthy, K., 191, 192, 208
McComb, R.D., 110, 111, 203, 240, 244
McCully, M.E., 214, 223
McDowell, E., 109, 203
McEvoy, R.C., 180, 181, 207, 393, 423
McFarlin, D.E., 349, 356
McGeer, E.G., 267, 268, 269, 462, 466
McGeer, P.C., 267, 268, 269
McGeer, P.L., 462, 466
McIntire, K.R., 109, 203
Mackay, B., 472, 474
McKay, R., 429, 464
MacKenzie, M., 21, 30
Mackey, K., 194, 208, 399, 424
McLean, I.W., 216, 223
McNeill, T.H., 164, 205
Mains, R.E., 360, 419
Makela, O., 18, 19, 30
Mallet, J., 167, 206
Malmfors, G., 392, 423
Mandel, P., 348, 355
Mandel, T., 278, 302
Mannweiler, K., 80, 83, 89
Mano, Y., 485, 492
Mansour, E.G., 467, 470, 473
Marangos, P.J., 333, 335, 354
Marcon, N., 416, 426
Marcucci, A.A., 100, 103, 142, 143, 144, 186, 201, 202, 207, 468, 473
Margolis, F.L., 333, 354
Mariam, J.M., 54, 87
Markey, K., 316, 318, 319, 353
Marrack, P.C., 284, 303
Marsden, H.B., 340, 355
Martin, R., 112, 113, 203, 399, 400, 424, 425
Martinko, J.M., 282, 302
Mason, D.Y., 145, 167, 169, 199, 204, 206, 209, 210, 223, 273, 274, 276, 285, 295, 299, 301, 304, 468, 473
Mason, T.E., 183, 207
Matsa, H., 428, 464
Matsuta, M., 482, 492
Matthew, D., 429, 464
Matthew, W.D., 25, 31
Matus, A., 435, 436, 464
Mayer, M.M., 481, 492
Mednick, M.L., 57, 87
Mehler, P.S., 412, 413, 426
Meier, C., 491, 492, 493
Mellors, R., 476, 492
Melnick, J.C., 282, 302
Mepham, B.C., 109, 203
Mera, S.L., 220, 224
Merchanthaler, I., 67, 88, 374, 376, 377, 378, 420
Mesulam, M.M., 58, 88
Meyer, D.K., 390, 423
Meyer, H.G., 93, 95, 97, 100, 101, 102, 114, 116,

127, 146, 149, 167, 200, 201, 203, 204, 205,
   238, 241, 244, 258, 269, 309, 352, 403, 404,
   405, 406, 407, 411, 425
Meyers, C.A., 374, 375, 420
Miani, N., 335, 354
Michell, G.F., 21, 30
Michetti, F., 137, 138, 204, 335, 354
Miettinen, A., 107, 202
Millar, R.F., 411, 425
Millar, R.P., 384, 422
Millard, P.R., 214, 215, 223
Miller, A., 274, 301
Miller, J.A., 481, 492
Miller, J.F.A.P., 281, 302
Miller, M., 390, 391, 423
Miller, R.A., 271, 301
Miller, R.G., 283, 303
Mills, K.M., 28, 31
Mills, K.R., 238, 241, 244, 309, 352, 403, 404,
   405, 406, 425
Milner, E.C.B., 13, 30
Milne, R.W., 21, 30
Milstein, C., 247, 260, 261, 268, 269, 310, 352
Minato, K., 295, 304
Minella, A.B., 271, 301
Mingari, M.C., 26, 31
Minowada, J., 295, 304
Mioduszewska, O., 297, 298, 304
Mirchandani, I., 298, 304
Mitchell, B.S.L., 109, 203
Mitchell, G.F., 278, 301
Miura, S., 145, 204
Modesto, R.R., 59, 88
Moeremans, M., 33, 79, 82, 86, 89
Mohler, M., 192, 193, 208
Moldenhauer, G., 259, 269
Molitch, M.E., 389, 400, 402, 423, 425
Molliver, M.E., 127, 128, 131, 203, 204, 316, 320,
   353
Momburg, F., 259, 269
Monge, M., 351, 356
Monti-Graziadei, G.A., 333, 354
Morales, A.R., 472, 473
Morecki, S., 278, 301
Morell, J.I., 155, 157, 191, 205, 208, 387, 388,
   423
Moretta, A., 26, 31
Moretta, L., 26, 31
Morgan, T.W., 293, 303
Moriarty, C.M., 93, 98, 202
Moriarty, G.C., 93, 98, 115, 116, 146, 150, 202,
   203
Morich, E.J., 259, 269
Morotta, C.A., 448, 455, 458, 465
Morris, B., 285, 303
Mortero, C., 180, 207
Mosher, D.J., 147, 177, 179, 180, 205
Mosier, B., 16, 30
Moss, R.L., 384, 387, 422

Moyle, W.R., 17, 30
Mozes, E., 279, 302
Mroz, E., 428, 464
Muck, K.B., 66, 88
Mueller, G.C., 68, 88
Muhlenthaler, M., 382, 422
Murant, F.G., 242, 244, 488, 489, 490, 493
Murphy, D.C., 335, 354
Murphy, M.J., 285, 303
Murray, N., 491, 493
Mushynski, W.E., 441, 446, 448, 449, 455, 456,
   458, 465
Mytilienon, C., 333, 354

Nadji, M., 472, 473
Naftchi, N.E., 135, 136, 186, 204, 207
Nagai, T., 267, 268, 269, 462, 466
Nagy, Z.A., 282, 302
Nair, R.M., 428, 464
Nairn, R., 282, 302
Nakamura, M., 361, 419
Nakane, P.K., 58, 59, 64, 87, 88, 195, 208,
   216, 223
Nakanishi, S., 361, 419
Nakazawa, N., 65, 88
Naor, D., 278, 283, 301, 302, 477, 492
Nash, D.R., 194, 195, 208
Nathanson, S.G., 282, 302
Naughton, S., 336, 355
Nauta, J.J.W., 187, 207, 323, 353
Neat, M., 472, 473
Neiman, R.S., 293, 302
Nell, E.E., 50, 53, 87
Nelson, W.G., 262, 263, 264, 269
Nestler, J.C., 189, 208
Nett, T.M., 410, 411, 412, 413, 425
Ng, P.-Y., 165, 172, 205
Nicolas, P., 383, 422
Nielson, A.J., 217, 224
Niewonhuys, R., 308, 311, 325, 352
Niitsu, Y., 65, 88
Nilsson, G., 367, 419
Nirenberg, M., 429, 464
Nirokana, N., 455, 465
Nishiitsutsuji, Uwo, J., 395, 424
Nisizawa, T., 282, 302
Nitecki, D.E., 279, 302
Nixon, R.A., 448, 455, 458, 465
Noack, M., 63, 88
Nobiling, R., 156, 158, 205
Nordal, H.G., 486, 493
Norman, A., 80, 89
Norrby, E., 486, 493
Norris, S.H., 59, 88
Norton, W.T., 348, 355, 435, 448, 464, 465
Nossal, G.J.V., 281, 302
Numa, S., 361, 419
Nunemacher, G., 418, 426
Nussbaum, J.L., 348, 355

Nygårds, A., 367, 419
Nygren, H., 63, 88

O'Connel, M., 107, 109, 202
O'Dowd, D.K., 339, 355
Oertel, W.H., 315, 353, 390, 423
O'Farrel, P.T., 243, 244
Ogawa, H., 65, 88
Okuno, Y., 183, 207
Oldham, R.K., 471, 473
Oldstone, M.B.A., 487, 493
Oliver, L., 382, 421
Olschowka, J.A., 127, 128, 131, 204
Olson, S.-O., 197, 198, 209
O'Neal, L.W., 418, 426
Orci, L., 80, 89
Ordonez, N.G., 472, 474
Ordonneau, P., 183, 186, 207
Orr, K.B., 284, 303
Osserman, D.E., 485, 492
Osserman, E.F., 295, 304
Osterhout, D.J., 246, 268, 432, 435, 459, 464
Ostermann, E., 29, 31, 246, 268, 430, 431, 433, 435, 438, 456, 464
Otani, F., 13, 30
Ottersen, O.P., 308, 314, 315, 352
Otto, H., 73, 74, 76, 77
Owman, Ch., 168, 206
Ozello, L., 295, 296, 304
Ozer, H., 295, 304

Paetkau, V.H., 281, 302
Page, N., 491, 493
Palay, S.L., 313, 314, 316, 328, 341, 353, 354, 355, 399, 400, 424
Palkovitz, M., 388, 423
Palutke, M., 298, 304
Pangalis, G.A., 299, 301, 304
Pant, H.C., 448, 465
Papamitriou, J.M., 296, 304
Papatestis, A., 485, 492
Paraskevas, F., 284, 303
Parish, C.R., 279, 302
Park, C.H., 467, 470, 473
Parkinson, J.A., 242, 244, 488, 489, 490, 493
Parr, J., 339, 355
Parsons, J.A., 100, 103, 164, 180, 181, 202, 207, 212, 221, 223, 384, 393, 415, 422, 423, 426, 468, 473
Pasi, A., 171, 206
Pasik, P., 311, 353
Pasik, T., 311, 353
Pasqualini, C., 411, 425
Pastan, I.H., 138, 139, 183, 184, 204, 207
Paul, C., 5, 30
Paull, W.K., 374, 375, 420
Pavessini, S., 133, 204
Payne, S.V., 213, 214, 223

Pearse, A.G.E., 216, 223
Pearson, J., 316, 318, 319, 329, 331, 332, 333, 353, 354, 367, 369, 419
Pearson, T., 267, 268, 269
Pecci Saavedra, J., 133, 204, 310, 313, 352
Peiper, S.C., 293, 302
Pelletier, G., 381, 399, 400, 421, 424
Pelliniemi, L.J., 107, 202
Peng, F., 267, 268, 269
Peng, J.H., 462, 466
Penz, G., 416, 426
Perdue, R.L., 54, 87
Peressini, S., 310, 313, 352
Perlman, H., 284, 303
Perlman, P., 284, 303
Perlo, V.P., 485, 492
Pernow, B., 367, 419
Pert, C.B., 394, 424
Perutka, S.J., 313, 353
Pesce, A.J., 59, 88
Peterfy, F., 18, 19, 30
Peterlini, D., 197, 209
Peters, A., 341, 355, 390, 391, 423, 447, 465
Petersen, R.O., 472, 474
Petrali, J.P., 28, 31, 33, 57, 72, 86, 87, 91, 114, 115, 116, 126, 127, 146, 149, 150, 185, 200, 201, 203, 204, 205, 238, 241, 244, 309, 352, 403, 404, 405, 406, 407, 411, 425
Petrelli, M., 467, 470, 473
Petrusz, P., 183, 186, 191, 192, 207, 208, 240, 244, 311, 312, 353, 374, 376, 377, 378, 420
Pfaff, D.W., 155, 157, 191, 205, 208, 384, 387, 388, 422, 423
Phifer, R.F., 183, 207
Philips, D.J., 52, 87, 274, 301
Phillips, R.A., 283, 303
Picart, R., 124, 125, 126, 203
Pich, A., 169, 206
Pickel, V.M., 322, 324, 353
Piekut, D.T., 135, 204, 219, 224
Pierce, G.B., Jr., 59, 88
Pilgrim, L., 315, 353
Pillavisetti, S.G., 470, 473
Pillez, A., 194, 196, 208
Pizzighella, S., 485, 492
Pizzo, S.V., 110, 111, 203, 240, 244
Plapinger, R.F., 57, 87
Platt, M., 416, 426
Plessman, U., 446, 465
Ploem, J.S., 54, 87
Polak, J.M., 216, 220, 223, 224, 389, 392, 416, 417, 423, 426
Pollak, V.E., 59, 88
Pollard, L., 295, 304
Poole, A.R., 52, 87
Porruissean, G., 491, 493
Porter, D.D., 66, 88
Porwit-Ksiatek, A., 297, 298, 304

Poskanzer, D., 485, 492
Poskitt, T.R., 479, 492
Poulsen, K., 156, 158, 205
Prage, C.A., 279, 302
Pressman, D., 13, 30, 282, 302
Preud'homme, J.-L., 145, 167, 204, 273, 274, 285, 299, 301
Price, D.L., 461, 462, 466, 486, 493
Price, P.J., 47, 87
Priestley, J.V., 187, 188, 207, 260, 269
Primus, F.J., 187, 197, 207
Prineas, J.W., 349, 356
Pritz, M.B., 187, 207, 323, 353
Proctor, J., 222, 224
Pullman, H., 63, 88
Purvis, K., 44, 51, 55, 86
Putnam, F.W., 5, 30
Puviani, R., 381, 421

Quaglino, D., 197, 209
Qualman, S.J., 220, 224
Quarles, R.H., 123, 203, 348, 349, 355, 356

Rabbitts, T.H., 3, 29
Rabei, S.Z., 472, 473
Rachibana, S., 65, 88
Radaskiewicz, T., 110, 167, 203, 206
Raff, M.C., 45, 87, 277, 301
Raine, C.S., 288, 290, 292, 303, 348, 349, 356, 435, 464, 487, 493
Raine, L., 68, 85, 88, 89, 172, 206
Rajensky, K., 15, 30
Rakic, P., 336, 337, 355
Range, M.S., 455, 456, 465
Ranson, D.H., 315, 353
Rantala, I., 169, 170, 206
Raymond, M.J., 53, 87
Raysdale, C.W., Jr., 322, 324, 353
Recht, L.D., 107, 202
Redick, J.A., 180, 207, 393, 423
Ree, N.J., 294, 303, 304
Reel, J.R., 168, 172, 206
Regidov, J., 390, 423
Rehfeld, J.F., 194, 196, 208, 389, 390, 399, 417, 423, 424, 426
Reichardt, L.F., 25, 31, 429, 464
Reichert, E.L., 288, 290, 292, 303
Reichlin, S., 370, 371, 372, 420
Reier, P.M., 107, 109, 202
Reimer, C.B., 52, 87, 274, 301
Reinecke, M., 395, 424
Reinherz, E.L., 487, 493
Reintra, K., 455, 456, 465
Reis, D.J., 146, 147, 148, 149, 152, 155, 205, 322, 324, 353
Reisert, I., 315, 353
Remington, J.S., 167, 206
Rende, M., 137, 138, 204

Renner, E.D., 220, 224
Repesh, L.A., 180, 207
Reth, M., 15, 30
Rhodes, C.H., 155, 157, 191, 205, 208
Ribak, C.E., 183, 207
Ricardo, M.J., Jr., 25, 30, 31
Rice, F.L., 127, 128, 131, 204
Rice, G.P.A., 487, 493
Richard, C.W. III, 364, 419
Richards, F., 28, 31
Richards, F.F., 17, 30, 277, 301
Richards, J.G., 192, 193, 208
Richardson, R.L., 471, 473
Rickert, D.E., 393, 423
Rivier, C., 428, 464
Rivier, J., 428, 464
Riviera, A.P., 485, 492
Roberts, E., 183, 207
Roberts, G.W., 216, 223, 392, 423
Robertson, A.A., 214, 223
Robinson, A.G., 107, 202
Rodning, C.G., 117, 122, 148, 152, 153, 154, 180, 203, 205, 207, 220, 224
Rodt, H., 286, 287, 288, 289, 303
Rodwell, J.D., 3, 4, 29
Roessman, U., 340, 355
Rognum, T.O., 292, 303
Rojas-Espinosa, O., 58, 87, 107, 202
Romano, R.L., 79, 89
Rosario, S.L., 107, 165, 172, 202, 205
Rosen, H., 411, 425
Rosenblatt, M., 370, 371, 372, 420
Rosene, D.L., 58, 88
Rosenstein, R.W., 17, 30
Rosset, J., 79, 89
Rossi, G.L., 115, 122, 123, 203
Roth, J., 80, 89, 394, 424
Roth, K.A., 399, 425
Roussel, G., 348, 355
Rowden, G., 335, 354
Rubinstein, A.E., 333, 354
Rubinstein, L.J., 339, 341, 355
Ruda, M.A., 325, 326, 327, 354, 365, 419
Ruggiero, D.A., 152, 205
Rutherford, A.V., 183, 184, 207
Rutisha, U., 5, 7, 30
Rutter, G., 80, 83, 89
Ryberg, B., 393, 423
Ryckewaerdt, J.J., 171, 206

Saavedra, J.M., 388, 423
Sachs, D.H., 279, 302
Said, S.I., 366, 419
Saito, A., 455, 456, 465
Saito, K., 183, 207
Salaza, F.J., 463, 466
Salvaterra, P.M., 317, 322, 323, 353
Samloff, I.M., 256, 268

Sammons, R., 199, 209
Samson, F.E., 447, 465
Sanders, S.K., 52, 87, 145, 205, 273, 301
Sano, Y., 167, 190, 206, 208, 311, 353, 374, 377, 384, 420, 422
Saraga, P., 295, 296, 304
Sarma, V.R., 10
Sarne, Y., 379, 420
Sasaki, M., 272, 301
Satoyoshi, E., 485, 492
Schafer, H., 73, 76, 89
Schafer, M., 400, 425
Schally, A.V., 135, 204, 374, 376, 377, 378, 420, 428, 464
Scharrer, B., 135, 196, 204, 306, 307, 308, 352, 358, 370, 377, 379, 390, 393, 394, 395, 419, 424, 460, 466
Scharrer, E., 135, 204, 245, 268, 306, 308, 352, 358, 379, 390, 397, 419, 424, 460, 466
Schechter, I., 229, 244
Scheidegger, D., 253, 268
Schenk, E.A., 49, 87
Schick, A.F., 72, 73, 77, 89
Schindler, E., 341, 355
Schlaepfer, W.W., 265, 269, 336, 355, 458, 466
Schley, C., 2, 29
Schlie, M., 340, 355
Schmechel, D.E., 315, 335, 353, 354
Schneider, M.D., 429, 464
Schnitzer, B., 298, 304
Schoenberg, D.R., 68, 88
Scholer, J., 374, 375, 420
Schoumacher, R.A., 471, 473
Schrader, J.W., 281, 302
Schraer, H., 165, 205
Schultzberg, M., 366, 419
Schwab, R.S., 485, 492
Schwartz, T.W., 196, 208, 417, 426
Scott, Z., 440, 465
Secarz, E.E., 274, 301
Sehested, M., 470, 473
Seif, S.M., 107, 202
Sekizawa, T., 272, 301
Seligman, A.M., 33, 57, 58, 72, 86, 87, 295, 304
Selkoe, D.J., 463, 466
Sell, S., 279, 280, 302
Semba, R., 335, 354
Seppala, M., 407, 417, 425, 426
Setalo, G., 135, 204
Seybold, M.E., 484, 492
Shaerer, F.C., 348, 355
Shaw, L.M., 472, 473
Shecket, J., 448, 465
Shehab, T., 370, 420
Shelanski, M.C., 456, 465
Sher, A., 15, 30
Shiloach, J., 394, 424
Shimiza, M., 374, 375, 420

Shin, H.S., 481, 492
Shinizu, A., 5, 30
Shinoda, T., 5, 30
Shivers, R.D., 191, 208, 387, 388, 423
Shore, S.L., 52, 87, 274, 301
Silverman, A.-J., 191, 208, 381, 385, 386, 420, 421, 422
Silverton, E.W., 10
Simon, C., 447, 455, 465
Sims, J., 3, 29
Sinden, J., 397, 424
Sinden, J.-A., 245, 268, 460, 466
Singer, S.J., 72, 73, 77, 89
Sipe, J.C., 487, 493
Sipple, J., 448, 465
Siraganian, R.P., 256, 268
Sirek, M.T., 416, 426
Sjoberg, N.-O., 168, 206
Sjoland, K., 168, 206
Skelly, D.S., 20, 30
Skirboll, L., 194, 208, 399, 424
Slater, R.J., 14, 30
Slaughter, C., 3, 29
Slot, J.W., 77, 89
Smart, Y., 214, 215, 223
Smet, L., 79, 82, 89
Smith, D., 147, 177, 179, 180, 205
Smith, D.B., 348, 355
Smith, P.F., 217, 223
Smolak, C.D., 448, 456, 458, 465
Snavely, F.C., 384, 422
Snyder, S.H., 312, 353
So, K., 298, 304
Sofroniew, M.V., 364, 381, 382, 419, 421, 422
Soifer, D., 448, 465
Somogyi, P., 187, 188, 207
Soner, G.L.I., 485, 493
Soria, C., 171, 206
Soria, J., 171, 206
Spicer, S.S., 183, 207
Spiegelberg, H.L., 284, 303
Spiers, R.D., 395, 424
Spoerri, O., 340, 355
Sprent, J., 282, 302
Sprinkle, T.J., 348, 355
Sproviero, J.F., 283, 302
Srisupnlack, S., 183, 207
Srouchi, P., 448, 465
Staatz, C.G., 299, 301, 304
Stanley, R.S., 333, 334, 354
Stass, S.A., 293, 302
Staub, J.-J., 416, 426
Steand, M., 476, 492
Steck, A.J., 488, 491, 492, 493
Steigleder, A., 63, 88
Stein, B.S., 472, 474
Stein, H., 286, 287, 288, 289, 303

Stein, L., 364, 419

Steinberger, A., 384, 385, 422

Steinberger, E., 384, 385, 422

Steinbusch, H.W.M., 133, 204, 308, 311, 325, 352, 353, 399, 400, 424

Steinert, P.M., 455, 465

Stengaard-Pedersen, K., 364, 366, 419

Stephano, G.B., 394, 424

Sternberger, L.A., 17, 24, 28, 29, 30, 31, 33, 57, 58, 72, 86, 87, 91, 92, 93, 95, 97, 98, 100, 101, 102, 104, 107, 113, 114, 115, 116, 126, 127, 146, 149, 150, 159, 167, 172, 185, 186, 196, 200, 201, 202, 203, 204, 205, 208, 230, 238, 241, 244, 246, 247, 248, 251, 252, 258, 262, 268, 269, 290, 295, 303, 304, 309, 352, 385, 386, 387, 403, 404, 405, 406, 407, 411, 417, 422, 425, 426, 429, 430, 431, 432, 433, 435, 438, 439, 441, 442, 444, 445, 447, 448, 449, 450, 451, 454, 455, 456, 458, 459, 462, 463, 464, 465, 466

Sternberger, N.H., 29, 31, 98, 103, 104, 108, 109, 113, 123, 136, 153, 159, 172, 202, 203, 204, 212, 219, 221, 223, 224, 242, 244, 246, 247, 252, 268, 290, 303, 341, 342, 343, 344, 345, 346, 347, 348, 349, 355, 356, 429, 430, 431, 432, 433, 435, 438, 439, 441, 442, 444, 445, 447, 448, 449, 450, 451, 454, 455, 456, 458, 459, 460, 462, 463, 464, 465, 466, 488, 489, 490, 493

Stieber, A., 46, 87

Stilman, M., 107, 202

Stolinski, C., 79, 89

Stollar, B.D., 477, 492

Stoner, G.D., 109, 203

Stoner, G.L., 485, 493

Stopa, E., 384, 422

Storm-Mathison, J., 308, 314, 315, 352

Straeblin, T., 20, 30, 242, 244

Streefkerk, J.G., 60, 62, 64, 88

Stromblad, L.-G., 197, 198, 209

Struble, R.G., 461, 462, 466

Su, Y.Y., 132, 204

Su, Y.Y.T., 315, 353

Subbarno, B., 16, 30

Suffin, S.C., 66, 88

Sugimoto, M., 270, 301

Sullivan, M.C., 188, 189, 208, 325, 328, 354, 399, 424

Sun, T.-T., 262, 263, 264, 269

Sundler, F., 107, 168, 202, 206, 306, 352, 392, 423

Susman, K.E., 412, 413, 426

Sutman, O., 271, 301

Sutmuller, P., 168, 206

Suzuki, F., 335, 354

Suzuki, I., 145, 204, 273, 279, 301, 302

Svehag, S.E., 26, 31

Swaab, D.F., 29, 31, 381, 382, 421, 422

Swallow, R.A., 183, 207

Swanson, K.A., 339, 355

Tabira, T., 342, 355, 485, 492

Tabuczka, P.M., 298, 304

Tada, A., 485, 492

Tada, N., 271, 301

Taggart, R.T., 256, 268

Takahara, T., 374, 377, 420

Takamiya, H., 73, 74, 76, 77

Takeuchi, Y., 167, 206, 311, 353

Tan, E.M., 483, 492

Tanabe, K., 335, 354

Tanaka, H., 72, 89

Tanigaki, N., 13, 30, 282, 302

Tappan, M.L., 315, 353

Tappaz, M.L., 315, 353

Tascos, N.A., 339, 355

Tashiro, T., 458, 466

Taugner, R., 156, 158, 205, 241, 244

Taussig, M J., 279, 302

Taylor, C.R., 168, 169, 206, 273, 274, 276, 291, 295, 299, 301, 303, 304, 467, 468, 473

Taylor, G.M., 77, 89

Taylor, R.B., 45, 87

Taylor, W.L., 367, 419

Terenius, L., 364, 366, 393, 419, 423

Ternyck, T., 28, 31, 63, 68, 88

Terry, R.D., 265, 269

Terry, W.D., 10

Thieme, G., 310, 352

Thomas, C.R., 270, 301

Thomas, N.C., 57, 87

Thompson, E.B., 135, 204

Thorell, J., 168, 206

Thorp, A., 310, 352

Thorpe, A., 395, 424

Tixier-Vidal, S., 124, 125, 126, 185, 203, 207

Tobet, S.A., 384, 422

Tolksdorf, G., 286, 287, 288, 289, 303

Tomashefsky, P., 165, 172, 205

Tomioko, H., 26, 31

Tonegawa, S., 11, 30

Totoric, T., 467, 473

Tougard, C., 124, 125, 126, 185, 203, 207

Towbin, H., 20, 30, 242, 244

Tragosics, B., 110, 167, 203, 206

Tramp, B., 109, 203

Tramu, U., 194, 196, 208, 400, 401, 425

Trapp, B.C., 349, 356

Traugott, U., 288, 290, 292, 303, 349, 356, 487, 493

Tridente, G., 485, 492

Triepel, J., 370, 394, 420, 424

Trisler, G.D., 429, 464

Trojanowski, J.Q., 265, 267, 269, 290, 303

Troncoso, J.C., 462, 466

Trost, T.H., 63, 88

Tsaraler, L., 429, 464
Tseng, S.C.G., 262, 263, 269
Tsuda, T., 107, 202
Tucker, L.W., 146, 147, 148, 149, 155, 205
Tucker, P.W., 3, 13, 29, 30

Uddman, R., 392, 423
Uekava, H., 282, 302
Ulbright, T.U., 418, 426
Ulrich, J., 350, 356, 462, 463, 466
Umekana, H., 335, 354
Urnas-Wallensten, K., 366, 419
Urushizaka, I., 65, 88
Utiger, R.D., 388, 423

Vaaland, J.L., 308, 314, 315, 352
Vacca, L.L., 135, 136, 165, 172, 186, 204, 205, 207
Vaerman, J.-P., 21, 30
Vaillart, C., 216, 223
Vale, W., 428, 464
Valenta, L.J., 411, 425
Valnes, K., 196, 209
van Camp, B., 79, 82, 89
Van der Kooy, D., 308, 311, 325, 352
Van Leeuwen, F.W., 169, 206, 381, 382, 421, 422
Van Orden, D.E., 180, 207
Van Orden, L.S., 180, 207
Van Vossel, A., 382, 421
Van Vossel-Daeninck, J., 382, 421
Vandehagen, J.J., 335, 354
Vandesande, F., 106, 196, 202, 208, 379, 381, 382, 383, 420, 421
Vandevelde, M., 488, 491, 492, 493
Vandvick, B., 486, 493
Vangove, S., 472, 474
VanLeeuwen, F.W., 29, 31, 232, 233, 244
Varga, J.M., 28, 31, 277, 301
Vaudry, H., 383, 422
Vaughn, J.E., 183, 207, 317, 322, 323, 353, 447, 465
Vaugn, J.M., 17, 30
Velasco, M.E., 340, 355, 448, 465
Verhofstad, A.A.J., 133, 204, 308, 311, 325, 352, 399, 400, 424
Vernon, S.E., 293, 295, 303, 304
Vidal, M.A., 21, 30
Vigh, S., 135, 204, 374, 376, 377, 378, 420
Villarreal, J., 428, 464
Vogt, A., 73, 74, 76, 77, 89
Vögtli, S., 456, 465
Voigt, K.H., 112, 113, 203, 399, 400, 424, 425
von Eschenback, A.C., 472, 474
Von Hungen, K., 435, 464
Von Mayersbach, H., 40, 50, 86

Wachsmuth, E.D., 167, 205
Wagener, C., 467, 473
Wagner, T.O.F., 410, 425

Wahl, L.M., 270, 301
Wahlstrom, T., 407, 417, 425, 426
Wainer, B.H., 265, 269
Wakabayashi, K., 241, 244
Walford, R.L., 283, 302, 477, 492
Wallace, J.A., 191, 192, 208, 311, 312, 353
Walles, B., 168, 206
Wallich, R., 284, 303
Wanatabe, K., 384, 422
Wang, A.C., 12, 30
Ward, S.M., 14, 30
Warner, N.L., 21, 30, 278, 302
Warren, B.P., 169, 206
Wasserkrug, H.L., 57, 58, 87
Watkins, W.B., 379, 381, 420
Watson, S.J., 364, 419
Waxdal, M.J., 5, 7, 30
Waxman, S.G., 339, 355
Weaver, C., 183, 207
Webb, S.R., 26, 31
Weber, E., 399, 400, 425
Weber, K., 446, 465
Webster, H. deF., 103, 107, 108, 109, 123, 136, 153, 202, 203, 204, 219, 224, 341, 342, 343, 344, 345, 346, 347, 348, 355, 356, 459, 466, 485, 492
Wegmann, W., 121, 203
Weigle, W.U., 281, 302
Weil, H.P., 63, 88
Weindl, A., 381, 382, 421, 422
Weiner, L.P., 486, 493
Weinstein, R.S., 165, 167, 205
Weisenburger, D.D., 220, 224
Weiss, L., 292, 303
Weiss, R.A., 262, 263, 269
Weith, H.C., 367, 419
Wells, M.R., 348, 355
Wendelschafer-Crabb, G., 147, 177, 179, 180, 205
Wenthold, R.J., 129, 130, 204
Westlund, K.N., 188, 189, 208, 325, 328, 353, 354, 399, 424
White, N., 230, 244, 388, 423
Whitehouse, P.J., 461, 466
Whittingham, S., 484, 492
Wilander, E., 168, 206, 393, 423
Wilbur, J.F., 388, 399, 423, 424
Wilkie, M.B., 191, 192, 208
Willard, M., 447, 448, 455, 465
Williams, T.H., 384, 422
Willingham, M.C., 138, 139, 183, 184, 204, 207
Wilson, D., 148, 152, 153, 154, 205
Wilson, I.D., 117, 122, 180, 203, 207, 220, 224
Wilson, M., 64, 88
Winchell, K.H., 348, 356
Winchester, R.W., 4, 10, 29
Winkler, C.F., 472, 473

Wisniewski, H.M., 448, 465, 485, 493
Witorsch, R.J., 155, 156, 205, 408, 410, 425
Wolf, G., 381, 420
Wolfe, H.J., 418, 426
Wolfgram, F., 348, 355
Wood, H.A., 261, 269
Wood, I., 255, 268
Woodcock-Mitchell, J., 262, 263, 264, 269
Woodhams, P.L., 167, 206, 216, 223, 392, 423
Wray, S.H., 485, 492
Wright, B., 310, 352
Wright, D.H., 213, 214, 223
Wu, H.L., 265, 269
Wu, J.-Y., 132, 192, 193, 204, 208, 313, 314, 315, 316, 328, 353, 354

Yahr, M.D., 333, 354
Yam, L.T., 472, 473
Yamada, S.S., 183, 184, 207
Yamaga, K., 282, 302

Yamashita, H., 190, 208
Yang, N., 472, 473
Yannihara, N., 398, 424
York, C., 333, 354
Yoskitaka, S., 65, 88
Young, E.W., 220, 224
Young, J.C., 66, 88
Yphantis, D.A., 455, 456, 465
Yu, Y.-Y., 370, 420

Zale, B., 351, 356
Zanderer, M., 283, 302
Zimmerman, E.A., 107, 164, 165, 172, 191, 202, 205, 208, 408, 425
Zimmerman, V.-J.P., 336, 355
Zipser, B., 2, 29, 429, 464
Zis, A.P., 335, 354
Zolman, J.C., 411, 425
Zomzely-Neurath, C., 333, 354
Zucco, M., 137, 138, 204
Zurbriggen, A., 491, 492, 493

Subject Index

A cells, 271, 282
Acetylcholine, 134, 265, 305, 309, 317
Acetylcholine receptor, 484
Acetylcholine-serotonin coexistence, 399
Acetylcholinesterase, 56, 316
Acrolein, 216
ACTH, see Corticotropin
α-Actinin
Adenocarcinoma, 467
Adenocarcinoma, differentiation from
    lymphoma, 295
Adenosine phosphoribosyl transferase, 256
Adjuvant disease, 488
Adrenalin, 130, 316, 329
Adrenal medulla, 329
Adrenocorticotropin, 171
Adult onset hypogammaglobulinanemia,
    incidence of autoimmune disease, 477
Affinity label, 15, 17, 275
Affinity purification, 261
Aging, T cell suppressor cell regression, 477
Aleutian mink disease, 477
Alkaline phosphatase, 167
Allelic exclusion, 11, 14
Allotype, 14
Aluminum poisoning, 462
    aberrant neurofilament phosphorylation, 463
    selective perikaryonal neurofilament
        phosphorylation, 462
Alzheimer disease, 267, 376, 461–464
    aberrant neurofilament phosphorylation, 463
    neurofilament kinase pathology, 463
    perikaryonal neurofilament phosphorylation,
        462
Amacrine cell, 132, 315
γ-Aminobutyrate, 305, 313, 314–316
γ-Aminobutyrate hapten, 308

γ-Aminobutyrate reuptake, 315
γ-Aminobutyric acid, 132
γ-Aminobutyric acid transaminase, 316
Aminoethylcarbazol, 57, 107, 188
γ-Aminoglutamic acid decarboxylase, 316
Aminopeptidase, 167
Aminopterin, 249
Amplification, see Staining intensity
Amygdala, 364, 366, 377, 382, 390, 392
Angiotensin, 156, 241
Anterior commissural nuclei, 155
Anterograde tracer transport, 187, 322
Antibody, 2
    hemolysis, 76
    idiotypic site, 309
    normal, 227
    retrograde uptake, 324
    size of idiotypic region, 229, 247
    tissue penetration, 25, 44, 65, 71, 78, 114, 117,
        126, 127, 129, 137, 138, 141, 183, 214, 220,
        345, 347, 376
Antibody absorption, 15
    liquid phase, 233–238
    solid phase, 236, 238–240
    see also Immunoabsorbent
Antibody affinity, 2, 6, 16, 17, 18, 19, 22, 28, 93,
    106, 200, 201, 225, 227, 229, 232, 236, 239,
    246, 247, 257, 258, 309, 374
Antibody affinity protection, 72
Antibody affinity purification, 27–29, 42, 43, 53,
    60, 63, 64, 77, 225, 226, 230
Antibody agglutination, 76
Antibody combining site, see Idiotypic region
Antibody conjugation, 35, 39–42, 59–68. See also
    Conjugated antibody method
Antibody dissociation, 17, 69, 95, 200, 201, 475,
    479

Antibody elution, *see* Antibody dissociation
Antibody genes, 256
Antibody heterogeneity, 5, 24, 245
Antibody heteroligating, 10, 248, 260
Antibody hinge region, 66
Antibody homocytotrophic, 27
Antibody labeled, *see* Antibody conjugation;
    Conjugated antibody method
Antibody liquid phase absorption, 243, 257
Antibody-producing cell, 194
Antibody production, 285
Antibody reaginic, 27
Antibody solid-phase absorption, 243, 257
Antibody specifically purified, *see* Antibody
    affinity purification
Antibody specificity, 1, 2, 3, 22, 85, 104, 225–268.
    See also Antiserum specificity
Antibody valence, 6, 19, 75
Antidiuretic hormone, *see* Vasopressin
Antigen, 1, 2
    affinity purification, 262
    purity, 227, 228
Antigen-antibody complex, 20, 100. *See also*
    Ferritin-antiferritin complex; Glucose-
    oxidase antiglucose oxidase complex;
    Immune complex disease; Peroxidase-
    antiperoxidase complex
Antigen-antibody reaction, 16, 19. *See also*
    Antibody affinity
Antigen-antibody reaction reversibility, 17, 18,
    28
Antigen conformation, 247
Antigenic determinant, *see* Epitope
Antigen receptors, 2, 4, 27, 272, 274, 277, 282
    A cell, 283
    B cell, 285
Antigens, shared epitopes, 228
Antiidiotype, *see* Idiotype
Antiserum specificity, 24
Apoperoxidase-antiperoxidase complex, 100
Araldite sections, 115, 217, 220
Arcuate nucleus, 222, 364
Area A5, 189
Ascites, 255
Aspartate, 129
Aspartate aminotransferase, 129
Astrocyte, 137, 329, 335, 336
    anaplastic, 339
    reactive, 339
Astrocytoma, 340
Auditory nerve, 129
Autofluorescence, 49
Autoimmune diseases, 287, 475–493
Autoimmune thyroiditis, 482
Autoradiography, 27, 32, 156, 165, 190–193,
    260, 274, 310, 316, 366
Avian leukosis virus, 186

Avian sarcoma virus, 138
Avidin, 169
Avidin-biotin complex method, 67–70
    aggregated proteins, 85
    quantification, 147
    resolution, 177
    sensitivity, 69, 172–175
    specificity, 259
    steric hindrance, 69, 174
Avidin-biotin method, 44
Axonal pathway identification, retrograde
    transport, 186–190
Azaguanine, 248

Background, 84, 225. *See also* Method specificity
Background identification, 145, 146
Basket cell, 316
Basket cell fibers, 173
Basophil, 27
B cell(s), 1, 2, 271, 272, 274, 277–280, 295
    helper, 295
    recirculation, 286
    resting, 286
B cell antigen, 277, 278
B cell differentiation, 285
B cell memory, 280
B cell receptors, 276
B cell tolerance, 280–282
B cell tumors, 291
Bed nucleus of hypothalamus, 364
Benzidine, 58
Benzoquinone, 63, 216
Benzyldiazapines, 192
Bifunctional reagents, 59
Bile canaliculi, 167
Bioactive peptides, 218. *See also* Regulatory
    peptides
Bioactive peptides, loss during tissue processing,
    see Hapten, loss during tissue processing
Biotin, *see* Avidin-biotin complex method
Bipolar cells, 133
Blast cell, 285
Blast transformation, *see* Tritiated thymidine
    incorporation
Blocking protein, 115
Blood-brain barrier, 488
    monoclonal antibody, 432
Blood group antigens, 109, 165, 227, 299
Bombesin, 397
Bombesin evolution, 395
Bouin's fixative, 103, 213, 292
Brain tumors, 265, 339–341
Breast tumors, 467, 472
    eutopic hormone production, 417
Buffers, 104
Bungarotoxin, 484
Burkitt's lymphoma, 298

Bursa of Fabricus, 271
Bystander cells, 272

C3 receptor, 287
Calcitonin, 418
Calcitonin evolution, 395
Calcium binding protein, 80
Calcium-dependent protease, 336
Calmodulin, 335
Canine distemper, 487, 488
Cap formation, 55, 285
Capping, 44, 279
Carbodiimide, 37
Carbonic anhydrase, 164
Carcinoembryonic antigen, 169, 470, 471
Carcinoid tumors, ectopic hormone production,
    417
Carcinoma poorly differentiated, 471
Carcinosarcoma, epithelial origin, 472
Carnosine, 305, 333
Casein, 169
Catecholamine development, 316
Catecholamines, 189, 316, 317
Cathespin D, 45, 52
Caudate-putamen, 187, 190, 323, 325, 364
cDNA, 363. See also Recombinant DNA
Cell membrane, 51, 77, 82, 117, 124, 138, 214,
    254, 270, 292, 342, 401
Cell membrane-Golgi complex pathway, 412
Cell permeability, see Antibody, tissue
    penetration
Cell sorter, see Fluorescent cell sorting
Cell surface fluidity, 44
Cell tolerance, 284
Cellular immunity, 2
Central gray, 382, 387
Centroblast, 286
Centrocyte, 286
Cerebellar cortex, 328
Cerebellar white matter, 173
Cerebellum, 313, 328
Cerebral blood flow, regulation, 131
Cerebral cortex, 121, 311, 317, 390, 392
Chemoarchitectonics, 245, 247, 395–397, 460,
    461
Chemotherapy, 471
Chloronaphthol, 58, 67, 189, 196, 107
Cholecystokinin, 194, 366, 389–392, 397
    hippocompal interneurons, 392
Cholecystokinin-dopamine coexistence, 399
Cholecystokinin evolution, 389, 390, 395
Choline acetyl transferase, 265, 309, 317, 461
Cholinergic-adrenergic colocalization in culture,
    317
Cholinergic synapse, 316
Chorionic carcinoma, 470
Chorionic gonadotrophin, 241

Choroid plexus papilloma, 339
Chronic relapsing allergic encephalomyelitis, 349
Cilia, 258
    monoclonal antibody, 432
Clear vesicles, 134, 135, 141, 305
Cloning of hybridomas, 250–252
ClonoPAP, 105, 107, 160, 243, 254, 255, 258,
    259, 260, 430, 431, 432, 435, 436, 437, 438,
    440, 441, 442, 444, 448, 449, 450, 451, 452,
    454, 457, 459, 462, 463, 489, 490
    mouse, 100
    rat, 100
Cobalt chloride, 188, 189
Coexistence, see Colocalization; Regulatory
    peptide coexistence; Regulatory peptide
    neurotransmitter coexistence
Colchicine, 376
Collagen I periodicity, 177
Colloidal gold, see Immunogold method
Colocalization, 112, 124, 134, 194, 197, 222, 260,
    307, 317–322, 397–401
    neuronal diversity, 399
Colon:
    endocrine cells, 169
    myenteric plexus, 390
    submucosal plexus, 390
Command neuron, 333
Complement, 7, 25, 44, 52, 76, 278, 476, 480,
    481, 482
Complement receptor, 278, 279
Concanavalin A, 277
Conjugated antibody method, 32–89, 144
    aggregated conjugate, 50, 51, 60, 67, 69
    aggregated proteins, 84, 85
    contamination by unlabeled antibody, 49, 50,
        59, 60, 85
    nonspecific binding of conjugate, 50
Contrasting color staining, see Dual antigens in
    same section
Coombs test, 476
Copulation, 155
Corpus striatum, 188, 312, 320, 397
Corticosterone, 377
Corticotropin, 118, 222, 237, 359, 362
Corticotropin-luteinizing hormone-releasing
    hormone coexistence, 400
Corticotropin-releasing factor, 135, 372–378
Cortisone, 374
Crossreactions, 2, 16, 24, 29, 180, 225, 226, 229,
    230, 232, 239, 240, 241, 244, 257, 291.
    See also Antibody affinity
Cryostat sections, 155, 260
Cuneiform nucleus, 189
Cuprizone, 349
Cushing syndrome, 416
Cystatin C, 197
Cysteine sulfanate decarboxylase, 315

Cysteine sulfonic acid decarboxylase, 313
Cytosol, 135
Cytotoxicity, 271
Cytotoxicity antibody-mediated, 478, 480, 482, 484
Cytotoxicity cell-mediated, 478, 484, 485, 487

Darkfield illumination, 84
Dehydration, 155
Demyelinating polyneuropathy, 490–492
Demyelination, 342, 487
Dendritic spine, 133
Dense core vesicles, *see* Secretory granules
Densitometer, 155
Dentate gyrus, 317
Development, 215, 468
Developmental changes of epitope distribution, 458–460
Diabetes, 122
Diabetes insipidus, 363
Diabetes mellitus, 414, 415
Diagonal band, 317
Diaminobenzidine, 57, 67, 70, 86, 96, 107, 128, 140, 145, 148, 155, 177, 185, 187, 188, 189, 195
    product intensification, 376
Diaminobenzidine reaction product:
    enzyme inhibition, 196
    sheltering of antibodies, 188, 196
Dianisidine, 58
Diazonium salts, 37, 38
Differential interference optics, *see* Nomarski optics
Differentiation, cell division, 191. *See also* Malignancy grading
Differentiation antigens, 289, 468–473
Difluorodinitrodiphenylsulfone, 59
DiGeorge's syndrome, 271
Dinitrophenyl hapten, 246, 277
Direct method, 42–44, 46, 48, 51, 52, 53, 68, 194, 210, 220, 260
DNA, *see* Recombinant DNA
DNA hybridization, 11
Dopamine, 152, 190, 196, 305, 309, 310, 316, 329
Dopamine-acetylcholine coexistence, 322
Dopamine-β-hydroxylase, 42, 128, 130, 309, 316, 325, 327
Dorsal horn, 365, 367
Dorsal horn nuclei, 189
Dorsal root, 367
Dorsomedial hypothalamic nucleus, 376, 388
Double-staining techniques, *see* Dual antigens in same section
Down's syndrome, 461
Dual antigens in same section, 37, 47, 54, 79, 193–200
    antibody removal, 194, 196
    simultaneous staining, 194, 199

Duodenum, 172
Duodenum enterocytes, 165
Duodenum goblet cells, 165
Dynorphin, 362, 363
Dynorphin-vasopressin coexistence, 399

Ectopic endocrine tumors, 416
Ectopic hormone expression, 363
Ectopic hormone production, index of malignancy, 470
Ectopic hormone secretion, 416
Educated cells, *see* Memory B cells
Efficiency, *see* Sensitivity
Electroblot, *see* Immunoblot
Electron hydrization, 36
Electron microscopy, 70–83, 114–142
Electron opacity, 72
Electrophoresis-electroblot, *see* Immunoblot
Embryonic antigens, 469
Endocrine tumors, 415–418
Endocytosis, 46, 277, 324, 411
Endogenous peroxidase, 86, 113, 114, 212
Endoplasmic reticulum, 126, 135, 141, 325
Endorphin, 222, 360, 363
    precursor heterogeneity, 400
Endorphin evolution, 395
Endorphin-vasopressin coexistence, 399
Endothelium, 110
Eng-Bibgee effect, 106, 107, 145, 147, 258, 259
Eng protein, *see* Glial fibrillary acidic protein
Enkephalin, 112, 167, 189, 260, 306, 360, 361, 362, 363, 364, 365, 366, 377, 392, 397
Enkephalin-acetylcholine coexistence, 366
Enkephalin evolution, 395
Enzyme histochemistry, 56, 245
    sensitivity, 165
    specificity, 164
Enzyme-labeled antibody method, aggregated proteins, 84, 85
Enzyme-linked immunosorbent assay, 18, 171, 252, 309
    hybridoma clone selection, 252
Enzyme-linked immunosorbent assay sensitivity, 259
Enzyme markers, 56
Enzyme product inhibition, 56, 67
Ependyma, 339
Ependymal cells, 335
Epidermis, 263
Epitope, 2, 16
Epitope density in tissue, 235–237
Epitope localization, 227, 247, 262
Epitope receptors, 270. *See also* Antigen receptors
Epitopes, effect of fixatives, 211
Epitope submolecular location, 262
Epon, 128, 217, 220
Epon sections, 145. *See also* Semithin sections
Equilibrium dialysis, 18

Equivalence zone determination, 98
Estradiol receptors, 191
Estrogen, 155, 169
Exocytosis, 77, 118, 119, 120, 382, 401
Exon, 11, 361
Experimental allergic encephalomyelitis,
    487–490
  capillary damage, 488
Experimental immune thyroiditis, 481
Extragonadal germ cell cancer, 471

Fab, 6, 65, 66, 71, 147, 186, 273
  fluorochrome labeled, 46
Facial nucleus, 325
Factor VIII, 110, 240
Familial dysautonomia, 330–333, 367
Fasiculus retroflexus, 385
Fast blue, retrograde tracer, 366
Fc, 6, 10, 21, 25, 44, 51, 52, 278
Fc receptors, 25, 26, 32, 46, 51, 52, 84, 105, 144,
    145, 210, 212, 272, 273, 278, 279, 283, 284,
    299
Feedback stimulation, 382
Feeder cells, 250
Ferritin, 92. *See also* Immunoferritin method
Ferritin-antiferritin complex, 100, 279
α-Fetoprotein, 227, 471
Fibrinopeptide A, 171
Fibronectin, 147
Fibronectin periodicity, 177
Fibrosarcoma, 468
First antibody, 105–107
Fixation, 211, 212–218
Flagellin, 274
Fluorescein antibody conjugate purification, 38
Fluorescein isothiocyanate, 33, 37, 38–42, 194
Fluorescence, 36
Fluorescence quenching, 36, 38
Fluorescent cell sorting, 46, 47
FMRF-amide, 394
Follicle-stimulating hormone, 126, 228, 241, 384
Foot and mouth disease virus, 168
Formaldehyde, 103, 117, 121, 213
  Schiff base formation, 308
Frozen sections, 106, 134, 211, 218, 308
F(ab')$_2$, 10, 51, 65, 271, 272

Galactocerebroside, 288, 351
β-Galactosidase, 56, 66, 274, 275, 278
Ganglioma, 340
Ganglioneuroma, 265
Gastric adenocarcinoma, 121
Gastric inhibitory peptide, 172, 197, 392
Gastric inhibitory polypeptide, 393
Gastric mucosa, 196
Gastrin, 180, 194, 196, 389, 390
Gastrin evolution, 389, 390
Gastrointestinal carcinoma, 470

Gene expression, 11
Genomic DNA, 363. 384. *See also* Genes,
    recombinant DNA
Germinal center, 286
Giant lymph node hyperplasia, differentiation
    from lymphoma, 298
Glial fibrillary acidic protein, 215, 335–341
  cell-free synthesis, 336
  development, 336
  posttranslational processing, 336
  in regeneration, 339
Glia-specific antigens, 308
Glioblastoma, 340
Glioma, 468
Glomerulonephritis, 478, 481
Glucagon, 169, 180, 197, 392, 393
Glucagon-α-endorphin coexistence, 400
Glucagon evolution, 395
Glucose oxidase, 33, 66
Glutamate, 305, 310, 314–316
Glutamate decarboxylase, 132, 192, 315, 328
Glutamate hapten, 308
Glutaraldehyde, 59, 61, 62, 63, 64, 73, 117, 127,
    214, 314
  Schiff base formation, 308
Glycentin, 197, 392
Glycomethacrylate, 214
Glycoprotein hormone α-subunit, ectopic
    production, 417
Glycosylation, 455
Golgi cell, cerebellum, 316
Gonadotroph, 119, 123
Gonadotropin, 471
Gonadotropin-releasing hormone, *see* Luteinizing
    hormone-releasing hormone
Goodpasture's syndrome, 479, 480
Granuloma, 169, 295
Growth hormone, 389
Growth hormone precursor, 389
Growth hormone-thyrotropin-releasing
    hormone coexistence, 400
Guanylate kinase, 248

Habenula, 317, 381, 385
Hairy cell, 273, 276, 299
Hapten, 15, 16, 18, 27, 133, 279
  loss during tissue processing, 133
Hashimoto's disease, *see* Autoimmune thyroiditis
Heavy chains, 260
Help, *see* T cell, helper
Hemangioblastoma, 111
Hemolytic plaque assay, 278
Hepatitis B antigen, 167
Hepatitis B surface antigen, 110
Hepatitis B virus, 281
Herpes simplex virus, 142
Herring bodies, 381
Heterocytotrophic interaction, 282

Hexachlorophene, 351
Hippocampus, 311, 317, 366, 382, 390, 392, 461
Histamine, 27
Histocompatibility, 15
Histocompatibility complex, 279, 282, 299
Hodgkin's disease, 168, 294, 295
Hog cholera virus, 47
Homocytotropic interaction, 282
Hormone precursor heterogeneity, 416
Hormone precursors, *see* Preprohormones
Hormone receptor endocytosis, 411
Hormone receptor regulation, 412
Hormone receptors, 401–414
    intracellular, 403
    membrane, 403
    secretion granule membrane, 403
Horseradish peroxidase, *see* Peroxidase
Hybridization probe, *see* cDNA
Hybridoma, 248. *See also* Monoclonal antibodies
Hybridoma clone selection, 250–252
    immunocytochemistry, 252
Hypogammaglobulinemia congenital, 271
Hypophysis, *see* Pituitary
Hypothalamo-hypophyseal tract, 219, 377, 384
Hypothalamus, 311, 327, 364, 370, 390
Hypoxanthine aminopterin thymidine medium, 249
Hypoxanthine-phosphoribosyl transferase, 248
Hypoxanthine-phosphoribosyl transferase genes, 256

Ia antigens, 279, 487
Ia region, 282
Idiotype, 4, 14, 476
    antibodies to, 477
Idiotype-antiidiotype networks, 282
Idiotypic receptors:
    B cell, 283, 284
    T cell, 283, 284
Idiotypic region, 17
Idiotypic site, 25
    size, 17, 29
IgA, 55
Ileum, 172
    mucosa, 152
Image analyzer, 155, 159–163
Immune complex disease, 480–482
Immune response, 1, 4, 152, 270–288
    control of, 15
Immune tolerance, *see* Tolerance
Immunization, *see* Immune response
Immunoabsorbent, *see* Antibody absorption solid phase, 28, 29
Immunoblot, 20, 107, 257, 262
Immunoblot one-dimensional, 241–243, 449
Immunoblot two-dimensional, 243, 441
Immunodiffusion, 20, 227, 228, 240
Immunoferritin method, 44, 72–78, 140, 274

aggregated conjugate, 73
aggregated proteins, 84, 85
contamination by unlabeled antibody, 85
estimation of antibody contents, 76
unconjugated immunoglobulin, 76
Immunoferritin method quantification, 147, 148
Immunoferritin method resolution, 177, 178
Immunoferritin method specificity, 83–86
Immunofluorescence, 34–55, 210, 214, 220, 260, 273, 274, 298, 299, 310, 316, 325, 364, 366, 367, 467
    cell surface, 44–47
    hybridoma clone selection, 251
    living cells, 44–47
    paraffin sections, 110, 167
Immunofluorescence counterstains, 49
Immunofluorescence dual antigen staining, 194
Immunofluorescence granular, 478, 484
Immunofluorescence linear, 478, 480
Immunofluorescence method specificity, 39, 42, 48–53
Immunofluorescence quantification, 47, 53, 54, 147
Immunofluorescence sensitivity, 44, 47, 49, 167, 168, 172, 259
Immunofluorescence sequential, 194
Immunogen, 281
Immunoglobulin, 1–31, 109, 110, 113, 117
    autoimmune, 475
    see also Antibody
Immunoglobulin A, 25, 26, 77, 122, 152, 180, 194, 286
Immunoglobulin carbohydrate, 7
Immunoglobulin chain homing, 10
Immunoglobulin chains, 199. *See also* Immunoglobulin heavy chains; Immunoglobulin light chains
Immunoglobulin class, *see* Isotype
Immunoglobulin constant region, 5
Immunoglobulin crossreactions, *see* Crossreactions
Immunoglobulin D, 27, 55, 271, 272, 277, 286, 287, 292
Immunoglobulin domains, 10
Immunoglobulin E, 26, 481
Immunoglobulin evolution, 4, 10, 12
Immunoglobulin formation, 77
Immunoglobulin fragments, 6
Immunoglobulin G, 6–10, 25, 26, 77, 79, 122, 194, 228, 285, 286
    carbohydrate, 324
Immunoglobulin genes, 11
Immunoglobulin heavy chains, 3, 4, 25
Immunoglobulin heterogeneity, 2
Immunoglobulin hinge region, 6
Immunoglobulin hypervariable region, *see* Idiotype
Immunoglobulin isotype, *see* Isotype

Immunoglobulin J chain, 25, 26
Immunoglobulin light chains, 3, 4, 228
Immunoglobulin M, 25, 26, 55, 194, 228, 256, 271, 272, 276, 277, 286, 287, 292, 293, 490
Immunoglobulin posttranslational processing, 286
Immunoglobulin production, 274
Immunoglobulin reduction, 9
Immunoglobulin variable region, 4
Immunogold method, 33, 34, 79–83, 140
  aggregated proteins, 84, 85
  cell membrane, 82
  contamination by unlabeled antibody, 85
  dual antigens, 79
  reagent stability, 79
  resolution, 82, 177
  surface replica electron microscopy, 83
Immunogold method quantification, 80, 83, 147, 148
Immunogold method specificity, 83–86
Immunosuppression, 1
Immunouranium method, 33, 72
Indirect method, 42–44, 48, 52, 53, 60, 68, 84, 225
Infectious mononucleosis, 294
Insulin, 180, 241, 393
Insulin evolution, 395
Intensification, see Staining intensity
Interleukin 1, 282
Interleukin 2, 283
Intermediate filaments, 265
Intermediolateral column, 366
Intermediolateral nucleus, 317
Interpeduncular nucleus, 317, 364, 370, 385
Intestinal mucosa, 191
Intestinal nerve plexuses, intrinsic regulatory peptides, 392
Intestine, brush border, 137
Intraperiod line, 341, 342
Intron, 11, 361, 362, 363
Ir genes, 278, 279
Ir region, 282
Isothiocyanate, 37, 38–42
Isotype, 5, 25–27, 194
Isotype shift, 11, 12, 27, 285

J chain, 286, 294
Jejenum, 172

Keratin, 262, 455
Keratin classes, 265
Keratin families, 265
Kidney:
  collecting tubules, 156
  tubulary absorption, 80
Kidney afferent arteriole, 156
Kidney cortical collecting tubules, 156

Labeled antibody method, see Conjugated antibody method
Lactotroph, 117, 120
Langerhans cell, 335
Lateral funiculus, 317
Lateral hypothalamic nucleus, 376
Lateral septal nucleus, 387
Lectins, 165, 294, 324
Legionnaire's disease, 220
Leukemia, 292
  blastic, hemoglobin, 293
  blastic transformation, 293
  chemotherapy, 293
  chronic granulocytic, blastic transformation, 293
  chronic lymphatic, B cell, 292
  chronic lymphocytic, differentiation
  lymphoblastic, 293
  lymphocytic, 295
  monoclonality, 292, 293
  polyclonal, 293
Leukocytes, 145, 167, 259, 298–301
Leukosarcomatosis, 476
Leydig cell, 384, 385
Ligand quantification, 149, 155, 403
Light absorption, 35, 36
Light chains, 260
Light microscopy, 54, 55, 103–114
Link antibody, 92, 93, 142, 143, 145, 149, 201, 273
β-Lipoprotein, 237, 360
Locus ceruleus, 128, 148, 159, 311, 316, 327, 364
Lordosis response, 387
Lucifer yellow, 190
  anterograde transport, 187
Lung tumors, 470
Lupus erythematosus, 482–484
  T suppressor cell response, 484
Luteinizing hormone, 119, 126, 217, 225, 228, 241, 384
Luteinizing hormone-releasing hormone, 29, 122, 168, 229, 232, 237, 238, 251, 262, 377, 378, 384–388
  adrenal receptor, 407
  ectopic production, 417
  gonadotrophic degrading enzyme, 412
  gonadotroph receptor, 403
  growth hormone colocalization, 389
  pancreatic islet receptor, 407
  syncytiotrophoblast receptor, 407
  trophoblast tumor receptor, 407
Luteinizing hormone-releasing hormone precursor, 386, 389
Luteinizing hormone-releasing hormone receptor, 401–408
Luteinizing hormone-releasing hormone release:
  estrogen effect, 387
  gonadotropin effect, 387

Lymphatic tissues, 285–288

Lymphocyte, 1, 270. *See also* B cell; Mononuclear cell; Natural killer cell; T cell

Lymphocyte markers, 271

Lymphocytic interstitial pneumonia, 298

Lymphocytic thyroiditis, 482

Lymphoid hyperplasia:
  polyclonality, 291
  reactive, 291, 294

Lymphoma, 169, 194, 197, 210, 285, 288–298, 467
  differentiation from adenocarcinoma, 295
  monoclonality, 291, 294, 298
  polyclonality, 291, 294, 298
  solid growth, 292

Lymphoma B cells, 295

Lymphoma T cells, 295

Lysozyme, 121, 152, 169, 180, 295, 325

Macrophage, 52, 259, 270, 271, 487. *See also* A cell

Major dense line, 341

Major histocompatibility complex, *see* Histocompatibility

Maleimide, 65, 66

Malignancy, 165, 169, 210
  multiple hormone coexpression, 417

Malignancy grading, 265, 285, 289, 290, 291, 295, 339, 340, 469, 471, 472

Mammary carcinoma, *see* Breast tumors

Mammillary body, 370, 382

Mantle zone, 286, 287

Marginal zone, 287

Mast cell, 27

Mating behavior, 384

Measles virus, 83, 486

Medial preoptic nucleus, 384

Medial septal nucleus, 317, 384

Median eminence, 164, 168, 190, 196, 370, 376, 381, 383, 384, 387, 388

Median forebrain bundle, 384

Medulla oblongata, 370

Medullary thyroid carcinoma, 418

Medulloblastoma, 265, 340

Melanocytes, 335

Melanocyte-stimulating hormone, 171, 222, 239, 360

Memory T cells, 280, 284

Menadione hapten, 277

Mercury bichloride fixation, 103, 345, 292

Metastasis, 289, 472, 472

Metastatic tumors, 468

Method specificity, 43, 48–53, 83–86, 90, 142–145

Microfilaments, 45, 137

β-Microglobulin, 282

Microspectrophotometer, 155

Microtubule-associated protein, 435

Microtubule-associated protein kinase, phosphorylation of neurofilaments, 456

Milk-fat globule membrane antigen, 473

Molluscan tetrapeptide, 112

Monamine oxidase, 316

Monoclonal antibodies, 6, 25, 29, 33, 42, 43, 44, 46, 47, 60, 82, 105, 106, 110, 113, 145, 147, 172, 188, 197, 201, 211, 212, 213, 219, 225, 226, 230, 235, 237, 240, 243, 244, 245–269, 309, 310, 322, 323, 366, 428–464, 485
  antineurofibrillar, 433, 435
  antineurofilament proteins, 433–463
  antiperikaryonal, 435
  antisynapse-associated, 433
  blocking of rabbit antibodies, 180, 260
  isotopically labeled, 260
  neurofibrillar group, 433
  to neurofilament phosphoepitopes, 448–455
  to neurofilaments, 432–458, 461–464, 265
  neuron-specific, 432
  to nonphosphorylated neurofilaments, 448–458
  perikaryonal-neurofibrillar group, 435
  selection for heterogeneity regions of antigens, 446, 447
  synapse-associated group, 433

Monoclonal antibody, broadly-reacting neuron-specific
  to acetylcholine receptor, 485
  to blood-brain barrier, 488

Monoclonal antibody production, 247–256

Monoclonal antibody selection, 250–252

Mononuclear cell, 1, 247, 253, 270

Mossy fibers, 328

Motilin, 31

Motoneurons, 267, 317, 387

Motor end plates, 317

mRNA, *see* Recombinant DNA

Muller cell, 339

Multiple myeloma, 6

Multiple sclerosis, 219, 288, 349, 485–487
  macrophage, 487
  T helper cells, 487

Multiple sclerosis plaques, T cells, 486, 487

Multiple sclerosis virus infection, 486, 488

Myasthenia gravis, 484, 485

Myelin, 341–352

Myelin-associated glycoprotein, 348, 349, 350, 351
  development, 348
  periaxonal, 348

Myelin-associated glycoprotein autoimmunity, demyelinating polyneuropathy, 490

Myelination, 486

Myelin basic protein, 135, 153, 242, 341, 342, 348, 350, 351, 488
  development, 342

Myelin development, 136

Myelin glycoprotein, 341
Myelin proteolipid, 341, 348
Myeloma cells, 247, 253
Myosin, 137

Naloxone, 363
Naphthol AS phosphate, 199
Naphthol phosphate, 66
Natural killer cell, 272, 284, 288, 485
Neocortex, 390
Neostriatum, 267, 309, 317
Nerve growth factor, 332
Neuroblastoma, 340
Neuroblastoma cells, 291
Neurocytochemistry, 305–356
Neuroectodermal tumors, 340
Neuroepithelial tumors, 340
Neurofibrillary tangles, 461
    selective structural compactness, 463
Neurofibroma, 333
Neurofilament-associated protease, 458
Neurofilament-associated protein kinase, 448,
    456
Neurofilament-associated protinease, 455
Neurofilament compactness, 451
Neurofilament heterogeneity, 13, 438–447
Neurofilament phosphoepitopes:
    heterogeneity, 449
    hapten inhibition of monolconal antibodies,
    451
Neurofilament phosphorylation, 448, 448–458
Neurofilament protein, 110, 265, 308, 340,
    433–463
    ancestral genes, 448
Neurofilament protein heterogeneity, 173
Neurofilament protein phosphoepitopes, 159,
    172, 246
    susceptibility to dephosphorylation, 441
Neurofilament proteins, developmental selection,
    439, 444
Neurofilament tangles, selective phosphorylation,
    462
Neurofilament transport, 447
Neurofilaments, 104, 265, 290
    buried nonphosphorylated epitopes, 449
    constrained conformation, see Neurofilament
        compactness
    developmental heterogeneity, 447
    enzymatic conversion of staining patterns, 450
    heterogeneity of phosphoepitopes, 450
    rephosphorylation in situ, 456
Neurohypophysis, see Pituitary
Neuromelanin, 329
Neuromodulators, 306
Neuronal diversity, 384, 427–466
    multiplicity of peptide precursors, 390
    regulatory peptide-neurotransmitter
        coexistence, 399

Neuronal enolase, 307, 308
Neuronal individuality, 357
Neuron-specific antigens, 254, 307
Neuron-specific enolase, 308, 333–335
Neuropathology, 328–333, 339–341, 461–464,
    484–492
Neuropeptides, see Regulatory peptides
Neurophysin, 164, 191, 192, 379
Neurosecretory granules, see Secretion granules
Neurosecretory principles, see Regulatory
    peptides
Neurosecretory substances, see Regulatory
    peptides
Neurotensin evolution, 395
Neurotransmitter, 305
    loss during tissue processing, see Hapten, loss
        during tissue processing
Neurotransmitter colocalization, 317–322
Neurotransmitter development, 329
Neurotransmitter haptens, 308, 309
Neurotransmitter pathology, 328–333
Neurotransmitter release, 316
Neurotransmitter reuptake, 311, 316
New Zealand black mouse, 476
Nickel ammonium sulfate, 189
Nociception, 189
Nociceptive stimuli, 366, 367
Nocireceptors, 365
Node of Ranvier, 341
Nomarski optics, 84, 109, 145, 219
Noradrenalin, 128, 152, 130, 305, 309, 316, 325,
    329
    effect of aldehydes, 308
Nucleus accumbens, 387
Nucleus basalis of Meynert, 267, 317, 461
Nucleus ceruleus, 155
Nude mice, 271

Olfactory protein, 307, 333
    development, 333
Oligodendrocyte, 135, 137, 152, 219, 288, 341,
    342, 348, 351, 486
Oligodendrocyte, satellite, 349
Oncofetal antigens, 469, 470
Opicoid receptor evolution, 394
Opioid receptors, 363
Opsonization, 52
Optical density index, 148
Optic tectum, 395
    intrinsic cholecystokinin neurons, 397
    intrinsic leu-enkephalin neurons, 397
    laminar segregation of bioactive peptides,
        397
Organum vasculosum laminae terminalis,
    387
Osmium tetroxide, 70, 103, 117, 121, 128, 185,
    212, 214, 217, 349
Oviduct, 169

Oxytocin, 29, 155, 169, 192, 232, 363, 377, 379–384
Oxytocin, evolution, 379, 395

Paired helical filaments, 461
Pancreas, 180, 241, 370, 470
Pancreatic endocrine tumors, 416
Pancreatic polypeptide, 397
Pancreatic polypeptide evolution, 395
Pancreatic somatostatinoma, 417
Paneth cell, 121
Paracrine secretion, see Private secretion
Paraffin sections, 103, 110, 127, 145, 155, 211, 220, 254, 259, 291, 468
  gluing on slides, 110
Paraformaldehyde, 127
Paraganglia, 329
Paragigantocellular nucleus, 189
Paranitroblue tetrazolium chloride, 66
Paraventricular nucleus, 135, 155, 164, 191, 197, 364, 376, 381
Parkinson's disease, 330, 399
Patch formation, see Capping
Pathology, see Prospective pathology; Retrospective pathology
Pepsin, 261
Peptide precursors, see Preprohormones
Peptides, see Regulatory peptides
Perfix, 215
Periaqueductal gray, 189, 311, 364
Periodate conjugation, 64
Periodate conjugation method, 62, 71
Periodide, 216
Periventricular thalamus, 364
Peroxidase, 33, 57, 59, 61, 92, 98, 274, 278, 323.
    See also Endogenous peroxidase; Retrograde uptake, peroxidase
Peroxidase-antibody conjugate:
  gel filtration purification, 60, 63
  lectin affinity purification, 62
Peroxidase-antiperoxidase complex, 94, 95 96–102, 107, 140, 145, 152, 273, 279
  baboon, 100, 143, 180
  chimpanzee, 165
  goat, 100
  hamster, 100
  maximum possible concentration, 100
  mouse, see ClonoPAP
  rabbit, 100
  rat, see ClonoPAP
Peroxidase-antiperoxidase method, see Unlabeled antibody peroxidase-antiperoxidase method
Peroxidase-antiperoxidase complex:
  sodium azide effect, 100
  storage, 99
Peroxidase-antiperoxidase complex stability, 102

Peroxidase-conjugated antibody method, 56–67, 259, 291, 292, 467
  aggregated conjugate, 64
  antibody fragments, 64, 65
  contamination with unconjugated antibody, 63, 85
Peroxidase-conjugated antibody method quantification, 147
Peroxidase-conjugated antibody method sensitivity, 67, 168–172, 233
Peroxidase-conjugated antibody method specificity, 83–86
Peroxidase-conjugated antibody method staining intensity, 67, 70
Peroxidase-conjugated protein A method, 171
Peroxidase-labeled antibody method, see Peroxidase-conjugated antibody method
Peroxidase-monoclonal antiperoxidase complex, see ClonoPAP
Phenylethanolamine-N-methyltransferase, 185
Pheochromacytoma, 265
Phosphatase, 33, 56, 66, 82, 165
Phosphatase treatment of sections, 450
Phytohemagglutinin, 277
Pinocytosis, 45
Pituitary, 112, 117, 119, 120, 124, 125, 164, 169, 171, 197, 239, 306, 335, 364, 379, 381, 389, 469
  LHRH-producing cells, 417
Pituitary adenoma, 164, 415, 416
Pituitary portal circulation, 135, 370
Placenta, 169
Plasma cell, 284, 285, 287
Plasmacytoma, 6
Plastic sections, see Semithin sections
Polyclonal antibody, see Antibody heterogeneity
Polyethylene glycol, 253
Polymeric conjugate, see Conjugated antibody method, aggregated conjugate
Polypeptide YY, 393
Postembedding staining, 114–126, 214, 218
  counterstains, 118
  serial sections, 118
Postembedding staining electron microscopy, 70
Postembedding staining embedding media, 117
Posterior hypothalamic nucleus, 376
Posttranslational processing, 14, 336, 357, 359, 360, 363, 370, 448
Posttranslational processing heterogeneity, 455
Preembedding staining, 126–142, 214, 218
Preembedding staining electron microscopy, 70
Preganglionic sympathetic neurons, 317
Pre-immune serum, 231
Preprodynorphin, 362
Preproenkephalin, 362, 364
Preprohormone heterogeneity, 13
Preproopiomelanocortin, 223, 237, 359–366

Preprosomatostatin, 367
Preprovasopressin, 383
Pretranslational heterogeneity, 3
Primary follicle, 286
Private interaction, 358, 377, 378, 394
Private secretion, 196
Procollagen, 147
Progesterone, 169
Prolactin, 117
Prolactin binding sites, 155
    prostate, 408
Prolactin cell, *see* Lactotrophs
Prolactin receptors, ovarian, 408
Prolylhydroxylase, 178
Proopiomelanocortin, *see*
    Preproopiomelanocortin
Propidium iodide, 325
Prospective pathology, 165, 169, 218, 220, 252,
    288, 291, 333, 339, 467–474
Prostate, 155
Prostate carcinoma, 252
Prostate-specific antigen, malignancy grading,
    472
Prostatic carcinoma, 472
Protease treatment of sections, 109–113, 213,
    214, 220, 292
Protein A, 21, 52, 63, 71, 79, 255, 274
Protein evolution, 180
Protein families, 2, 262, 265
Protein heterogeneity, 3, 13
Protein S-100, 137, 335
Proteoglycon, 178
Prozone phenomenon, see Eng-Bibgee effect
Pseudocyanine, 36
Purkinje cell, 167, 313, 325
Putamen, 267

Quantification, 47, 53, 54, 80, 83, 117, 141,
    146–163, 339, 343, 387
    antibody dilution, 156
    antigen as variant, 149
    area measurement, 159
    cell counting, 152
    deposit enumeration, 147, 148, 200, 201
    optical density, 148–152, 153–163
    steric hindrance, 147

Rabbit antibodies, blocking of monoclonal
    antibodies, 260
Radial glial fibers, 336
Radioimmunoassay, 20–24, 105, 240, 241, 251,
    291, 386
    hybridoma clone selection, 251
    see also Radioimmunobinding assay
Radioimmunobinding assay, 241
Raphé nuclei, 133, 188, 189, 310, 311, 325, 364
Raphé-striatal pathway, 310

Rat nucleus, 377
Receptors, 83. *See also* Antigen receptors; Fc
    receptors; Hormone receptors, named
    hormones
Recombinant DNA, 25, 361
Red blood cell receptors, 272
Red cell adherence test sensitivity, 166
Regulatory peptide coexistence, *see* Colocalization
Regulatory peptide interneurons, 392
Regulatory peptide-neurotransmitter
    coexistence, 306
Regulatory peptide precursors:
    evolutionary conservance of C terminal
        regions, 393
    heterogeneity of N terminal regions, 393
Regulatory peptides, 306, 308, 357–426
    colocalization, 364, 397–401
    C-terminal portion shared with precursor, 374
    ectopic processing, 376
    evolution, 359, 362, 394, 395
    evolutionary conservation of C terminal
        sequences, 390
    feedback stimulation, 376
    modulatory action, 399
Regulatory peptides posttranslational processing,
    359, 360, 363, 370, 374, 380, 383. *See also*
    Preproopiomelanocortin
Remyelination, 350
Renin, 156
Reticular formation, 311
Reticulosarcoma, 168
Retrograde tracer uptake, 322–328
Retrograde transport, 186–190
Retrograde uptake, peroxidase, 165, 172, 187,
    365
Retrospective pathology, 103, 212, 218, 220, 265,
    289, 328, 331, 339, 468
Rhodamine disulfonic acid, 38
Rhodamine isothiocyanate, 33, 37, 38, 194
Rosenthal fibers, 339
Rossette formation, 279

S-100 protein, 71
Sarcoidosis, 294
Scharrer concept, 135, 306, 358, 359, 390, 394
Schiff base, reaction with aromatic hydroxyl
    groups, 308
Schmidt-Lantermann incisure, 348
Schwann cell, 335, 341, 342
Second antibody, 21, 43, 52, 53, 70, 90
    effect on method specificity, 43
    see also Link antibody
Secondary follicle, 286, 287
Secondary response, *see* B cell memory; T cell
    memory
Second messenger, 401
Secretin, 392

Secretion granule receptors, 403, 411
Secretion granule recycling, 412
Secretion granules, 124, 126, 134, 135, 141, 150, 233, 261, 305, 381
  gene product contents, 400
Secretory granule-vesicle coexistence, 398
Section adherence to slides, 220
Semiprivate secretion, 306, 358, 370, 393
Semithin sections, 193, 217, 220, 221, 349, 370
Senile dementia, Alzheimer type, 461
Senile plaques, 461
Sensitivity, 43, 60, 49, 51, 67, 69, 70, 72, 80, 96, 102, 103, 105, 149, 163–175, 219, 225, 232, 259
Serial sections, 193
Serotonin, 133, 167, 188, 191, 192, 305, 309–312, 325, 365, 329
  aldehyde modified crossreactivities, 310
  effect of aldehydes, 308
Serum sickness, 481
Shiverer mouse, 350
Signal intensification, see Staining intensity
Signal intensity, 43, 60, 135, 164. See also Staining intensity
Signal to noise ratio, see Sensitivity
Silver halides, 67, 376
Slide preparation:
  confinement of drops, 104, 259
  poly-L-lysine, 210
Slow virus, 477
Slow virus infection, 483, 486
  autoimmune disease, 476
Sodium azide, 99, 100
Solid-phase immunoassay, 18
Solid-phase radioimmunoassay, 18
Solitary nucleus, 189, 382
Somatic mutation, 3, 13, 270, 285
Somatostatin, 121, 167, 169, 180, 191, 196, 261, 367–372, 377, 392, 393
  secretion granule receptor, 412
Somatostatin cryptic peptide, 370
Somatostatin evolution, 395
Specificity, see Antibody specification; Method specificity
Spinal cord, 311, 325, 370, 390
Spinal thalamic tract, 365
Spurr's low viscosity resin, 122, 214, 220
Staining intensity, 44, 67, 69, 107, 172, 173, 185, 186, 376
Stellate cell, cerebellum, 316
Stria medullaris, 382, 385, 392
Stria terminalis, 364, 370
Striatum, 311
Striosome, 397
Subacute sclerosing panencephalitis, 486
Substance P, 135, 167, 189, 260, 306, 316, 325, 330, 332, 366, 367, 389, 392, 397

Substance P evolution, 395
Substance P-serotonin coexistence, 399
Substance P-thyrotropin-releasing hormone coexistence, 400
Substantia gelatinosa, 364, 366
Substantia innominata, see Nucleus basalis of Meynert
Substantia nigra, 190, 267, 311, 316, 333, 382
Sulfatide, 351
Sulfonyl chloride conjugation, 38
Superior colliculus, 189
Suppression, see T cell, suppressor
Suprachiasmic nucleus, 219, 381, 392
Supraoptic nucleus, 155, 164, 197, 364, 376, 381
Surface immunoglobulin D, 292
Surface immunoglobulin G, 301
Surface immunoglobulin M, 292, 299
Surface replica electron microscopy, 83
Surface villi, see Hairy cell
Surgical pathology, see Prospective pathology
Sympathectomy, 333
Sympathetic ganglion, 290, 331, 366
Synapse, 129, 131, 133, 135, 138, 141, 246, 311
  monoclonal antibody, 433
Synaptic thickening, 130
Synaptic vesicles, see Small clear vesicles
Syncytiotrophoblasts, 237
Syphilis, 50, 53, 92, 167

Tanycytes, 339
Taurine, 305, 313, 314
Taxonomy, 180
T cell, 2, 82, 259, 271, 272, 287, 298
  helper, 47, 272, 283, 288
  natural killer, see Natural killer cell
  suppressor, 47, 272, 282, 283, 284, 288, 295, 476
T cell antigen, 277, 278
T cell receptors, 276
T cell tumors, 291
Tegmentum, 316, 370
Terminal dysoxynucleotidyltransferase, 293
Testosterone, 384
Tetanus toxin, 324
Tetanus toxin retrograde tracer, 190
Tetramethylbenzidine, 58
Thalamus, 365
T helper cell, see T cell, helper
Thioguanine, 248
Thrombosis, 171
Thryotropic hormone, 241
Thymic aplasia congenital, see DiGeorge's syndrome
Thymidine incorporation, 277, 279
Thymocytes, 274
Thymosin, 271
Thymostimulin, 271

Thymus, 271, 283
  in myasthenia gravis, 484
  reticuloepithelial cell, 271
Thyrotropic hormone, 225, 228
Thyrotropin-releasing hormone, 388, 389
  precursor heterogeneity, 400
Tinctorial staining, 468
Tinctorial staining sensitivity, 164
Tissue permeability, see Antibody, tissue
    penetration
Tissue preparation, 210–224
Tolerance, 115, 274, 280–282, 283, 475, 480
  abrogation, 476, 477
Tolerogen, 281
Toluene diisocyanate, 73
Toxoplasma gondii, 167
Toxoplasmosis, 294
Transferrin, 169
Trigeminal nucleus, 325
Tritiated thymidine incorporation, 276, 280, 285
Trophoblastic tumors, 407
Tropomyosin, 137
Troponin C, 335
Trypsin, 112, 113
Trypsin treatment of sections, 109, 450
Tryptamine, 310
Tryptophane hydroxylase, 312
T suppressor cell, see T cell, suppressor
Tuberculosis, 294
Tubulin, neuron-specific, 307
Tumor, prognosis, 470
Tumor chemotherapy, 291, 468
Tumor classification, 285
Tumor differentiation, 468–473
Tumor prognosis, see Malignancy grading
Tyrosin hydroxylase, 147, 148, 152, 155, 190,
    194, 309, 316, 329, 330

Undifferentiated tumors, 467
  antigen expression, 470
Unlabeled antibody, resolution, 175–180
Unlabeled antibody double PAP sequence, 171
Unlabeled antibody method, 90–209
  antiferritin-ferritin 4-layer sequence, 138
  combination with retrograde uptake studies,
    186–190
  counterstaining, 107, 145
  double peroxidase-antiperoxidase complex
    sequence, 135, 186
  double serum antiperoxidase sequence, 186
  ferritin-antiferritin sequence, 186
  4-layer affinity-purified antiperoxidase
    sequence, 149, 183
  4-layer antiferritin-ferritin sequence, 183
  4-layer serum antiperoxidase sequence, 149,
    171, 172, 183, 467
  glucose oxidase-antiglucose oxidase sequence,
    186, 197

hemocyanin marker, 279
heterologous 3-layer sequence, 180, 183
heterologous 4-layer sequence, 183
light microscopy, 103–114
peroxidase-antiperoxidase complex from
    species heterologous to first antibody, 142
peroxidase-conjugated immunoglobulin as
    third layer, 183
peroxidase-F(ab')$_2$-antiperoxidase, 183
prozone phenomenon, see Eng-Bigbee effect
quantification, 117, 141
serum antialkaline phosphatase-phosphatase
    sequence, 199
simultaneous staining with retrograde tracer,
    186–190
staining intensification, 185, 186
Unlabeled antibody method quantification,
    146–163
Unlabeled antibody method resolution, 167
Unlabeled antibody method sensitivity, 96, 102,
    105, 164–175, 180
Unlabeled antibody method specificity, 90,
    142–145
Unlabeled antibody peroxidase-antiperoxidase
    method, 90–209, 212, 214, 219, 220, 225,
    258, 273, 291, 292, 298, 299, 316, 366, 367,
    467
  autoradiography on same section, 190–193
  bioactive peptide localization in transmitter
    reuptake identified cell, 192
  dual antigen staining, 402
  4-layer heterologous sequence, 259
  product intensification, 376
  quantification, 146–183, 200, 201, 387
  sensitivity, 103, 233, 259
  staining of Lucifer yellow in vivo labeled
    neurons, 190
  transmitter identification of photoaffinity
    receptor-labeled cells, 192
Unlabeled antibody protein A method, 183
Urinary bladder, 390
Urinary bladder carcinoma, 470
Urinary bladder transitional carcinoma, 165, 169,
    470, 471

Vasoactive intestinal peptide, 134, 197, 306, 392
Vasoactive intestinal peptide-acetylcholine
    coexistence, 398
Vasoactive intestinal peptide evolution, 395
Vasopressin, 29, 106, 112, 135, 164, 169, 191,
    192, 196, 219, 232, 239, 363, 372, 377,
    379–384
  corticotropin release, 191, 382
  evolution, 379, 395
Vasopressin-leu-enkephalin coexistence, 399
Vasopressin receptor:
  distal convoluted tubules, 407
  pituitary pars intermedia, 407

Ventral horn, 317, 382

Vestibular nuclei, 328

Vibratome, 211

Vibratome sections, 127, 145, 218, 219, 316, 342

Vibrissae, 325

Villous cell, *see* Hairy cell

Vinblastin, 45

Vitamin D, 80

von Recklinghausen's disease, 333

von Willebrand factor, *see* Factor VIII

Waldenstrom's paraproteinanemia, 490

Western blot, *see* Immunoblot

Wheat germ agglutinin, 324, 325
   anterograde transport, 325

Wheat germ agglutinin retrograde uptake, 189, 325

Wolfgram protein, 341, 348

Zamboni's fixative, 214